Crime and Science

The New Frontier in Criminology

Also by Jürgen Thorwald

The Century of the Detective
Science and Secrets of Early Medicine
The Century of the Surgeon
The Triumph of Surgery

Crime
and
Science

The New Frontier in Criminology

Translated by Richard and Clara Winston

Jürgen Thorwald

A Harvest Book

Harcourt, Brace & World, Inc., New York

Contents

I   At the Limits of Detectability: Forensic Serology

II Clues in the Dust:
Forensic Chemistry and Biology

List of Illustrations

x

ACKNOWLEDGMENTS ARE MADE FOR THE FOLLOWING PHOTOGRAPHS:

Different types of bloodstains, *Almay*, Paris.—Susan Hayes, Marie-Ange Robitaille, Pamela Mason, Pierre Jaccoud, Edward H. Coolidge, *A. P.*, Frankfurt, London.— Photomicrographs of bloodstained fibers, Bayerisches Kriminalamt, Munich.— R. R. A. Coombs, Walter Bird, London.—Schematic representations of the principle of mixed agglutination, R. R. Coombs/Barbara Dodd, *Identification of Blood Stains.*—Detective in house-to-house search, Leonard Richardson, *Daily Express*, London.—Hildegard Wassing's and Peter Falkenberg's bodies, Samuel Sheppard, Marilyn Sheppard's pillow, *dpa*, Frankfurt.—Friedrich Lindörfer, Photo: Hortig, *8-Uhr-Blatt*, Nuremberg.—Exhibits in the Jaccoud case, Keystone, Munich, Paris. —Pamela Coventry, locality where her body was found, *London Express*, London. —Lattes test, Ponsold/Berg, *Lehrbuch der gerichtlichen Medizin*, Thieme, Stuttgart. —Helmuth Daube's house, Roland Scheidemann, Düsseldorf.—Normal blood, agglutinated red blood cells, Fritz Schiff, *Die Technik der Blutgruppenuntersuchung*, Springer, Berlin.—Linda Baud, *Schweizer Illustrierte*, Zurich.—Karl Landsteiner, Süddeutscher Verlag, Munich.—Graeme Thorne, Stephen Leslie Bradley, Stephen Leslie Bradley's house, *Sydney Morning Herald*, Sydney.—Paul Jeserich, Helmuth Daube and Karl Hussman, Ullstein, Berlin.—Albert Guay and his wife Rita, *U. P.*, Paris, London.—The adhesive tape method, Wissenschaftlicher Dienst der Stadtpolizei Zurich/Kriminalpolizei.—All other photographs, courtesy of the author.

I

At the Limits of Detectability:
Forensic Serology

1

The mysterious death of the nine-year-old schoolgirl Lucie Berlin, with the search for her murderer, was unquestionably the crime of the year 1904, at least for the capital city of the German Empire.

On the morning of June 11 the mist had not yet entirely cleared above the River Spree, which winds through the city of Berlin, when "Skimmer" Teske and his assistant Barthold set out in their skiff to traverse the river between the Alsen Bridge and the Weidendamm Bridge, near the Friedrichstrasse Station. It was Teske's daily job to skim a section of the river, removing the flotsam and jetsam which might otherwise spoil the appearance of the young metropolis. Toward eight o'clock, as Teske was approaching the riverbank by the Reichstag, he caught sight of a curious, oozing bundle behind the rudder of an anchored tug. He rowed toward it until he was close enough to make out a piece of wrapping paper, spattered with blood, tied with loose cord to some object beneath it that bobbed up and down on the slight waves.

Recalling the many fetuses and newborn infants he had fished out of the Spree in the course of a decade, Teske mused: "I suppose some woman's tossed in another one she wanted out of the way." His work had hardened him. But when he brought the bundle into his boat with his net, and lifted the paper aside, he gave a start of horror. What he saw was the headless and limbless torso of a ten- or eleven-year-old girl, with breasts already distinctly budding. There were bloomers on the corpse and a red woolen petticoat. Otherwise the child's body was naked.

Teske and his helper rowed to the nearest landing on the other side of the river, on Schiffbauerdamm, and Barthold ran to the Fifth Precinct station. A telegram was immediately dispatched over the private wire to police headquarters at Alexanderplatz—the great red building where since 1885 Berlin's criminal police, as the detective force was called, had been trying to set up a German Scotland Yard. As yet Berlin did not have any of those homicide commissions which were later to enhance the reputation of the city's detectives. The view still prevailed that the officials charged with the investigation of a murder must vary from case to case—one set for robbery and murder, another for sex crimes. Nevertheless, day and night two inspectors of the criminal police force were on hand at Alexanderplatz. Their job was to go to the scene of capital crimes without delay, accompanied by specialists and a forensic-medical expert.

As a result, only twenty minutes elapsed before several carriages arrived at the bank of the Spree, where Teske and Barthold had landed their skiff. Inspectors Wannowski and Wehn leaped from their carriages, followed by Dr. Schulz, Police Chief von Borries, Counselor Dieterici, and Assistant District Attorney Dr. Lindenau. There was a reason for this turnout of top brass. Only a few days before in nearby Charlottenburg the body of a woman had been found drifting in a canal. So far, the police had obtained not the slightest clue to her identity. An aroused public and a vigorous press were now keeping close watch on the police.

After a preliminary examination of the torso, Dr. Schulz declared that the child had been the victim of a particularly brutal sex crime. In view of the violent public reaction that could always be expected when such crimes involved children, Police Chief von Borries ordered his men to solve the case "at all costs."

In the summer of 1904 Berlin detectives were trying hard to make a name for themselves in that science of modern criminology which had begun in Paris twenty-five years earlier. There, Alphonse Bertillon of the Sûreté had developed the first reliable method for identification of criminals. It was based on the fact that every human being differs from every other in the exact measurements of various parts of his body, and that the sum of these measurements yields a characteristic formula for each individual. *Bertillonage* had largely put an end to the criminal's ancient trick of hiding behind different names, clothing, style of hair and beard; it had brought the first rays of nineteenth-century scientific thinking into the field of criminology. In the meantime, Bertillon's method of measurements had been superseded by the discovery of fingerprinting. In 1901 Scotland Yard established the first fingerprint file in Europe, and Bertillon fought a losing battle for the continuance of his system. Nevertheless, Bertillon's work marked the introduction of a new method in criminology, which no longer depended on interrogation of witnesses and the intuition or cunning tricks of experienced detectives. Criminology was now laying full emphasis on objective scientific evidence. Photography had become an important weapon in the detective's arsenal and was already widely used to preserve the exact appearance of clues and of the scenes of crimes. Out of the combination of law and medicine had developed the special discipline of forensic medicine, and progressive police forces in Europe frequently called upon its services. Forensic medicine, collaborating with chemistry, was engaged in studying traces of poison, sperm, and other substances on the bodies of victims or at the scenes of crime. Naturally, the clues that most frequently came to forensic physicians for identification consisted of bloodstains, which seemed to everyone the most direct and the most betraying marks of crime.

Ever since 1896 the Berlin police had maintained an identification service, a Bertillon file of measurements, and a register of missing persons and of crimes. These were all housed in headquarters on Alexanderplatz. Thanks to the new register, not ten minutes had passed since Police Chief von Borries issued his order to solve the crime at all costs when a clerk reported to him that a nine-year-old girl had been missing from a house in the northern part of Berlin since Thursday, June 9. The description fitted the trunk and the clothing found on the body. The child was Lucie Berlin, youngest daughter of a cigar maker named Friedrich Berlin, who lived at 130 Ackerstrasse, an apartment house. An officer of the local precinct was dispatched to bring the father of the missing girl to where the body had been found. Von Borries, who was much concerned about his reputation with the public, waited on the bank of the Spree while a steadily growing crowd of the curious gathered. By the time Friedrich Berlin arrived—a pale-faced man of fifty in workman's smock and indoor slippers—the police had to clear a path for him through the crowd. Friedrich Berlin recognized his daughter by a scar on her chest, cried: "Oh, Lucie," and sank to the ground in a faint; the local reporter who described this scene in next morning's newspaper was not even exaggerating for effect. Von Borries sent the cigar maker home in his own carriage; the Police Chief was aware that such gestures went over well with the press and public. He then promptly dictated a proclamation which was to be published in all the newspapers and posted on all the advertising columns of Berlin:

ONE THOUSAND MARKS REWARD! At 7:45 A.M. today the torso of Lucie Berlin, born in Berlin on January 8, 1895, was washed up in front of the building at 26 Schiffbauerdamm. Head, arms, and legs of the corpse were severed with some sharp instrument. The girl was last seen playing in the yard of her home at 130 Ackerstrasse from noon to around one o'clock on the ninth of this month, and had been missing since then. She was tall for her age, was wearing a russet-brown wool dress, a black pinafore, white stockings, brown bloomers, buttoned shoes. She had a rectangular gold locket around her neck, on a black velvet ribbon. Evidently the girl was the victim of an indecent assault. Persons who can offer information regarding her whereabouts from June 9 to 11, or who encountered her, are requested to communicate with the police at headquarters on Alexanderplatz or at any precinct.

Berlin, June 11, 1904   Police Chief von Borries

The Police Chief appointed Inspectors Wannowski and Wehn heads of the investigating commission and Precinct 59 as center for the local inquiries. Wannowski was a quiet, taciturn, keen-minded man. Wehn, by contrast, was lively, given to gesturing and pantomime, highly imaginative and easily roused to enthusiasm. Neither of the two had any inkling, as they took on their assignment, that they were undertaking a case which was destined to turn the eyes of all Berlin upon the scientific detection of clues and, moreover, upon the most obvious and spectacular phase of such detection: bloodstains and the possibilities of analyzing them, as developed by physicians, chemists, and criminologists up to 1904.

2

Wannowski and Wehn took charge of things by nine o'clock in the morning. Their first act was to instruct the detective patrols of Berlin, which were constantly on the prowl for sex criminals, pimps, and pickpockets, to concentrate on the area around Ackerstrasse. The patrols were to seek any suspicious-looking men who might have been seen on Thursday afternoon or later with a nine-year-old girl. Meanwhile, at Alexanderplatz headquarters and at Precinct 59, detectives stood watch to receive evidence when witnesses reported—as was bound to happen as soon as the Police Chief's proclamation was distributed. Much useless testimony had to be expected, of course—but there was always the chance of something important.

The two detectives then went out to Ackerstrasse, a street lined with endless, dreary gray tenement houses. While they were there, a messenger from the morgue reached them, bringing the first results of the autopsy performed on Lucie. At this time Berlin did not yet have an Institute of Forensic Medicine, like Paris; there was only an academy for instruction in public health, which was located in the morgue itself. But its director, forty-six-year-old Professor Fritz Strassmann, was a great believer in medico-criminological co-operation, then being promoted especially in Paris and Lyons. Strassmann himself, aided by his assistant Dr. Schulz, had performed the autopsy on the torso. In his brief report he stated that in all probability Lucie Berlin had been strangled. Her vagina had been torn by rough fingers. It seemed certain that the wounds had been inflicted when the child was already close to death from strangulation and the activity of the heart had ceased. The removal of the limbs had been done by unskilled hands. Death itself had ensued probably about an hour after her last meal, which had consisted of "pork, potatoes, and cucumber salad."

The tenement house at 130 Ackerstrasse was a dark, four-story structure in which nearly a hundred families lived in cramped, low-ceilinged apartments. A passage through the front part of the building and an arched gateway led to a squalid interior court and, from there, over worn wooden steps, into a warren of narrow hallways, toilets on the landings between floors, the doors of the apartments dark brown with age. Detectives Ball and Ogotzek, who accompanied Wehn and Wannowski, were at home in this slum section of the city. They knew the working men and women, the pensioners and handicraftsmen, who lived in this gray sea of houses, alleyways, saloons, and dives, side by side with the female and male prostitutes, pimps, swindlers, and thieves who nightly swarmed out over Berlin. The *Berliner Morgenpost* had meanwhile distributed posters and extras all over, so that news of the crime had been carried to the last corner of Berlin. Women, children, the unemployed and the unemployables, thronged inquisitively around 130 Ackerstrasse. Police from the local precinct had just rescued a shoemaker named Petercit from a hail of stones and sticks. Someone had called the man a "bratchaser," the name given in local dialect for debauchers of children, and a band of street boys had promptly set upon him.

In Friedrich Berlin's cramped kitchen on the first floor of the side wing, Wannowski found the entire family assembled: husband, wife—a worn-out woman of fifty—the elder son, nineteen, and a younger son, Hugo, who worked as an errand boy. Patiently soothing the woman's grief and the men's fits of rage, Wannowski found out what the members of the family themselves knew of Lucie's disappearance. The child had come home from school at eleven o'clock on June 9, had played in the yard for a while, and had bought two cents' worth of candy at "Frank's" store. After returning from the store Lucie had waited for her father, who came home for the big noon meal at twelve fifteen. They had eaten well, pork cutlets, potatoes, and cucumber salad, and then Friedrich Berlin had left again for his job in the cigar factory. Shortly before one o'clock the girl had asked for the key to the toilet, which was on the landing half a flight up, just a few steps from her door. Twenty minutes later Hugo had come home for his dinner. He had missed Lucie and found the toilet locked. Thereupon he had gone down into the yard, had heard a variety of contradictory stories from the women and children of the tenement, and had gone on searching for his sister until evening, going around to acquaintances to ask whether they had seen Lucie. Finally, after Friedrich Berlin returned home from work in the evening, the family had decided to call the police.

Wannowski wanted to know whether Lucie had been a trustful child. Not a bit of it! Who could be trustful in this neighborhood? The brat-chasers lurked on every street corner with their candy and money. Two days before Lucie's disappearance a little girl from the other end of the block had come home clutching a few copper coins as her reward, and with her underwear torn. They had always warned Lucie: "Don't go anywhere with anyone you don't know."

While Wannowski was talking, Inspector Wehn looked around the place. If Lucie had been kidnaped, or had voluntarily gone out on the street and been picked up there, someone, either the child or the criminal or both, must have passed through the arched entrance in the front building shortly after one o'clock. The superintendent, Möbius, said that at noon an organ-grinder had played his instrument in the yard, and as always many people had stood around or at the windows to listen. Inspector Wehn asked all the tenants who thought they had any information whatever to come to the superintendent's apartment, where Ogotzek and Ball questioned them.

By late afternoon the two inspectors had winnowed the bewildering mass of data that poured into Precinct 59 and into headquarters on

Alexanderplatz, and had collected a few facts that might prove useful.

There was, for example, the tailor Gusta Rese, who had been working at the window of his apartment opposite the tenement house in which the Berlins lived. He said that he had observed a man "between thirty and forty" coming out of the entrance, holding a girl by the hand, toward two o'clock in the afternoon. They had gone off in the direction of Humboldthain, a big park in the vicinity. The man had caught his attention because "the seat of his pants was unusually big and fitted very badly."

A carpenter named Gryczykowski, who lived in 131 Ackerstrasse, said that at one o'clock he had seen two men whom he did not know at the entrance of Lucie's building. One of them had later spoken to a child. A Frau Rehrkorn and her daughter, also of Ackerstrasse, had observed two men with a little girl who was carrying a paper bag. One of the men had gone away, the other had led the girl toward Humboldthain. He had been wearing a straw hat and a dark suit with ill-fitting trousers that sagged in the back. In addition, there was a nine-year-old child named Greta Schreiber. The girl gabbled that nobody wanted to believe her because nobody wanted to say anything bad about Lucie in front of her mother, but Lucie hadn't gone to the toilet at all. She had run right down the stairs past Greta herself and out through the yard into the street. Finally, a twelve-year-old girl named Adametz told of a bearded young man who had spoken to her shortly before noon on June 9. She described him as wearing "dragging" pants and a straw hat. He had shown her a large green bottle. When she ran away, the man stopped in front of Frank's store. Lucie Berlin had gone into the store at just this time.

Wannowski was far too seasoned a detective not to be aware of the unreliable nature of the testimony of children. But the curious repetition of the themes of ill-fitting trousers, straw hat, beard, offers, and the park seemed significant. Could Lucie Berlin have been less cautious than her mother thought? Had she been lured by a stranger's promise when she went to buy candy shortly before noon? Had she asked for the toilet key only as a pretext for leaving the apartment? Wannowski's suspicions were further strengthened by the statements of a hack driver named Krüger; Krüger said he would "take his oath on it" that at about noon on June 9 he had seen a man walking in Humboldthain "slightly lame in one foot and holding a girl by the hand."

At five o'clock in the afternoon detectives from the morals squad called on all the known streetwalkers in Ackerstrasse to query them.

9

(By that time, every single one of them reported a limping man with ill-fitting trousers.) At six o'clock Detectives Siegel and Blume knocked at a door only a few yards from Friedrich Berlin's apartment. This was the address of Johanna Liebetruth, a registered prostitute of many years' standing. She had been released from the Barminstrasse jail only that morning, about the time the body was found in the Spree; she had been serving a short sentence for "insulting a customer." Johanna Liebetruth was thirty-two, a tall, buxom woman with a rather flattened nose. She greeted Siegel and Blume with the wariness of the recent jailbird.

At the table in her small kitchen sat a stocky man in his forties, with dark-blond hair and a mustache. While he ate, a black dog crouched at his feet. As a matter of form, Siegel asked for his identification. He was Theodor Berger, a junk dealer who lived at 70 Bergstrasse. Johanna Liebetruth explained he was an old friend who had come to celebrate her release with her. In a sudden access of sentimentality she added that he'd been wanting to marry her for eighteen years and now—in a few days—they were going to have their wedding. Siegel was well acquainted with this longing of "his" prostitutes for the respectability of marriage, and so paid no special attention to this announcement. Nevertheless, it had a certain effect on him, for he did not scrutinize Berger—who went on nonchalantly tucking in his meal—as closely as he might otherwise have done in his eternally alert lookout for pimps. He had another problem on his mind at the moment, and so he asked whether Johanna Liebetruth knew a man who fitted the description he had from Wannowski.

When the woman realized that the detectives were not interested in her, but in Lucie Berlin, she became even more sentimental and garrulous. Sobbing, she assured the policemen that she knew the "poor kid" very well; the girl used to call her "Auntie" and often ran errands to the store for her. In her opinion, the murderer could only be one person—Otto Lenz, the pimp of another prostitute named Emma Seiler, who lived in the basement of the same building. Emma had given him his walking papers only a few days ago because she'd seen him fooling around with "brats," that is, little girls. The fellow limped, she said, wore baggy pants and a straw hat, and had often played with Lucie Berlin. In fact, he'd often taken her on his lap or had her dance to music, while staring at her "in a funny way."

Siegel felt a certain uneasiness. It seemed, somehow, all too pat. But then he went downstairs to the basement and called on Emma Seiler, who was just lacing herself into her corset for her evening round of the streets. She went right on dressing in Siegel's presence, cursed Lenz, called him a "low-down brat-chaser," and confirmed everything Johanna had said. Her readiness to offer a list of the dives where Lenz hung out and might be found again put Siegel on his guard. But since he was unable to justify this feeling, he passed his information on to Wannowski without comment.

On Sunday afternoon, twenty-four hours later, Lenz was picked up in a dive called the Bouillon Cellar. He had shaved his beard and wrapped his straw hat in newspaper, preparatory to throwing it away. Though a strong, broad-shouldered man, he was shaking with terror when the police made their arrest. He admitted that he had known Lucie, and did not deny that he had watched her dancing and taken her on his lap. But killed her? He swore he had never harmed anyone, let alone a child. Wannowski confronted him with the witnesses on Ackerstrasse. They insisted, with but one exception, that he was the man they had seen with the little girl. Only Krüger, the hack driver, was not quite sure. But when Lenz put on his straw hat, he exclaimed: "That's the guy."

The result was that on June 13 Lenz was remanded to prison—where a crowd of prisoners awaiting investigation or trial received him with threats and curses. Nevertheless Wannowski had the feeling that he was on the wrong track. That feeling grew stronger when a man named Brandengeier, an agent for the Iduna Insurance Company, asked to see him. Brandengeier declared that if the murder had been committed by two o'clock in the afternoon on June 9, Lenz could not possibly be the murderer, because on June 9 he had hired Lenz as a subagent and had been with him every minute of the day until two o'clock. They had lunched together in the restaurant called Norddeutsche Stuben. Lenz, he said, had formerly been an insurance agent before he fell into the hands of Emma Seiler; he was a weak man who would easily lose his head and might well have shaved off his beard out of fear of being taken for the murderer.

Wannowski did not regard insurance agents as the most trustworthy of people; but since he already had qualms, he began checking Brandengeier's statements. What he found out about Lenz left him with the nasty impression of a rootless, rotten existence; but the fellow had been seen lunching with Brandengeier and there seemed little possibility, therefore, that he could have abducted and killed Lucie Berlin. Wannowski did not release Lenz, but he instituted a new search for the murderer. Several dozen policemen were set to combing the entire area between Ackerstrasse and Humboldthain, as well as the numerous allotment gardens of the vicinity, in hope of clues. If the child had been killed outside the building, there ought to be some clues or pieces of missing clothing in the neighborhood. But the hunt ended in such total failure that Wehn for the first time considered the alternative possibility: that Lucie Berlin had not left the house at all, but had been dragged into another apartment, a cellar, or the attic, there to be killed and the body later taken to the river by the murderer.

Wannowski was dubious, but Wehn pressed him to make another search of 130 Ackerstrasse from roof to cellar. Wannowski had little hope of any result, and none came to light; but some persistent feeling made Wehn look into the question of the denunciation that had led to the arrest of Otto Lenz. The fact that it had come from Johanna Liebetruth, and that the woman's apartment was almost next door to Friedrich Berlin's, seemed significant, and Wehn asked Detective Siegel for a fuller account of his talk with the prostitute. In this way he heard about Theodor Berger for the first time. Johanna Liebetruth herself could not possibly be guilty of the murder, since she had been in jail when it occurred. Wannowski therefore looked into Berger's background. His investigation began as a pure formality, a shot in the dark.

There seemed to be nothing in the records against Berger. If the man had actually been only an old flame of Johanna's, who had come by that day to celebrate her release, there was nothing to link him with the murdered child. But then a fact turned up which changed the direction of the search. On the afternoon of June 14 Detectives Ball and Ogotzek reported that Theodor Berger was by no means a guest. Rather, he had been living at 130 Ackerstrasse with Johanna Liebetruth ever since she had moved in six months before. The Bergstrasse address in his identity papers was sheer camouflage. It seemed he had rented a room there for form's sake from a tailor; in reality the room was occupied by someone else. His claim to be a junk dealer was obviously a cover-up also. Now and then he turned up at taverns and cheap eating places with odds and ends for sale; but he could not possibly have lived on his earnings from such stuff.

Camouflage of this sort was customary among pimps, and Wannowski accordingly concluded that Berger was Johanna Liebetruth's pimp who had so far managed to evade the morals squad, like many another. Pimps, however, were not necessarily murderers; and it somewhat reflected to his credit that on Monday, June 13, Berger had actually appeared at the Registry and asked for the banns to be posted for his marriage to Johanna Liebetruth. In following various leads, however, Detective Ball had had a talk with Johanna's seventy-five-year-old father, a wood-turner by trade. It seemed that Johanna had been born in 1872, and that Berger had "seduced" her when she was only fourteen. Berger had set up house with her in a room on Tieckstrasse when the girl was sixteen, and thereafter he had sent her out "on the prowl," telling old Liebetruth: "I'm not working any more. Your daughter can feed me." They had been living together for eighteen years, she earning the money, he drinking, gambling, and hiring Johanna out for private "artistic performances"—in Hamburg, Düsseldorf, and other cities, as well as Berlin. These performances consisted in her undressing for a select audience and then being "at the disposal" of the gentlemen. Old Liebetruth called his daughter lazy, lustful, servile, and so stupid that for eighteen years she had gone on hoping Berger would marry her. Berger was a dirty dog who'd served his first jail sentence when he was only sixteen, for "indecent acts on a public street," and had been sent up time and again ever since for all kinds of trouble; he'd done time in Hamburg and other cities, too. When the detective informed him that Berger was shortly going to marry Johanna, old Liebetruth replied that if it were true, something unusual must have happened, because Berger had been wriggling out of the marriage for eighteen years.

The old man's hatred for Berger was obvious, and could be discounted; but even so there were points in his story which suggested the value of further investigation. Most of all, there was the remark that something unusual must have happened to make Berger consent to a marriage he had fended off for eighteen years. As yet, Wannowski could not really define the suspicions that these words aroused. For the present, he tried to find out about Berger's earlier convictions. If they had been imposed in Berlin, they must be in the files somewhere. Obtaining data from other places was more difficult, since there did not yet exist a central file for the State of Prussia, let alone for Germany as a whole. Nevertheless, Wannowski sent inquiries to Hamburg, Düsseldorf, and other cities.

On the morning of June 15, Wannowski, Wehn, and a large number of policemen descended on Ackerstrasse. They visited all the apartments on the same hallway as Friedrich Berlin's and Johanna Liebetruth's, and those on the hallways above and below. Everywhere, they asked the same questions: What was known about Berger's behavior toward children? Was he considered a violent man? Had he been in the building around noon on June 9, and had anyone noticed him outside the Liebetruth apartment? Who had ever seen him with Lucie Berlin, and how had he acted toward the child? Who had noticed Berger on June 10 or 11, and had anyone heard any unusual sounds in the Liebetruth apartment from June 9 to June 11?

Information was hard to elicit. Every family, every individual in this run-down neighborhood, had their own troubles. Scarcely anyone paid any attention to his neighbors' activities. But after about an hour Wehn came across a woman of eighty on one of the upper stories, Anna Müller, who lived alone in a single room. On June 9 she had been going upstairs with a pot when Lucie went to the toilet. The child had offered to carry the pot up to the old woman's room for her, but Anna Müller had said no thanks, and toiled on. During this time, however, Theodor Berger had come out of Johanna Liebetruth's apartment in his shirtsleeves and had looked at the child, then watched the old woman until she was out of sight upstairs. She had felt annoyed at Berger's look because it seemed to be saying: Come on, old lady, make it snappy and beat it. But it hadn't occurred to her to attach any importance to the meeting. Of course Lucie Berlin had known Berger well and called him "Uncle."

Wehn picked up another piece of information from a Frau Marowski, who had rooms directly above Johanna Liebetruth's. After reflecting for a while she stated that on June 9, between one and two o'clock, she had heard through her open window a child's voice screaming "No." The voice had come from down below. But she had attached no importance to the incident. Such testimony could, of course, be the product of error or fantasy; it could have been imagined after the news of the murder came out. But it was hard to believe that the stolid tailor Nölte and his wife, who lived directly beneath Johanna, had also had the same fantasy. On June 9 at 1:30 P.M. they had heard a sound of falling "that did not stop all at once, as if arms or legs were hitting the floor in succession." Nölte had remarked to his wife: "Sounds like the baby's fallen out of bed."

Toward noon Wannowski and Wehn returned to headquarters on Alexanderplatz, leaving instructions with the detectives to watch every movement of Theodor Berger and Johanna Liebetruth from now on. They found the first documents on Berger's previous convictions in their office. Old Liebetruth had not exaggerated: embezzlement, fraud, breach of peace, drunken violence, procuring, and obscenity—the charges added up to a pretty portrait. In 1896 Berger had been sentenced to a year in jail in Hamburg, and had made a jail-break.

But still Wannowski hesitated. Aside from Anna Müller's statement, he still had nothing substantial that linked Berger himself with Lucie Berlin on the afternoon of June 9 or later. But he was spurred to action at last that afternoon when a new witness named Gertrud Römer was brought to him. She attested that on the morning of June 11—the day on which the gruesome torso was fished out of the water—she had seen a man on the riverbank near the Reichstag, carrying a large rectangular package and leading a black dog on the leash. Her description of the man fitted Berger, of the dog the black cur that had crouched at Berger's feet the time the police had called on Johanna. Could it be that she had seen Berger when he was carrying part of Lucie Berlin's corpse to the river, leading the animal in order to look like a good citizen up early in order to walk his dog? Wannowski waited no longer; he ordered Detective Blume to arrest Berger and Johanna Liebetruth and have them brought to Alexanderplatz headquarters.

At this time word reached Alexanderplatz that some fourteen-year-old boys had seen a tuft of hair drifting in the Charlottenburg ship canal. Boatmen pulled it out of the water and found that the hair belonged to a child's head, to which two arms were tied crosswise with string, the remains of some red woolen cloth, and a newspaper: the head and arms of Lucie Berlin. Wannowski and Wehn hastened to the scene, where they found an excited crowd and the Chief of Police—who, having been at a fire nearby, had at once sped to the canal to demonstrate his omnipresent zeal. Wannowski, reporting Berger's arrest, was praised for it and in the next breath scolded for not yet having secured a confession. Controlling the impulse to answer back, Wannowski examined the bundle, saw that the paper was the remains of an issue of the *Berliner Morgenpost,* and waited until the horrible remains were on their way to Strassmann and Schulz at the morgue. Then he raced back to Alexanderplatz to pick up Berger. Ignoring the man's alternately arrogant and toadying protests, he took Berger with him to the morgue and straight to the table in the autopsy room where Lucie Berlin's head and arms were at that moment being laid out. Wannowski was using a method dating back to the beginnings of detective work—one which would seem sheer barbarism to humanitarian reformers, but had often driven murderers to immediate confession. Berger turned white and trembled; but he was either innocent or so hardened by his many dealings with the police that he quickly mastered himself. In a tight voice he asked what they wanted of him. Why had they brought him here? Then, without waiting for a reply, he added that he had nothing to do with the child's death. Wannowski gave up his effort to extort a confession by shock tactics and took his prisoner back to Alexanderplatz.

A few hours later the newspapers came out with extras announcing the story of the new finds in the canal, and exhorting the police to solve the crime speedily. Late in the afternoon of June 15 Wannowski and Wehn began interrogating Theodor Berger and Johanna Liebetruth. For five hours without a pause Wannowski questioned Berger on his activities between June 8 and June 11. He tried to trap the man in contradictions and persuade him at least to admit that he had seen Lucie Berlin in the hallway outside his apartment at noon on June 9. Berger, scarcely thirty-five, but with the dissolute features of a man ten years older, displayed an actor's assortment of faces: now indignantly respectable, now assertive, now humble and flattering, now insisting on his honor and his irreproachable love for children. But throughout that long grilling he did not deviate from his account of how he had spent the days from June 8 to June 11.

On June 8, his story went, he had gone with Johanna to jail, where she had to report for her three-day sentence. On the way back he had run into an acquaintance named Mulatto Albert on Unter den Linden. They had walked together for a while, and on Friedrichstrasse had met a music-hall singer. Berger had offered Mulatto Albert and the girl Johanna Liebetruth's apartment for a rendezvous. Later he had gone to a night spot, The Golden Cow, and had spent the night there, had got into a brawl early in the morning, and finally started for home. At half past eleven his sister had visited and fixed him a lunch of herring and potatoes. At one fifteen she had left. Then he had gone to sleep, he said, until evening when he took the dog out for its walk. On Brunnenstrasse he'd met a girl who had no place to stay. She had spent the night with him in Johanna's apartment, and on the morning of June 10 vanished; Berger did not recall her name and was rather dim about her appearance. June 10 he had slept most of the day, and did not hear about Lucie Berlin's disappearance until the afternoon. He had gone for a short walk, then slept again until the morning of June 11, when Johanna came home from jail. It was only from her, he said, that he learned Lucie's body had been found. When confronted with Anna Müller's statement about his presence in the hallway with Lucie Berlin on June 9, he said that was just the crazy talk of a half-blind and half-deaf old idiot. He called the neighbors' statements about suspicious noises in the apartment imagination, and dismissed Gertrud Römer's testimony as the babble of a dumb streetwalker.

Even though Berger had not been able to describe his alleged bed-mate of the night of June 9, or name a single person who could corroborate his story, by late that evening Wannowski had no illusions about the situation. With the evidence he had in hand, he could never put Berger on trial. Things looked up, however, about eleven o'clock that evening, when Wehn reported the results of his interrogation of Johanna Liebetruth. Wehn, too, had taken hours; for a long while the woman had maintained a stubborn silence—until at last she began expostulating that the arrests were "screwing up" her marriage to Berger. Her silence broken, Wehn managed to extract the following story from her.

She had come home from jail at eleven o'clock in the morning on June 11, and found Berger lolling on the bed. In the hallway she had met neighbors and heard about Lucie Berlin. She told Berger, who at once said that Lenz must have done it, and she had agreed. But shortly afterward they dropped the subject of Lucie Berlin and began quarreling. She admitted that she was extremely jealous. When she noticed that a pillowcase bearing the inscription "Sweet dreams" was not in its usual place, she suspected that another woman had been in the apartment during her absence. Berger finally admitted that he had lent the apartment to Mulatto Albert and his singer. Then they had made up. But in the afternoon, when she was tidying the bedroom, she opened a large hamper and noticed that another, smaller basket which she kept inside it was missing—a child's wicker suitcase. Suspicion rose again and she once more accused Berger of infidelity. She knew him only too well. When he'd had too much to drink, he "needed a woman right away—he was like a bull at those times." (She said this with a touch of pride.)

She kept after him until he confessed that on the night of June 9 he'd taken another woman to the apartment. He had had no money, he said, and so had finally given her the little wicker suitcase to pay her off. Johanna Liebetruth had by now fallen into such a fury of jealousy that she began to scream. Berger then closed the windows and barked at her to stop fussing about a worthless suitcase; then he had embraced her and actually declared: "You know, Jo, it's good to have you back," then added: "Tell you what, I'm going to marry you." She had been "stunned"; for in jail a fellow prisoner had boasted that her boy friend was going to marry her as soon as she got out, and Johanna had remarked: "Berger would sooner spend ten years in the pen than marry me." But now Berger insisted that if it weren't Saturday and already too late, he would post the banns at once, but that he would go to the Registry first thing in the morning on Monday. At that she had been "happy enough to forget all about our argument." And Berger had actually kept his word; she'd spent the last few days in ecstasy, until the police came along and "screwed up" everything.

Years later Wannowski remarked that that evening, when Wehn finished his report, they had looked at one another with the same thought in their minds. Wannowski had already had a glimmering of it when he first heard about Berger's sudden decision to marry. But here was a new clue: the wicker suitcase. Why had Berger suddenly declared his "love" and made his marriage offer when the quarrel broke out over that suitcase? Encountering the child in the hallway, had he lured her into the apartment under some pretext? Had he, half drunk as he was, been seized by that uncontrollable sexual impulse Johanna Liebetruth had described with pride? Suppose, then, that the child began to scream once she found herself alone in the apartment with him. Had he throttled her, violated her, and then, to conceal his act, cut up the body and packed parts of it into the suitcase, so that he could take it to the river during the night, or at dawn? Was that why the wicker suitcase had become so sensitive a point with him that he volunteered to marry Johanna Liebetruth rather than face a quarrel about it?

Returning to Berger, Wannowski continued his routine questioning for a while, then suddenly asked whether Berger knew Johanna Liebetruth's wicker suitcase. He thought Berger turned pale and began to tremble again. If so, the man quickly recovered. Nevertheless, he made a slip, for he said he had never seen any such suitcase. Did any reference to the suitcase seem so dangerous that he denied something he could not very well deny, after having lived so long in Johanna's apartment? Or was he so sure of Johanna that he could count on her never saying anything that might incriminate him? Even when Wannowski repeated part of what Johanna had said, he seemed to consider for a moment, as if debating whether to persist in his denial. But then he tried to dismiss the "matter of the suitcase" casually, as if he had merely forgotten it. Oh yes, he had given the suitcase to that girl. But no matter how much the inspector urged him to recall the name and appearance of the woman, since it would provide him with an alibi, he could not remember. Only after prolonged questioning did Berger come up with something about a black jacket and a white straw hat. He didn't care what a girl's name was, or what she was wearing, he mumbled, but about other things entirely. The girl had had stinking little breasts.

Shortly before midnight Wannowski sent Theodor Berger back to his cell. By now he was convinced that there had never been any such bed companion. He would, however, ask for witnesses who might have seen a girl in black jacket and white straw hat, accompanied by a man of Berger's appearance, entering 130 Ackerstrasse on the night of June 9, or leaving the building with a wicker suitcase the following morning. Then Wannowski went to look in on Wehn and Johanna Liebetruth. He knew her type well, knew the curious mixture of instinct and sentimentality in the psyches of such women. He was familiar with their longings for petit-bourgeois respectability. Although Johanna Liebetruth was Berger's abject slave, although her dearest wish was to marry him, and although she did not mind his criminal habits—far from it—there were limits. Certain crimes, a woman of her type would not accept. If she thought he had murdered a child, that was the end. And so Wannowski took over the interrogation with a single aim in view: to sow distrust in the woman.

Why, he asked, did she think Berger wanted to marry her all of a sudden, after having put it off for eighteen years? Was it because he wanted to deflect her attention from the suitcase? And what had become of the suitcase, really? Did she believe the story Berger had told her? If she, Johanna, spent the night with a man, would she be content with an old wicker suitcase for payment?

"Certainly not!" Johanna retorted, proudly.

Then why did she believe Berger could have palmed off the suitcase on the other woman? Or had he done something else with it? Something he was afraid would come out? Hoping these thoughts would prey on her dull mind, Wannowski had Johanna Liebetruth taken back to her cell.

3

On the morning of June 16 the *Berliner Morgenpost* carried a highly emotional story:

"The population of Berlin will breathe a sigh of relief, as if freed from a nightmare, to learn that the real killer of little Lucie Berlin has at last been apprehended. The horrible crime that snuffed out this young life will be duly punished. The fearful act of violence was committed in 130 Ackerstrasse itself, in an apartment next door to that of Lucie's parents. While the mother was anxiously looking for her daughter, the child gasped out her life under the knife of an inhuman monster, separated by only a thin partition from her parental apartment. A procurer named Berger . . . is the murderer."

One may well ask how the *Morgenpost* could be so certain about it all. Wannowski and Wehn were personally convinced that Berger was the criminal; but there was a vast difference between this and possessing the requisite legal evidence. To be sure, a police search of the Liebetruth apartment yielded several issues of the *Berliner Morgenpost*. This proved that the newspaper was read in the apartment, and bits of the paper had been found sticking to Lucie Berlin's arms. What was more, the search also uncovered a knife wrapped in old underwear. The weapon was sent to Professor Strassmann, who was to decide whether it could have been the "instrument of mutilation." But these finds added up to nothing by themselves.

Throughout the sixteenth of June, Wannowski and Wehn spelled each other as interrogators. Berger did not yield an inch. He had not lured Lucie Berlin into the apartment, violated her, killed her, nor packed the body into the suitcase and thrown it into the Spree. What little progress was made was in the interrogation of Johanna Liebetruth. Wannowski's carefully planted seeds of suspicion were sprouting. She seemed to be brooding blackly over the suggestion that Berger had been ready to marry her only to silence her about the suitcase. But she was still wary of saying anything that might be harmful to Berger. Wehn picked up only a few possibly useful details, during spells when her antagonism took the upper hand. Berger, he learned, was prone to violence. He sometimes started beating Johanna so hard that she had to flee by jumping out of the window. He had threatened her with a knife. As far as she knew, he was not partial to children. But when he was in the grip of his sexual impulses, he did not care who it was, so long as it was female.

During a pause in the questioning Johanna, talking at random, revealed that Lucie had been in her kitchen the day before she had to go to jail. The child had played with the dog on the floor, and had kicked her legs in the air. Lucie already had full, white thighs. Berger had been watching her.

But however significant such details seemed, none of it was proof. In the course of that long day Wannowski began to feel that there was no hope of Berger's breaking down and confessing. As for Johanna Liebetruth, even if she blurted out everything she knew, she could only blacken

Berger's character. She could not produce any real evidence because she had not taken part in the crime. Again and again Wannowski's mind reverted to the wicker suitcase. If his guess were correct, and Berger had carried the dismembered body of Lucie Berlin to the river in that suitcase and then thrown the thing into the water either with the body or after it, the suitcase must be floating in the Spree, as well as the dead girl's legs. Hence it ought to turn up. If it were found with parts of the body in it, or with some traces of recent use, it would certainly be a vital piece of evidence against Berger. For the first time the idea of bloodstains came to Wannowski's mind; he could almost see a wicker suitcase floating in the Spree, splotched with Lucie Berlin's blood. That very night he and Wehn went to the examining magistrate, Dr. Massmann, and urged that notices be posted asking the public to look for the missing suitcase.

On the morning of June 17 the citizens of Berlin learned that a wicker suitcase was being sought in connection with the murder of Lucie Berlin, and that this suitcase might be of crucial importance in convicting the murderer. The particulars were listed: the suitcase was two feet long, a foot wide and eighteen inches high; the wickerwork was rather loose, the catch damaged, so that the lid easily sprang open. A special inquiry also went out to all barge men whose boats traversed the length of river where the corpse was found.

That afternoon word reached Alexanderplatz that the final fragments of Lucie Berlin's corpse had been found. A cabman had noticed a suspicious package in the river. It contained—wrapped in the brown wrapping paper of a Berlin department store—the dead child's right leg, still with shoe and stocking on. Shortly afterward someone noticed a second soaked package near Schiffbauerdamm. It contained the other leg. But Professor Strassmann, who duly examined the finds, could tell nothing more about the murderer.

The thought of a bloodstained suitcase continued to obsess Wannowski and Wehn. Their sense of frustration was transmitted to Examining Magistrate Massmann, who took them to task for this exclusive concern with a missing suitcase. Why not search the Liebetruth apartment for blood, which should surely show up there if Berger was the murderer? He was told that policemen and officials of the Identification Service had already gone over the apartment to no avail, but this did not satisfy Massmann. Perhaps, he suggested, those people had not had enough experience in detecting traces of blood. He suggested that the one chemist in Berlin who had made a name for himself in that field be asked to conduct a new and more thorough hunt. That man was Dr. Paul Jeserich.

Jeserich, son of a Berlin furniture mover, had first studied the chemistry of foods, but he had early become interested in the criminological aspects of chemistry, and had spent many years testing for poisons. In the eighties he went on to study a wide variety of stains and similar clues, photographing them with apparatus he made himself. Thanks to photomicrography, he could detect clues at the scenes of crimes which had previously been passed over. A heavy-set, mustachioed, self-assured man who liked good food, playing the zither, and sailing, he could throw himself into his work with single-minded devotion. In the field of testing bloodstains he had acquired a degree of experience altogether extraordinary for his time.

4

On the day Jeserich arrived at 130 Ackerstrasse, the scientific study of bloodstains had already passed through memorable phases. The pioneers of forensic medicine in the middle of the nineteenth century had faced the problem of determining whether the spots at the scene of a crime, or on a suspect's clothing, actually came from blood. Experience had taught that not every reddish spot meant blood. Bloodstains could be brown, tan, yellow, green, even gray. Much depended on the age of the stain and on the effects of temperature, dampness, or light. As a first step in scientific procedures, bloodstains of all kinds and colors had been kept on plates, to permit the identification of suspicious spots by comparison.

The development of microscopy, and the discovery that blood consists of red blood cells (erythrocytes), white blood cells (leucocytes), and a watery fluid (serum), had suggested the idea of identifying bloodstains under the microscope by the typical shapes of red blood cells. But these cells lost their shape and lumped into an amorphous mass when the blood dried. Microscopic examination yielded results only when a solution of caustic potash and alcohol was mixed with the dried bloodstain. If the substance in question was blood, the red blood cells separated out of the lump, unless the stains were too old or too small. Besides this, the technique did not always work.

In 1863 the German scientist Schönbein had discovered another method for demonstrating the presence of blood. He had observed that the coloring matter of red blood cells, hemoglobin, contained an enzyme which caused hydrogen peroxide to form a white foam. Contact with the hemoglobin resulted in a violent reaction, the hydrogen peroxide breaking up swiftly into hydrogen and oxygen. The hemoglobin attracted the oxygen because of its ability to bind oxygen in the lungs of men and animals, whence it was carried by the blood to the organs of the body, where it released the oxygen again. The hydrogen peroxide reaction was so sensitive that it revealed the presence of blood even where the blood had been washed off and could no longer be discerned under a magnifying glass. Unfortunately, in the following several decades it had been found that not only blood, but also other substances such as rust, saliva, sperm, and certain shoe polishes, would produce the same reaction. Thus the Schönbein test was fallible, too.

The same was true of the blood test developed by the Dutch scientist Van Deen around the same time. While conducting experiments with alcoholic extracts from the West Indian guaiac, a shrub, he had noticed that the solution turned blue when it was mixed with turpentine and blood. Here, too, the effect depended on the power of hemoglobin to bind oxygen; hemoglobin extracted the oxygen from the turpentine and transferred it to the guaiac. Even faded bloodstains many years old formed the telltale blue within minutes. Finally, around the turn of the century, O. and R. Adler developed another blood test. Their reagent was a chemical developed by the firm of Merck: benzidine. It too proved extraordinarily sensitive, coloring the solution blue in the presence of mere traces of blood. But since the benzidine test would now and then react to such materials as rust or iodine salts, it was—like the two earlier tests—only good for determining whether suspicious traces were present; other methods would have to be called on to prove that the reacting substance was in fact blood.

The earliest method of checking for blood had likewise been devised about the middle of the nineteenth century. Ludwig Teichmann, working in Cracow, Poland, had made the following observation: If particles of a suspected blood spot were dissolved with the addition of sodium chloride and glacial acetic acid and the whole mixture warmed, crystals formed only in the presence of blood. These *hematin* crystals represented definite proof that blood had been found. The test might come out negative if the blood traces were on rusty pieces of metal; but if it were positive, the presence of blood was certain.

The search continued for some method of identifying bloodstains which would be 100 per cent reliable. Toward the end of the nineteenth century such a technique became available. It involved the spectroscope, which can detect the nature of every chemical substance by the characteristic lines in its spectrum. Hemoglobin has a characteristic absorption spectrum; and spectroanalysis can deal with the most minute quantities of the sought-for substance. Around the turn of the century, however, this method was still little used by specialists in forensic medicine.

Nevertheless, by that time a whole arsenal of methods had been developed for detecting blood. Some criminologists had even attempted to deduce the course of a crime from the location and shape of blood spatters. The French researchers, Florence and Fricon, had worked out a whole system for classifying bloodstains caused by dripping, splashing, spurting, or grazing contact. Round stains, or roundish jagged stains, for example, indicate that the blood fell vertically; oblong stains result from impact at various angles. Blood that spatters perpendicularly but with no great force against a vertical plane leaves stains quite different in appearance from blood spurted obliquely to left or right, or up or down. Blood falling vertically upon horizontal surfaces produces different types of stains according to the height. Blood oozing out drop by drop and falling upon the same spot can easily be identified by the shape of the stain. Spurting arterial blood can be distinguished from splashed blood. The stains formed by dragging a bleeding body are quite different from those imprinted on a vehicle that has run over or hit a person or animal.

Multifarious as these researches were, on one point they had all failed up to the turn of the century. There was no way of distinguishing between the bloodstains left by a human being and those of an animal. The urgency of this problem was obvious. Proof of blood alone usually did not mean much in criminal cases. The suspect on whom bloodstains were found could claim that the blood came not from the victim, but from some animal, or from meat. Conversely, every poacher tended to claim that stains on his clothing were from his own blood. "I had a nosebleed," was an argument heard daily. Now and then microscopic examination even confirmed this, for the blood would be mixed with cells from the nasal mucous membrane. On the other hand, the absence of these cells did not prove much, for they do not always show up in a nosebleed.

For a time the French scientist Barruel had attempted to identify blood by its odor. The blood of cattle boiled with sulphuric acid yielded the typical odor of a cow barn, Barruel maintained, while the blood of men so treated smelled like human sweat. Then for some fifty years, there were efforts to follow up the caustic potash–alcohol test with microscopic examination of the red blood cells. In man and mammals these are circular disks without nuclei (except for camels and llamas, in which these cells are elliptical); other vertebrate animals, from birds to fishes, have nucleated, oval red blood cells. So far, so good, but there was still no way to tell the blood of most mammals from that of men.

Fresh blood made it easier since the red blood cells differ in size in men and animals. Those of man are largest, with a diameter of 0.0003 inches; in cattle the average diameter is 0.00025, in goats 0.00015 inches. Fine measurements of this sort sometimes gave difficulties even with fresh blood; moreover, the method was useless for dried blood, because in the drying process the original shape of the cells was distorted. Even when the cells could be separated from the coagulated mass, their original form and size could not be restored. Thus all measurement was impossible. As for the white blood cells, they seemed to offer no help at all in this matter.

When Jeserich received the assignment to search the Liebetruth apartment, just three years had passed since this vexing problem had been solved virtually overnight. On February 7, 1901, Paul Uhlenhuth, Assistant Professor at the Institute of Hygiene at the small German University of Greifswald, announced in the *Deutsche medizinische Wochenschrift* that he had developed a method for distinguishing human from animal blood, no matter how small the traces. There was a story behind this communication, which was initially received with skepticism. Back in 1890 Emil von Behring had worked out the principle of antitoxins. When animals were inoculated with small quantities of diphtheria toxin, their blood serum, the watery component of the blood, formed antibodies against diphtheria. These substances distinctly promoted recovery in diphtheria patients. From that time on, scientists made haste to find other curative serums. A new branch of science came into being: serology. In the course of such serological research Uhlenhuth, in the summer of 1900, had observed a curious phenomenon. When he injected large quantities of protein from chicken eggs into rabbits and later mixed the blood serum of these rabbits with the white of an egg, the rabbit serum possessed such an "anti-effect" upon the chicken's egg proteins that these proteins were, so to speak, knocked out of the clear solution and fell to the bottom as a cloudy precipitate. If, on the other hand, Uhlenhuth tested the same serum against the white of eggs from gulls, pigeons, or turkeys, nothing happened. When, however, he injected the protein of a pigeon's egg into a rabbit, a substance developed in the rabbit's blood serum which would precipitate the protein of pigeon eggs.

Pursuing these experiments, Uhlenhuth injected blood from a chicken into a rabbit to determine whether the rabbit serum would also generate antibodies against the blood proteins. Sure enough, he obtained a serum that produced a flaky protein precipitate as soon as it was mixed with the blood serum from a chicken. This same serum was completely ineffective when mixed with blood or blood serum from human beings, cattle, dogs, or pigs. But if Uhlenhuth injected cattle blood into other rabbits, he obtained a serum that specifically precipitated cattle blood. Obviously, there were unequivocal differences among the proteins in the blood of different species. Within a few months Uhlenhuth could produce special rabbit serums for precipitating the proteins in the blood of human beings and many different types of animals. He could thus identify blood of almost any type within a few minutes. His method had only one flaw: blood from closely related animals, such as the horse and donkey, could not be distinguished because the proteins were too much alike. This was also true of the blood of human beings and apes.

In December 1900 Uhlenhuth began testing his method on dried bloodstains of different origins and ages—with success. Even very small and extremely old traces of blood could be differentiated. It sufficed to dissolve a bit of the bloodstain in a salt solution, then test the liquid with a number of rabbit serums containing a wide variety of antibodies. As soon as a whitish precipitate formed the identity of the bloodstain was clear; it had to be the blood for which there were antibodies in the particular serum.

Once the doubts were dispelled, Uhlenhuth's method stirred great enthusiasm in criminological circles. In 1902 Julius Kratter, Professor of Forensic Medicine at Graz, Austria, thought he had discovered possibilities for error in Uhlenhuth's "precipitin test," as it was now called. But Uhlenhuth showed that the errors were due to improper preparation of the materials by Kratter's Japanese assistant Okamoto, whose bloodstain solutions were insufficiently clear and clean and whose test serums were too concentrated. Henceforth, Uhlenhuth insisted, the test serums must be obtained from official sources, either from the Institute of Hygiene in Greifswald or from the world-famous Robert Koch Institute in Berlin. Moreover, he recommended that the serums be checked each time by applying them to samples of known blood and observing the reaction.

After some time, instances cropped up when the material underneath the bloodstain, such as tree bark, confused the issue. Such cases were exceptional. Nevertheless, Uhlenhuth introduced a further precaution. Before every blood analysis, a solution of the substance on which the stain had been found was tested to see whether any disturbing precipitation effect could be produced. Refined in this way, Uhlenhuth's test for the differentiation of human and animal blood did not fail a single time. In a large number of trials it proved to be the decisive factor in a conviction or an acquittal. No one who had ever seen it done doubted for long that it was one of the great, fundamental discoveries in scientific criminology. Soon it would be used everywhere. But in June 1904 the precipitin test was still the specialty of a few German and Austrian experts in forensic medicine.

Even a man like Paul Jeserich did not officially apply the method, although he knew of it. To the great majority of criminologists it was as unknown as it was to the public—including the knowledgeable Berlin public.

5

On the morning of June 20 Paul Jeserich thrust his stocky figure in among the sizable group of men gathered in Johanna Liebetruth's kitchen. Wannowski, Wehn, and Examining Magistrate Massmann were present, along with several people from the Identification Service, but Jeserich was soon the center of attention. Although the members of the Identification Service, founded only eight years before, had applied themselves to learning the methods of identifying bloodstains, Jeserich the outsider was still the expert on this subject. In addition to the kitchen, Johanna Liebetruth's apartment consisted of a bedroom. The rooms, now that they were unoccupied, made an even worse impression on the detectives than before. Everything was filthy and disagreeable. The cracked, smoke-stained ceilings were low, the floorboards crude, rough deal. The cracked panes of the small windows were dusty and flyblown. The bed was unmade; dirty clothes littered the floor.

Jeserich inspected the floors, the tattered rugs, the walls, the furniture, and finally the clothing in and outside the clothes closet. He had a good many objects wrapped in clean paper to be taken to his laboratory. Included were a rug, the large hamper, Berger's underwear and shoes, all the knives, a cleaning rag, and finally the trap of the kitchen sink drain. In his experience blood occasionally lingered in the trap after a murderer or abortionist had cleaned up.

Jeserich then took blotting paper soaked in hydrogen peroxide and pressed it against suspicious spots on the floor. Only one spot—a rather large reddish stain under the bed—foamed up. Jeserich had the stained floorboards sawed out and wrapped. At a few other places in the kitchen he pried dirt from between the floorboards and put it into envelopes. Finally, between the sink and the stove, he found some interesting spots on the kitchen wall. He had this section of wallpaper ripped off and added to his collection. After the rooms and their furnishings had been photographed, the place was put under police seal. Jeserich returned to his laboratory and went to work.

For the next three days, Jeserich's interim reports to Wannowski and Wehn were totally discouraging. No blood could be found on the rug, on the pieces of clothing, in the sink drain, on the knives, the floorboards, or the dirt from the cracks. Hydrogen peroxide and tincture of guaiac did produce slight reactions here and there from spots on the clothing. But if these were blood, careful washing had removed so much that there could be no positive proof. The only bloodstains of any importance were found on the wallpaper. But these were unquestionably bedbug blood; the legs of crushed bedbugs were distinctly visible under the microscope.

By the evening of June 23 it was clear that the hunt for bloodstains had failed. The wicker suitcase remained the last hope of bringing Berger to justice. For no matter how many reasons there were for suspecting him, the only proof left must be that suitcase. As Wannowski was leaving Professor Strassmann after a final conversation on the afternoon of June 23, even this point began to seem treacherous. Assuming that the suitcase could be found, and assuming that it had floated in the river with the dead girl's body, would there be any chance of finding bloodstains on it? Was it conceivable that bloodstains would not be leached out by the water?

Strassmann replied that if even a tiny trace of blood still clung to the wicker, the Uhlenhuth reaction could probably demonstrate the nature of the blood—the reaction was superlatively sensitive. It all depended on whether the blood had already dried before the suitcase came into contact with the water.

Friday, June 24, and Saturday, June 25, passed. Wehn had the vagrants who spent their nights near the Spree rounded up and asked whether they had noticed any wicker suitcases drifting in the river. Nothing came of this inquiry. Then, late on Sunday afternoon a Frau Buchholz, the wife of a coal dealer, came to the headquarters of the Tenth Precinct with her nephew, a barge man named Wilhelm Klunter, who lived in the nearby suburb of Gross-Wusterwitz. Klunter had gone to visit his aunt that afternoon, and in the course of the visit the talk had turned to Lucie Berlin. It turned out that Klunter had not read a newspaper for weeks and knew nothing about the case. Hence he had not reported finding and fishing out of the waters a small wicker suitcase with a sprung lid and nothing inside it but a hairpin. He had stuck the suitcase under the staircase in his home in Gross-Wusterwitz.

The sergeant on duty took Klunter over to Alexanderplatz at once. Wehn was called from his Sunday dinner by telephone. Excited, but filled with nervous apprehension, he asked Klunter to go home as quickly as possible and fetch the suitcase. Nevertheless, it was next morning, June 27, before the barge man returned to Alexanderplatz with it.

Wehn was there, waiting for him, and inspected the wickerwork with care. Within twenty minutes he was convinced that this suitcase fitted the description Johanna Liebetruth had given of it. The size, type of weaving, color, and damaged catch all agreed. Small particles of newspaper and wrapping paper, which reminded him of the wrappings around the parts of the child's body, were stuck to one of the ends of the suitcase. On that same end were several reddish spots that might well be from blood. Wehn informed Wannowski and had Johanna Liebetruth brought in to watch her reaction when she saw the object.

On entering Wehn's room, Johanna exclaimed instantly: "Why, there's my suitcase." She went up to the table and with mounting feeling examined the suitcase on all sides and tested the catch. Her suitcase had been a bit more saggy, she finally said. But this was explicable. The wicker had swelled in the water and tightened up. Johanna had no doubt that it was hers, and Wehn could sense her suspicions of Berger growing. He readily answered her when she asked where the suitcase had been found; for what he had to tell her could only speed the process of making a breach between her and Berger. When she heard that the suitcase had been fished out of the Spree only a few hundred yards from the spot where the torso of Lucie Berlin had been found, she broke out into ugly imprecations and, dropping all restraint, rattled off the names of a dozen persons who would be able to identify the suitcase. Wehn immediately ordered a roundup of these witnesses and had all who could be found quickly brought directly to Alexanderplatz—prostitutes and semiprostitutes, workmen and their wives. Some were only partly sure they recognized the suitcase; others, in particular several women who had recently been "subletting" a bed in Johanna Liebetruth's apartment, identified it without question.

A trial showed that the suitcase fitted neatly into the large hamper in which it had always stood. Immediately after this test, the precious object was taken to Professor Strassmann and Dr. Schulz. Schulz calculated, from the measurements of Lucie Berlin, that it would have been quite possible to pack her corpse into the suitcase. Schulz proceeded to examine under the microscope the reddish spots on the side of the suitcase. This was one of those lucky cases in which the red blood cells could be distinguished without difficulty; thus there was no question that the stains came from blood. Embedded in the bloodstains were fibers of wool that had obviously been stuck to the basket by the drying blood. The microscope showed them to be the same as fibers from Lucie Berlin's skirt. The blood must have been dry before the suitcase was thrown into the water; that alone explained the fact that the stains had not been washed away.

In the presence of Professor Strassmann and Paul Jeserich, Dr. Schulz performed the Uhlenhuth test with all the care and solemnity proper for so novel a procedure. Working in the autopsy room of the morgue, he followed Uhlenhuth's instructions to the letter. From the bloodstain on the suitcase he obtained a clear, reddish solution. He then prepared another solution from an unstained part of the wicker, and a third solution of known human blood. Into each solution he dropped Greifswald serum containing human blood antibodies, in a dilution of 1:1000. If the bloodstain were from human blood, within two minutes at the latest a ring-shaped cloudiness, gradually thickening, should form in the test tube, the cloudiness of precipitating proteins. In fact, it took only 70 seconds for the precipitation to begin in two of the test tubes. Only the test tube containing the solution made from clean wicker showed no precipitation of proteins. There could be no doubt that the spots on the suitcase came from human blood.

On December 12, 1904, Berger—still denying the charges—was brought to trial in the Second District Court of Berlin. For the crowds which streamed toward the courthouse in the foggy morning, and certainly in the minds of many of the jurymen, the verdict was already a foregone conclusion. Berger's defense attorney Bahn—later to become a famous criminal lawyer—fully realized the key importance of the Uhlenhuth test. He did everything he could to shake the demonstration that the stains on the suitcase had been human blood. He reminded the jury of the objections Kratter had raised to the Uhlenhuth method as late as 1902. He quoted the Berlin forensic physician Strauch, who had at various times made capital of the fact that Uhlenhuth could not distinguish human from ape blood. Strauch, who was something of a wit, had attempted to make a count of the apes in Europe ("except for the Rock of Gibraltar") which theoretically might produce bloodstains that could be taken for human blood. In Berger's case, however, such speculations were purely farcical. Finally Bahn insisted on calling August von Wassermann to the witness stand, to testify as an expert.

Wassermann—later to become world-famous as discoverer of the Wassermann test for syphilis—had come within a day of anticipating Uhlenhuth's discovery. A thirty-five-year-old assistant at the Berlin Institute for Hygiene, he had independently hit on the same method of identifying bloodstains. He and his associate Albert Schütze published their work on February 8, 1901, just one day after Uhlenhuth. Undoubtedly Bahn counted on his feeling a certain bitterness for the man who had robbed him of the glory. But Wassermann was far too honorable to be influenced by such feelings. He testified that the prosecution scientists had worked with care and precision, and that he agreed with their conclusions.

On December 23, 1904, the deathly-pale Berger was permitted to say a last word before sentencing. His declaration struck many as a piece of arrant blasphemy, coming from a man of his sort: "I am just as innocent as Christ when he stood before the Pharisees and Pilate said: There is no fault in this man," he said.

The jury pronounced Theodor Berger guilty of killing Lucie Berlin; the court sentenced him to fifteen years in the penitentiary.

6

Forty-five years later, in the summer of 1950, a French criminologist and journalist who as a young man had witnessed the trial of Theodor Berger, and who had also known Wannowski, wrote:

"When I think back today on those misty December days in 1904, I must admit that never in all these years have I been bothered by any doubts regarding the guilt of that unsavory figure on the witness stand. He was indeed the murderer of Lucie Berlin. The finding of the suitcase closed the circle, and the proof that the stains were human blood welded the ring of evidence.

"Today, when identification of bloodstains has become standard practice in criminology throughout the world, it is difficult to imagine the impact made by Uhlenhuth's discovery in 1904. It laid the basis for criminological or forensic serology, which since dominates the field. With that discovery began the building of the structure of blood testing as we have it today; and the case of Lucie Berlin was a symbol of that beginning. Nevertheless, I have often thought of the defense attorney Bahn and wondered why he did not stand up and cry out to the jury: 'Gentlemen of the jury, even if we concede that the blood on this suitcase is human blood, does that prove that it is the blood of Lucie Berlin, as everybody in this courtroom assumes? Where is there the spark of proof that this blood differs from the blood of millions of other people, any one of whom might have come into contact with this suitcase? You are all bemused by this new and wonderful way of demonstrating the presence of human blood from even the tiniest speck. But we forget that there is no proof of *whom* this blood came from; no one can possibly say whose blood it is. Not one scientist or criminologist on the face of the earth is able to declare that the blood on this suitcase is Lucie Berlin's blood.' I dare say such an appeal would not have altered the verdict pronounced on Theodor Berger. The sum total of the incriminating evidence was too convincing. Nevertheless, there would have been sense to such an expostulation. Like all human agencies, criminology could not take two steps forward at once. In December 1904, after the means for distinguishing human and animal blood had been devised, only a few persons of imagination looked forward to the next task: to demonstrate that a given bloodstain came not from a human being in general, but from a particular human being. The possibility seemed an absurd dream, and no one suspected that the scientific basis for at least partly achieving this dream had already been laid in that same year of 1901 in which Uhlenhuth contrived his method."

The Frenchman who wrote these lines at the age of nearly seventy was right on several counts, and especially so in regard to the strange double significance of 1901 for the development of forensic serology. In fact, on November 14 of that year an inconspicuous paper was published in the *Wiener klinische Wochenschrift*. It bore the title "On Agglutination Phenomena of Normal Human Blood" and contained the essence of what the French writer had called the next task. The name of the author was Karl Landsteiner.

The paper began: "Some time ago I observed and published the fact that blood serum of normal persons can frequently agglutinate the red blood corpuscles of other healthy individuals." Landsteiner pointed out that there must be differences in the blood of different persons which produce an incompatibility reaction, manifested by agglutination of the corpuscles. "The aforementioned agglutination," he concluded, "can also be produced with serum that has first been dried, then dissolved. It even succeeded with a solution made from a drop of blood dried on canvas, preserved for two weeks, and then dissolved."

Karl Landsteiner was thirty-three years old and assistant to Professor Anton Weichselbaum at the Institute of Pathology and Anatomy of the University of Vienna.

A shy young man, devoted entirely to his profession, his work at the University's First Surgical Clinic had made him aware of the helplessness of medicine in dealing with many illnesses. This had led him to withdraw from practice and return to medical research. He was particularly interested in pathology, bacteriology, and serology.

The fact that red blood cells clumped—or, to use the scientific term, agglutinated—was not unknown in 1901, for such agglutination sometimes led to death. The process had been observed by those daring physicians who had attempted the first transfusions of fresh blood from the veins of healthy persons into the sick and old. Statistics from 1871 reported 146 deaths out of 263 transfusions! From this fact, the famous Viennese surgeon Theodor Billroth had reasoned that there must be different types of blood which were not compatible. But his hint was ignored. The German physiologist Leonard Landois had noticed that mixing animal with human blood, or mixing the blood of different animals, led to agglutination. But no one had properly studied the phenomenon. Pathologists examining the blood of corpses who had never received a transfusion had the impression that many as yet unknown diseases led to clumping of the blood cells. Agglutination thus seemed to be a problem of pathology rather than a phenomenon of healthy blood.

No one can say what prompted Karl Landsteiner in 1900 to experiment with mixing the blood cells and blood serums of different persons. It was just one more of those innumerable experiments which sprang from the desire to penetrate more deeply into unknown territory. One winter day Landsteiner took blood from nimself and from several of his colleagues: Dr. Störk, Dr. Pletschnig, Dr. Sturli, Dr. Erdheim, and the laboratory assistant Zaritsch. He separated the serum from the cells by centrifuging. Then he distributed the serum from Dr. Störk's blood among six test tubes. To each of these tubes he added blood cells of one of the participants. In the first tube, in which Störk serum was mixed with Störk blood cells, nothing happened. Likewise nothing in the combination Landsteiner-Störk; his own blood cells seemed to be compatible with Störk's serum. But in the other four test tubes, in which blood cells from Pletschnig, Sturli, Erdheim, and Zaritsch were mixed with Störk serum, there was instantaneous agglutination of the cells, visible to the naked eye. An experiment with six portions of Landsteiner serum worked out in the same way; this serum was compatible with Störk cells and with Landsteiner's own, but promptly agglutinated the cells of the other four men.

Dr. Pletschnig's blood serum behaved quite differently. It accepted the blood cells of Störk, Landsteiner, Zaritsch, and Pletschnig himself, but not those of Sturli and Erdheim. With Zaritsch it was still another matter. His serum left his own cells and those of Störk, Pletschnig, and Landsteiner unaffected, but clumped those of Sturli and Erdheim. Finally, the blood serums of Sturli and Erdheim showed a third possible reaction. These were compatible with the blood cells of Störk, Landsteiner, Sturli, and Erdheim, but not with those of Zaritsch and Pletschnig.

Sample after sample yielded the same sort of result. From this Landsteiner deduced that there were characteristics in everyone's blood which were either compatible or not. The distribution of these characteristics seemed to follow a certain regularity. The serum of one group of persons, to whom he gave the designation Type A, agglutinated the blood cells of a second group, B, but never those of its own group. The serum of all persons in Group B did not clump the cells of its own group, but invariably those of Group A. The serum of Group C agglutinated the cells of Groups A and B, but those of Group C were not agglutinated by the serums of Groups A and B. According to these rules, Landsteiner and Störk belonged to Group C, Sturli and Erdheim to Group A, Pletschnig and Zaritsch to Group B.

This led to the following conclusions: there were two kinds of cell characteristics in human blood, A and B. But the serum of certain individuals held a mysterious factor which acted against the cell characteristic B, making its existence impossible, so that only characteristic A remained. The serum of another group of human beings held a factor opposed to cell characteristic A (which eliminated that characteristic from the person's blood). The serum of a third group of persons contained a factor opposed to both A and B, both of which were therefore absent from the red blood cells. Thus Landsteiner had identified three groups, A, B, and C. He named the factors in the serum which produced agglutination in the cells to which they were opposed "agglutinins," and the characteristics of the blood cells agglutinogens. A year later, in the spring of 1902, Dr. Adriano Sturli himself and Alfred von Decastello happened on a fourth blood group. A small number of persons had blood which did not clump the cells of either Group A or Group B. This blood contained no agglutinins, which meant that its cells must have both cell characteristics, A and B. Sturli and Decastello called this blood "typeless." A few years later the "typeless" blood was rediscovered by the Czech scientist J. Jansky and the American W. L. Moss. Unfortunately, Jansky and Moss created some confusion by giving numerical designations to the groups which Landsteiner had identified with letters. In 1911, finally, Professor von Dungern of Heidelberg and his assistant from Warsaw, Ludwig Hirszfeld, proposed the designations which have since become standard. Landsteiner's Group C became Group O and the "typeless" category Group AB. The blood groups now recognized are thus: A, B, AB, and O.

As has so often happened in the history of the sciences, in 1901 no one in Vienna, let alone outside that city, grasped the importance of Landsteiner's discovery. No one realized that here was the cause of fatal complications in transfusions. Generally overlooked as Landsteiner's findings were, it is rather remarkable that another young man in this same Vienna should have seized on the idea of applying these experiments to the field of criminology.

The young man in question was Max Richter, who in 1901 was employed as an assistant in the Institute for Forensic Medicine of the University of Vienna. He quickly saw that the new tests would complement the Uhlenhuth test for human blood, with the result that bloodstains of specific human beings could be identified. In the spring of 1902 Richter got in touch with Karl Landsteiner. At this time Blood Group AB had not yet been discovered. The methods for determining blood groups were just being developed. Richter's line of thought was the following: Thanks to the Uhlenhuth reaction it was possible to check the alibis of many suspects who claimed that the stains on their clothing came from animal blood. However, there was no way to check their claims that the blood was their own, not some victim's, because one person's blood could not be distinguished from another's. Might not Landsteiner's discovery be turned to good use here? If, for example, a solution from a bloodstain caused agglutination of a suspect's blood cells, that would prove that the stain was not from the suspect's own blood. One question, however, still had to be answered: were the anti-A or anti-B factors of serum, which Landsteiner had found, still present and active in dried blood-stains?

In the summer of 1902 Richter undertook the first experiments to determine blood groups from bloodstains. At first, as Landsteiner had done, he tested the blood serums of six volunteers, in this case prison inmates, for their respective agglutinating effects. Then, having established their serological reactions, he dropped specimens of blood from those convicts on cloth, glass, and wood, and let the spots dry. After periods of varying length (three days to four weeks), Richter dissolved his synthetic bloodstains. It was fairly easy to scrape them off the glass and wood; on cloth, he had to cut out particles of the cloth along with the blood. He now centrifuged out red blood cells from fresh blood taken from the same six convicts and made suspensions of the cells in physiological salt solution. He placed one drop of each of the six suspensions on a hollow-ground slide and examined the slide under his microscope, with the drop hanging down. Often a full hour of patient observation was necessary. Sometimes nothing happened. But in other cases the dry bloodstain within the drop slowly dissolved and produced clumping of the red blood cells. The reaction followed the same lines as with fresh blood, except that the agglutination was considerably feebler. Stains more than a week old produced scarcely any result. Nevertheless, after his summer's work Richter was convinced that the technique would be valuable for his purposes.

In November 1902 he went to Karlsbad to attend a convention of German naturalists and physicians. He gave a talk on his work. But, like Landsteiner, he made little impression; Uhlenhuth's discovery put everything else in the shade. Blood group studies seemed a strange preoccupation, at most of marginal interest. Dashed, Richter returned to his Institute.

Thus the first attempt to make criminological use of the discovery of blood groups was passed over, as unremarked as the discovery itself. Landsteiner was too unassuming to fight for his new approach. He went on quietly pursuing a research program whose full value was to dawn on a later generation; in the course of it he made two more discoveries without which criminological blood testing today would not be possible. In model experiments he showed how the anti-A or anti-B factors attached themselves to the cells to which they were "opposed": anti-A to cells of Group A, anti-B to cells of Group B, anti-A and anti-B to cells of Group AB. The cells as it were took on a load of factors that were "hostile" to them. This happened even when the cells themselves were no longer recognizable as such, as a result of coagulation or drying in bloodstains, and so could not overtly manifest their chemical combination with specific anti-factors. This "loading up" or absorption could be demonstrated by indirect methods. If the serums which had been brought into contact with dried bloodstains were removed after a while, it turned out that they had lost their anti-factors, released these "antibodies" as they are now called, to the cells in the bloodstains. Suppose, for example, that a serum containing known A antibodies were mixed with dried blood of Group A and after a while removed. If fresh cells of Group A were now added to the serum, they did not agglutinate.

In further experiments Landsteiner proved that it was even possible to reverse this process of "loading up"; the A or B antibodies in serum could be freed from the red blood cells under the influence of heat.

The significance of these experiments for the near future was ignored in 1904-05. Disheartened, Landsteiner turned to other fields of research. In 1908 a major epidemic of infantile paralysis in Vienna prompted him to study poliomyelitis. He succeeded in transmitting the disease to monkeys and thus showed for the first time that the disease was not the outcome of a variety of infections, but was caused by a specific type of virus. Much other fundamental work followed. But none of it brought him the fame he deserved. After the outbreak of the First World War Landsteiner worked in a Viennese hospital for three years. He hoped that once the war was over he might obtain recognition and a secure place of work in research. When this hope, too, was shattered, he left his native city in 1919, accompanied by his wife and two-year-old son, and accepted a position as pathologist in a hospital in The Hague. Two years later the Rockefeller Foundation took notice of him. Simon Flexner, one of the great trail blazers in American scientific research, invited him to New York. Thus Landsteiner turned his back on Europe, prepared to take up again in the New World the investigation of the many unsolved problems of blood groups. No one bade him farewell, no articles of tribute were published; and possibly the whole science of criminalistic blood testing, which he had fathered, would never have come into being had it not been for another man like Max Richter who looked at Landsteiner's work with the unbiased eyes of youth and saw its potentialities.

7

September 7, 1915, was a curious and historic day. On that day a small, somewhat stooped man of about fifty appeared at the Institute of Forensic Medicine of the University of Turin in northern Italy. He was dressed in his Sunday best, a suit of peasant cut and indefinable greenish-black color. Tucked under his right arm he held a flat package wrapped in newspaper; his brown hat sat so clumsily that anyone could see he was not used to headgear of this sort. When he entered the Institute, he removed his hat and pressed it against his chest with his left hand, while respectfully holding out a letter to the first student he encountered.

The letter was meant for Dr. Leone Lattes, lecturer and research assistant at the Institute of Forensic Medicine. The student showed the man the way to a large, high room where Lattes was working with other young scientists. Lattes, at that time twenty-eight, a limber, lively native of Turin, opened the letter. It was from a Dr. Bertola, whose practice was in a working-class district of the city. He was sending Lattes a patient of his, a construction worker named Renzo Girardi, Bertola wrote. Girardi had a "family problem" with which he had come to Bertola, who found himself unable to aid the patient. From the little he knew of Lattes' current project, Bertola thought it possible that Lattes would be able "to relieve the poor devil."

Lattes led Girardi to his desk and invited the man to "tell me all about it." Even before speaking, Girardi deposited his package on the table, opened it, and took out of it a white shirt, which he unfolded. Lattes observed two brownish-red spots on the lower half of the shirt front. Raising his eyebrows, he asked whether Girardi was involved in a crime. The man shook his head vigorously. Then he began to tell his story.

On a Sunday at the beginning of June, three months before, he had gone to his native village a few miles outside of Turin to visit friends. He had gone to a tavern with them and had not returned home until late at night. His wife, Andrea, was very jealous. She had greeted him with accusations and revilings. It was nearly morning before he had finally got to sleep. But the real drama had begun after he awoke and took off his Sunday shirt, for he had sat up arguing with his wife so late that he had fallen asleep without undressing. To his dismay he saw on it two spots which seemed to come from blood. The worst of it was that his wife found the spots and instantly renewed her charges, insisting that the blood came from some other woman; now she was certain he had been unfaithful.

Since that morning Girardi's family life had been an inferno. His wife never stopped berating him. She had gone to soothsayers and fortune-tellers who had confirmed her opinion that Girardi had been philandering. The quarrels over the spots on Girardi's Sunday shirt had assumed such proportions in the course of the past three months that Girardi by now dreaded going home. Even if it might bring him peace, he refused to admit he was guilty, because he knew that he had not touched another woman.

The poor man had given considerable thought to the mysterious bloodstains. There were three possible causes for them.

1) He customarily bought the meat for the family's Sunday dinner, and prepared it by cutting away the bone before he turned it over to his wife. He had done the same on the Sunday in question, and had already been wearing his Sunday shirt at the time. It was possible that he had suddenly felt the call of nature and had taken care of it without washing his hands first, thus unwittingly smearing the blood from the meat on the front end of his shirt.

2) On that Monday morning when he took off his shirt, he had left it lying on his bed for a while. A woman friend of his wife's, Teresa Einaudi, had come into the house and offered to help make the bed. Teresa had been in the bedroom alone for a little while. Later Girardi had found out that she had been "unwell" at the time. And since he knew that Teresa Einaudi was not a very cleanly person, he thought it barely possible that she might have used the tip of his shirt for a purpose for which it was not intended.

3) Since his wife had so long been tormenting him with her jealousy, Girardi suspected that she herself might have smeared blood on the shirt, perhaps hoping to make him confess to infidelity.

Girardi concluded his story by averring that he was a poor man, but that he would willingly give everything he owned if Lattes could prove that the spots did not come from some other woman, but in one of the other ways he had suggested. Dr. Bertola had assured him, he said, that if anyone in Turin could provide such proof, it was Dottore Lattes.

Bertola had good reason for thinking so. Lattes, after completing his medical studies in 1909, had put in some years at German universities. In Munich he had met Max Richter and learned of Richter's earlier experiments. Thus, he had become interested in the fascinating problems of agglutinins and agglutinogens. A gifted linguist, he had read every-thing that was published on the question of blood groups. In the course of this research he had come across various papers by American, French, and Italian scientists who were trying to determine whether the ag-glutinins in blood serum remained in dried bloodstains. Their results had been contradictory, and these uncertainties had reinforced Lattes' desire to investigate the grouping of bloodstains. Up to the autumn of 1915, however, he had given his major energies to his lectureship at the University of Turin and had made scarcely any significant practical experiments.

It struck Lattes as both odd and comical that it should be a marital dispute, not a crime, which spurred him to action. But he felt sorry for the poor little fellow and moreover regarded this problem thus brought to him as a sign from fate. He would take on the job, he said, on condition that Girardi would prevail on his wife and Teresa Einaudi to come to the Institute of Forensic Medicine. Girardi rather dolefully gave his promise to do his best. Lattes then took a blood sample from the workman's ear lobe and waited to see what would come of the af-fair. To his surprise, both women turned up two days later. They talked and gesticulated wildly, both at once, the one ranting against her hus-band's bold-faced lies and the other against Girardi's insulting insinua-tions. But in the end both consented to give samples of their blood.

The first stage of Lattes' work, determining the blood groups of the three persons involved, presented no difficulties. The technique was well developed by now. Renzo Girardi turned out to have Group A. Andrea Girardi Group O, and Teresa Einaudi Group A.

Then began the crucial experiment: determining the blood group characteristics of the spots on Girardi's shirt. The simple practice of treating the bloodstains with the blood of suspects and observing the reaction—what Max Richter had done thirteen years earlier—did not satisfy Lattes. Since Richter's time, this branch of knowledge had been enlarged. It was now known that blood groups were distributed among the population in definite percentages: 40 per cent had Group A, an-other 40 per cent Group O, 15 per cent Group B, and about 5 per cent Group AB. Professor von Dungern and Ludwig Hirszfeld in Heidelberg had shown in 1911 that the thing was hereditary, and even that the inheritance followed certain laws which, however, had not yet been fully investigated. Lattes was now aiming for extremely precise results.

During that September of 1915 Lattes went to work with a degree of meticulous care which would elicit faint smiles from scientists of a later generation. His first task was to restore the dried blood and its serum as far as possible to its original degree of liquidity. For this purpose he cut both spots out of Girardi's shirt and weighed the cloth on his finest balance. The weight of one patch of cloth came to .0944 grams. Lattes then counted under the magnifying glass the number of linen threads forming the warp and woof of the stained cloth. He found 180 warp and 65 woof threads. Next he cut several pieces out of the un-stained part of the shirt, of approximately the same size as the stained fabric. Once again he counted threads and finally had a piece likewise containing 180 lengthwise and 65 transverse threads, which he weighed. The balance showed a weight of .0649 grams. Subtracting this weight from the weight of the bloodstained patch, he obtained the weight of the dried blood. It had long been a rule of thumb in research that the dry components of blood represented some 20 per cent of the total weight. Lattes therefore soaked his bloodstained pieces of cloth in dis-tilled water measured precisely to equal four times the weight of the dried blood of the stain. He thinned the resultant solution with physio-logical salt solution, making a 50 per cent dilution to avoid too concen-trated a serum. He then placed the vial in an ice chest. Now and again he pressed the cloth with a glass rod, to speed the dissolving of the dried blood. By the following day so much had dissolved out that Lattes was able to remove the now white specks of cloth from the dark-brown solution. This meant that all the dried serum contained in the stain had been transferred to the solution, along with all the agglutinins which might still be active in this serum.

Following Richter's procedure, Lattes placed a drop of the solution on each of two dimpled slides. Then he added a drop of fresh Group A blood cells to one drop, a drop of Group B to the other drop. With suppressed excitement, he examined the drops under the microscope. After half an hour, he saw what he had hoped for: the cells of Group B were distinctly agglutinated, but not those of Group A. In other words, the anti-B factor of the serum was still operative after three months. And the blood that had caused the spot belonged to Group A. Lattes repeated his experiment several times, always with the same result.

Thus, the possibility that the bloodstain came from Girardi's wife was excluded. It could only be from Teresa Einaudi or from some unknown person, or from Girardi himself. Since Teresa Einaudi, as she freely admitted, had indeed been "unwell" on the day in question, Lattes tried to determine microscopically whether the bloodstain might have come from menstrual blood. Cytology—the science of body cells—had learned that the cells of the vagina differed from other body cells, and that such vaginal cells were present in menstrual blood. Forensic medicine was beginning to make use of this fact. Since Lattes could find no vaginal epithelial cells in either of the two bloodstains, Teresa Einaudi was also excluded from the list of suspects. Lattes himself had a strong sense of Girardi's innocence. The chances were great that the blood had come from himself. To discover how Girardi might have stained his own shirt, Lattes asked the workman to come in for an examination. The cause was quickly uncovered. Girardi suffered from prostate trouble which he had never noticed, but which led to occasional bleeding of the urethra.

"This result," Lattes wrote in the report he published on the case in 1916 in the *Archivo di Antropologia Criminale, Psichiatria e Medicina Legale,* "restored peace to the family." Of far more importance than the case itself, bordering as it did on the comic, was the fact that determination of blood groups was thereby made part of criminology.

Even before Lattes' paper appeared, the Girardi case was being discussed in medico-legal circles in Turin. It reached the ears of an examining magistrate engaged in the investigation of a homicide. He sent Lattes the coat of a man named Aldo Petrucci who had been arrested in connection with the crime. Petrucci was a habitual criminal, and had been found with bloodstains on his coat which were regarded as highly incriminating. He denied any knowledge of the killing and offered the oldest of all alibis: that the blood had come from his own nosebleeds and had nothing to do with the blood of the murdered man. The bloodstains were only four days old, and had been proved to be human blood. But that fact alone did not suffice to refute Petrucci's story.

Lattes obtained the blood group of the corpse from blood taken out of the heart, then went straightway to Petrucci's cell for a sample of the suspect's blood. The victim's blood group was A, Petrucci's O. In examining the bloodstains on the coat, Lattes followed the same circumstantial procedure he had applied in the Girardi case, and arrived at an unequivocal result: the serum from the spots agglutinated red blood cells of Groups A and B. It therefore contained anti-A and anti-B factors, hence belonged to Group O. This was at least proof that the blood did not come from the victim and might have come from Petrucci's nosebleeds. On the basis of this finding, the police looked further into the case and Petrucci was completely exonerated.

This episode became a decisive turning point in Lattes' life. He would henceforth be passionately devoted to the cause of criminological serology. His paper, published in 1916, included a report on the Petrucci case, and he was confident that his method would be widely adopted. Unfortunately nothing of the sort happened. But Lattes had a temperament that was not easily discouraged. To be sure, he had to wait until 1923 before the next blood group case was referred to him—but he continued to delve into general theory.

The First World War halted criminological progress in Europe for several years. Lattes himself was kept from his work by military service. By 1922, however, he had done so much in the way of blood group research that the book he published that year, *L'Individualità del sangue nella biologia, nella clinica, nella medicina legale,* became an international textbook on the subject. In it he took up the problems of blood transfusion; he also dealt with the hereditability of blood groups, whose laws were so important to forensic medicine for solving one of the most common legal questions, the determination of paternity, especially of illegitimate children. But a central feature of the book was its discussion of group determination in bloodstains. Lattes had tried to simplify the involved procedures of his first tests. Chance had frequently come to his aid in this. Once he let flakes of blood dry on wood and other smooth surfaces. Then, without lengthy preparation, without weighing and dissolving, he placed the flakes in the slide of a microscope, added the suspension of test blood cells, slid a cover glass over the drops, and found that the serum agglutinins of their own accord dissolved in the corpuscle suspension and clumped the opposing blood cells. Thus all the complicated dissolving procedures he had used in earlier tests were rendered superfluous. Lattes had devised the simplest method for determining blood groups in stains.

At first glance this procedure seemed inapplicable to stains on absorbent textiles. But Lattes found a way to make artificial flakes of blood. He would first make an extract from the bloodstained spot, then drip this slowly onto a slide. A fan dried a drop at a time until a small encrustation of blood resulted.

Thus Lattes (by now Professor of Forensic Medicine) was thoroughly prepared for the problem that faced him in 1923 when he was called upon to assist justice in Modena. Thanks to his simplified slide technique, he was able to identify several one-and-a-half-year-old bloodstains on a silk cap. From the bloodstained clothes of a murdered man he determined the victim's blood group, which turned out to be B. The bloodstain on the silk cap likewise contained Group B blood. Confronted with this evidence, the murderer confessed.

The next case was marked by special circumstances. The trousers of a suspect had numerous red stains. Lattes soon determined that these stains came from red wine, not blood. But there remained a stain on the inside of the trousers pocket which undoubtedly came from human blood. The suspect desperately protested his innocence. He did not attempt to plead a nosebleed, but he could not say where the blood came from. The spots were three weeks old. Lattes found his blood group to be A, and the stain on the pocket belonged to the same group. Hence it could very well have been the suspect's own blood. Examining the stain under the microscope, Lattes found the limbs of a crushed flea which must have been engorged with the man's blood before being killed. With this one bit of evidence disposed of, it became clear that the innocent suspect had come under suspicion only because of an unfortunate chain of circumstances.

By 1925 Lattes' work had progressed so far that he was ready to publish a second account. As yet there was not a single report from any other quarter of the use of the method for criminological purposes. Consequently, Lattes now defined its value. To be sure, it could not tell unequivocally that a bloodstain came from one particular person; that could scarcely be expected, since Blood Group A alone, for example, was shared by 40 per cent of the human race. The procedure was again of no avail wherever the blood group of a victim coincided with that of a suspect. But blood group determination of bloodstains did permit the criminologist to narrow the circle of possible culprits. Suspects could be ruled out if the bloodstains on their clothing did not coincide with that of the victim. And if a suspect asserted that stains on his clothing were his own blood, these statements could be checked. Finally, it could help convince an accused murderer that the jig was up, when he could offer no credible explanation for stains that corresponded with the blood of a victim.

Appreciation for the method was gathering. Thus, a tribute came in from Georg Strassmann, the son of Berlin Professor Fritz Strassmann, when he delivered a lecture at Innsbruck in September 1924 to a meeting of German and Austrian forensic scientists. The subject of the lecture was the various means of determining paternity. In the course of it, however, he mentioned the importance of blood group determination to the criminologist. In every case of violent death or death from unknown causes, he urged, the victim's blood group should be determined at once, in order to have ready comparative data to check against any bloodstains that might later be discovered.

It was even more significant when Fritz Schiff, the thirty-six-year-old

Berlin serologist, promoted Lattes' method. Schiff saw to the publication of Lattes' book, "The Individuality of Blood," in German translation as early as 1925. Thanks to his influence, the German Society for Forensic Medicine invited Lattes to its annual meeting in 1926.

Schiff's opening address was a ringing cry for the new methods. "Today, twenty-five years after the discovery of blood groups, the German Society for Forensic Medicine is discussing the Landsteiner reaction for what is probably the first time," he declared. "Certainly forensic medicine cannot be accused of having prematurely rushed to put the Landsteiner reaction to practical use. . . . The credit for having applied it in practical cases must go to our Italian guest Lattes. . . . His procedures permit us to investigate bloodstains which can no longer be weighed with an ordinary chemical balance, which in other words weigh less than one tenth of a milligram. . . ."

Lattes could return to Turin with fair confidence in the future of his method: in those days, Germany was the leader in the field of criminology. If his method were accepted there it would be adopted everywhere. Still it was another year and a half before German authorities were faced with a case in which a bloodstain test decided the issue.

8

Seven persons heard cries that rent the stillness of the night over Gladbeck, a town in the industrial area of western Germany, in the early morning hours of Friday, March 23, 1928. These were two school principals and their wives, a doctor's housekeeper, the machinist of a coal mine, and a police sergeant. None of them bothered to find out who was screaming for help.

Nocturnal brawls had become more and more common in the restive Ruhr district, and the police sergeant was hardened to the point of indifference. He only paused briefly on his rounds. The machinist turned on the light, looked at the clock, saw it was 3:30 A.M., and tried to go back to sleep. He did not suspect that only a few feet from the door of his house on Schultenstrasse a man had just been killed. School Principal Deese, who lived on the ground floor across the street, at 11 Schultenstrasse, awoke at the same time, as did his wife. Deese went to the window in his nightshirt. But he could not see the scene of the murder—

the sidewalk in front of his house—because his garden hedge hid it from view. He observed a man's shoulders and head appear above the hedge and then vanish, as if stooping, appear again and vanish once more, and finally cross the street, where the figure was lost in darkness. Deese asked his wife the time, was told that it was three thirty-five, and shivering went back to bed.

Principal Adolf Daube, who likewise had an apartment in 11 Schultenstrasse, also slept in a room that faced on the street. He got up, looked at the clock, saw that it was three thirty, and went into his son's room. Nineteen-year-old Helmuth Daube was about to take his final secondary school examination, the *Abitur*, and had gone with some fellow students to the neighboring town of Buer. There the "Alte Herren," a prestigious student fraternity of the time, had arranged a beer party for potential new members—a procedure not unlike an American fraternity "rush." Daube found his son's bed untouched, but reassured his wife, who felt vaguely anxious about the boy, and went back to bed.

An hour later the doorbell rang wildly at the house of Dr. Lutter, whose housekeeper, Elli Mehring, had similarly heard and ignored the cries for help. When Dr. Lutter stumbled to his door, he found two miners on their bicycles. They reported that a short distance down the street lay a dying man; they had come upon him while on their way to work. Lutter threw on some clothes and ran to the spot. In the dim light from the bicycle lamps he made out a dark figure stretched on the ground—head on the curb, feet toward Principal Daube's garden gate. The doctor quickly ascertained that the person on the ground was dead, not dying. There was a frightful slash in the neck, reaching down to the spinal column. The face was so smeared with soot and dirt as to be unrecognizable. Over the pavement two pools of blood were spreading, one of which lay at some distance from the corpse on a slightly higher level of the sidewalk.

Lutter asked the miners to wait a moment, and since No. 11 was in total darkness he ran to his own telephone. It was 4:45 A.M. when he called the police. Detective Trampert asked him to stand guard until the police arrived. Then he rang up his superior, Inspector Klingelhöller, chief of the Gladbeck Criminal Investigation Department, as well as Detective Captain Pest, and the head of the regular police, Major Preuss. He also got in touch with the Criminal Investigation Department of the neighboring city of Recklinghausen, which according to the organization chart was to maintain a special murder commission for the towns and villages of the vicinity. Pest, Preuss, and Klingelhöller arrived at Schultenstrasse at 5:10 A.M. Preuss was not a detective and took little part in the actual investigation. As for Pest and Klingelhöller, much of what they did and what they omitted doing in the next several hours can be understood only if we consider the then current conditions of the criminal branch of the Prussian police force.

Since the end of the First World War, the Prussian criminal police force had a splendid record in Berlin and other large cities, but only a sad one in the provinces. The local police forces had pretty much to fend for themselves. The training of detectives left a great deal to be desired. Efforts to recruit able young people, with training in law, technology, or economics, were confined to Berlin and a few other large cities. There was scarcely any specialization in specific crimes; and permanent homicide commissions like Berlin's were either unknown in the rest of Prussia, or purely theoretical.

When the postwar crime wave reached an unprecedented crest toward the end of 1923, ordinary policemen without any special training were simply transferred to the criminal police. A year later the entire criminal police force of the State of Prussia was nationalized. Before the effective date of this measure, many local police heads promoted their friends and fellow party members among the detectives, without regard for ability or merit, simply in order to assure their own followers high rank in the national police service.

Forty-nine-year-old Detective Pest of Gladbeck had been appointed an inspector in 1918 and a captain in 1925 without any testing of his qualifications. Forty-two-year-old Inspector Klingelhöller had passed an examination in 1922; but his knowledge in the field of homicide investigation was pitiable. Nevertheless this state of affairs does not explain everything that happened that night of March 23.

When Pest and Klingelhöller, along with several assistants, arrived at Schultenstrasse, the carbide lamps from the miners' bicycles provided the sole illumination. It had occurred to no one to bring a floodlight, and none was sent for. Since the bicycle lamps were hardly adequate, the police decided to wait for daylight and the arrival of the homicide commission from Recklinghausen.

But Recklinghausen sent only a single man with the impressive title of Detective Director Schönermark, with a bloodhound. Although the criminal police in Recklinghausen had five detective captains and twenty inspectors, it had at its disposal no regular homicide commission—as it should have had, according to the organization chart. The bloodhound nosed about a bit, but did not take up any trail. Schönermark then felt his duty was done and left, instructing Inspector Klingelhöller to take over the investigation. After a cursory glance at the dead man's throat wound, Klingelhöller announced that the case was one of suicide. He had read in the newspapers that several young men of late had been ending it all by cutting their throats in this manner. In his subsequent report Klingelhöller supported this view by the following enigmatic statement: "At first I asked myself whether the case was one of murder or suicide. I considered the second possibility because in consequence of the throat wound the assumption of this possibility was justified."

It was decided to call in the district health officer, Dr. Marks, to examine the body. Assistant Detective Kraemer, sent to fetch the doctor, returned to report that Dr. Marks had no time now; he had to appear in court that morning. Neither Klingelhöller nor Pest could screw up their courage to remind Marks that he was officially obliged to check on such a case immediately. Since they did not dare touch the body before an official physician had seen it, they continued to wait. Nothing happened until shortly before six o'clock, when Principal Daube (wakened by conversations and the barking of the dog) looked out on the street. Recognizing Dr. Lutter, he went out to inquire what all the fuss was about. A moment later he knelt down beside the body, crying out: "My God, it's my son."

Before Daube staggered back into the house to tell his wife the terrible news, Dr. Lutter, who helped him to his feet, heard a few confused references to the boy's outing at Buer and the meeting of the fraternity in the Hotel Zur Post. Dr. Lutter thereupon proposed to Major Preuss that he himself telephone a doctor of his acquaintance who was a member of the same fraternity and might know something about the party in Buer. He ran to his house and was soon back with the information that in addition to the dead boy, two other students from Gladbeck had taken part in the beer party: Karl Labs of 5 Lambertistrasse and Karl Hussmann of 67 Hegestrasse. Hussmann came from abroad and was living with the family of Principal Kleiböhmer, who happened to be one of Dr. Lutter's patients.

At this point Captain Pest finally took things somewhat in hand. He sent Klingelhöller to check on Karl Labs and Detective Kraemer to make inquiries about Hussmann. In the general confusion he made no objection when Major Preuss and Dr. Lutter simultaneously announced that they would try to reach the Kleiböhmers' house by telephone and ask Karl Hussmann for information.

Klingelhöller arrived at the home of Karl Labs between 6 and 6:30

A.M. Labs was sleepy, but immediately became wide awake when he heard what had happened. They had all been together in Buer, he confirmed: Daube, Hussmann, he himself, and another student named Brettschneider. They had left the Hotel Zur Post at 2:10 A.M. He remembered the time exactly because there was a clock in front of the hotel. Since the streetcars had stopped running, they had walked the two or three miles to Gladbeck—Hussmann and Daube in front, he and Brettschneider behind. Brettschneider had taken his leave of them in Gladbeck, at the Heinrichstrasse intersection. He, Labs, had caught up with the two others and continued on with them as far as the Gladbeck town hall. Here their ways parted. Hussmann and Daube had walked on down Rentforterstrasse. That was the last Labs had seen of the two. He himself had gone to bed at three twenty. His brother, who slept in the same room with him, could confirm the time.

Then Hussmann had been the last person with Daube, Klingelhöller asked. He had, Labs replied, and since both were tipsy, they had walked along singing. Had Daube ever talked of suicide, Klingelhöller inquired further. Labs shook his head. He thought the idea absurd. It did not occur to Klingelhöller to inquire about the relationship between Hussmann and the dead boy. He had made up his mind that the case was one of suicide, and his petit-bourgeois imagination ruled out the thought that a young man who had enjoyed the benefits of higher learning might have been involved in a crime.

Meanwhile Dr. Lutter had succeeded in reaching Karl Hussmann by telephone. Hussmann answered the call at once. This rather surprised Lutter, who knew the Kleiböhmer house, having made professional calls there. The telephone was on the ground floor, in Principal Kleiböhmer's study, which was locked at night; the key was usually hung up in the stairwell. But Karl Hussmann himself lived on the fourth floor. Hussmann reacted to Dr. Lutter's tidings without particular emotion: "What, Helmuth is dead?" he asked, and offered to get dressed and come right over. He had barely hung up the phone when Detective Kraemer rang the doorbell. He had seen light in the hall, but was distinctly surprised when the door opened so promptly. Karl Hussmann, a tall, strong young man with a tousle of dark hair, stood before him in nightshirt and bare feet, and invited him in with a friendliness which took him aback at first. He was still more taken aback by the sight of Hussmann's feet. They were filthy, "like a workman who hadn't washed his feet for weeks." Kraemer, too, considered students as in a higher class. Moreover, he was already convinced by Klingelhöller's idea of suicide. Therefore he only asked whether Hussmann could give him any information about Daube's last actions. Hussmann readily replied: After parting with Labs, he and Daube had walked together to the intersection of Schultenstrasse and Rentforterstrasse. Here Daube had wanted to take his leave, but Hussmann had persuaded him to walk him home, even though that meant something of a roundabout way for Daube. They had parted in front of the Kleiböhmers' door, and Daube had gone home alone. That was all he knew.

When asked when they had parted and when he himself had reached his room, Hussmann became less glib. All he could volunteer was the fact that he had had to use the toilet several times because of all the beer they had drunk that night. The toilet was on the stair landing between the second and third floors. The last time he had gone down he had heard the telephone ringing, and while talking to Dr. Lutter the doorbell had also rung; that was why he had been on the spot so quickly to open it.

Kraemer thanked the young man and bicycled back to Schultenstrasse. A little later Hussmann followed him, hastily dressed in black oxfords, gray trousers, and a sports jacket, which he had put on right over his nightshirt. He arrived at the Daubes' house on his bicycle shortly before Klingelhöller's return. Leaning the bicycle against the fence, the young man greeted Dr. Lutter, who introduced him to Major Preuss. He cast only a few hasty glances at the corpse of his friend; standing some fifteen feet away, he repeated his story to the Police Chief.

Meanwhile day broke. Inquisitive miners and their wives pressed against the barrier the police had set up. The corpse still lay untouched on its back between the blood and another wet spot at its feet, now visible, which could not possibly come from blood. A detective at last photographed the scene. The pictures later proved useless because they had not been taken from all directions and were printed without a scale. Toward seven o'clock Klingelhöller returned, and Hussmann was introduced to him. The inspector requested the student to come closer to Daube. Hussmann nervously refused. Asked whether Daube had ever spoken of suicide, he replied with alacrity—unlike Labs: Yes, two years ago. At that time Daube's love affair with Principal Kleiböhmer's daughter had broken up, and he had thought of committing suicide. Daube had been a weak and vacillating person. Then Hussmann asked whether he might go into the house to offer condolences to his dead friend's parents. Klingelhöller had no objection. It caught his attention, however, that Hussmann circled around the blood on the ground; and as he observed this the detective instinctively looked at Hussmann's shoes. He thought he saw some dark-red blotches that reminded him of blood. Astonished, he followed the young man into the house and caught up with him in the vestibule.

Hussmann seemed totally surprised when the inspector asked him about the stains on his shoes and fell to studying the shoes closely. They were wet through and through, and there were several bloodstains on the uppers which could not be very old. Quickly recovering his poise, Hussmann replied that it must be the blood of a cat which he had caught "poaching" in his foster-family's garden a few days ago—on April 21, to be exact—and had killed.

Klingelhöller asked whether these were the shoes he had worn on his way home from Buer.

Yes, he had worn these shoes.

And why were they so wet?

It had rained during the walk home.

At this moment the first suspicion stirred in Klingelhöller, though not suspicion of murder. Rather, he thought that Hussmann might have been a witness of his friend Daube's suicide, had stepped into one of the puddles of blood, and was now reluctant to admit it. Might both have courted the same girl? Did Hussmann perhaps feel some guilt in the matter? But gullible as he was, the inspector asked Hussmann to remove his shoes. They were given into the keeping of Detective Rehlinghaus while he himself returned to the street.

There Captain Pest had laboriously arrived at a second decision. He sent a detective to the home of Dr. Meyer, the examining magistrate who would be in charge of the case, in the hope that Meyer could provide them with the requisite doctor. It was eight fifteen when the examining magistrate drove up and at least took purposeful action on a few matters. Klingelhöller reported to him in so many words: "Here is a typical case of suicide." Meyer merely glanced at the scene and asked: "Where is the weapon Helmuth Daube used to cut his throat? Did he swallow it?" The assembled detectives gaped in dismay. Meyer also called their attention to a bloodstained shirttail sticking through the fly of the dead man's trousers. To lose no more time, he requested Dr. Lutter to examine the corpse. Lutter had no knowledge of forensic medicine at all. But when he opened the trousers, he saw at a glance that Helmuth Daube had been emasculated with several cuts of a knife. Within a moment, the whole suicide theory collapsed, and Pest and Klingelhöller had to face the humiliating fact that they had wasted three crucial hours.

Captain Pest saved the situation by promptly appointing Klingel-höller head of a "temporary homicide commission," composed of the detectives who happened to be present. Klingelhöller, now determined to prove his mettle, swung completely around and jumped to the conclusion that Hussmann was the murderer. He ordered the student placed under guard in the Daubes' kitchen, while he himself drove to Hege-strasse to inspect Hussmann's room. Principal Kleiböhmer was not especially cordial and the first inspection was more than hasty. Nevertheless, Klingelhöller found the blue coat, blue suit, socks, and green hat that Hussmann had worn on the night of the murder. He looked for bloodstains on the clothing, but at the moment found nothing, and hurried back to Schultenstrasse with his booty.

Meanwhile Dr. Lutter, who in this crisis was fast developing a personal interest in criminal investigation, went to the Daube kitchen and asked Rehlinghaus whether he could see the student's shoes. What was on them were indubitably bloodstains. They were as large as pfennig coins, and must have splashed down from above. The surface blood had hardened to a film but beneath the blood was still liquid. Lutter estimated that the drops of blood had fallen on the shoes in the early hours of the morning. It occurred to no one, however, to make a record of Lutter's observations. While examining the shoes, Lutter turned to Hussmann and remarked that the blood was incriminating evidence against him. Hussmann thereupon became agitated and asserted that he sometimes had nosebleeds. Had his nose bled any time last night, Lutter asked. Hussmann said no, but at once asked Rehlinghaus whether frogs had blood. Because during the night he had happened on a frog on the street and had torn it "to pieces"; that must be where the blood had come from. Rehlinghaus listened in some perplexity to these wild words, and was relieved when Klingelhöller returned and asked Hussmann to put on his blue coat and come into the brighter light of the sunroom. There a bloodstain below the lapel immediately became visible. Hussmann's agitation increased; he now spoke of having had a cut on his finger. It turned out, however, that this wound was insignificant and had long ago healed. Klingelhöller thereupon decided to return to Principal Kleiböhmer's and conduct a more thorough search of Hussmann's room.

Detective Trampert was meanwhile ordered to take the shoes and clothes to the Gladbeck police station. Experienced bloodstain testers would have been horrified if they had witnessed the procedure. No material was more suitable for sopping up fresh bloodstains than the newspaper in which Trampert wrapped the shoes. The clothes were simply bundled together without wrapping. At the police station no one stopped curious officers and clerks from unwrapping and examining the evidence. The newspaper was damp. Whether it had absorbed blood was never determined. In any case, the dampness of the paper confirmed the fact that the shoes had been wet. And in fact Trampert found the soles and uppers soaked through, while the socks Hussmann had worn were completely dry. Trampert concluded that the shoes could not have got wet on the walk home, but must have been washed afterwards. There was not a trace of mud on the shoes. Detectives Baumann and Collesie observed this, but did not bother to set down these data. Unlike the shoes, the coat and trousers were dry. The detectives noticed several spots on the front of the coat that showed plain indications of having been washed and rubbed. Around these spots they found encrustations, the size of pinheads, which were obviously blood. They found a reddish streak in the inside of the right coat pocket, as though "a bloodstained hand had been thrust into it." No record was made of this observation either. No stain was marked. Later on there was no way to determine how many of the stains had been destroyed on the way to the police station, inside the station, and even afterwards.

Klingelhöller, now convinced that he had found the murderer, thought it best to take Hussmann along with him on a second search of the young man's quarters. But the distinctly hostile attitude of the Kleiböhmers caused him to confine his search to Hussmann's bedroom on the fourth and his study on the second floor, and omit the other places which had been accessible to Hussmann during the night, such as the stairwell and toilet. It occurred to him to ask the student whether he had had a handkerchief with him during the night. Hussmann said he had. Where was it? After a moment's hesitation Hussmann replied that it must be under his pillow. No handkerchief was found there, nor could it be located anywhere.

Detective Aschenbach, who had accompanied Klingelhöller, forgot to photograph the bed on which Hussmann claimed to have slept for a few hours that night (with interruptions). As a matter of fact, the bed looked as if it had been unused and rumpled deliberately rather than from the natural movements of a sleeping man. Nor was any search made for blood splotches on the floor or traces of blood in the drains. Aschenbach did pick up a shirt with a single streak of blood on the cuff. During the search Hussmann's agitation increased to such a pitch that his face became "livid." When Klingelhöller opened a briefcase that

Hussmann had taken with him to Buer, the young man leaned against the wardrobe to keep from falling. The briefcase contained objects intended for the party: an invitation card, a book of student songs, a fraternity badge. In among these things lay the buckskin sheath of a big jackknife; but the knife itself was missing. Klingelhöller, convinced that he had found a new clue, asked where the knife was. Hussmann replied that he had lost it. A burglar had tried to break into the Kleiböhmers' house on April 20, he said; he had rushed out into the garden, taking the knife with him for a weapon. He must have dropped it out there. What part of the garden? Hussmann no longer remembered. Then why had he taken the empty sheath with him to Buer? He did not know; probably it had been in the briefcase and he had overlooked it, Hussmann replied.

No proper record was kept of these significant details. Hussmann was asked to come along to the police station. There Trampert called Inspector Klingelhöller's attention to the fact that Hussmann's shoes had been thoroughly soaked. Klingelhöller thereupon sent a detective to question the other two students, Labs and Brettschneider. The detective returned with the information that both students had come home from Buer with dry shoes, which indicated that Hussmann must have lied about the reason for his wet shoes. Like Trampert, Klingelhöller concluded that Hussmann had washed his shoes after coming home from committing the murder. Klingelhöller did not, however, think through the problem of the bloodstains; otherwise he would have asked himself how, when, and under what conditions fresh blood could have fallen on the shoes washed *after* the crime. Several detectives were dispatched with the assignment of searching the Kleiböhmer garden for the lost knife. These men combed the place for several hours, but found no knife.

At last, at three o'clock in the afternoon, the district health officer, Dr. Marks, was ready to undertake an autopsy of the victim at the Gladbeck cemetery. As it turned out later, this was largely useless for criminological purposes. No one thought of determining the dead boy's blood group. Apparently Dr. Marks had never read Georg Strassmann's paper on the importance of this step.

In the afternoon Hussmann was for the first time "officially" interrogated by Klingelhöller at the police station. The record of the hearing —all of four pages long—contained only a few references to the incriminating evidence and not a single question about the motive that might have prompted Hussmann to kill Helmuth Daube. Nevertheless, at five o'clock Klingelhöller took Hussmann to Examining Magistrate

Meyer to obtain a warrant for his arrest. But the inspector's summary of the evidence was so slender that Meyer released the young man after half an hour's discussion. Assistant District Attorney Neef, who had listened to the proceedings, remarked sarcastically: "If a workman were suspected of such a crime, he would have been arrested immediately on the basis of these same facts. But I guess Hussmann is too well known here. . . ." Perhaps there was something to this charge. Be that as it may, Klingelhöller really had not put together enough evidence for a warrant. Through initial indecision and incompetence he had wasted the crucial first hours. Hussmann was now free and able to dispose of all remaining clues. All that Klingelhöller retained as possible evidence was the material he already had in hand: a pair of shoes, a coat, a suit, a shirt, and the traces of blood on these articles.

9

In March of 1928 there was not a single official in the whole region around the cities of Recklinghausen, Essen, and Gladbeck who had much knowledge of developments in the field of blood group testing. On March 24 a messenger from Klingelhöller appeared at the Chemical Investigation Office in the city of Recklinghausen. This office usually processed industrial analyses, but occasionally it performed Uhlenhuth tests. The messenger turned Hussmann's shoes, coat, suit, shirt, stockings, and a single glove over to the head of the office, Dr. Baumann, and asked whether Baumann could determine whether the blood came from Hussmann or from Daube. Baumann replied that he could say whether the blood was human, that was all; he did not mention the possibility of determining the blood group; he evidently knew little about this field and was unaware that an immediate determination of blood group should be made in an institute of forensic medicine equipped for the purpose.

In preparing his experiment, Baumann found stains on the shoes, on the front of the coat, in the right coat pocket, and on the right leg of the trousers. He also discovered certain spots on the coat on which some liquid had run down, and then been rubbed away. In his report he did not mention that he carried out the usual tests for blood, which had by now been standardized for decades. He undertook the Uhlenhuth test at once, cutting the spots out of the cloth and dissolving the blood on the shoes in physiological salt solution. On March 27 Dr. Baumann informed Inspector Klingelhöller that he had found human blood on all the articles. That same day Baumann inspected the clothes and shoes once more, and found more spots. In his second report he did indicate his awareness that material should be saved for possible subsequent testing. But since he again cut spots out of the coat and the lining of the pockets, and dissolved more of the spots on the shoes, only a few of the traces remained—and most of these were the smallest. On March 28 Baumann reported by telephone that with the exception of one spot on the lower part of the coat, he had found human blood everywhere. He evidently thought that his part of the job was done.

To a man like Klingelhöller, the determination of human blood (as in the time of the Lucie Berlin case) seemed a conclusive bit of evidence. He had meanwhile been on the lookout for possible motives for the crime. The investigations he conducted in person or through other detectives were neither thorough nor systematic. Nevertheless, from the elder Daubes and several fellow students, some remarkable facts had come to light about the relationship between Karl Hussmann and Helmuth Daube.

Hussmann had been born in Guatemala. His father was a German who had acquired a coffee plantation in South America before the First World War. In 1921, while en route to Europe, he had died on shipboard of tropical dysentery. Hussmann's mother, also German, was related to Principal Kleiböhmer's wife. Her husband had regarded her as too unstable to raise their children, and had named Principal Kleiböhmer as their legal guardian. Karl was the youngest; the elder boys were at the Universities of Göttingen and Munich. Kleiböhmer also administered the inheritance of the Hussmann sons, which was invested in Dutch funds. Karl Hussmann had said of himself that "somehow there are strains of tropical Central America in my nature." According to his fellow students and teachers, he could on the one hand be exaggeratedly courteous and gentle, on the other hand domineering and brutal. After some hesitation three of his fellow students, Kahmann, Stackwitz, and Harsch, admitted that they were afraid of Hussmann. Kahmann said: "In his class everyone said that Hussmann is perverted. . . . He went after little boys." It was also charged that Hussmann was a sadist: "He liked hitting people with thin rods or umbrella ribs. . . ." "He liked killing cats. . . . " "He was always friendly to a person's face, but nasty behind his back."

Hussmann's relationship to the murdered boy certainly had odd overtones. According to everyone's account, Helmuth Daube had been a gifted, somewhat unworldly and dreamy boy. When Hussmann failed to be promoted in 1926, he dropped into the same class as Daube. Soon the older boy set out to win Daube's friendship. In 1927, when Daube and Ilse Kleiböhmer fell in love, Daube had admitted to his mother that Hussmann could not tolerate his "loving" anyone else, for which reason he had more than once tried to break away from his peculiar friend. He had had a certain experience with Hussmann on a hiking trip, which, however, he had not revealed to his father and mother. Of late Hussmann had been trying to persuade the boy to go to the University of Erlangen with him; but Daube had told his parents that he would not do so, that it was better if he and Hussmann attended different universities.

Against this background, the results of Dr. Baumann's blood analyses struck Klingelhöller as virtual revelation. Did not the proof of human blood refute all of Hussmann's stories about cat blood and frog blood? Klingelhöller evidently concluded that he could force a confession out of Hussmann if he surprised him with the scientific evidence that the stains came from human blood. On March 27, at 8:30 P.M., Klingelhöller arrested Hussmann and interrogated him in the presence of Detectives Mikfeld and Baumann. The questioning went on until one o'clock in the morning. A report full of gaps, taken down from memory, was the only later record of this interrogation. Not till the following day was a "stenographic interrogation" held, that is, one taken down word for word by a stenographer. It showed all too bluntly that Klingelhöller had not the vaguest notion of how bloodstains might have been evaluated. He was forever repeating the same question: How did the blood get on the shoes? How did the blood get on the coat? Where did the blood on the trousers come from? Klingelhöller had counted on the mere phrase "human blood" to throw Hussmann off balance, and had not prepared a single precise question. He did not say: "The blood on your shoes dripped from a certain height. It did not arise from contact with the pool of blood on the scene of the crime, because I saw you step around that pool. It is not cat's blood and it is not frog's blood. It is human blood. You did not remember having any nosebleeds. Can you give me any other explanation for the bloodstains on your shoes except that you attacked Helmuth Daube from behind, cut his throat, and had your right foot forward to support yourself while doing so? Is that how the blood fell on your shoes?" Because of the inadequate autopsy, and his own total lack of training, Klingelhöller could not construct the possible course of the crime. It soon became evident that his supposed trump card, "human blood," did not scare Hussmann. The young man quickly realized that the inspector felt inferior to him. He pounded on the table, drank glass after glass of water; his face twitched and he occasionally grew angry and insulting. But each time he recovered his self-control in a way astonishing for his age. He had only contempt for the blood test. "Sheer nonsense," he said. "Why, that's rot . . . idiocy . . . go ahead, write down 'rot.' "

Nevertheless, on the following day Examining Magistrate Meyer issued the warrant he had refused on March 23. He did so because Hussmann persisted in offering impossible explanations for the bloodstains. He could easily have withdrawn his former statement and recalled that he had had a nosebleed after all; that would at least have accounted for the human blood. Instead he insisted with mysterious consistency that he had come into contact only with animal blood. He now even alleged that a week before the night of the murder he had been at the Gladbeck slaughterhouse and had stepped into pools of blood; probably he had spattered blood on himself at the same time.

On the night of March 28, after the shock effect of Klingelhöller's "human blood" had failed, it suddenly occurred to Dr. Marks to try blood group determination of the bloodstains. He told the inspector he had heard of a Professor Müller-Hess in Bonn who "is supposed to be a whiz in this field." Since he himself had neglected to find out Daube's group, he now hoped that Müller-Hess would be able to obtain it from the blood on Daube's clothes. As for Hussmann, Marks took a sample of his blood on March 29. It was not until the afternoon of March 30 that a policeman arrived at the Institute for Legal and Social Medicine on Theaterstrasse in Bonn, bearing a large box. It contained, crudely packed, a test tube with a sample of Hussmann's blood, all the dead boy's clothing, and the articles of Hussmann's clothing which had already been examined at the Chemical Investigation Office in Recklinghausen.

Viktor Müller-Hess, who had taken over the direction of the Institute for Forensic Medicine of Bonn University in 1922, was forty-five years old at this time. A thickset, round-headed man, he had the kind of vitality which predestined him to a leading role in the field of forensic medicine. He had many ideas about blood tests, and kept up to date, reading all articles about new methods.

Müller-Hess had Hussmann's clothes put on a clotheshorse, in order to reconstruct their normal position; that simplified both the finding of bloodstains and conclusions about their origin. To his dismay he saw that of all the original splotches and spots, at best two still lent themselves to the Lattes group determination method. He was faced with the typical botchwork of ignorant testers, who had ruined most of the test material. Only Hussmann's coat and shoes preserved a few sizable flakes of blood which could be peeled off and which therefore promised useful results in a blood group test.

In the past two years Müller-Hess had had a good deal of experience with the Lattes method. He had found that it was vital to examine every stain as quickly as possible, because the agglutinins were apparently much shorter-lived than Lattes himself thought. Why the devil had the stains not been brought to Bonn as early as March 23, Müller-Hess angrily asked himself.

There was of course no trouble about determining Hussmann's blood group. He had Type O. Determination of Daube's blood group from the bloodstains on the clothes was not quite so simple, but proved possible; it led to the determination of the blood group as A. When Müller-Hess next proceeded to add fresh A and B cells to the still usable flakes of blood from Hussmann's coat, he found that both types were agglutinated. There was no doubt of the results: the spots on the coat belonged to Group O. They could therefore not be from the victim, but might be from Hussmann himself. In testing the remaining large splotches of blood on Hussmann's shoes, however, the result was different. These spots belonged to Blood Group A—Daube's group. Müller-Hess scraped off every flake of blood he could; the result in every case was Group A.

Next Müller-Hess proceeded to look for further usable clues on Hussmann's coat. He found something that had hitherto escaped all the detectives—a tiny cut on the collar of the coat, which corresponded with a cut of equal size on the jacket collar beneath. The cuts looked as if a knife had slipped in the course of a struggle. This observation confirmed his suspicion that there might be Group A bloodstains on the coat also. But although he came upon a spot that had been obviously washed and scrubbed, there was not enough blood left for his tests. In order to have some idea of the extent to which the coat had been stained with blood, Müller-Hess sprayed it with hydrogen peroxide. Foam formed on many spots of the coat and of the trousers where they showed beneath the coat, but there was no foaming wherever suit jacket and trousers had been covered by the coat.

After studying the records of the case, Müller-Hess drew his own conclusions. From a photograph of the throat wound he concluded that the deadly wound in the throat had been inflicted from left to right, and that the murderer must therefore have stood behind his victim. The incision was jagged, as if it had been started and stopped several times; Daube had evidently tried to wrest the knife away. This would also account for the wounds on his hands and forearms. Experts in forensic medicine like Müller-Hess were aware that a killing of this sort could be accomplished without the murderer's being bloodied. Trousers and shoes might be stained if one foot were placed ahead of the other, as the murderer took a firm stance during his crime. It sometimes happened that the murderer stained himself with his own blood, because his nose knocked violently against the back of the victim's head, and thus he suffered a nosebleed. This might explain both the staining of Hussmann's clothing with his own blood and also his curious refusal to admit to a nosebleed as the explanation for the bloodstains.

Müller-Hess sent his report early in April: "The very few bloodstains which were left for me to examine on Hussmann's coat belong to the same group as Hussmann himself. . . . Whether there may have been other stains on the coat that could have come from the murdered Daube, like the spots on Hussmann's shoes, could no longer be determined, since the available stains had been already removed for tests elsewhere. . . . The case could have been better clarified if the sparse stained material had been used for tests that could have thrown significant light on the facts. Moreover, it would have been of great value if the position, form, and size of all the bloodstains had been determined before their removal."

On March 31, while Müller-Hess was still occupied with his tests, a workman named Kowalsky reported at the police station in Gladbeck. He said he had been working in Principal Kleiböhmer's garden, and "of his own accord" had found in some loose earth the knife that belonged to Karl Hussmann's knife case—the knife that Hussmann alleged he had lost in the garden on March 20. Oddly enough, this knife was found at a spot that had been searched very thoroughly by detectives on March 23.

Faced with these latest developments and the reports from Bonn, Chief District Attorney Lingemann of Essen, who had at last entered the case as the responsible higher authority, called in two experienced men from Berlin. These were Ludwig Werneburg, forty-five, who had studied law and had been a detective inspector since 1919 (he was at present both head of the Armed Robbery Department and one of the foremost homicide commissioners of the capital), and Rudolf Lissigkeit, thirty-two, likewise a detective inspector, and an experienced investigator of homicides. The two men arrived in Essen on April 1 and studied the documents before proceeding to Gladbeck. Lissigkeit noted: "We felt that the ten-day-old crime could hardly be solved any longer, so badly had everything been blurred by the incompetence and lack of technical knowledge on the part of the detectives who had conducted the investigation thus far. We might just as well have bought our return ticket at once. The lost time could no longer be recaptured."

As always in such situations, the local authorities did not hail Werneburg and Lissigkeit with enthusiasm—if only because the two new detectives had to interrogate all the others in order to put the results of the previous investigation into a shape which might possibly be useful in court.

Once this was done, they systematically set about reconstructing the motive and a logical course of action for the crime. The hints about Hussmann's homosexuality were swiftly substantiated. Hussmann's behavior while being held for trial was partly responsible for this. In jail he tried to be transferred to the cell of a young embezzler to whom he addressed ardent love letters, which began with the salutation "darling" and contained such sentences as: "If I were with you, nothing would matter." Patient, tenacious questioning of his fellow students also finally brought to light the incident of the hiking trip in the Eifel mountains, which had led to coolness between Hussmann and Daube. In 1926, during a school outing, the class had spent the night in a youth hostel. "Hussmann visited Daube in his bed," the other boys related. But that was not the only significant incident. The accounts of Hussmann's efforts to involve younger boys in sexual relations continued to mount up. There was talk of Hussmann's engaging in obscene dances during another class outing. "He behaved like an animal. . . . We were afraid of him," one boy reported. Inspectors Werneburg and Lissigkeit took down statement after statement on the fateful relationship between Daube and Hussmann. Daube, the weaker of the two, had repeatedly tried to break free, but was again and again subjugated until at last he had seemingly summoned up the strength for a final break. There were other indications of Hussmann's mistreatment of his friend. A fellow student named Harsch reported: "More than once I saw him inflicting pain on Helmuth Daube . . . so that Daube's eyes filled with tears from the pain. . . ." Three other students, Schöller, Erpenbock, and Kappen, described another episode they had witnessed on an outing to Lake Laach. During a ride in a carriage, Hussmann, his face distorted, had forced Daube onto his lap by twisting his thumb so that Daube screamed in pain.

Did not all this point to a vengeful, sadistic homosexual who had subjugated Daube and killed him when the boy broke away from him, perhaps after one last nocturnal quarrel—killed him so that he would never belong to anyone else?

The motive seemed logical. What would decide the case, Werneburg and Lissigkeit thought, was so accurate a reconstruction of the order of events that the suspect would confess when confronted with it. The first point would be to prove that Hussmann had lied when he asserted that Daube had accompanied him to the Kleibӧhmers' house and then gone home alone. Since this would have meant a considerable detour for Daube, he could hardly have arrived in front of his home at three thirty, when the screams were heard. It seemed much more likely that Hussmann had gone home with Daube.

Werneburg and Lissigkeit finally arrived at the following reconstruction: Hussmann had walked Daube home. There Daube had given Hussmann a final refusal: he would not go to Erlangen with him. At that, Hussmann had attacked him from behind, perhaps at the moment Daube stepped up to the garden gate to urinate, an act which excited Hussmann. The mysterious wet spot on the sidewalk suggested this possibility. Hussmann had cut Daube's throat, and while doing so had got some blood on himself, probably from his own nosebleed. Only his shoes were heavily stained with blood—possibly when he turned the dead boy on his back—for the body must have lain face downward at first—to emasculate him. Hussmann had wrapped the "prize of this mutilation"—for such was the euphemism of the day—in his later vanished handkerchief, and hurried home. There he had wiped all the bloodstains he could see from his clothing. In particular, he had removed his shoes and washed them. That explained why they had been so wet. Then he had been given ample warning by Dr. Lutter's telephone call. Detective Kraemer had come; as soon as the detective left, he had changed his clothes and put on the washed shoes. Before leaving the house he disposed of the betraying "trophy" and handkerchief, probably by throwing both into the toilet. It was then, in all likelihood, that some drops of blood had fallen on his shoes. On this occasion he may also have left other bloodstains on the steps. Hurriedly, without noticing the blood on his shoes, he had gone to Schultenstrasse, where after a while Klingelhӧller had observed the stains on the shoes.

Werneburg and Lissigkeit were convinced that the crime had taken place in precisely this manner, and that an organized search for evidence conducted within the first twenty-four hours would soon have persuaded Hussmann to confess. Instead, Hussmann had been given ample warning, and no one had thought of tracking down the bloodstains in any consistent and careful manner. When Werneburg and Lissigkeit attempted to use the scanty belated findings of Müller-Hess in interrogating Hussmann, they found their plan blocked by Hussmann's defense attorney, Ruschen, a lawyer of great experience. Ruschen perceived the peril of even the tiniest bloodstain, if the two Berlin detectives were permitted to fit it into the framework of their reconstruction in the course of questioning the suspect. The tactics of these clever criminologists were quite a different matter from the clumsy frontal attack of Klingelhöller. Ruschen therefore had his client decline to testify except at the trial. At the same time, the lawyer bent every effort to find some innocent explanation for the presence of Group A bloodstains on Hussmann's shoes. He discovered a Widow Stratmann who alleged that there had been some sort of street brawl that same night on Hegestrasse, near the Kleiböhmer house, which had left a pool of blood on the sidewalk. Ruschen maintained that Hussmann had unknowingly stepped into this pool. Of course the fracas had taken place four hours before the time Hussmann was going home (allegedly accompanied by Daube), which meant the blood would long ago have dried on the pavement and could not possibly have stained the upper part of Hussmann's shoes. But Ruschen knew the methods that aroused feelings of uncertainty in judges and jurors. He produced further witnesses for even more farfetched allegations. At the Hotel Zur Post in Buer that fateful night another guest had been struck in the nose and had had a nosebleed. This had actually happened, though the fraternity party had been in another room, so that Hussmann never even laid eyes on the other man. Nevertheless, the incident served to confuse the issue of the bloodstain.

The trial was held in Essen from October 16 to October 30, 1928. Up to the last moment the inexplicable Group A blood on the shoes remained a major piece of incriminating evidence. The court seemed swayed by the reconstruction of Werneburg and Lissigkeit. Yet in spite of all this, the jury acquitted Hussmann, stating that it was not entirely convinced of his innocence, but not convinced beyond a reasonable doubt of his guilt.

The Daube case nevertheless focused the attention of criminologists all over the world upon the problems of identifying bloodstains and testing for blood groups. Even before the trial began, a major article appeared in the *Kriminalistische Monatshefte* pointing out the crucial importance of immediate blood group determinations. The author was Werneburg; the title, "The Practical Importance of Blood Group Examination." In the case in question, the police had sadly bungled things. This led to a sequel of official investigations, to charges, countercharges, and self-defense. But perhaps the very mismanagement of the case unforgettably dramatized how it should have been handled.

10

At the end of October in this same year, 1928, at the time the jury was considering its verdict in the Hussmann case, a young physician in Innsbruck, Austria, was just about to complete his studies and receive his doctorate. Two months later, on January 1, 1929, he accepted a post as assistant at the Institute of Forensic Medicine of the University of Innsbruck. That was more or less a matter of chance; young Franz Josef Holzer had hardly planned to go into forensic medicine. He had, in fact, been in no hurry to launch himself on a career, meaning to continue his education for a while by studying chemistry. Upon hearing this, gruff Professor Karl Meixner demanded whether he intended to spend his life looking into test tubes. If so, the young man would find plenty of test tubes at his Institute of Forensic Medicine.

Thus it was more or less provisionally that Holzer came to the Institute in January 1929, and soon turned his attention to serology. Professor Meixner was occupied with determinations of paternity; but there had also been several criminal cases in Tyrol which lent themselves to blood testing and serology.

Ever since the previous fall, the Halsmann case had been a subject for lively discussion at Meixner's Institute, as well as in the press. A university student named Philipp Halsmann had gone mountain climbing with his father on the eastern slope of the Olperer Massif in the Zillertaler Alps. He had returned alone, reporting that his father had had a fatal fall. Examining the terrain, Meixner had found some suspicious items: a blood-splotched stone which would have been an excellent murder weapon, and a blood-specked trail leading to the site of the fall. The story of the accident seemed full of holes. The investigation was still under way when Holzer started work on the third floor of the ancient building at 44 Müllerstrasse. The subsequent trials, in which Halsmann was first convicted of killing his father, then acquitted, but above all the public excitement over proof by bloodstains, formed the background against which Meixner began creating a special laboratory for blood studies, at the very time that Holzer was hired by the Institute as a serologist.

Thanks to the spur Lattes had given to the practice of group determination, the subject was far better understood by 1929. It had been discovered that the serum agglutinins, the anti-A or anti-B substances in bloodstains, behaved in a highly unpredictable manner. Their effect on the sample red blood cells depended on numerous factors: their original strength, which varied from person to person; their age; the degree of heat or cold to which they had been exposed; and so on. Often they lost their potency in a surprisingly short time. Now and then that potency was preserved far longer than was normal. A bothersome complication was the discovery that anti-A agglutinins in the serum of Group O blood could differ from the anti-B agglutinins in persistence and strength. This meant that the anti-A substance might survive in the dried serum of a Group O bloodstain, but the anti-B substance be severely attenuated or disappear entirely. If such a stain were treated with sample cells, the A cells would clump, the B cells would not. Thus the blood would seem to belong to Group B, whereas in fact it was Group O. This, to be sure, was an extreme but still possible case. In another extreme case the anti-B substance might vanish from a Group A bloodstain, so that it would seem like a Group AB. Lattes' test did not work with Group AB because the serum contained no agglutinins. If, therefore, a test produced no agglutination at all, several conclusions were possible. The blood might be Group AB, or it might be blood of another group which had lost its agglutinins in the process of drying. Results of the Lattes test must thus be taken with more than a grain of salt.

The search was on for a more reliable procedure. Lattes, too, had considered the possibility of not searching for the agglutinins in the dried serum of a bloodstain, but examining directly the group characteristics of the red blood cells, which must likewise be present in every bloodstain. But since the cells in dried form lost their shape and clotted in crusts, there was no way to determine their group by direct observation. Lattes had therefore turned back to Karl Landsteiner's experiments of 1902–05.

Landsteiner had shown that the cells in dry blood lose their shape and ability to clump, but retain their group characteristics. He had further demonstrated that between these characteristics and the antibodies of serum an "attraction" existed, and that the group characteristics in completely dried crusts of blood still attracted serum antibodies. If the group characteristics of the clotted red cells in a bloodstain were more stable than the antibodies of the serum, there ought to be a way to determine the type of these group characteristics by attraction, or to put it another way, by "absorption" or "nonabsorption" of the serum antibodies.

Lattes tried several times to find this route, as did other scientists of various nationalities: Popoff, Martin and Rochaix, Higuchi, and others. Their experiments all bore out the fact that the characteristics of blood cells (the agglutinogens) in bloodstains were far more stable than the antibodies of serum. It seemed all the more urgent, therefore, to find a way to identify these agglutinogens directly. But such efforts encountered many difficulties. If, for example, one had a Group A bloodstain and added anti-A serum to it, the A agglutinogen absorbed A agglutinin, but only to a certain extent, to the point of "saturation." Its capacity for absorption differed from case to case; much depended therefore on the quantity of serum and the strength of the anti-A substance it contained. If absorption were complete, a further test with Group A red blood cells would easily reveal whether the serum was "void" of agglutinins, that is, ineffective, for it would no longer agglutinate the test cells. But if remnants of A agglutinins were left in the serum, the results tended to be ambiguous. The question therefore was: How could the quantity and strength of the serum which was mixed with unknown bloodstains be so adjusted that all the antibodies contained in it were absorbed? All sorts of calculations were tried, but because of the many unknowns they did not yield clear results. Nevertheless, the idea of detecting the blood groups in unknown stains by finding the agglutinogens themselves seemed a promising approach.

Fritz Schiff, in Berlin, attacked the problem repeatedly. He asked himself whether the whole circumstantial procedure followed in previous experiments would not be superfluous if a technical device were found for measuring precisely how much potency an anti-A or anti-B test serum lost after it had been mixed with a bloodstain. If the agglutinating powers of a test serum could be measured before and then after mixture with the stain, and it could be determined whether it had lost anti-A or anti-B effectiveness, and if so how much, there would no longer be any obscurities. For example, if an anti-A serum of, say, effectiveness 100 were reduced to effectiveness 50, whereas an anti-B serum lost none of its effectiveness, the bloodstain must belong to Blood Group A. If anti-B serum lost a considerable quantity of effectiveness, but not anti-A serum, the stain would belong to Blood Group B. And if the effectiveness of both serums was undiminished, the stain must belong to the O group.

Such was the situation when Holzer went to work and tried out a number of procedures based on Schiff's ideas. After many experiments he finally found a simple and practical method. He employed dimpled slides such as are used in chemistry for spot tests, the examination of extremely tiny quantities of material. These slides were thin slabs of glass into which eight tiny wells had been ground. Holzer placed two such slides side by side on his laboratory table. Then, using a pipette, he placed four drops of physiological salt solution in each well of the first slide. He then dropped four drops of the anti-A test serum he wished to use to test a bloodstain into the first well of this slide and stirred the resulting mixture. He then transferred exactly four drops of this mixture to the next well—so that the serum in this well was only half as strong as the mixture in the first; it was diluted in the proportion of 1:2. Proceeding with this method of dilution, Holzer moved on from well to well, until in the eighth he had attained a dilution of 1:256.

He repeated the same process with anti-B serum on the second slide. There, too, he had a series of dilutions running from 1:1 to 1:256. Holzer then prepared two suspensions of fresh red blood cells: one suspension of A cells and another of B cells. Into each well of the series of anti-A serum dilutions he dropped a quantity of A cells, making sure that the quantity remained constant; he followed the same procedure with B cells in the B serum dilutions. After from ten to thirty minutes he examined the specimens for agglutination. He could now determine up to what degree of dilution his anti-A or anti-B serum would continue to agglutinate blood cells. Strong serums were effective up to a dilution of 1:256; weak ones only to a dilution of 1:128, 1:64 or 1:32. In every case, however, the strength (or "titer," to use the technical term) could be measured. As soon as the strength was known, Holzer proceeded to test a bloodstain of unknown group. The serums of various dilutions were mixed in micro test tubes with flakes of the bloodstain or blood-soaked bits of fabric and placed in a refrigerator for twenty-four hours. Then the contents of the test tubes were centrifuged, separating out the surplus anti-A or anti-B serum from the solid components of blood in the stain. Holzer removed the surplus serum from the tubes and proceeded with them as he had done with the fresh serums, again using dimpled slides. Both were diluted once more to from 1:1 to 1:256. Again Holzer took his A and B suspensions of cells—taken from the same sample of blood that he had used to check the original titer. Now he could determine the extent to which each of the serums had remained unaffected or lost strength because of its mixture with the unknown blood group. In other words, he checked what chemists call the "loss of titer." If, for example, his original anti-A serum had been effective to a dilution of 1:128, and if after use its effectiveness ceased at a dilution of 1:16 or 1:32, the titer had fallen by three or four degrees of dilution—a sign that the bloodstain had absorbed a considerable quantity of anti-A. If the effectiveness of the anti-B serum, on the other hand, was unchanged, the bloodstain belonged to Group A.

After a series of experiments Holzer simplified his procedure still more by not checking, applying, and checking again anti-A and anti-B serum. Instead he used Group O serum, which contains both anti-A and anti-B antibodies. In October and November 1929 he undertook the first experiments on twenty-nine artificially dried bloodstains of individuals of known blood group. Each of the stains contained from 10 to 15 milligrams of dried blood. His "blindfold" tests turned out to be 100 per cent accurate. These results encouraged him to communicate his findings to Leone Lattes and to ask him for dried bloodstains of various ages. Lattes responded enthusiastically. He sent Holzer seven test stains whose group characteristics he alone knew. Holzer identified five of them correctly. On eight bloodstains sent to him from Vienna, he achieved a perfect score. Meanwhile he went on trying to improve the reliability of his procedure. He found that lowered potency of a serum could be regarded as proof of the presence of the corresponding blood group only if the loss in titer extended to several dilutions. A single dilution never sufficed, because even blood of Group O could slightly weaken a serum. Often, too, blood of Group A lowered the strength of an anti-B serum to a slight extent. Control experiments with the Lattes test, which Holzer ran parallel to his own experiments, confirmed his belief in his own work. The Lattes test gave correct results in a considerably smaller fraction of the cases than his own method.

Nevertheless, the day came when Holzer was faced with a disturbing setback. He went wrong thirteen times on sixty-five new bloodstain samples from Vienna. Eleven times the titer of the anti-A serum fell distinctly, although there was no A blood in the stain. The bloodstains in question had been sent on filter paper. Did this mean that errors were possible, as in the Uhlenhuth test, because different substrates absorbed serum antibodies? Holzer began checking all the materials on which bloodstains might be found: textiles, papers, soil, stones, etc. He discovered that filter paper indubitably affected the strength of blood serums even when it was completely free of blood. Here was a warning that the new method would have to be supplemented by checking the base material of a bloodstain, or the results might be misleading.

In the spring of 1930 Holzer finally ran a series of very special tests. Meixner's predecessors, like most specialists in forensic medicine, had established a "museum" containing evidence presented in former crimes. At the Institute Holzer found all of a hundred such items with bloodstains on them—clothing, weapons, blankets, bones, soil, and plants—souvenirs of now forgotten crimes. Holzer applied his method to this material and found that even bloodstains decades old had not lost their powers of absorption. On one ancient blackjack he found bloodstains from several different blood types. His curiosity stirred, he looked up the old records and found that this blackjack had been used to kill four persons in the course of a robbery.

In the autumn of 1930 Professor Meixner asked his assistant to write up his method and its results—by then Holzer had conducted 387 individual experiments. Meixner also arranged a spot for his assistant on the agenda of the 19th Congress of the German Society for Legal and Social Medicine, held, that September, in Königsberg. Holzer, a slender, unassuming person, set out for East Prussia rather halfheartedly, expecting that his fate would be the same as that of Landsteiner, Richter, or Lattes. But he was fortunate: his method had closed a gap that had been all too obvious for years, and three months after the congress the *Deutsche Zeitschrift für die gesamte gerichtliche Medizin* published his paper—"A Simplified Procedure for Group Determination of Dried Blood by Agglutinin Formation." Only a few months later he was called in to solve a major crime, the first in which his method was decisive.

11

What took place during the overcast morning hours of November 18, 1931, in Imst, a town not far from Innsbruck, was a little drama of small farmers against the background of the Depression.

Its scene was a peasant house on the northwestern edge of Imst, where a muddy dirt road turned off from the main highway at the Church of St. John, and wound along a brook to Rose Garden Gorge. The house, built up against a cliff, was a weather-beaten old place with small windows and many rooms, cellars, attics, stables, corridors, woodsheds, and hidden corners. It was three stories high and was inhabited by eight persons. Three of them, a tenant named Johanna Brugger, her son, and another tenant named Franz Häussler—all three occupied rooms in the attic—were only silent witnesses of the events. The drama took place among the other five, who lived on the ground floor and second floor. All these people but one belonged to the Mair family.

The owner of the house was a farmer and cattle dealer, Franz Mair, a lean, sharp-faced, dark-haired man in his forties. In 1928 he had bought the house for a few thousand schillings; ever since he had lived on the ground floor with his housekeeper and mistress, Adelheid Staudacher.

In his barn Mair had three cows, a pig, and a goat. He tilled a few fields, hayed a few meadows, and earned most of his livelihood by cattle trading without much regard for the borderline between honesty and cheating. Grasping to the point of avarice, unable to read or write, crude and unfeeling, he did not have a single friend. Adelheid Staudacher, whom he had brought home with him from a cattle-trading tour, was housekeeper, bedmate, and mother of a newborn child. She put up with Mair, although he beat her and gave her no wages. No one knew what attached her to Mair: need, fear of unemployment, sexual enslavement, or the hope that her child would someday inherit Franz Mair's property.

The other Mairs lived on the second floor: Franz Mair's alcoholic stepmother Anna and her grown sons Wilhelm and Karl, one of whom worked for a butcher in Imst, the other on the roads.

Shortly after seven o'clock on the morning of November 10 a young man of twenty-five in a gray-green jacket and rough laced boots stopped in front of the police station in Imst. He called to District Inspector Gabl, who happened to be looking out the window, that his brother Franz had been assaulted. Gabl had been stationed in Imst long enough to know the Mairs by sight. He recognized the young man as Karl Mair, stepbrother of the cattle dealer.

Inspector Gabl fetched his bicycle from the shed and rode up to Rose Garden Gorge. At the door of the house he found Adelheid Staudacher and one of the neighbors, Josef Baumgartner, a worker in a textile mill. Baumgartner seemed excited, while the housekeeper—looking older than her age in shawl and ragged smock—led the inspector silently, without tears, into the low-ceilinged room to the right of the vestibule. The furniture consisted of little more than an old bed. At its foot hung a black coat and a patched vest, both splotched with large bloodstains. A lean figure was lying on the bed, in socks, trousers, and bloody shirt, head hidden under bandages. Beside it stood the village doctor, Dr. Jenewein.

There was no hope, the doctor told the policeman; there was nothing to do but wait for death. Mair had received at least six blows on the head. One blow had exposed the brain.

Gabl heard the story from the housekeeper and Baumgartner. Franz Mair regularly rose at five o'clock in the morning to take care of the animals. This morning, as always, he had wakened his housekeeper after crawling out of the feather bed. While he was out in the barn, Adelheid Staudacher prepared the pig feed in the kitchen, and ten or fifteen minutes later she followed him. In the barn she found Franz feeding the cows and his stepbrother Karl, who as Adelheid said had not been working for some time "on account of some ulcers"; instead, he had slept all day or "just hung around shirking work." Adelheid Staudacher had filled the pig trough, milked the goat, and returned to the kitchen. At six Franz Mair brought the pail of cow's milk to the kitchen, and promptly returned to the barn. That was Adelheid Staudacher's account. The rest of the story came from Baumgartner, the neighbor. He had found Franz Mair lying in the barn, beaten to a pulp.

Baumgartner, who had a room in a nearby house, had got up at six to go to work at the mill. About six twenty, as he was going to light the carbide lamp on his bicycle, he found that his matches were all damp. He saw a light in Franz Mair's barn and opened the barn door, which was next to the house door, intending to ask for a few matches. In the light of the kerosene lantern that dimly illuminated the stalls he saw a figure lying on the floor, near the pigpen, legs in the urine of the gutter, head turned toward the right side of the barn. He recognized Franz Mair at once, and sprang to the conclusion that a cow had kicked him. He shouted for the housekeeper and with her help carried the injured man into the bedroom.

Baumgartner had then jumped on his bicycle, while Adelheid Staudacher went to the bottom of the stairs and called Karl Mair and Anna Mair. She had had to shout before both came down; they looked into the room, but backed away from the gruesome sight. When Baumgartner returned he found Anna and Karl Mair standing at the front door. The doctor, when he arrived, declared that he did not think the injury an accident, and sent Karl Mair to alert the police.

That was all Baumgartner and the housekeeper could say. No one had heard any noise or quarreling—Adelheid had heard nothing although the kitchen was separated from the barn only by a rough wall.

Gabl went into the barn. The kerosene lantern was still burning on the right-hand wall. In the corner in front of the pig trough Gabl found a large, bright-red pool of fresh blood. At the sight, so he reported later, he "realized at once that this case exceeded my powers." He needed help. He therefore sent Baumgartner with a message to the police station. Shortly afterward District Commander Federspiel and Inspectors Eller and Strohmeier arrived at the house.

Federspiel was a man of some experience in investigating the scene of a crime. But since he had neither cameras nor other aids, he could do nothing for the present but seal off the barn and telephone to Innsbruck headquarters for help. While waiting, he heard the story from Gabl, questioned the housekeeper and the neighbor once more, gave his inspectors instructions to look around the house and to question the tenants on the top floor. When he heard that Anna and Karl Mair had gone back up to their rooms on the second floor, he went upstairs. He found Anna Mair in the kitchen with a bottle of schnapps. Karl Mair was sitting by the stove in the other room, wearing heavy work shoes, trousers, and a patched, filthy shirt. He was staring sleepily into space, did not stir, and merely murmured a greeting when Federspiel sat down facing him and asked what he had to say about the murderous assault, why he had been hanging around the barn early in the morning, and when he had left it. Federspiel knew many young men of Karl Mair's type, especially in the mountain villages. Begotten in drunkenness, as children set to heavy work, sent to school irregularly, they constituted the flotsam of society and the Depression. Slow in thought and expression, most of them were harmless; but others had a dangerous, low cunning and dark, instinctual hatreds.

Karl Mair answered slowly and deliberately. He had waked early, although he could not go to work with the road crew because of his sore arm. But he was used to rising early. He had wakened his brother Wilhelm and his mother, so that she could prepare their breakfast soup. Now and then he helped his stepbrother Franz with the morning chores, and so this morning he had put on his felt slippers and gone down to the barn shortly after six o'clock. But he found the chores already done. He therefore returned to the house, just in time for the soup. Afterward his brother Wilhelm had left for his job at the butcher's. He himself had taken off his shoes, lain down on the bench in front of the stove, and had a little snooze. He had not wakened until he heard Adelheid Staudacher's screams. Then he had hurriedly put on his leather shoes, which were standing at the foot of the bench, and run downstairs. He reached the bottom of the stairs just as Franz was being carried past him into the house, and had gone along into the bedroom. But he never could stand the sight of blood and had stayed only a moment or so. Later he had bicycled to the police headquarters.

Federspiel noted a discrepancy between Karl Mair's account and Adelheid Staudacher's statement. She had said that the dying man was already laid in the bedroom when Karl Mair and his mother came down the stairs. Was this a mistake or dull-minded forgetfulness? While Mair talked, Federspiel's glance had several times fallen upon his right shirt sleeve, where there were a few tiny, brownish-red spots that might have come from spurting blood.

Recollection of the big pool of blood in the barn prompted Federspiel to ask about the slippers which Karl Mair said he had worn to the barn in the morning. Karl Mair stooped without a word and fumbled behind the stove. Finally he pulled the shoes out and pushed them over to the inspector. For a moment Federspiel thought he must be mistaken. But then he was sure: on the leather toe-piece, and on the sides as well, were some dried, reddish-brown spots. He looked fixedly at the man. But Karl Mair seemed neither to see the spots nor to be aware of them. Only when Federspiel put the shoes on the table in front of him and asked where the blood came from did the man show faint signs of possible emotion. He stared at the shoes, then ran his tongue over his lips. Then he replied, after some moments of thought, that he remembered where the blood came from. The day before he had helped an acquaintance slaughter a calf.

Meanwhile Inspectors Eller and Strohmeier had been looking around the house. But there were so many nooks and corners in the place, and every nook filled with so much dirt and junk, that there was no prospect of doing a thorough job without days of work. Just checking the feed mow above the barn, and the adjacent haymow, filled with hay but also with scrap wood and rusty implements, would require hours of hard labor. From the ancient wooden structure feed hatches led directly down into the barn. The fore part of the haymow extended over the front wall of the house, making a sort of bridge over the doorway. The wall of an old shed served as a support for its other end. There was an opening in this bridgelike upper story, through which the hay could be pitched. A ladder hanging near the barn door led up to this opening, so that with the aid of the ladder the haymow could be reached from the outside. The feed mow and haymow—unlike the lower part of the barn—could be reached by a direct connection with the living quarters of the house, through the second floor. Behind the feed mow was the privy, which could be entered both from the mows and the rooms of Anna Mair and her two sons.

The policemen had climbed into the haymow from outside, and were just descending the stairs inside the house from the second floor to the first, when Adelheid Staudacher came out of the room in which the dying man lay. For the first time she seemed excited; she held out Franz Mair's bloody jacket and vest, which had been hanging at the foot of his bed. The seams and linings in jacket and vest had been ripped open by powerful hands. The housekeeper burst out with the explanation that Franz Mair had always carried all his cash and his bankbook on his person. She knew that because he often showed her his wealth, to drive home what riches she would be letting slip if she did not stick it out with him. He carried at least two thousand schillings in a wallet and a bankbook showing at least six thousand schillings in his account. Now both were gone, ripped out of the clothes.

The girl was so worked up over this that she was at a loss to say whether Franz Mair was still alive. Nor did she care. The matter of the clothing had fully occupied her attention. She had never received any affection in the Mair house, and she had none to show in return.

Eller hastened upstairs to inform Federspiel. He found him in the kitchen with Anna Mair; the woman, slightly drunk, was volubly explaining that her son Karl was a fool who could never tell a story straight after it had happened. She herself had gone to the barn to call him for breakfast, and her stepson Franz was perfectly alive and well. After breakfast—such was her story—Karl had snoozed by the stove. When "that woman" called for help, he had jumped up and started to run downstairs in his stocking feet. She had reminded him to put on his felt shoes. Then both of them had run down. At the door, the injured man had been carried past them both. They had followed into the bedroom, and Karl had laid pillows under his stepbrother's head.

Federspiel was a simple man, but he had learned to observe carefully and to draw his conclusions carefully. Anna Mair's account differed so conspicuously from that of her son and from Adelheid's that the inconsistencies could not be overlooked. Why did she emphasize that Karl

Mair had worn his slippers and not his shoes on the way to see the dying man? And why the detail about Karl's putting a pillow under the injured man's head? Why did she say she had been in the barn to call Karl for breakfast? Had she been eavesdropping when Federspiel questioned Karl Mair and heard the bit about the bloodstains on the slippers? Was she trying to provide a credible alibi for her son? For if Karl Mair had been wearing the slippers, as his mother claimed, when the injured man was carried past him, and if he had stepped close in order to push a pillow under his stepbrother's head, the story could be that the bloodstains had dripped or sprayed on the slippers then, not at the time of the murder.

At this point in Federspiel's reflections, Eller came in with the news that Franz Mair had been robbed. Full of suspicions, Federspiel called a halt to the interrogation and ordered Karl Mair to be taken to head-quarters—where he could not be coached by his mother. The slippers were also sent to headquarters for safekeeping. Eller and Gabl were ordered to search Adelheid Staudacher's room, the home of the neighbor, Josef Baumgartner, and the entire second-floor apartment for the money and the bankbook. Federspiel himself began making inquiries among the neighbors of the Mairs.

Federspiel was inclined to distrust quick conclusions and initial suspicions. There was the possibility that some outsider had broken into the barn in the pre-dawn darkness and attacked Franz Mair because he knew the man's habit of carrying his money on him. In these hard times there were innumerable desperate men around. Nor could the possibility be excluded that one of Mair's enemies, a victim of his sharp dealing, had profited by the opportunity of catching him alone early in the morning. There was no certainty that Baumgartner, who had allegedly discovered the crime, was not its perpetrator. And there always remained the consideration that Adelheid Staudacher herself, exploited and abused as she was, might have taken part in the murder, perhaps as the accomplice of some young lover. Then, again, she might only have stolen the money when she was alone with the dying man.

But by the time Federspiel returned from his rounds of the neighbors shortly after twelve o'clock, these alternatives seemed highly improbable. There were several dogs around who barked at every stranger who turned off from the main road. Baumgartner was one of the few people who was on friendly terms with Franz Mair, and not one of the neighbors thought him capable of "killing a fly." Everyone said that Adelheid Staudacher was a timid, cowed creature who never left the house and scarcely knew anyone, let alone having a young lover or accomplice. On the other hand, the combined testimony of the neighbors built up to a picture of savage conditions in the Mair household—a picture of envy, avarice, hatred, and violence.

Before Franz Mair's widowed father (now dead) had married Anna Mair, he had lived with his son Franz in a small house in another part of Imst. Franz had counted on inheriting the entire farm. But then the two stepbrothers, Karl and Wilhelm, had been born. Franz had hated his stepmother and "her gang" from the very first, had fought with the boys and occasionally threatened them with his knife—not entirely without reason. Anna Mair came from a family of drinkers. She was considered miserly and a gossip. Karl was thought to be dim-witted, but no less avaricious and spiteful for all that. Wilhelm was an exception in this family. When the father died, in 1921, the house had been the scene of bitter quarreling until Franz Mair put the others out, paid them off, and finally bought for himself the house on the road to Rose Garden Gorge. But no one in the town had liked Anna Mair, and six months ago Franz had been forced to take her and her sons in once more, this time as tenants for a rent of forty schillings a month. Nevertheless, Anna's hatred for this stepson who now owned his own home was, if the neighbors could be believed, more vicious than ever. And Karl, so it was said, was full of bitterness and hatred.

Shortly before Federspiel returned to the house, Franz Mair quietly gave up the ghost. Abandoned and disregarded, he lay on his bed. Federspiel, to his relief, found a message waiting for him: a homicide commission was already on the way to Imst from Innsbruck. It was headed by Examining Magistrate Stettner of Innsbruck; the doctor assigned to it was Josef Holzer.

Holzer and Stettner, accompanied by Detectives Mayr, Guth, and Zanoll, arrived at the Mair house at one o'clock in the afternoon. After hearing Federspiel's report, Holzer made a preliminary examination of the dead man. He found that Franz Mair had received eight blows with a very sharp object on his head, the side of his face, his neck, and his back. At one point on his back his jacket vest and shirt had been pierced clean through. From the position of the wounds, Holzer assumed that the victim had been attacked by surprise while his back was turned. After the blows on the head he had fallen to the floor and had received still more blows. These facts having been established, the body was sent to Innsbruck for autopsy.

Holzer next went to the barn, where he wanted to know the dead man's exact position; he prepared a drawing, and directed that the scene of the crime and the pool of blood be photographed from various angles. Then he took samples from the pool, and set about searching for more traces of blood. The task was extremely difficult because of the condition of the barn; the stalls had not been cleaned for a long time and splashes of urine and manure reached up to the ceiling. Only along the wall where Franz Mair's head had laid did Holzer find, at a height of two feet, several suspicious fresh splotches. He peeled these spots off the wall, along with their underlay of dirt, dust, and plaster. Otherwise, there were no visible spots. But when Holzer stepped out of the barn and went across to the opposite supporting wall of the haymow, he noticed numerous bloodstains. These, however, seemed to him quite old. Nevertheless, he took several samples. He carefully inspected the door to the stalls, and then the ladder leading up to the haymow. At the latter, he paused in surprise. What he saw on the rungs were only tiny, diaphanously thin reddish smears. But his practiced eye recognized them as bloodstains. He called Stettner and Federspiel. All three had the same thought: if they believed that Karl Mair might have had a part in the murder, these stains pointed to the ideal way for Mair to reach the second floor without being seen by anyone after the crime. Stettner, Holzer, and Federspiel climbed the ladder into the haymow, reached the corridor to the privy without difficulty, and from there entered the apartment of Anna Mair and her sons. Along the way, Holzer looked for more bloodstains, but found none. When, however, he went to the corner by the stove, where Karl Mair had been sitting while Federspiel questioned him, he once more came upon several bloodstains, although these were by now almost invisible traces. Otherwise, the rough, filthy floor seemed to have no blood on it.

Since evening was approaching, Holzer and the other members of the homicide commission drove over to headquarters and inspected the slippers. Federspiel had seen correctly. The leather tip and the side of the right shoe showed bloodstains. It was already growing dark when Karl Mair was brought before the commission. Holzer examined his clothing. He, too, found the sprinklings of blood on the shirt which had already attracted Federspiel's attention. They were so minute, however, that it seemed dubious whether a serological check would yield results. Otherwise, there seemed to be no blood on the clothing, until Holzer used a flashlight to examine Mair's trousers. Suddenly, low on the right trouser leg he saw spots that obviously came from blood, fairly fresh blood. He made Mair remove his trousers and shirt, took a sample of blood from the man's ear lobe, and swiftly motored back to Innsbruck.

On November 11 Meixner's autopsy confirmed Holzer's theory of an attack from behind. Meanwhile Holzer determined the dead man's blood group as O. Then came Karl Mair's blood group—which luckily turned out to be A. Thus the first prerequisite for successful work was established. The subsequent tests determined that all the bloodstains were of human blood. The one exception were the older stains on the shed wall; these were cattle blood. The police thereupon made inquiries and learned that the carcasses of slaughtered animals had often been strung up against this wall. So far, everything checked out perfectly. Holzer proceeded to make the necessary experiments for determining the blood groups in the stains.

Meanwhile, Adelheid Staudacher surprisingly found the stolen money. On November 12 she was throwing hay down from the mow into the mangers for the cows. When she returned to the barn several hours later, she found schilling notes lying in the manure, and the bankbook as well, wrapped in a newspaper. The police picked out of the straw, hay, and manure a total of sixteen hundred schillings; the wallet and remainder of the money did not turn up, however. Inspector Gabl assumed that the cows must have chewed up the rest of the bills and the wallet; wallet and bankbook had obviously been concealed in the hay and been accidentally thrown down along with the feed. This discovery confirmed the conjecture that the murderer lived in the house and had made his way out through the haymow after the crime. Federspiel interrogated Karl Mair, and accused him of killing and robbing his stepbrother. But Mair showed no signs of emotion. In his heavy fashion, he declared that he had had nothing to do with it; he hoped he would fall down dead if there were anybody who could prove he had—if there were a single person who had seen him outside his mother's apartment after six o'clock in the morning. When the interrogation was over, Federspiel had to concede that Mair's brain might work slowly, but it worked cogently. It was true that no one had seen him committing the crime. No one had observed a weapon in his hand, no one had found a weapon. Not a single schilling of the stolen money had been found on his person or in his room. No one had observed him leaving the barn and climbing the ladder to the second floor, and no jury would convict him unless more conclusive evidence were found.

Holzer, meanwhile, was busy with his blood group tests. Since the bloodstains were fresh, it seemed likely that the agglutinins had been preserved, which would make the Lattes technique feasible. But he obtained not a single usable result with it. That was understandable in the case of the stains on the ladder; they were too diminutive. On the slippers, the felt had so deeply absorbed the blood that the agglutinins could scarcely be activated. But the stains on the trousers consisted of dark-brown to black encrustations of blood, a quarter and an eighth of an inch square; these should have yielded some positive results.

Next day Holzer tried his own method. Even this failed to detect the blood groups of the stains on the ladder. In testing the stains on the slippers—some from the felt, some from the porous leather toe-pieces— Holzer took the precaution of using different O serums with anti-A and anti-B factors. When he tested one spot on the leather part of the slippers with the first of his test serums, it turned out that neither anti-A nor anti-B factors were weakened. Only the activity of the anti-B serum underwent a slight reduction—as could happen with Group O serum. That seemed to prove that the stains belonged to Group O—the dead man's blood group. There remained only the base underlying the stains, the felt and the leather parts of the slippers, to check. But when Holzer looked at his results, he suffered an acute disappointment. Both felt and leather produced a wide variety of loss in titer of the anti-A and anti-B factors in the test serum. When he repeated his tests with a stronger serum, the felt and leather samples weakened the serum just as much as the bloodstains. By ill luck what he had were two of the few materials which could play havoc with his results.

He therefore set about examining the last bloodstains at his disposal with all the more excitement. These were the stains on Karl Mair's trousers. He chose an O serum that was still effective in a dilution of 1:64 and exercised the greatest care with each successive step. When absorption was completed, when he had removed the excess serum from the bloodstain, tested it for its remaining activity, and finally tested the absorptive capacity of unstained bits of cloth taken from the trousers, he at last found that he had a set of results which could not be doubted. The serum had lost neither anti-A nor anti-B antibodies; the cloth of the trousers did not cross up the results of the test in any way, and therefore the stains belonged to Group O, the victim's blood group.

Holzer, wanting to make absolutely certain, undertook a comparison test with the samples from the pool of blood in the barn and the blood-stains on the barn wall. In both cases they were unquestionably the blood of Franz Mair and Group O blood. For control purposes Holzer tested whitewash and dirt from the wall, as well as clay from the floor of the barn. The underlying material did not affect the reactions of the bloodstains. And the group determination of samples from the wall and from the pool of blood produced exactly the same results as the test of the stains on Karl Mair's trouser leg. Only when he had reached this point did Holzer inform Examining Magistrate Stettner of his results. He added the comment that his findings were no proof of Karl Mair's being the murderer; they merely provided a strong indication and supplied the basis for purposeful interrogation.

He had hardly needed to point this out, for Stettner proved to be one of the few men of law who could properly evaluate and intelligently use the possibilities of bloodstain findings. After he had read Holzer's report and once more gone through the record, he quickly realized the importance of Holzer's blood group determination of Karl Mair's trousers. He himself had meanwhile questioned Adelheid Staudacher several times about the order of events when she and Baumgartner carried Franz Mair into the bedroom on November 10. Baumgartner had been too confused to remember every detail. But the girl had it all impressed vividly on her mind, and had never deviated an iota from her initial statement that she and Baumgartner had laid Franz Mair down before she went to call Anna and Karl Mair while Baumgartner went for the doctor. She had had to call very loudly, and she was certain that neither of the two had come anywhere near the victim; both had announced that they could not stand the sight of blood and had retreated hastily.

Stettner's first question, therefore, was: How and under what circumstances could blood have splashed up as high as two feet on Karl Mair's trousers during the moment he was in the room? Since Karl Mair could not answer this question, Stettner went on: What other innocent explanation could Karl Mair suggest for the fact that there were fresh bloodstains on his trousers, that they were not animal blood, not his own blood, and could only have come from a person with the same blood group as the victim? When, how, and where had Karl Mair met a person of Blood Group O by November 9 at the latest, and met him in such a way that this person's blood stained his trousers?

Karl Mair resisted the interrogation for two weeks. It took ten days before the dull-witted man realized that only a specific statement about an encounter with a man of a certain type of blood could save him. He resorted to the explanation that he could remember nothing because his head had been injured in an accident while he was doing road work. At last, on December 3, he decided to make a partial confession: he admitted having taken part in the robbery and named as his accomplice a certain Josef Hetschnig. Hetschnig was the murderer, he said; he himself had only stolen the money. Finally, after another four days, he broke down completely and confessed that he had invented Hetschnig —fellow prisoners in the jail had suggested this trick to him. He admitted that on the morning of November 10, shortly before six o'clock, he had been alone in the barn with Franz Mair and had struck down his stepbrother with a hoe which he had placed in the barn days before. After his stepbrother fell to the floor, he had struck several times more, until he thought him dead. Then he had ripped bankbook and cash out of his jacket and vest and, taking the hoe with him, had climbed the ladder to the haymow. Here he hid the money and bankbook in the hay, and went to his room. He cleaned the hoe with a rag, burned the rag in the stove, and placed the murder weapon in a shed at the back of the house. He pushed the slippers under the stove, not noticing that there was blood on them. He had also failed to notice the small splashes of blood on his trousers and shirt. Then he had eaten his soup, pretended to sleep, and waited for the body to be discovered. Everything he and his mother had said about their lingering in Franz Mair's bedroom had been untrue. He had scarcely looked at the wounded man, because he feared that his stepbrother would still be able to see and have the strength to denounce him. As for the reason for the crime: he had always hated his stepbrother. He had not planned to rob him, he maintained, and had thought to take the money only after his stepbrother lay on the floor apparently dead. He refused to answer when asked whether his mother had influenced him and had known of the murder beforehand.

On March 8, 1932, he was tried in the district court in Innsbruck. That same day the jury declared him guilty of first-degree murder.

12

From 1932 on, the Holzer absorption test became the preferred method of group determination for bloodstains, although it did not completely replace the Lattes test. The results of the Lattes test could now be checked by means of a second method. These checks brought to light both previously suspected defects of the Lattes test, and some of its special virtues. Its chief drawback was that it almost always failed in cases of older bloodstains. On the other hand, it became clear that the Holzer method had its limitations. Stains had to be fairly large for accurate testing—in general at least the size of a fingernail, if absorptions were to be achieved. More serious was the fact that the blood group which had decided the issue in the Mair case—Group O—in a good many cases proved troublesome. If the test serums were not weakened, the theory was that Group O must be present, and in the overwhelming majority of cases it was. But the agglutinogens in the blood cells could weaken or vanish like the agglutinins in the serum. That meant that a Group A bloodstain could have lost its A agglutinogens and thus give the impression of belonging to Group O. Although this might seem like hairsplitting, hairsplitting was essential for exactitude. The Holzer procedure remained the preferred method for determination of blood groups A, B, and AB. But it did not afford certainty in every case for Group O. As an alternative, in favorable cases the Lattes test could be applied. If in this test A and B cells were agglutinated, the group was certainly identified as O. But since this was possible only in favorable circumstances, a one-step method for determining Group O remained a problem awaiting final solution.

Holzer's method was still being tested when in October 1933 he plunged into the greatest adventure of his young life, impelled by his hunger for more serological knowledge. He sailed to New York to join Karl Landsteiner, who in 1930 had at last been awarded the Nobel Prize for his discovery of blood groups.

Holzer had written to Landsteiner and received a gracious reply, whereupon Meixner gave his assistant a three-months leave. Holzer took a loan for the to him dizzying amount of $150. On that he hoped to live for three months in New York. Such was the beginning of his New York apprenticeship.

Landsteiner, then sixty-five, received Holzer with the paternal kindness for which he was noted: he always warmed to honest zeal and scientific talent. The three months turned into a year. Holzer spent part of the time in Landsteiner's laboratory and animal rooms at the Rockefeller Institute, part working for the Department of Health in Albany. He received a stipend of $200 a month which allowed him to pay the salary of a substitute in Innsbruck. In the course of time he came to know Landsteiner as scientist and as man. He saw how the old man lived almost exclusively for his work, became familiar with his eccentricities (such as Landsteiner's horror of whistling, so that at the slightest such sound he would cry out, "Who is whistling there?"), spent much time with him in his apartment on 86th Street—deliberately without a telephone—and in his summer house on Nantucket, which had been bought with the money from the Nobel Prize.

When Holzer returned to Europe in 1934, he was probably the only forensic serologist in Austria and Germany who had actually worked under the great Landsteiner himself. Above all, he was the only one who had personal knowledge and experience of two new discoveries which had been communicated to European forensic scientists only by brief publications of Landsteiner and his associate, Philip Levine.

The first concerned the fact that human blood, in addition to the by now classical Groups A, B, AB, and O, possessed other "individual characteristics." Ludwig Hirszfeld had earlier pointed out that Blood Group A could be subdivided into two groups of different strengths, A_1 and A_2. Philip Levine, born in Kletsk, Russia, who had come to New York at the age of eight and had been working with Landsteiner since 1925, had found in experiments with rabbit anti-human serum that there were substances in human blood that absorbed this serum exactly as Group A blood cells absorbed anti-A serum. Landsteiner and Levine had found two such substances right at the outset. They called these blood factors, and designated them M and N. These factors occurred separately in human blood, or together as MN. They were also hereditary and distributed among the population in a specific proportion: M could be found in the blood of 30 per cent of all persons, N in 20 per cent, MN in 50 per cent. In 1927 Landsteiner and Levine tracked down another blood factor, P, likewise hereditary and present in 25 per cent of human beings, but missing in the remaining 75 per cent.

European serologists—chief of them Fritz Schiff—had utilized the discovery of these new hereditary factors to improve the determination of paternity. They had sought primarily to determine the presence of M, N, and P in fresh blood by means of the absorption method. Holzer, too, studied the application of these factors to paternity cases. (Later, he liked to tell some of the experiences he had had in the course of this work. There was, for example, the story of the workman's wife who had had a very severe confinement and was supposed to receive blood transfusions from her husband, if it were compatible. Holzer determined the blood groups and blood factors of husband, mother, and baby, and incidentally discovered that the husband could not possibly be the infant's father. When he mentioned this to the woman in a private moment, she exclaimed: "How can you know that, you strange man?" But then she candidly admitted he was right, and explained that her husband was often away from home and her neighbor, a shoemaker, had, in her phrase, "helped her out.") However, Holzer had too great an interest in the criminological possibilities of the new blood factors to confine himself to questions of paternity.

Since his return from New York, there had been much experimentation in Europe also, and new knowledge had been gained in the field of blood testing and its applications to practical criminology. The old tests for determining the presence of blood had been improved and supplemented. The hydrogen peroxide test had turned out to be tricky, for the chemical destroyed bloodstains completely unless its action was quickly cut short. New methods replaced this old test: the formation of acetone-hemochloride crystals, or the hematoporphyrine fluorescence tests. In 1937 Walter Specht of Jena placed the phenomenon of chemical luminescence in the service of criminology. In his procedure a chemical—later simply named *luminol*—was sprayed in darkness wherever invisible bloodstains were suspected. In the presence of blood, the chemical glowed in the dark.

But important as all these new methods were, the discovery of blood factors seemed more important. If a way were found to determine the subgroups A_1 and A_2, as well as the factors M, N, MN, and P, in bloodstains, the chances of identifying the owner of the blood were enormously increased. Perhaps more factors would be discovered. It would then be possible to set up whole formulas for the blood of an individual, like the formulas for fingerprints—at least as far as fresh blood was concerned. The decisive question was: Could these factors and subgroups be determined in dried bloodstains by means of the absorption method?

In 1938 Holzer transferred to Berlin. He became the assistant of Viktor Müller-Hess, who in 1930 had moved from Bonn to Berlin University. From now on Holzer worked in the Berlin University Institute for Forensic and Social Medicine, grappling with the problem of making subgroups and factors as detectable in bloodstains as the major blood groups now were. The absorption method proved to be the only one that promised success; but it could be used only in some cases, and only with large, fresh bloodstains, for tracking down A_1 and A_2 and the factors M and N. Nevertheless, by November 1941—shortly before the Second World War put a halt to all further research work—Holzer could claim that he had succeeded in detecting M and N factors in bloodstains.

On October 29 in that year a sixty-year-old accountant for the Mitropa Restaurant, Adolf Stephan, was killed and robbed in his office in

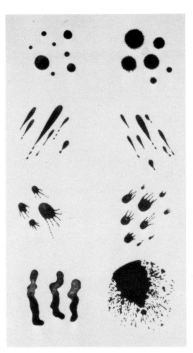

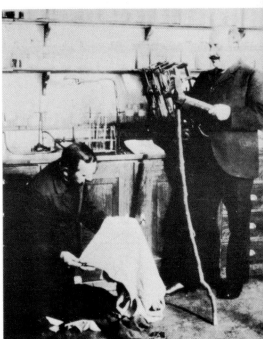

TOP LEFT: Different types of bloodstains caused by dripping or spattering from different directions

TOP RIGHT: The Berlin forensic chemist Paul Jeserich in his laboratory with an assistant, examining an ax and bloodstained clothing

Experiments to determine the kind of bloodstains caused by single or repeated blows with the blade and head of an ax

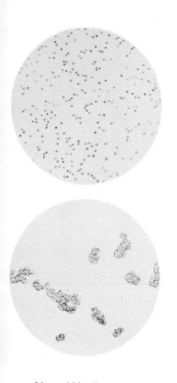

TOP: Normal blood
BELOW: Agglutinated red blood cells

Karl Landsteiner, the discoverer of the agglutination of human blood

Lattes test. Left, with agglutination; right, without agglutination

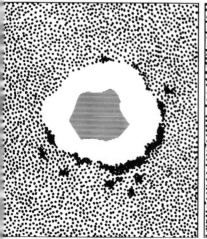

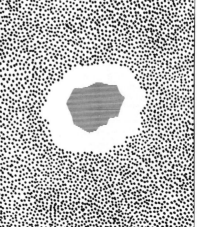

Helmuth Daube and Karl Hussmann

Principal Daube's house, the scene of the crime

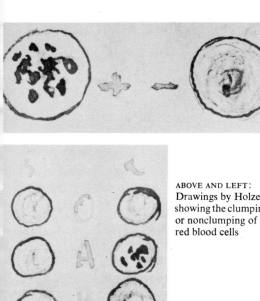

ABOVE AND LEFT:
Drawings by Holzer
showing the clumping
or nonclumping of
red blood cells

Franz Joseph Holzer

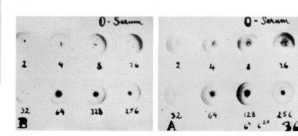

Dimpled slides such as Holzer used in his experiments

Blackjack used by Holzer in his experiments

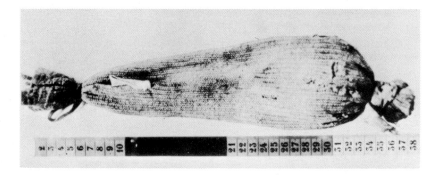

the Stettiner Railroad Station in Berlin. Holzer found the dead man's blood to be Group A, and the factors MN. A few days later Pavel Vacko, nineteen, who worked as a silver polisher for Mitropa, was arrested on suspicion of murder. There were numerous bloodstains on Vacko's clothing, especially in his right trouser pocket, and on a brass clock weight that he kept in his room. Holzer found Blood Group A and the MN factors in all the stains. When Vacko finally confessed, he described how he had used the clock weight as the murder weapon and later thrust it into his right trouser pocket. The freshness of the bloodstains had greatly helped Holzer's work.

At this time, however, the above-mentioned *second* important discovery of Landsteiner and Levine, with which Holzer had been involved in New York, had just strikingly proved its merits in cases of crime. Landsteiner's and Levine's discovery was truly astonishing. To sum it up briefly: they had found that not only did the blood possess group characteristics, but so did all the secretions of the human body: saliva as well as tears, semen, or sweat. The two scientists had demonstrated that the secretions of each individual displayed the same groups as his blood. And during the first half of the year 1939 England was the scene of two crimes which, by the very sensation they created, pointed up the criminological value of this discovery.

13

On January 18, 1939, an eleven-year-old child, Pamela Coventry, disappeared in Hornchurch, Essex. Pamela, a pretty girl with chestnut hair and bright, clear face, was the daughter of an electrician who lived in a tenement on Morecombe Close in the Elm Park district of the town. After lunch, at 1:40 P.M. Pamela had started for school. Her short way led down South End Road to Coronation Drive, a street lined with row houses. A five-minute walk along Coronation Drive brought one to Benhurst Avenue, where the school was.

When the child had not returned home by five o'clock, her mother went to the school building, found a teacher still there, and learned that Pamela had not attended the afternoon session. The teacher had taken it for granted that the child was sick. When she learned that Pamela had not been ill at all, but had set out for school, she recalled that two other pupils, Vivian Hall and Susan Baker, had waited in vain for Pamela on the corner of Coronation Drive and Benhurst Avenue; they had explained that they were late for school because of waiting. Mrs. Coventry, who could not recall that Pamela ever dawdled on her way to school, took the addresses of Vivian and Susan, and went to their homes. But the two girls could only confirm what the teacher had already said. They had waited on the corner until shortly before two o'clock, throwing snowballs to while away the time.

Pamela's mother, still hoping that Pamela might have run into a playmate and decided to play truant, hurried back to Morecombe Close to see if the child were back by now. But she found the flat empty, and toward six o'clock she finally went to the nearest station of the Essex Constabulary.

The police put through the usual missing-person report but hoped the child would return of her own accord. When this hope proved vain, several police search patrols set out in the darkness. It was not until the following morning that Charles Judd Horsman, a night watchman from Hornchurch bicycling down Wood Lane, a narrow road through snow-covered fields, discovered a small female corpse lying in a ditch surrounded by bushes, at the back of the military airdrome of Hornchurch. It was the body of Pamela Coventry.

She lay naked on a rotting mattress in the snow, only her neck covered by her petticoat. Her knees were pushed up to her chin, her legs trussed tightly to her body with insulated cable wire. A piece of friction tape was stuck to the wire, and the kind of twine gardeners use for pea vines.

Chief Inspector Baker of the Essex Constabulary was well aware of the excitement that murders of children produce in the public. He appealed to Scotland Yard for help. Chief Constable Horwell of the Yard charged Inspector Bridger with the on-the-spot investigation and called on Sir Bernard Spilsbury, the leading practitioner in English forensic medicine.

By the time Bridger arrived in Hornchurch, one fact had been determined with certainty: Pamela Coventry had been sexually assaulted. Moreover, every experienced policeman could see that the child had been brutally strangled. Since Pamela had been seen as she turned into Coronation Drive, but had not arrived at the Benhurst Avenue intersection where her friends were waiting for her, the first hypothesis was that the crime had been committed in London and the body returned to

Hornchurch as a blind. On this grim January day Coronation Drive was covered with snow under a gray sky. At any rate Pamela must have been picked up there shortly before two o'clock, perhaps by a waiting automobile. Bridger could already see the mountain of routine work that lay before him: the endless searching, the going from house to house asking questions. Such procedures came to nothing because even the most innocent-seeming husband and father might conceal a sex criminal. Bridger was all too familiar with this exhaustive and exhausting groping in the dark, which yielded results only if by chance there had been a witness or some fortuitous clue could be found establishing a link between the murderer, the victim, and the scene of the crime.

After making his first inspection of the scene, Bridger felt little hope of any such clue. Cable wire, friction tape, and a bit of twine were hardly objects that could point to a particular person as the criminal. Bridger asked the dead child's parents to list all the clothing and objects that Pamela had worn or carried on her last walk. Since everything had vanished except the petticoat, these things might constitute a lead. Toward ten o'clock in the morning of January 19 Bridger summoned all available Constabulary forces and had the fields, streets, gardens, sheds, cellars, and the airfield combed for the missing objects. The R.A.F. commander supplied three hundred men to help the police.

Shortly after ten, Bernard Spilsbury arrived with his instrument case —composed, reticent, and gentlemanly as always. The child lay in the icy morgue. But years of operating in morgues had hardened Spilsbury. Though his hands were stiff with cold, he worked as deftly as ever. Evidently the child had resisted her attacker valiantly. Her hands and arms were covered with wounds. Her jawbone bore the marks of a violent blow from a fist. But data of this sort were at the moment of little help to Bridger.

Spilsbury untwisted the wire trusses and forced the bent legs down. On the skin below the chest was a cigarette stub; it rolled to one side, and Spilsbury picked it up with a pair of pincers. Obviously the murderer had smoked while he tied his victim, and in his excitement had not noticed that the half-smoked cigarette was caught between chest and thigh.

Spilsbury was most thorough and studious, with practically no interests outside his profession, but he was not a researcher or a serologist. As a matter of routine, he placed the cigarette stub with the wire, the friction tape, and the string, as materials for the Scotland Yard Laboratory, which had been established in 1935. What now seems an extraordinary feature of this case is that Spilsbury did not take a sample of the child's blood. This omission possibly came about from his somewhat forbidding manner, doubtless owing to shyness, which kept all those present from drawing the attention of such an important expert to his failure.

Roche Lynch, a puny little chap whom no one would bother to look at twice, could be regarded as a pioneer of scientific criminology in England. Outwardly, he had only one thing in common with Spilsbury: he too affected a carnation in his buttonhole. Lynch was at this time just fifty; his principal job was that of Director of the Department of Pathological Chemistry at St. Mary's Hospital in London. For years he had been considered the foremost London specialist in toxicology and blood testing. He regularly analyzed the blood samples that Spilsbury turned over to him, and in the past nine years he had frequently received bloodstains for testing from Scotland Yard. Since Scotland Yard had set up its Metropolitan Police Laboratory, they had Dr. James Davidson, director of the laboratory, and John Thomas, a young serologist, to handle questions of bloodstains; but in 1939 Roche Lynch was still the leading practitioner in forensic serology. Like Spilsbury, he was not a researcher or discoverer, but he had a keen interest in new developments and followed what was being done outside of England. He telephoned Chief Constable Horwell and asked to have the cigarette butt from Pamela's corpse sent over to him. He might possibly be able to find a clue in the dried saliva.

Horwell replied that Superintendent Cuthbert of the Metropolitan Police Laboratory had taken possession of the cigarette. It was being studied at the moment, and had already been found to be a hand-rolled cigarette. The smoker must have been in the habit of rolling his cigarettes from collected butts, for there were scatterings of charred tobacco in it.

Lynch repeated his request, mentioning that he was thinking of a novel experiment in blood group serology; it might be possible to determine the killer's blood group even without a bloodstain, solely from the saliva adhering to the cigarette. And so, while four hundred policemen and soldiers were searching Hornchurch and its vicinity for Pamela's clothing, a detective sergeant brought the cigarette end to Roche Lynch's laboratory.

The earliest research that led to the discovery of blood group characteristics in saliva and other bodily secretions now lay fifteen years in the past. On June 2, 1925, an article was submitted to the American *Journal of Immunology* by K. Yamakami, Director of the Department of Forensic Medicine of the Imperial Japanese University of Hokkaido. Written in English, it was entitled "The Individuality of Semen, with Reference to Its Property of Inhibiting Specifically Isohemoagglutination." Yamakami maintained that human semen, just like blood cells, could absorb anti-A or anti-B serums; therefore it possessed group characteristics just like blood, and these characteristics corresponded to the blood group of the individual. He himself belonged to Blood Group A. In examining his own saliva by means of the absorption method Yamakami had found that his saliva, too, showed the same group characteristic. He had concluded that this factor could be useful for tracing the originator of semen stains.

This observation was so unusual that it would scarcely have been credited if Landsteiner and Philip Levine had not made the same discovery at the same time, and independently of Yamakami. When they confirmed the Japanese report, by an article of their own in the *Journal of Immunology* not long afterward, Landsteiner's name sufficed to attract a certain amount of international attention to the discovery. Other blood group specialists in Finland and Germany took up the problem. Gradually it was discovered that semen, vaginal secretions, saliva, sweat, tears, gall, mother's milk, and other secretions all revealed the same group characteristics as the blood: A, B, and AB. For the time being there was some uncertainty about Group O. Doubts had briefly arisen as to the regularity of the phenomenon, when it turned out that the saliva, semen, or sweat of some individuals did not contain group characteristics. The obvious conclusion, to be sure, was that such persons fell into the O blood group. But disconcertingly their blood then proved to be Group A or B. Their saliva or semen should have been likewise Group A or B, if the findings of Yamakami, Landsteiner, and Levine were generally applicable.

The doubts remained until Fritz Schiff of Berlin and his Japanese assistant Sasaki undertook a series of experiments and uncovered a peculiarity of the group characteristics in bodily secretions which was accepted as doctrine for the next few decades. People were apparently divided into two classifications. The members of one set had group characteristics in their secretions; the members of the second set did not. Schiff in 1932 dubbed these "secretors" and "non-secretors." Numerically, 86 per cent of the human race seem to be secretors and 14 per cent non-secretors.

Thus, within a few years, serology had amassed a large body of knowledge that appeared to be potentially useful to criminologists. That usefulness seemed enhanced when the Finnish scientist Putkonen pointed out that the group characteristics in the body's secretions were enormously greater than those in blood; he reckoned the degree of concentration at 300:1. Thus it should be possible to determine blood groups from secretory spots when no trace of blood was present. The sweat on a piece of clothing, the spot of semen on the body of a victim, the saliva on an envelope, a stamp, or a cigarette, should reveal the blood group of the person who had left these clues.

Once again it was a Japanese who took the lead. In 1928 K. Fujiwara, Director of the Institute of Forensic Medicine in Niigata, reported a crime which had been solved by means of blood group determination from seminal stains. A sixteen-year-old girl, Yoshiko Hirai, who went from village to village selling fortunetelling slips, had been found strangled. Witnesses had seen the girl at 7:30 P.M. on her way from the village to the railroad station. She must have been raped and killed shortly afterward. Fujiwara found whitish spots which contained well-preserved semen cells on the girl's body. Her blood group was O. Fujiwara tested the semen spots by the absorption method, adding anti-A and anti-B serums, and thus determined that the semen had the group characteristic A. Meanwhile the police had arrested two suspects. One of them was a twenty-four-year-old mentally retarded beggar named Mochitsura Tagami, who straightway confessed that he had committed the murder. The second suspect, Iba Hoshi, denied all guilt. The police were on the point of accepting Tagami's confession and releasing Hoshi when Fujiwara asked for time to determine the blood groups of the prisoners. The results proved that Tagami, who had made the confession, could not possibly be the criminal; his blood group was O. Hoshi, on the other hand, had Group A. Confronted with the data, Hoshi confessed; that Fujiwara knew his blood and his semen had something in common impressed the man's simple mind as a form of witchcraft.

Once more forensic serologists in Europe followed through with studies of their own. Leone Lattes showed that it was possible to detect the blood group of a man who had sealed a letter from the traces of saliva on the envelope flap. Holzer solved a murder on the basis of traces of saliva left in a car. In 1938 Galloro developed a simple method for determining components of a person's blood group from the saliva left on the tip of a cigarette. This method, likewise based on absorption, could place the smoker of a discarded cigar or cigarette butt as belonging to Blood Groups A, B, or AB, provided that he belonged to the group of "secretors."

This was the situation in research and criminological practice when on January 21, 1939, Roche Lynch received the cigarette stub that Bernard Spilsbury had found on Pamela Coventry's body. Lynch went to work with his characteristic painstaking precision. He had none of Spilsbury's personality, and made up for this lack by diligence and extra care.

In preparation for the intended tests, he wished to confirm the new method for himself. He assembled a number of cigarettes, some unsmoked, others smoked by laboratory assistants with known blood groups. He removed tiny bits of paper from the tip of each and placed them in physiological salt solution until he thought the traces of the saliva would have dissolved into the solution. Then he began applying anti-A and anti-B serums, according to the rules of Holzer's absorption method.

Roche Lynch was still waiting for his results when the search squads in Essex came upon the first pieces of Pamela Coventry's missing clothing. The shoes the child had worn were found in a lot on South End Road. Near the Elm Park railroad station two buttons from her blazer, together with a piece of the wire that had been used to tie her, turned up. These objects were wrapped in a January 11 copy of the *News Chronicle* fastened with the kind of friction tape that had been found beside the child's body. Finally, school insignia were found that had been torn off Pamela's blazer. It appeared certain that the murderer was still lingering in the vicinity of Coronation Drive, and was trying to throw his pursuers off his scent by strewing objects that had belonged to the child over a wide area. After the insignia, however, nothing more was found. None of Pamela's other clothing—her cream-colored cap or her blazer, her brown stockings or underwear—turned up.

Bridger now placed his hopes in a house-to-house questioning all along Coronation Drive. Had anyone seen the child? Had anyone noticed a man with a child? Had an unknown driver taken a child into a car? Was anyone in the neighborhood unusually fond of playing with children?

Bridger's work had reached this point when Chief Constable Horwell called him to London and informed him that Roche Lynch had completed his tests on January 23. He had repeated them several times to eliminate all doubts, and now felt sure of his conclusions. His control experiments —determining the blood group of his assistants from the saliva on their cigarettes—had been 100 per cent successful.

Bridger returned to Hornchurch grateful for the lead, although not fully understanding the scientific point involved. He found a mountain of paper dealing with the results of the house-to-house inquiries. But the pickings were distinctly lean: rumors, gossip, accusations, the sort of thing that such dredgings always bring up from the depths of human baseness. Nevertheless, he decided to repeat the procedure, with more precise inquiries and the use of written questionnaires. Where, in what house or apartment, during the noon hours of January 18, was there a man or youth who had been alone for a while, who smoked cigarettes which he rolled himself out of used tobacco?

The families who lived on Coronation Drive were all working-class people whose men went out to jobs; none of them would have been at home in the middle of the day. To Bridger's surprise, the new series of questions produced a result by January 26. The search narrowed down to two men, one of whom could be eliminated after a few hours of closer investigation because he was sick and permanently bedridden. But the second, a twenty-eight-year-old factory worker named Leonard Richardson, had stayed home from work on January 18 because of some temporary illness. He had been at home alone. His wife had recently given birth and was still in the hospital. Richardson was a heavy smoker who rolled his own cigarettes. What was more important, he worked in a chemical factory where smoking was forbidden during work. He therefore slipped off to the men's room at intervals, rolled a cigarette, and took a few puffs; then he would put it out and tuck the half-smoked butt into his tobacco tin. That would explain—if he were the criminal—why there were charred bits of tobacco in the cigarette end that had been found on Pamela Coventry's body.

Bridger had had a good deal of experience with sex crimes. He knew that persons with pathological sexual instincts could fall into a state of sexual overstimulation when their wives were away for some time, and might be capable of sudden, dangerous reactions. On January 27, therefore, he set out to see Richardson, with a view to gaining an impression of the man. Richardson, short, rather stocky, with an expanse of brow and a head somewhat too large for his body, was extremely co-operative and self-assured. He promptly declared his willingness to do all in his power to help solve the crime. If he were uneasy at all, he betrayed his feelings at most by the way of hastily rolling and smoking one cigarette after another. The way he moistened the paper with his tongue, and frequently ran his tongue over his lips while smoking, reminded Bridger of Lynch's finding, which had initially struck him as so peculiar and mysterious. From that moment on he began considering how he could ascertain Richardson's blood group. British law gave him no way of demanding a blood sample from the man; and his sixth sense told him that Richardson, for all his pose of being accommodating, would flatly refuse to give a sample.

Bridger left Richardson with his suspicions heightened. But how was he to obtain a blood sample unobtrusively? On the afternoon of January 27 he asked Horwell for advice. Horwell could only suggest that he appeal directly to Roche Lynch. Bridger therefore went personally to London and called on the Home Office Analyst at St. Mary's. Lynch, who as usual went right on with his laboratory work, for he hated being interrupted, casually suggested that Bridger get hold of some of Richardson's dirty laundry, best of all used handkerchiefs; he was confident that he could identify the suspect's blood group from his nasal mucus.

Next day Chief Inspector Baker obtained a search warrant. When the detectives appeared at the apartment, Richardson once more behaved with the utmost good nature. While Bridger's men searched chiefly for Pamela Coventry's missing clothes, for bloodstains and other possible signs of an act of violence, Bridger looked for dirty clothes. He finally found a laundry bag with a number of heavily used handkerchiefs. Richardson unsuspectingly admitted that he had used these during the past week. Bridger had the handkerchiefs wrapped up and sent a sergeant off with them to London. Only then did he himself participate in the general search. Richardson remained friendly and helpful. And after several hours nothing had been discovered that might have connected him with the murder—no trace of Pamela Coventry's clothing, no signs of violence. The whole flat was neat and had been cleaned with exemplary care. But then a policeman found a heap of newspapers—many issues of the *News Chronicle*. Remembering that the murdered girl's blazer buttons had been wrapped in a January 11 issue of that newspaper, Bridger looked through the heap. All the issues from January 4 through January 12 were there—except for the issue of January 11!

Hopes now rose that some incriminating evidence might after all be discovered. And sure enough, in the garden one detective came upon cable that looked like the wire used to tie Pamela. Somewhat later another detective found black friction tape resembling the tape with which the *News Chronicle* package had been fastened. Bridger called off the search after he had discovered tiny bloodstains on a raincoat that Richardson said he had worn during the past week. He sent the raincoat to Roche Lynch, and the wire, the tape, and Richardson's tobacco tin to the Metropolitan Police Laboratory. Then he and Baker waited in suspense for the results of the tests in London.

On January 30 the Police Laboratory reported on its findings. The cigarette paper used by Richardson was of the same type as the paper in the cigarette end found on the corpse. However, the brand of paper was very widely used, so that the identity did not signify too much. The same was true for the wire found in Richardson's garden; it, too, resembled the wire on the body in all testable characteristics; but it was a mass-manufactured product, although the manufacture of part of it had ceased seven years earlier. Part of the cable—green—was of very unusual type —600 O.H.M., seven strand. This certainly could and did point to the suspect. The friction tape was likewise of a well-known brand, manufactured in large quantities. But the tape from Richardson's apartment and the tape found with Pamela Coventry both showed defects in the weaving that were not typical of the brand. As for the tobacco tin, it contained, along with fresh tobacco, bits of burned tobacco and half-smoked cigarettes. The tobacco had been sent to the specialists of a tobacco firm in Bristol so that it could be compared with the tobacco in the cigarette butt.

All these finds tended to incriminate Richardson. With all the more eagerness Bridger now waited for the completion of Roche Lynch's tests.

On January 31 Lynch reported his results. He had checked the bloodstains on the coat. They were human blood, but in the state of scientific knowledge of that time the size of the stains was insufficient for blood grouping. To his intense disappointment, however, all efforts to get a blood grouping from the paper of the cigarettes Richardson was known to have smoked or from the highly significant cigarette end found with the corpse proved unavailing. Richardson happened to be what is known as a non-secretor and his saliva could not be grouped at all.

Bridger knew that it would not be easy to persuade a jury of Richardson's guilt. He was well aware of the coolness felt by British jurors for scientific evidence of all kinds. He knew their general distrust of all novelties they did not understand. For this reason he tried to extract a confession from Richardson by totting up all the evidence he had against him: the cigarette paper, the wire and tape. But the stocky man with the big head remained unshaken. He denied everything; he composedly continued his denials even after the verdict of the tobacco experts arrived from Bristol: that the tobacco in the cigarette butt and in Richardson's tobacco tin was exactly the same type. Bridger once more searched Richardson's apartment, hoping to find some additional clue. But all his rummaging was in vain. Everything was tidy and clean.

In April 1939 Richardson was indicted for murder in the Central Criminal Court of London. But the trial came to an abrupt end on the fifth day. The foreman of the jury handed Mr. Justice Hawke a note stating that the jurors would be unable to convict Richardson. A formal verdict of "Not guilty" was returned, and Richardson left the courtroom a free man.

A reporter from the *Daily Herald* who accompanied Richardson in a car to his house ended his account of the car ride with a description of the triumphant Richardson who, before reaching Elm Park, heaped loose tobacco on cigarette paper and rolled himself a cigarette with visible satisfaction.

Thus the first spectacular crime involving an attempt at determination of blood grouping from saliva ended with the criminological value of the method left in doubt. But in that same year England, and London, provided another and even more spectacular case which focused upon the same problem. Once again the scientific precision of the method was dramatized and the reluctance of juries to recognize it confirmed.

14

In May of 1939 Chief Inspector Leonard Burt of Scotland Yard was still many years away from the era of his greatest triumphs in crime detection. That time came after the Second World War when (by then Commander of the Special Branch) he arrested the "atom spies" Alan Nunn May and Klaus Fuchs. But from the beginning of his career as a constable in the streets of London's East End up to the spring of 1939, he had already had a remarkable record as a member of the Murder Squad.

Called to the scene of a murder in a villa in Branksome, Bournemouth, on the night of May 21, 1939, he thought at first that it was an affair of no special importance. To be sure, Branksome was in the territory of the Dorset police, who as a rule appealed to Scotland Yard for help only in difficult cases. But Burt rather prided himself on his instincts about a case, and here his instincts suggested nothing extraordinary. He set out rather coolly with Detective Sergeant Dyke.

The villa in which the crime had taken place was situated some distance off Poole Road, behind a garden full of shrubs and trees. The house belonged to Walter Dinivan, a well-to-do man who owned a garage and several rental houses. Thrifty in spite of his wealth, he had divided his villa into two large apartments. The upper apartment was occupied by two old ladies, Miss Young and Miss Lancefield; in the lower flat Walter Dinivan, widowed, sixty-four, lived with his granddaughter, Hilda Dinivan. Hilda's brother, a telegrapher in the Royal Navy who had been serving in the Far East for several years, had recently come home and was staying with his grandfather.

On the night of May 21 the young people had left the house shortly after seven o'clock to go to a dance. Dinivan stayed home, sitting in his favorite chair by the fireplace. Hilda and her brother returned sometime after eleven o'clock, and found the window of the living room unwontedly dark. They knocked repeatedly, but no one came to the door. At last they went around to the side of the house, where they could see through a window into the rear part of the living room. The lamp was out, but the electric fire in the fireplace glowed. By its light Hilda saw her grandfather stretched out on the floor, his face pressed against the rug, his feet toward the fireplace. A dark pool spread around his head.

For a moment Hilda and her brother thought their grandfather had suffered an attack of weakness, and vomited. The boy ran back to the front door, and smashed the glass, expecting to be able to turn the key from the inside. To his surprise, the key was not there. He then broke the glass entirely out of the panel, squeezed through into the hall, and opened a window so that his sister could climb in. When they turned on the light in the living room, they saw that Walter Dinivan's head lay in a pool of blood already partly coagulated. His skull had been bashed by many blows, but the old man was still breathing.

Hilda's brother called an ambulance and the police. Dinivan was taken to Boscombe Hospital. There he died in the course of the night, shortly before three o'clock, without being able to give a hint as to who his murderer had been.

When Superintendent Swain of the Dorset police called in Scotland Yard, Bernard Spilsbury also was sent for. He arrived even before Burt. His conclusions from the autopsy were as follows: The murderer had first tried to strangle Dinivan, and had apparently failed. He completed his job with brutal blows on the head. A hammer must have served as the murder instrument. Spilsbury found no signs that Dinivan had attempted to defend himself. Either he had been assaulted by an unexpected intruder, or else the murderer was an acquaintance whom Dinivan had trustingly admitted. The two ladies on the upper floor of the house had heard unusual noises toward eleven o'clock but had attributed no importance to them. Nevertheless, this suggested that the murder had taken place shortly before eleven.

The investigation had reached this point when Chief Inspector Burt and Detective Sergeant Dyke reached Poole Road. Shortly afterward, Superintendent Cherrill, head of the fingerprint division of Scotland Yard, arrived. They examined the scene carefully. Close to the spot where the dead man had lain stood a table holding Dinivan's whiskey bottle and the glass he usually drank from. But there was also a beer bottle and a second glass. Neither the beer nor the other glass had been on the table when the young people left the house. During their absence, therefore, Dinivan must have entertained someone. The beer glass had been knocked over and some of the contents spilled on the table. Cherrill found a large number of fingerprints. He obtained the prints of Hilda and her brother, for purposes of comparison, and drove to the morgue to secure the dead man's fingerprints. All the fingerprints were either those of Dinivan or his grandchildren except for one thumbprint on the beer glass, for which there was no explanation. It might be the unknown murderer's.

Meanwhile Burt, Dyke, and some of the Dorset police officials had made some interesting discoveries. A small safe in the wall of the living room had been opened and pillaged. The key to the safe, which the dead man had always carried in his pocket, lay inside the empty safe. The murderer had also taken nineteen pounds from Dinivan's pocket; Dinivan had given his granddaughter some money that afternoon, and she had observed him counting the money he had with him. His rings had also been stripped from his fingers; his watch and gold chain were likewise missing. On the floor lay a brown paper bag crumpled in such an odd manner that it seemed evident it had held a hammer.

The most curious finds, however, were a hair curler and a number of cigarette ends. The hair curler lay on the rug beside the sofa. Dyke, who knew something about such beautification devices, identified it as a French type. The cigarette stubs seemed ordinary enough; but it was curious that some of them lay not only on the rug beside the sofa, but also on a silk cushion on the sofa. They had not been stubbed out, and nevertheless the silk showed not the slightest sign of singeing.

When Burt showed Hilda the curler and asked whether she used that kind, she showed signs of embarrassment. Her brother, less inhibited, explained that it was a little awkward, but both of them knew that Walter Dinivan liked to receive woman visitors and occasionally brought home streetwalkers from Bournemouth. But that was his affair; the young people felt that they had no right to interfere.

The detectives, of course, promptly considered the possibility that a prostitute had been Dinivan's unknown late guest, and that she and a male accomplice might have killed and robbed him. Dinivan had not been a cigarette smoker. The curler and the butts might suggest that a girl had kept the old man occupied while the actual murderer stole into the house. Superintendent Swain therefore ordered several detectives to make inquiries among known prostitutes.

Burt, however, continued to eye the cold cigarettes on the easily singed cloth of the cushion and on the rug. He was more and more inclined to think that the cigarette stubs had not been carelessly dropped in the course of a conversation, but that they as well as the curler had been deliberately placed there in order to lure the police off on a false trail—precisely, the trail to the Bournemouth prostitutes. When he found another cigarette butt behind a second cushion, where supposedly it might have dropped before or after sexual intercourse, his suspicion became a certainty—for if that cigarette had been lit, it would surely have left marks of burning, if not started a fire. At the same time he recalled the Richardson case and the blood group tests that Roche Lynch had carried out with a cigarette. He wrapped all the butts in tissue paper and asked Dyke to take them to Roche Lynch. "Ask him," he said, "if there is a chance of establishing the blood group of the person who used them."

Dyke returned in the afternoon with word that Roche Lynch would undertake the tests; that, in fact, he was extraordinarily interested in the case. However, he was so busy at the moment that it would be several days before he could have results on his tests. Burt was somewhat annoyed at having to wait so long; he felt oddly impatient. But he made good use of the time. While the Dorset police were concentrating on prostitutes and their acquaintances, he looked for other persons who might have been on so familiar a footing with Dinivan that he would have admitted them late at night and given them beer. Hilda Dinivan gave the names of all her grandfather's cronies and acquaintances. Among others she mentioned Joseph Williams, a retired old soldier whom Dinivan had known for decades. Williams lived ten minutes' walk away, on Ingworth Road. But Hilda asserted that Williams was over seventy and much too infirm to kill anyone, so that Burt postponed checking on the man until he had dealt with the other acquaintances. He had questioned a dozen or so with no more result than he had got from the prostitutes. Some of the streetwalkers admitted they had known "old Dinny," but none of them owned a hair curler of the type that had been found in Dinivan's living room; they laughed at the old-fashioned curler, the kind Grandmother used to wear, they said. Nevertheless, one of the prostitutes said something that prompted Burt to look up Joseph Williams after all. She mentioned that up to May 21 Williams had been broke all the time, but lately he had had his pockets full of money.

Burt quickly found out that Williams owned the house in which he lived, that it was mortgaged to the limit and he had not paid the interest for a long time—until a few days previously, when he had suddenly paid an installment. On May 25, therefore, Burt and Dyke went to call on him. They found him living in one utterly filthy room, with an indescribable stench. For years Williams had been making much of his being a veteran of the Indian Army; an old sword lay on the table, which, besides a few chairs, a stove, and a bed, constituted the room's only furniture.

Apparently Williams had been prepared for Burt's coming by the newspapers' accounts of the activities of the police. The old man, who looked nothing but skin and bones, screeched at the Chief Inspector out of a toothless mouth: "Busybody Burt!" He swung the sword around. "I'll show you the way to go home." Sheer rage flashed behind his thick glasses. "I know you. I know what you're after. But you shan't bloody well get it." Then he dropped into a chair, still clutching the sword. "Oh yes, Inspector, I can account for every minute of the day poor Dinivan was murdered. Queer thing, you know, I saw him . . . on the seventeenth. We met in the street outside, and he insisted on taking me in and giving me a drink. But he wouldn't lend me all the money I needed. Oh no—only five pounds. And that he got out of his safe."

Williams suddenly fell silent, apparently realizing that he was speaking of dangerous matters; and from then on he refused to say another word about the case. When Burt asked him for his fingerprints, so that he could prove he had had nothing to do with the murder, he waved the sword wildly again and shouted that he knew his rights, he knew the tricks the "bloody rozzers" used to catch the innocent.

Burt and Dyke left Williams' den with little accomplished. Burt was therefore all the more pleased when he returned to London and heard the results of Roche Lynch's tests. The smoker of the cigarette stubs was in fact a "secretor"; it had therefore been possible to determine his blood group. It was the same for all the cigarettes, Blood Group AB, the rarest of all groups. This fact enormously narrowed the circle of possible murderers. Lynch suggested that the detectives obtain the saliva of suspects for him or, if possible, that they let him obtain the sample himself, for saliva had to be handled with special care, because it could easily be broken up by bacteria.

From that first meeting with Williams, Burt realized that it would be altogether pointless to ask the old man for a saliva sample—he would refuse as scornfully as he had refused to let his fingerprints be taken. Cunning was called for. But he had the man watched, with orders that he be informed at once if Williams dropped into a pub for a beer or a drink. A few days passed before word came that Williams was at a pub in Branksome. Burt and Dyke hurried to the place. They pretended they had just dropped in, met Williams by chance, and had meanwhile abandoned all suspicions of him. Burt wrote later in his memoirs: "There wasn't any difficulty persuading him to have a pint." Burt offered his pack of cigarettes, and Williams took one. As Burt tells the story: "When he finished the cigarette he threw the stub away and took another. Dyke moved to pick it up." Meanwhile, Burt distracted Williams' attention by arguing about horses. Before long Dyke had a fistful of cigarette butts which were sent off to London the very next morning.

Burt's experience with general detective work had made him cautious. Nevertheless, his first suspicions of Williams soon grew into a conviction that Williams was the murderer. That conviction was confirmed when at last the report came from Roche Lynch: "The person who smoked the last batch of cigarettes and moistened them with his saliva is a secretor and has Blood Group AB."

Burt himself was far too great a believer in "direct investigation" to overvalue the results of the saliva tests. But they certainly impressed him. Theoretically, in spite of the rarity of the blood group, it was conceivable that some other person of Group AB had murdered Dinivan. But practically . . . ? In any case, Burt now had enough evidence in hand to justify his concentrating all further investigation on Williams exclusively.

A few hours later he and Dyke once more stood at Williams' door. When Williams opened the door and recognized his callers, he croaked in fury: "What the hell do you want?" He let them in, but went on protesting: "Me kill old Dinny? I couldn't kill a cat." In a fury of self-righteousness he said mockingly: "Oh, if you like; take a dekko around the place."

Burt seized upon the unexpected invitation. From a coal shed Dyke brought out a bundle of old brown paper bags. They were all of the same sort as the bag the murderer had left behind in Dinivan's living room. Williams watched the detectives packing up their loot. "Paper bags?" he said with a scornful glare. "I used to be a greengrocer. Also a fishmonger. All greengrocers have paper bags."

While Burt and Dyke looked around the messy room, Williams tossed his wallet on the table. Maybe they wanted to see his money too. All right, they could go ahead. But they'd have a time proving he had a single note from Dinivan. He'd just won at the races. Blue Peter in the Derby.

While he was ranting on, Burt discreetly noted the numbers of the bank notes.

That about exhausted all the possibilities of finding evidence at Williams' house. Burt and Dyke left the old codger, who had meanwhile worked himself up to wild threats again. As far as Burt could see, this visit had yielded only one profitable thing: a neighbor had given him the address of Williams' wife, who had left him some time before.

Burt went to see the worn old woman. And he made a surprising discovery: she used the very type of hair curler that had been found at the scene of the crime. Of course she must have left a few of them around her husband's place at one time or another, she said. Comparison at the laboratory in London showed that Mrs. Williams' curlers and the one found in Dinivan's living room were in fact the same kind: an old-fashioned brand manufactured in France. But at this point the investigation ground to a halt. No one had seen Williams in the vicinity of the Dinivan house on the day or night of the crime. There were no witnesses who had even seen Williams leaving his own house that night. For several weeks Burt and his men probed in vain. Burt finally saw that the one remaining possibility was to arrest Williams, take his fingerprints, and make a thorough search of his premises. The question was whether a magistrate would regard the few bits of incriminating evidence and the one big item—the agreement of the blood groups—as sufficient for an arrest warrant.

Burt first decided to pay a last call on Williams, hoping that the old fellow would have cooled down and would be feeling cocky again. Perhaps the right line to take would be to treat him with deliberate friendliness and pretend to ask pardon for having suspected him unjustly. Burt therefore started a rumor that he had been convinced of Williams' innocence.

After thus preparing the ground, Burt and Dyke paid their third visit to Ingworth Road on June 20. Williams received the two detectives, his toothless mouth pursed in a malicious grin. "Innocent, that's what I am —innocent, and even you can't pin it on me." And sure enough, as proof of his clean conscience, he made the very gesture Burt had been hoping for. He held out his hand to Burt, offering to let his fingerprints be taken.

"How's that for confidence, eh, mate?" he croaked. Burt took the fingerprints, suppressing all signs of his eagerness. Then Williams showed them out and slammed the door behind them.

Dyke drove at once to the fingerprint department of Scotland Yard. That same night Cherrill called Burt and excitedly informed him that the thumbprint on the beer glass found at the scene of the crime was identical with the print of Williams' right thumb. Now Burt was sure that any magistrate would authorize Williams' arrest.

Next day Burt, this time accompanied by Superintendent Swain, stood for the fourth time at Williams' grubby door. They informed him that he was under arrest. Only for a moment did he seem alarmed. Then he resumed his pose of unconcern. "Arrest me? You're not going to arrest me, are you? The whole thing's ridiculous."

In the courtroom he behaved with enormous impudence. He called out to the press photographers: "Take a pretty picture, lads." He snarled at the magistrate: "There'll be a sensation when I don't go to the whist drive tonight. . . . I am just as innocent as you are, sir, that's all. Of course I don't know whether you did it or not. . . . "

Williams stuck to his guns throughout the following weeks, during which Burt made every conceivable effort to obtain some direct testimony to support the circumstantial evidence against the prisoner. But there was nothing to be done; no incriminating witnesses could be found. And the circumstantial evidence itself was not very impressive, although it had convinced Burt: the fact that Williams had suddenly come into money; his admission that he had asked Dinivan for money; the hair curler; the paper bags; the thumbprint; and the coincidence of the blood groups as determined by the saliva test of the cigarette butts.

In October 1939 Williams was tried at the Dorset Assizes before Mr. Justice Croom-Johnson and a jury. Led into the courtroom, he put on a show of jauntiness. "Here we are. Keep on smiling." He kept interrupting the proceedings with shouts of "I am innocent." He snarled at the prosecutor: "That's a lie!" or "I hate people to tell lies." His defender, Norman King, had difficulty silencing him and persuading him to apologize for his outbursts. Rarely had a defendant made so disagreeable an impression upon judge and jury. Nevertheless, Norman King seemed calm and confident when he began his summation for the defense on October 14.

Within a few words it became clear what he was aiming at: the uncertainty of jurors when confronted with the new phenomenon of saliva testing. King gave the question of the thumbprint a wide berth; he did not want the jurors to think about this piece of evidence, which he could hardly wave aside altogether. But what about the hair curler? With a wave of his hand, King swept that argument away. It might be that Mrs. Williams had left some old curlers around the defendant's home, but did that prove that they really corresponded to the curlers at the scene of the crime? And how many old curlers of this sort were there probably lying around London? As for the paper bag—had anyone observed Williams carrying a murder instrument into Dinivan's house in one of his old paper bags? No one! How many thousands and tens of thousands of similar bags were there in London?

King's speech for the defense had reached this point when he raised his voice and delivered his main argument. Deliberately, he had left the question of the saliva traces until the last. The prosecution, he declared, based its charges against Williams very largely on the circumstance that cigarette ends had been found at the scene on which allegedly tiny remains of saliva of Blood Group AB had been found. It further alleged that saliva on cigarettes that Williams had smoked showed the same blood group. Yet the assertion of the serologists that a person's blood group was indicated by his saliva was so novel that the prosecution expert could not even claim that the foundations of this doctrine were sound. Scientists could go ahead and accept the demonstration of blood groups in human saliva if they were so minded; but he, King, must ask the honorable members of the jury (and he held up the tip of a cigarette) whether any of them was prepared to make the life or death of a defendant dependent on such a scrap of paper! Could any of the jurors observe the dried saliva on the cigarette tip? None could. And could any of the jurors imagine that the blood group of a human being could be determined from these invisible traces? He himself found it incredible. And he must leave it to the jurors whether they wished to decide the guilt or innocence of an old man on the basis of an invisible smear of saliva—an old man who had certainly made a spectacle of himself in court, but whose uncontrollable excitement could after all be understood when one considered that he was helplessly and desperately fighting against the injustice that was being done to him.

Williams looked at his defender with obvious complacency and licked his lips. His smugness was justified, for when the jury returned they acquitted Williams of the charge of murder. Embittered, with the chagrin of the hunter who is turned from his quarry, Burt listened to the verdict. Williams left the court with the air of a victor, followed by one of those reporters who partly out of honest conviction, reformism, and humanitarian ideals, partly out of pure joy in sensationalism, frequently become the partisans of persecuted innocence and all too often hit upon imaginary innocents. This reporter—his name was Norman Rae—thought he would be able to turn in a brilliant scoop on Williams' return to freedom. Thinking the old man would be more communicative after a good rest, Rae took him to a hotel in the vicinity of Dorchester. Drinking his first double whiskey, Williams offered the toast: "To the hangman! To the hangman who has been cheated of his victim." Then he bathetically decided that he did not want to stay in the hotel; he wanted to go back where he belonged, to Poole. If Rae did not want to drive him there, he would take the next bus: "I want to see their faces when I walk up Main Street."

With his firm faith in the man's innocence, Rae found this impulse quite forgivable. And so they drove to Poole, and Williams enjoyed his victory. Then he returned to the hotel with Rae. But in the middle of the night Rae heard fists pounding on the door of his room. When he opened it, there stood Williams—but not the Williams he had seen in court, bold and waggish. This was a weeping, shaking old man. "I couldn't sleep," he whimpered. "Christ, I couldn't get to sleep at all.

I've got to tell somebody. You see, the jury was wrong. . . . The jury was wrong," he repeated. "It was me."

Rae struggled to master his disillusionment and to calm the ghostly-looking, shaking old man. After a while he managed to get Williams to bed, and next morning the old fellow seemed to have forgotten everything; he once more played the part of an aggrieved innocent. Rae returned him to Poole. The dream of a great news story was shattered. Rae did not write a word about the nocturnal confession. For according to British law, Williams could not be tried twice for the same crime, even if he had been wrongly acquitted. Rae did not reveal the long-preserved secret until 1951, after Williams had died an octogenarian.

The Williams case proved that diagnosis of blood groups from traces of bodily secretions was a dependable method. It gave the criminologist a new procedure for determining possible suspects or for excluding falsely accused persons from a group of suspects. It offered far wider possibilities than the mere analysis of bloodstains. But four more years were to pass—until the summer of 1943—before such a test was to lead to a confession and conviction. Now the scene shifted to New York. The scientist involved was a member of the original group of researchers around Karl Landsteiner, the father of blood grouping. He was Alexander S. Wiener, a Brooklyn-born biochemist, and at the time in question barely thirty-six years old. But he had already made a name for himself in the still new and promising field of blood factor research. He was among the discoverers of the Rhesus factor which was soon to acquire great importance in general medicine. That fact alone assured him a place among the prominent serologists in the world. Consequently, much attention was paid to his role in the solving of a crime which took place in March 1943 in New York, in the very midst of the storms of the Second World War.

15

On the night of March 30, 1943, an unknown woman was found dead in front of the stoop of a rooming house at 337 West 30th Street. Inspector Conrad Rothengast, head of the 3rd Detective Squad, reached the scene of the crime at 3 A.M. on March 31. The corpse lay on the sidewalk directly in front of the building, her head and trunk propped against the wall of the house. The nearest street lamp and what lights were on in the French Hospital, across the street, gave only a dim illumination. By his car's headlights Rothengast saw that she was a woman in her fifties, with graying hair; she wore a greenish dress and a cheap coat of black-and-white patterned wool. There were a stocking and a high-heeled shoe on her right leg; the left leg shone bare and white. The left shoe had vanished. Oddly, the missing stocking was found in a long, narrow paper bag that lay beside her on the pavement.

Detective John A. Hawthorne, a handsome, broad-shouldered member of the Homicide Squad, had reached the scene before Rothengast. He was kneeling beside John J. Brennan, a sergeant from the precinct station on the same street, directing his flashlight at the unmistakable strangulation marks on the woman's throat. Behind him stood a man in the uniform of a night watchman. On the lower step of the stairs that led up to the totally dark entrance of 337 another policeman was holding a small, stocky man of South European appearance, who in spite of his rugged features was staring dully into space with a helpless expression.

Hawthorne briefed Rothengast on what he had learned. He had heard the story, he said, from the man in the night watchman's uniform, Edwin J. Finnerty, who was responsible for guarding the adjacent building, 335, which held the offices of the periodical *The Rural New Yorker*. At 2:30 A.M. Finnerty had come out of the old building to smoke a pipe in front of the door. He was used to the nocturnal noises of the city, and tonight things seemed to him oddly quiet. For that reason he heard the clicking of the front door to the rooming house next door, which was on a higher level, and looked up the stoop. Because of the high balustrade along the stairs, he could not see the steps themselves; but he made out the outlines of a man moving backward down the stairs, as if pulling some burden behind him. After a short time the figure vanished behind the balustrade, and Finnerty heard a sound as if a heavy bundle were being laid down. He suspected that some tenant of the rooming house who owed his rent was stealing out of the building with his possessions. Hearing the noise of footsteps moving rapidly away, he walked the few steps down the street. He was just in time to catch sight of a small man moving toward Ninth Avenue and mingling with a crowd of post office employees who were leaving the Central Post Office, nearby, their night shift ended. Finnerty wondered what could have happened to the apparently heavy baggage the man had had with him. The stairs and sidewalk were so poorly illuminated that he did not notice the shadowy bundle beside the steps. He returned to his own building. But after a while curiosity impelled him to go out and look once more. This time he went to the foot of the stoop. To his horror, he discovered the dead woman, and at the same time he heard footsteps, this time approaching from the Eighth Avenue direction. Their rhythm reminded him of the pace of the unknown man from the rooming house who had left in the opposite direction five or ten minutes before. Finnerty concealed himself in the entrance to 335, where he could watch the street. A moment later a man hurried past him, small as the unknown man he had observed before. With a folded newspaper under his arm, this man climbed the stairs to the rooming house, opened the door, and closed it behind him. While Finnerty was considering whether to wait a moment longer or call the police, he heard a noise at the door again. Once more he recognized the top part of the stranger's body as the man moved down the steps. Carrying a longish object wrapped in a newspaper or paper bag, the man set off toward Eighth Avenue. He must have seen the dead woman, but he went past her without pausing for a second.

Finnerty decided to follow the man, who was now heading toward Pennsylvania Station. On the corner of 33rd Street Finnerty caught sight of a cruising police car and informed the policeman, who followed the stranger and stopped him. Frightened, he explained in broken English that his name was John Manos and that he had done nothing wrong; he came from Greece and was working as a cook in the Bronx. Not know much English, ask boss, he good worker, hard worker.

The policeman asked where he lived. Manos replied that he had a room at 337 West 30th Street. Why had he left the house several times during the night? Manos said he had been hungry the first time. He'd been sick all day, and so he'd gone out to get something to eat and buy a newspaper. After he got back he saw an empty wine bottle in his room, and since he was a neat man, he didn't like empty bottles standing around. So he had gone out once more to throw the bottle into the litter can on 33rd Street. He had wrapped up the bottle because he didn't want anyone to see it and think he was a drinker. No streetwalkers or drinkers were allowed in his rooming house.

The police drove Manos and Finnerty back to West 30th Street. There they convinced themselves that the night watchman's information was correct, and that Manos could not have passed the dead woman without seeing her. But Manos shook his head—rather vaguely and apathetically. He insisted he had not seen her. He had never seen her before, either.

Such was the story that Hawthorne told Inspector Rothengast, while the policemen stood on the steps guarding John Manos. Meanwhile a number of people gathered inquisitively. One man pressed forward, glanced at the dead woman's face, and cried out that he knew her. Someone else also recognized her. Both gave her name as Alice Persico. She lived with her brother a few houses down, at 311 West 30th Street. The brother's name was Peterson—Ernest C. Peterson. Alice had formerly been married to a Greek named Persico, but her husband had left her. She was seen around, and was a pretty heavy drinker. Did she have friends? Hawthorne asked. Did she take up with men? The witnesses shrugged. Maybe. They'd better ask her brother. Or her husband. The husband lived somewhere in Brooklyn.

Rothengast sent for specialists of the identification service and for the medical examiner, who would pass on the cause and the time of death. He sent Hawthorne into the woman's apartment to search for clues there. Then he ordered the policeman guarding Manos to take the man up to his third-floor room. He himself followed them. Manos opened his door. When he had said he was a neat man, he had not been exaggerating. The old brick building was somewhat the worse for wear. But in Manos' sparsely furnished room everything was scrubbed and orderly. The linoleum floor gleamed. Everything was in its proper place. When a man living alone declared that he had gone out at night to a rubbish container some distance away in order to get rid of an empty wine bottle, he would generally be thought a liar. But in the present case the appearance of the room suggested that he had been telling the truth.

Manos stood somewhat hunched between the policemen repeating in a babble of Greek and English the same sentences again and again: "Not me. . . . No one in my room. . . . Never have woman in room. . . . Clean room self. . . . Never saw dead woman."

Meanwhile the men from the identification squad had come up. They had already taken the dead woman's fingerprints, and they now took Manos'. Then they set about searching his room thoroughly. Rothengast questioned the maid who took care of the rooms on the second story. She confirmed the fact that Manos cleaned his own room. He lived all alone, worked in the Bronx from late afternoon to early morning, and was saving his money to buy a farm when he returned to Greece. The day before he had been ill and had not left his room. Rothengast also questioned the tenant in the room next door. He was an old man who also had been sick and confined to his bed for two days. During the day and all through the past night he had been suffering a good deal of pain and had been unable to sleep. He thought it altogether impossible that a murder could have been committed in Manos' room at any time during the past twenty-four hours. The walls were so thin that every noise came through. All he had noticed was that Manos had gone out at about 2 A.M., returned, and gone out again.

By four o'clock in the morning the men of the identification squad were finished. They had found nothing worth noticing; all fingerprints were those of Manos himself. The fingerprints on the empty bottle of port wine, bearing the label "Riverside," were also his own. Meanwhile, Hawthorne had returned from his visit to Alice Persico's apartment. The murdered woman's room was a complete mess—it was obvious that she had long led an irregular life. Ernest Peterson did not even know when his sister had last been at home. According to his statement, they hadn't had much to do with one another. Alice Persico had had several lovers, among them a jealous and violent man named Pete Coyle, whom she was frightened of because he often beat her; Peterson remembered his sister once saying that Coyle would kill her someday. He had no idea where Coyle could be found. Hawthorne immediately ordered a search for Coyle.

When Rothengast and Hawthorne came out on the street again, the body was about to be taken to Bellevue Hospital. Dr. Benjamin Vance, the assistant medical examiner, reported that she had been strangled by obviously very powerful hands. He could not state the time of death precisely as yet. Then he left for Bellevue. Rothengast had the entire stairway and the fronts of the other houses searched for the missing shoe, without success. A policeman rummaged through the trash container into which Manos had been going to throw his empty bottle of Riverside wine—likewise in vain.

Since nothing more could be done at the scene before daybreak, Rothengast phoned District Attorney Pagnucco, who spoke ten languages, including Greek. Rothengast asked him to come to the police station and question Manos in his native language. When Pagnucco addressed his first words in Greek to the man, Manos' face lit up a little, and his replies became much more detailed and comprehensible. But they remained the same in essence: "I did not kill her. I never saw her before. She was never in my room. Nobody ever visited me in my room."

By seven o'clock in the morning, after several hours of questioning, Pagnucco gave up. He had the Greek taken to a cell and discussed with Rothengast what their next steps should be. As things stood, there was no proof at all that Manos was the murderer. It seemed highly improbable that he could have managed to kill a woman in his room and drag his victim through the house and out to the street without being seen by anyone. Finnerty, the night watchman, could testify only that Manos was the man who had passed him several times and who had entered and again left the rooming house. He could not state that Manos was the same man who had come backward down the stairs dragging something after him. All he could say was that the two men seemed to have had the same way of moving. It was quite possible that the murderer did not live in the rooming house at all. He could have lured Alice Persico from the street into the unlocked vestibule and for some unknown reason strangled her. On the other hand, the fact that the dead woman was brought out to the street argued against this possibility. A murderer from outside the house would not care whether his victim were found in a strange building. Still, it was a possibility.

There was only one trivial matter that impelled Pagnucco not to release Manos immediately. That was the narrow paper bag, with Alice Persico's stocking in it, which had been found on the sidewalk. Pagnucco himself was a wine drinker and therefore knew this type of bag well. It was a bag made to hold wine bottles; and Manos' Riverside bottle fitted precisely into this paper bag. That might be one of those curious coincidences which occasionally led detectives astray. Nevertheless, Pagnucco decided to keep Manos in custody, not as a suspect, but as a material witness, until he found out more about this murder.

On the morning of March 31 Rothengast had a crew of detectives go through the rooming house making further inquiries and searching for the missing shoe. Their initial results were more than disappointing. Although every tenant of 337 and the neighboring houses who could be reached was questioned, not one had ever seen John Manos and Alice Persico together. Some of them knew Alice Persico; one man claimed he had seen her on the night of March 30 very much alive on Ninth Avenue—but not with Manos. As for Manos himself, nothing incriminating could be discovered. He had immigrated from Greece as a youth and had never left New York. He worked, slept, worked, saved. He had never been seen drunk, never with women, never violent, although his hands were extraordinarily strong. As a child he had worked in a Greek candy factory, and his hands had been strengthened by kneading sticky masses of sweetstuffs.

A thorough check of all the other tenants of the rooming house showed that everyone had an alibi for the night of the murder. Orelio Persico, the dead woman's husband, was also looked up in Brooklyn. He had separated from his wife because she was loose and drank too much. He had been completely out of touch with her for a long time, and could prove that he had not been in Manhattan on the night of her death.

Hawthorne likewise tracked down Pete Coyle, the man Alice Persico's brother had suspected. But Coyle was severely ill with a lung ailment and had been in a Manhattan hospital for the past three months; he was unable to leave his bed. All other investigations similarly led to nothing. The autopsy, too, yielded no results. In the dead woman's stomach red wine was found—a fact that pointed back to Manos and his bottle of Riverside wine but was not much in the way of evidence for a jury.

Rothengast and Pagnucco now considered releasing the little Greek who had lived so lonely and blameless a life in New York. Then Hawthorne, carefully examining the paper bag with the woman's stocking in it, came upon an almost invisible number at the bottom of the bag: G 12 E 1—probably the mark of a manufacturer's series. A detective set out to check in all the liquor stores between 34th and 59th Streets. On the second day of this exhausting task he found a place on 41st Street which was using bags of this same series. More important was what the detective learned about Riverside wine; the brand was so uncommon that it was sold only in this store. The sales clerks could not, however, recall anyone of Manos' appearance; their volume of business was far too large to recall a single customer.

About the same time Devers, another member of the Homicide Squad, made an additional discovery. Behind a trash can on 30th Street he found a bundle wrapped in newspaper which contained Alice Persico's missing shoe, also a woman's hat, a man's undershirt, and two handkerchiefs knotted at both ends. A query to the office of the medical examiner yielded the statement that there could be no doubt about the diagnosis "strangulation with strong hands"; the handkerchiefs could not have been used to commit the murder. Why they were in the bundle remained a mystery. Rothengast had the undershirt and handkerchief checked for laundry marks, hoping to obtain a clue to their owner. But that proved a false trail. Pagnucco and Hawthorne therefore went to

Manos' room once more. They decided to examine the Greek's clothes to see whether he owned undershirts and handkerchiefs of the type that had been found.

It was evening, and Manos' room was dark when they opened the door. Pagnucco could not immediately find the light switch, and Hawthorne therefore switched on his flashlight. The cone of light scurried across the floor and suddenly caught two small spots near the bed. Pagnucco was the first to notice them and called to Hawthorne to hold his light on the place. Perhaps the spots were wiped bloodstains which for some reason had been overlooked during the first search of the room. But the two spots were distinctly whitish; it seemed unlikely that they could have come from blood. Nevertheless, they were possibly important. Pagnucco cut out the piece of soiled linoleum and placed it in a specimen box. Hawthorne took it to the office of the medical examiner and asked for a check to determine whether it was faded blood or something else from which conclusions might be drawn. Pagnucco meanwhile looked through Manos' few possessions. He found only an undershirt, two shirts, and two handkerchiefs; the undershirt and handkerchief looked more or less like the articles found behind the trash receptacle. While Pagnucco was standing indecisively in front of the chest of drawers, wondering how he could prove that the articles had belonged to Manos, he recalled remarks that Dr. Vance, the assistant medical examiner, had made about investigations at the scenes of crimes: that it was advisable to look not only for bloodstains, but for traces of saliva or other physiological secretions. Vance had also mentioned that serological examinations of sweaty clothing might yield indications of specific individuals. Perhaps, Pagnucco thought, the underwear might be soaked with sweat; and so he also sent the undershirts and handkerchiefs from both the trash can bundle and Manos' drawer to Bellevue Hospital.

These materials reached the laboratory of the chief medical examiner on April 18. Twenty-five years had passed since the by now almost legendary pathologist Charles Norris had succeeded, in 1918, in doing away with the inadequate and corrupt coroner system and creating the office of chief medical examiner. Norris had introduced into New York the principles of European forensic medicine. A few years before his death, in 1934, he had finally won his long fight to have a chemical and toxicological laboratory, under the direction of Alexander O. Gettler, attached to his office. It was not until 1938, under Norris' successor Thomas A. Gonzales, that the first serological laboratory was established in New York to study blood and bloodstains in the manner pioneered by European criminologists.

This relatively late beginning seems odd when we consider that Landsteiner and Levine, the pioneers of blood group research, were working in the heart of New York. Nevertheless, it augured well for the laboratory that it was put in the charge of Alexander Wiener. At this time the discovery of the Rhesus factor was a matter for the future; and Wiener had not yet won international renown as a talented and daring researcher. But at the age of thirty-one he was already considered a coming man. His initial interests had been hematology and serology. When he joined the group of workers around Landsteiner in 1935, he began comparative studies of antigens in men and monkeys—work which subsequently led to the discovery of the Rh factor. While Landsteiner always remained a man of pure research, Wiener combined the talents of the research scientist and the practical administrator. In 1935 he became head of the Blood Transfusion Division of the Jewish Hospital of Brooklyn, and with the aid of his lawyer father sponsored several bills, later passed by the New York State Legislature, which would enable courts to order blood group tests in cases of disputed paternity. He also fought for the use of serological tests of bloodstains in crimes.

How little was known about forensic serology and its possibilities in the world's greatest city in 1938 became evident when Wiener was first appointed. When Thomas A. Gonzales called a press conference to launch the laboratory, the reporters' first question was: "Tell us, Doctor, what's this serological business all about?" Gonzales made an effort to explain some of the basic facts about bloodstains and blood group testing. The result was that on the following morning Wiener found himself described, amid more or less muddled expositions, as the "blood detective." But he took the nickname in good part. During the following five years, he and his single assistant, Eve B. Sonn-Gordon, labored to persuade the police as well as the press of the value of serological work in an ever increasing number of crimes.

When Hawthorne brought in his new material, Wiener and his assistant first tested the articles from Manos' room, the two shirts, the undershirt, and the handkerchiefs. One of the shirts, the undershirt, and one handkerchief had been so carefully washed that the tests showed no results. The second shirt, however, seemed to have been worn briefly and then put aside; and one handkerchief had been used. Applying the absorption method to sample extracts from the soiled shirt and handkerchief, Wiener found the anti-B serum so heavily absorbed that he could say with certainty that the user belonged to Blood Group B.

The undershirt and the two knotted handkerchiefs that had been found along with Alice Persico's hat and shoe were then tested in the same manner. The shirt showed no absorption; but the handkerchiefs did: anti-B serum was markedly weakened in several stages. Both handkerchiefs came from a man of Blood Group B.

Wiener now asked Pagnucco for a sample of the Greek's blood. The little man, who had never heard of blood groups, made no objection. A few hours later it was determined that Manos had Blood Group B. Since the blood groups of all autopsied persons were automatically taken and recorded by the office of the medical examiner, only a look in the file was needed to find out that Alice Persico had belonged to Blood Group A.

Since the shirt and handkerchief from Manos' drawer had shown Group B as definitely as his actual blood, the first part of the test had once more demonstrated the reliability of group determinations from bodily secretions. On the other hand, the handkerchiefs in the bundle could certainly not have come from Alice Persico. They must have been used by someone with Group B blood, hence possibly Manos. But the crucial test remained.

Pagnucco had been mulling over the possible significance of the spots on the linoleum floor ever since their discovery. He once more studied the record of Manos' arrest and was struck by the repetition of one particular statement in a number of different phrasings: "Nobody ever visited me in my room. . . . I did not kill her. . . . I never saw her before. . . She was never in my room. . . . I never had a stranger in my room." If the spots on the floor of Manos' room came from blood or some other secretion that corresponded with Manos' blood group— well and good. But if they showed another group, that is, if they had come from somebody else, then Manos must have lied when he repeatedly asserted that no one else ever entered his room.

Wiener made a smear from one of the linoleum spots, dyed it, and examined it under the microscope. He saw large numbers of mucous cells. This at any rate suggested that the spot might have come from a slimy, edemic fluid. Next he applied the Uhlenhuth precipitin test. As he himself later wrote: "The extract gave strong positive reactions in the precipitin test with anti-human serum even in high dilutions. Therefore the stains contain a human fluid—almost certainly human edema fluid." In a telephoned explanation to Pagnucco, he explained: "This is the type of fluid that usually seeps out of a person's mouth during strangulation."

Pagnucco waited in extreme suspense for the outcome of the last decisive tests of the groupings. On April 21, 1943, he and Rothengast at last received Wiener's final report. It read: "In the grouping tests, the extracts [of the spots] inhibited the anti-A serum but not the anti-B serum, proving that the secretion came from a Group A individual." This meant that Manos had lied and that a stranger had been in his room. Here too was proof that the person had been someone of Blood Group A—the group of the murdered woman This news was so exciting that Pagnucco saw Manos already as good as convicted. But Wiener pointed out the limits of scientific proof. To be sure, they could show that Manos had not told the truth when he insisted that nobody had ever visited him in his room. Certainly there were now strong indications that Alice Persico had been killed in Manos' room, and that in cleaning up Manos had overlooked the fluid that had dripped from her mouth. But suppose Manos should change his mind, suppose he revised his statement and suddenly declared that he had forgotten, there had been other persons in his room after all? He could easily "recollect" peddlers or salesmen who had called on him and who, after all, unknown and untraceable as they were, might easily belong to Blood Group A.

The real value of the findings, Wiener said to encourage the disappointed Pagnucco, was as a basis for eliciting a confession from Manos by further interrogation. The rest was up to the skill of the detectives and the prosecutor.

A few weeks later Pagnucco was able to report that Manos had confessed. He did not reveal how it had happened until Manos entered a plea of guilty in General Sessions Court and was sentenced by Judge Freschi to ten to twenty years in Sing Sing. The authorities had not applied pressure to Manos. Instead, they had spent weeks explaining to the rather slow-witted man the principle of blood group tests, without speaking about his own case at all. On July 8, at the end of the sixth week, they had suddenly confronted him with the results of Wiener's tests, pointing out that these proved him a liar, and had then offered a reconstruction of the crime. The poor fellow broke down. "I never thought I would be caught," he exclaimed in despair. He then described what had occurred.

Manos actually had not known Alice Persico before March 29th. But he was friendly with other women on West 30th Street, whom he occasionally took up to his room when he came home from work at night, to drink a glass of wine and, as he put it, to get for himself what he needed as a man and to give them what they needed. No one had ever seen him with these women because the visits took place late at night and all of them "behaved quietly and decently"; Manos did not want any difficulties with his neighbors or landlady. On the night of March 29 he had met Alice Persico on the dark street. He had—so he maintained—had a glass of wine already and mistook her for one of his other female acquaintances.

When he asked her whether she would "come upstairs," she followed him through the dark house without a word. He realized his mistake only after he had switched on the light in his room. Moreover, he saw that this strange woman was already quite drunk. He was afraid that she might behave noisily, which could easily lead to "trouble" with the landlady. He therefore told her to beat it, but she only laughed, picked up his bottle of Riverside port wine, and drank until she tumbled onto the bed and fell asleep. He had sat there worrying about "trouble" until she awoke and became noisy. She reached for the bottle. He feared she would throw the bottle through the windowpane and rouse the whole house. And so he put his hand around her neck to silence her. But in his agitation he gripped too hard, and she fell back dead.

All this had happened on the night of March 29, when his neighbor in the next room was not yet sick. Nobody therefore had heard the commotion. All Manos could think of was how to dispose of the body. First he pretended illness in order not to have to leave his room. He stayed with the corpse all day and night. During this time he carefully cleaned the room and wiped all footprints from the floor. He waited until the main lights were turned out in the French Hospital and the street became quite dark. Then he dragged the body down the stairs to the street. On the steps a shoe fell off. Manos picked it up and stuffed it into his jacket pocket, which also contained an undershirt and a couple of handkerchiefs he had knotted around his head while cleaning. Alice Persico's hat fell off on the stairs; he picked that up too. After he had propped the body against the high iron fence in front of the house, he walked down to Sixth Avenue. There he found a newspaper, wrapped up the hat and shoe, in his agitation including the undershirt and handkerchiefs, and threw the package away. He then returned home by a roundabout route, saw that the dead woman lay where he had left her, and only now noticed that she had also lost a stocking on the steps. He went to his room and stuffed the stocking into the wine bottle bag. Then he remembered that Alice Persico had drunk from his wine bottle and perhaps left fingerprints on it. He therefore wrapped up the bottle to throw it away at a greater distance. It was while he was on this mission that the police caught him and brought him back to his victim. At this time he still had the paper bag with Alice Persico's stocking under his jacket. In an unobserved moment he managed to drop it to the ground beside the corpse.

That was Manos' story. Pagnucco thought it left some questions open, in particular whether he had not actually tried to take by force from Alice Persico what, in his phrase, he "needed as a man," after luring her to his room with promises of some kind. His account of mistaking her for another woman sounded implausible. But the Assistant District Attorney had no way to refute it, nor any way of penetrating the psyche of the lonely little man with the hard face and strong hands for whom New York had never become a home. Perhaps he had actually never lost his fear of the foreign environment and the Moloch of a city, and had killed in a fit of terror, thus destroying his dream of someday going home to Greece.

16

The late Pierre Argent has provided an excellent summary of the postwar situation in criminology:

"As the criminal police slowly began to resume normal work during the first decade after the Second World War, bloodstain testing remained at best where it had been at the beginning of the war. I believe, however, that we must underline the phrase 'at best,' for owing to the war there was considerable retrogression. The basic methods for blood determinations developed in Europe were now practiced on a world-wide scale, but everywhere there were still inadequately instructed detectives and inadequately trained scientists who committed many sins of omission. The method of securing bloodstains left much to be desired, and was often restricted to stains that could be seen with the naked eye. Analysis of clues at the crime scene, leading to reconstruction of the crime itself, was the province of a few individuals who still had a good deal to learn. To be sure, the Uhlenhuth method for the testing of animal and human blood was generally accepted. But the postwar years revealed how few scientists really understood the technique of applying this method, and how dependent it was upon a high level of exactitude on the part of serum producers or the testers. As for blood group determination from blood or secretory stains, the two fundamental methods of Lattes and Holzer had been widely adopted—but by no means widely enough to come through the interlude of the Second World War unimpaired. Even in countries with a long scientific or criminological tradition, there were astonishing lapses. The problems of determining Blood Group O in stains, as well as the problems of demonstrating blood factors, had remained unsolved because of the war. When the improved technology of the postwar era made it possible to deal with more minute stains, the limits of traditional methods were more plainly to be seen.

"Thus an enormous effort was needed to shape a scientific criminological apparatus out of the wreckage that had survived the war—an apparatus that could cope with the requirements of the new mass-society. Anyone who has encountered the inadequacies and mistakes particularly in the field of blood testing and forensic serology which came to light in the course of the detective work of the postwar period, will realize that the above statements do not express the case at all too harshly."

The kind of setback Argent was referring to was nowhere more evident than in the young Federal Republic of Germany. A case occurring in 1956 vividly illustrates the state of affairs.

The criminal police of Düsseldorf, capital of the State of North Rhine-Westphalia, could be considered one of the more competent urban police forces in the Federal Republic of Germany. On the morning of February 8, 1956, a man named Julius Dreyfuss reported to the Third Precinct that his car, a Mercedes 170 S, license number R 209-448, had disappeared. The chauffeur, Peter Falkenberg, twenty-seven, had driven Frau Dreyfuss home the night before. Then he was supposed to take the Mercedes to the garage, after which he would have been off duty. His day usually began at 8:45 A.M. On Friday morning, however, Falkenberg had not shown up for work. A telephone call to the garage yielded the information that the Mercedes had not been delivered there the night before. Dreyfuss had also called Falkenberg's landlady and learned that he had not been seen at his home since the previous morning.

A police clerk took down Dreyfuss' statement, and treated the matter as an auto theft—what with the economic boom in Germany and the rapidly increasing motorization of the country, car theft had become a common crime. Moreover, there were various innocent explanations for Falkenberg's disappearance. Perhaps he had taken the car to make an impression on a girl; perhaps he had stayed out somewhere during the night and had overslept.

Soon a Frau Hendrich, who lived near the main railroad station of Düsseldorf, reported that a black Mercedes had been parked at the curb in front of her house with its headlights on full and no owner in sight. Its license number was R 209-448. Dreyfuss was informed and asked to have it brought over to the police station, where he would pick it up. This was done; but when the car arrived in the yard of the Düsseldorf central police headquarters, the whole affair took on another and more sinister aspect.

Detective Secretary Hansen glanced into the parked vehicle and started as he observed brownish-red spots on the upholstery. He opened the unlocked front door on the left side and saw that the driver's seat was completely splattered with stains, drops and splotches that were obviously from blood. A large quantity of relatively fresh, coagulated blood clung to the rear seat, and there was a pool of blood on the floor in front of the driver's seat.

Chief Inspector Botte of the homicide squad was called in. There were unique reasons for the speed and thoroughness with which Botte examined the Mercedes. Since November 1955 Botte had headed a special commission that was trying to clarify a car murder committed on October 31 of that year. The victims had been a pair of lovers: the twenty-six-year-old baker Friedhelm Behre and his somewhat younger sweetheart Thea Kürmann. The two had been last seen at the Czikos Restaurant in Düsseldorf on October 31, 1955. They had left in Behre's blue Ford, supposedly to visit Thea's aunt. The couple vanished and could not be traced until November 28. On that day the owner of a trucking firm was standing by a dredged pond in the vicinity of Düsseldorf, whiling away time by throwing stones at a dark object drifting some distance away in the water. After a while he realized that it must be an automobile. He called some of his men to help, pulled the car ashore, and found two corpses on the rear seat. They were identified as Friedhelm Behre and Thea Kürmann. The condition of the bodies suggested that they and the car must have been in the water for about a month. The killer or killers had apparently fallen upon them while they were petting, pulled them out of the car, knocked them out, deposited them on the rear seat, and then driven the vehicle to the edge of the pond and let it roll into the water so that the two drowned.

This murder had stirred all the more excitement in Düsseldorf because it was the second of its kind. In January 1953 another automobile murder had taken place and had since defied all the efforts of the Düsseldorf detectives to solve it. Late at night on January 7, 1953, a Düsseldorf lawyer, Dr. Servé, had met a young workman named Hüllecremer and gone with him in his car down to the end of Rotterdamer Strasse. There was a homosexual relationship between the two. They had paid no attention when another car passed their own parked car. A few moments later the door on the driver's side was wrenched open. For a moment a figure loomed up, the face masked by a woman's stocking drawn over it. Then came the sound of a shot. Servé was struck by a bullet from a .32-caliber pistol, and collapsed, dying. The man who had fired the gun squeezed into the driver's seat and tried to start the motor, while behind Hüllecremer a second unknown climbed in and struck him on the head with a hard object. Strangely, as he did so he whispered to Hüllecremer that he did not want to kill him, but that Hüllecremer must play dead. When the killer did not succeed in starting the motor, he took Servé's wallet, and he and his companion vanished into the darkness. Hüllecremer pulled himself together and called the police. This crime was still unsolved.

These earlier cases explain Botte's intentness as he inspected the bloodstained interior of Julius Dreyfuss' Mercedes on February 8, 1956. He did not yet know that at this very hour a distraught woman who gave her name as Frau Wassing was at the desk of his own Third Precinct, accompanied by a girl whom she introduced to the desk man as Ingrid Krug.

The woman explained to the detective on duty that her twenty-three-year-old daughter Hildegard had been missing since the night before. The Wassings were a refugee family from the former German eastern provinces, which since the end of the war had become part of Poland. Hildegard Wassing had a job and supported her mother, and had hitherto scarcely associated with men. Last Sunday she had gone to the Weber Dance Hall with Ingrid Krug. The two girls had met a fellow named Peter who told them that he worked as a chauffeur in the Ministry of Education. Hildegard had made a date with him for Tuesday night. Peter had called for her at six thirty on February 7, and Hildegard's younger brother had noticed that he drove a black Mercedes 170 S. She had not returned home. Ingrid Krug knew no more about Peter than his first name; she offered the vague description that he was about thirty, slim, and fair.

The desk man informed Botte, who before he had finished his inspection of the Mercedes thus found his worst forebodings confirmed. It seemed virtually certain that "Peter" was the chauffeur Peter Falkenberg, who had apparently used his employer's car on February 7 to go out with Hildegard Wassing. The bloodstains in the car suggested that the unknown "car murderer" had struck again. Botte got in touch with his superior Dr. Wehner, head of the Düsseldorf detective force, and was assigned to the case together with Chief Inspector Tabbert.

Shortly before eight o'clock next morning, in the small village of Lank-Ilverich near Düsseldorf, a gardener set out for his place of work. As he was passing the fields of a farmer named Hasebrink, he noticed the remains of a burned haystack about a quarter of a mile from the last farmhouse in Ilverich. Out of curiosity he went up to it, and a moment later recoiled in horror from the sight of the charred bodies of a man and a woman.

Reports of the gruesome find reached Düsseldorf within two hours. Wehner guessed that the bodies might be those of Peter Falkenberg and Hildegard Wassing, and sent Botte and Tabbert to Lank-Ilverich at once. They learned that the haystack had gone up in flames on the night of February 7. Late that night a black Mercedes had also been observed in the neighborhood. The fire itself had broken out around 1:30 A.M., but the farmer's son-in-law, who woke up at the sound of the crackling flames, had let it burn, since it was far from the farm and there was nothing he could do about it anyhow. The two corpses had therefore been lying in the ashes since that night. They were so badly burned that at first glance identification seemed impossible.

The Institute of Forensic Medicine of the Düsseldorf Medical Academy was informed, and sent one of its men to the scene. He determined at once that the male victim had been killed by blows on the head. (A short time later, in the course of the autopsy at the Institute, the hole made by a bullet from a small-caliber weapon was found between chin and spinal column.) The female victim had likewise received a number of blows on the head. Pieces of her woolen gloves had survived the flames, and a key ring was found under the man's body. Two detectives returned to Düsseldorf with the keys and gloves. The keys opened the door of the apartment in which Falkenberg had a room, and the door to his own room as well. Frau Wassing recognized the gloves as her daughter's. Corroboration was provided by examination of the victims' teeth —they were indeed the missing Düsseldorf couple. They must have been attacked in the Mercedes at some unknown spot, killed, and driven to the haystack in Lank-Ilverich. There the murderer or murderers had attempted to burn their bodies, then driven back to Düsseldorf and left the Mercedes near the railroad station, where it had been found on February 8.

As soon as the first accounts of the new automobile murder were published in the Düsseldorf newspapers, the memory of the Servé and Behre-Kürmann murder cases was revived. The phrase "Lovers' Lane killer" was on everyone's lips; and the newspapers insistently demanded that the police solve the crimes. A special homicide commission was appointed, consisting of Inspectors Tabbert and Botte, with Superintendent Junge of München Gladbach assisting. None of the three could have imagined how strenuous a task confronted them.

Experience has taught that "Lovers' Lane murderers" are by and large persons whose sexual behavior strays from the canons of "normality." Normality of course is a highly variable factor. Nevertheless it seemed an obvious first step for the detectives to check all persons known or suspected as sexual deviants who had been seen in the area where the bodies were found before and during the night of the crime, who frequently passed through that area, or who knew the victims well.

In the course of this search Detective Böhm of Düsseldorf called at police headquarters in the town of Büderich. Here he was told of a young man whose parents lived close by the spot where the bodies of Peter Falkenberg and Hildegard Wassing had been found. The young man did not live with his parents, but he came to see them regularly in his Volkswagen. Neighbors stated that he was so "violent" he had once attacked playing children with a manure fork. Otherwise, he had little contact with people and was generally regarded as an "outsider." His name was Erich von der Leyen. On February 23 the special homicide commission sent Detectives Kossmann and Weierstall to investigate this young man.

Erich von der Leyen's parents lived in Büderich, close to the burned haystack. Until 1945 the father, Siegfried von der Leyen, had been bailiff of two farms in East Prussia. Like most of his fellow countrymen, he and his family had fled from the advancing Soviet armies. Eventually they wound up in Büderich, where until 1955 von der Leyen had been in charge of a small farm. After a while agricultural work became too heavy for him, and he had opened a laundry. His fate was rather typical of that of many Germans who had not broken under the strain of losing home and property, but had tried to build up a new life in alien surroundings. His son Erich had become separated from the family during the flight from East Prussia—he had then been fifteen—but had found his parents again in West Germany. Suddenly thrown into a new world, he had had difficulty adjusting. For a time he had studied agriculture and nursery gardening, and had helped his parents on the farm; after a while he got a job as a paint salesman.

At present Erich von der Leyen was living in a furnished room he rented from a family named Ehren in Veert, near Geldern. In 1954 he changed jobs, became a salesman for agricultural machinery, and drove around to farms in a maroon Volkswagen placed at his disposal by his company. He lived quietly and frugally, had very little to do with young people of his own age, but visited his parents regularly. He gave the impression somehow of being "different" from most people.

Detectives Weierstall and Kossmann found little to incriminate Erich von der Leyen during their initial inquiries. But when they called on von der Leyen himself on February 24, they were struck by the fact that he could not say precisely where he had been at the time of the murder, the evening of February 7, or the rest of the night. He finally stated that he had been at home in Veert; but the Ehren family could not confirm this alibi because they usually went to bed by eight o'clock and did not know whether their boarder had been at home. The detectives asked to see the trip logbook which every salesman of the agricultural machinery firm was required to keep, in order to check his whereabouts. But the logbook had been kept "in a highly unofficial manner." Many entries were missing. Their suspicions were aroused, however, when they discovered that the data for February 7 and 8 had been entered afterward, on February 9, and that the traveling times set down for drives from place to place were totally implausible.

Nevertheless, these details would have remained inconclusive if examination of the Volkswagen had not revealed suspicious stains. There were spots on the front seat covers which looked so much like bloodstains that Weierstall took possession of the covers from all the seats. He also thought bloodstains were present on a green leatherette coat and on von der Leyen's jacket.

Von der Leyen could not offer any explanation for the origin of the blood, if that was what it was. He recalled having carried poultry, and once a rabbit he had run over, in his car. He had also been holding a girl friend's dachshund, and had played with the animal in the car. The dog had been in heat recently, he said. Von der Leyen's girl friend confirmed these statements. Finally Weierstall and Kossmann asked von der Leyen to go with them to Düsseldorf. There the seat covers and von der Leyen's clothing were turned over to the Institute of Forensic Medicine, whose director, Professor Kurt Böhmer, was asked to determine whether the stains were blood, and, if so, what kind of blood and what blood group.

On the afternoon of February 25 the Institute reported by telephone to Inspector Tabbert. The bloodstain on the seat cover was indubitably human blood. The stains on the coat and jacket were also blood of some kind; further data would be ready on February 27.

On the basis of this von der Leyen was taken into custody and once again asked for a credible explanation of the bloodstains. It was pointed out to him that the seat cover on the front seat was indubitably stained with human blood; therefore all his talk about poultry, rabbits, and dogs was wasted words. It was also pointed out that the murderer of Peter Falkenberg and Hildegard Wassing had driven the Mercedes with its bloodstained seats from the burned haystack to the vicinity of the Düsseldorf railroad station, where he had presumably changed to another car and so could have smeared blood from his own clothing on the seat covers of that other car. But von der Leyen continued to insist that he had had nothing to do with the murder, nothing whatsoever. Oddly enough, he did not try to concoct any alibis. He swore that no one else had ridden in his car; no one could have caused the bloodstains. If anyone should know where those stains came from, it was he. But he had not carried human blood into his car. He did not offer any of the favorite allegations of nosebleeds or cut fingers. He made no objection to having a sample of his own blood taken, so that his blood group could be determined. But he repeated again and again that it could not be human blood. He also now recalled that he had laid the chickens and the rabbit on a sheet of plastic; therefore the blood could not have come from them. The only explanation was his girl friend's dog; the bitch in heat was the sole possible source of the bloodstains.

On February 26 detectives searched von der Leyen's room in Veert. It was so tiny that there was not even room for his clothes; his few possessions were in a wardrobe in the adjoining room, which was occupied by another boarder. The detectives brought back to Düsseldorf some gray cord trousers and a pair of shoes. Both seemed to be stained with blood, and were sent at once to the Institute of Forensic Medicine.

Meanwhile other detectives were trying to check on von der Leyen's statement that he had been home in Veert on the nights of February 7 and 8. They were able to find witnesses who had seen von der Leyen as late as the afternoon of February 7. But then there was a gap until the morning of February 8—a gap that could not be closed. The police were unwilling to release their prey, and therefore obtained a warrant from the Düsseldorf police court charging him with having killed two persons, Peter Falkenberg and Hildegard Wassing, on the night of February 7, 1956, "out of a murderous impulse, for the satisfaction of the sexual instinct, for gain, or some other base motive."

On February 28 and March 1 the full report of the Institute of Forensic Medicine finally came in. All the Volkswagen seat covers had been checked. There had been blood on the rear seat also. The bloodstains on the front seat came from persons of Blood Groups A and B. The principal stains on the cord trousers were likewise blood; many splashes had been too small for testing, but the large stains unquestionably had come from human blood.

As for the blood grouping of the stains on the trousers, various spots had shown blood group characteristics A or AB. Since control tests of the unstained cloth had demonstrated that this particular textile could produce absorption of anti-A serum, the finding of Group A might not be accurate; the presence of Group B was, however, incontrovertible.

The significance of this result was heightened when the Institute added that von der Leyen himself had Blood Group A_2. In the course of the autopsies of the victims it had been found that Falkenberg's blood was Group B. Checking the records on Friedhelm Behre and Thea Kürmann, the detectives discovered that both had had Blood Group B. Faced with these facts, and given the knowledge that von der Leyen himself could not be the source of Blood Group B stains in his car, the homicide commission became convinced that they had a man who was at least involved in the automobile murder.

On the basis of these findings, Junge, Botte, and Tabbert launched on a series of interrogations which would, they felt certain, result in a confession. But within a few days they had to admit to themselves that their slight-bodied prisoner was either one of the most resolute "deniers" they had ever encountered, or was in fact an innocent man. Von der Leyen kept repeating with desperate consistency that there could not possibly be traces of human blood in his car or on his clothes; the blood must have come from the dachshund bitch. He maintained that he had definitely not worn the cord trousers since October 1955, when they had been washed and had lain in his wardrobe, until February 12, when he had gone out with his girl friend and had then put on the clean trousers. Afterward, the dachshund had jumped onto his lap several times. He unwaveringly insisted that he had not been in Lank-Ilverich at the time of the crime. True, his logbook was not very well kept; he'd never been good at record-keeping.

Junge had von der Leyen's statements checked. As it happened, his landlady remembered that she had washed the trousers in October and put them away. For one moment, moreover, the landlady thought she recollected his having been at home on the night of February 7. She recalled his sitting with her and listening to a radio broadcast entitled "North against South." But then it turned out that this program had been broadcast on February 8. Nevertheless, in the face of von der Leyen's steadfast denials Wehner began to have his doubts. He appealed to the Institute of Forensic Medicine for confirmation that the blood groupings were correct, that the blood really was human and the possibility of dog blood out of the question. He received this confirmation. There seemed, therefore, no explanation but that von der Leyen was lying with incredible consistency, day after day.

In this apparently hopeless situation Wehner and Junge hit on the idea of having the age of the bloodstains checked. Both of them knew that dating bloodstains was still a highly problematic matter. But they hoped that for once a valid result might be obtained, which would tell them whether the stains could have been produced around the time of the double murder. Wehner appealed to the Technological Detection Department of the West German Federal Criminological Office, which had been established in Wiesbaden in 1951. The biological section was in charge of a relatively young man, Dr. Otto Martin—a quiet, reticent, dreamy person, wholly devoted to his scientific work. Martin was a biologist who had turned his attention to criminological analysis of traces of soil, fiber, plants, and so on; but he had also studied bloodstains. He was noted for his extreme precision and conscientiousness, which seemed to qualify him for study of extremely microscopic clues.

Upon receiving Wehner's first teletype message from Düsseldorf, Martin asked for more precise data on the matter. Only after he had learned that there was evidence for the date the cord trousers had last been washed did he agree to attempt the analysis. Within a few days he sent word to Düsseldorf that the bloodstains on von der Leyen's trousers could not be older than a month or more recent than two weeks. Thus the trousers might very well have been stained at the time of the murder. But possibility was no proof—and von der Leyen's assertion that the staining had taken place after February 12 might also be true. Nevertheless, the detectives intensified their efforts to destroy what they now regarded as the prisoner's fabric of lies.

During March 6 and 7 there were moments when von der Leyen seemed on the point of giving up. Driven wild by the incessant questioning, he cried out: "Either I did it unconsciously, or I didn't do it." And again: "I almost believe myself that I was the one." But he repeatedly pulled himself together and denied any part in the crime. The contradiction between the findings of the Institute of Forensic Medicine and von der Leyen's staunch assertions of innocence prompted the homicide commission to order a psychiatric examination of the prisoner. Moreover, on March 6 the commission asked the prosecuting attorney to authorize the use of the American "lie detector." Since this apparatus has long encountered profound skepticism in Europe, the prosecuting attorney's office refused the request. The commission thereupon decided upon an unusual step. On March 7 Superintendent Junge went to Wiesbaden to ask Martin to check the findings of the Düsseldorf Institute of Forensic Medicine. For if one accepted von der Leyen's insistence that he and his car could not be stained by human blood, then there could be only one conclusion: the determination of blood type by Professor Kurt Böhmer and his Institute had been wrong. The prisoner's strong stance had begun to convince his persecutors.

When Junge arrived in Wiesbaden, he did not suspect that in the course of determining the age of the bloodstains on the cord trousers Martin had already discovered something startling. First of all, he had found some bloodstains which no one in Düsseldorf had evidently looked at. The Düsseldorf finding that only the two larger stains had reacted to human blood, and that there had not been enough material in the other bloodstains for a determination, seemed to him to bespeak rather careless work. Moreover, in his microscopic examination of the stains, Martin had found the blood mixed with a glistening white secretion. In it were glycogenous epithelial cells, a sign that the blood might be of menstrual origin. This seemed a significant finding, since it had not yet been determined whether in the course of the automobile murders there had been any assault on the female victims. His doubts about the Düsseldorf findings once aroused, Martin had gone ahead on his own account, out of curiosity, to check the Düsseldorf tests for blood type and blood group. He was therefore fully prepared when Junge arrived with his request. He promised to inform Wehner by telephone as soon as his own tests were completed.

Junge returned to Düsseldorf on March 8. Late in the evening of March 9 Wehner's telephone rang. Martin was calling from Wiesbaden. He apologized for the lateness of the hour, but what he had to say seemed of crucial importance. The blood on von der Leyen's trousers could not possibly be human blood. It was dog's blood, mixed moreover with vaginal epithelial cells which signified that it had come from an animal in heat. The blood group determination meant nothing at all, since animal blood, too, has group characteristics.

Wehner got in touch with one of Böhmer's assistants the first thing in the morning. The man was incredulous, but agreed to run a series of control tests.

A day passed. On the afternoon of March 12 Wehner received a curious document from the Institute. In roundabout language the error was acknowledged. The spots on the seat covers of von der Leyen's car were also not human blood, the new report stated. The explanation offered for this fateful error was that the serum from the Behring Company in Marburg, which had been used for the Uhlenhuth precipitin test, was labeled as anti-human serum but also reacted to canine blood.

Wehner, Junge, and Botte lacked the scientific background properly to assess this explanation. For them, the one staggering fact was that an unassailable authority had admitted one of the most shocking errors they had encountered in the whole of their careers. That afternoon Erich von der Leyen was released from jail. But his sufferings could not be undone, any more than the basic question could be suppressed: How was it possible, more than fifty years after discovery of the Uhlenhuth reaction, for forensic medicine to go so far astray?

Before Wehner wrote up his report to the Police Section of the Ministry of the Interior, he turned to Martin once more in order to obtain his authoritative opinion. In view of the controversial position of the Federal Criminal Office, Martin had to be rather reticent. Nevertheless he said that he was quite familiar with the products of the Behring Pharmaceutical Company and had never run into such a peculiar serum, which reacted to both human and canine blood. Nor did he know how anyone could in practice make such a serum. He himself had used Behring serums, but, like any experienced laboratory worker, he had always tested each serum for specificity before using it, and had moreover made a practice of employing several serums from different producers. Had these normal precautions been taken in Düsseldorf?

With the end of the war, German criminology did in fact face a critical situation. The Robert Koch Institute, which had been the chief supplier of test serums until the occupation of Berlin, ceased production. Government control over serums, which had been exercised by the Paul Ehrlich Institute in Frankfurt ever since the days of Uhlenhuth, had broken down during the chaos of the early postwar years. At last the Behring Company had taken up the task, on its private initiative, of supplying essential serums to criminologists. As things stood, it was more important than ever before to observe certain rules which had existed since the days of Uhlenhuth, the foremost of which was that the tester must check every serum for its specificity before applying it. If this were done, a serologist could not make mistakes due to inadequate serums. Whatever excuses the Düsseldorf Institute offered, there could be no excuse for the failure of the serologists themselves to obey this fundamental rule. If the serums had actually been faulty, the laboratory workers at Düsseldorf should have discovered that fact before using them.

As it turned out, the Falkenberg-Wassing case was never completely solved. Wehner pursued the matter for years, and assembled a mass of evidence that gravely incriminated Werner Boost, a twenty-eight-year-old Düsseldorf workman. On June 10, 1956, Boost was caught by a hunter just after he had hidden his motorcycle in the woods and was creeping up on a pair of lovers in a Volkswagen. Weapons were found in his home, and another workman testified that Boost had partly led and partly forced him to participate in a number of more or less criminal acts. Slowly, Wehner gathered evidence to indicate that Boost had been the leader in the Servé-Hüllecremer crime of January 7, 1953. His accomplice confessed to being the man who had warned Hüllecremer and only stunned him instead of killing him. Although there were indications that Boost had also committed the Behr-Kürmann and Falkenberg-Wassing murders, he was convicted only for the murder of Servé, and on December 14, 1959, sentenced to life imprisonment.

17

Was the von der Leyen case an aberration, a solitary failure on the part of forensic science? Not at all. Nor were such inadequacies or blunders in blood testing limited to Germany, or to the continent of Europe. They could be found even in scientifically advanced America.

On the night of July 3, 1954, there began in Cleveland, Ohio, a drama which was "sensational" in the most literal sense of that much-misused word. The scene of the events was Bay Village, a suburban community on the shores of Lake Erie. It was inhabited by prosperous middle-class people whose breadwinners went into the city by day and drove back to their comfortable homes at night.

Flourishing in the midst of this seemingly solid, well-ordered society was Bay View Hospital, owned by the family of an osteopathic physician. Dr. Richard Allen Sheppard and his three sons, Dr. Richard, Dr. Stephen, and Dr. Samuel Sheppard, ruled what amounted to a medical "empire" in the hospital and the Fairview Park Clinic. As affluent members of the community, they enjoyed widespread respect and admiration, though this was also, as with all successful people, mingled with subliminal feelings of envy.

Perhaps "success" was most conspicuous in the life of Dr. Samuel Sheppard, the youngest of the Sheppard boys. He was barely thirty, but already head of the hospital's department of neurosurgery. Slender, dark-haired, he was generally regarded as a good-looking young man. Sam Sheppard lived in a white, thirty-thousand-dollar house on the lakefront. He had married a high-school sweetheart, Marilyn, and the couple now had a seven-year-old son, Chip. Sam Sheppard also had a black dog and three cars, including a Jaguar that cut quite a swath in Bay Village. He shared ownership of a motorboat with the Mayor of Bay Village, John Spencer Houk. People in Bay Village were well informed concerning Sheppard's finances. They knew that his annual income amounted to at least thirty-three thousand dollars. It was vaguely to his discredit that he spoke in a rather stiff, bookish manner, and that he gave an impression of some aloofness. But none of this jeopardized his popularity as a man or a doctor—until that fateful night of July 3.

A few minutes before dawn on July 4 the insistent ringing of the telephone wakened Mayor Houk. He heard his friend Samuel Sheppard's voice saying: "For God's sake, Spen, get over here quick. I think they've killed Marilyn." Houk, the owner of a meat market, and a genial, well-liked politician, awakened his wife. Both dressed hastily and drove the short distance to the Sheppard house. Houk found the door of the house on Lake Road unlocked. He stumbled over Sheppard's medical bag, which was lying in the hallway, and immediately afterward saw Sam Sheppard in the den. Bare to the waist, his trousers dripping wet, he was slumped in a chair. His face showed some discolored, swollen spots, but no open wound. Sheppard seemed completely dazed; he groaned, apparently from pain.

When Houk asked what had happened, he said: "I don't know exactly, but somebody ought to do something for Marilyn." He added: "I don't know. I just remember waking up on the couch and I heard Marilyn screaming and I started up the stairs and somebody or something clobbered me and the next thing I remember was coming to down on the beach."

While Sheppard was talking, Houk's wife dashed up the stairs which led from the living room to the second-floor sleeping quarters. As Sheppard's explanation trailed off, she came down the stairs again, exclaiming: "Call the police, call an ambulance, call everything!"

The left-hand bed in the Sheppards' bedroom was a ghastly sight. In the midst of the tangled bedclothes, her head about halfway down the bed, her feet over the footboard, lay Marilyn Sheppard. Her face was an almost unrecognizable mass of bloody wounds; her pajama top had been pushed up to her shoulders, exposing her breasts. Some parts of the bed seemed to be soaked in blood; the walls all around were covered with splashes of blood.

Houk called the Bay Village police, an ambulance, and Sheppard's brother Richard. Then he went on trying to extract more information from Sam. Meanwhile his wife looked in on the Sheppards' son Chip. The boy was sound asleep in his room, as if nothing had happened. The black dog, Koko, lay in the hallway close to the front door, without making a sound.

Patrolman Drenkhan, a twenty-eight-year-old navy veteran, was the first policeman to arrive at the Sheppard house. He went straight up to the bedroom. A little later—at 6:10 A.M.—Sheppard's brother Richard came rushing in. He thought medical help might still be possible and looked for a knife in the kitchen, with the idea that he might open Marilyn's chest and try cardiac massage. But when he entered the bedroom he saw that there was nothing to do; his sister-in-law was quite dead. She had been so frightfully beaten that it was impossible to count the number of blows that had struck her. The murderer must have acted in a fit of savage frenzy. From the body temperature Richard Sheppard estimated that Marilyn could not have been dead more than two hours.

Richard Sheppard stepped into the bathroom to wash after touching the corpse. His glance fell on a cigarette butt, without filter tip, floating in the toilet bowl. This surprised him because his brother did not smoke at all, and Marilyn had been only a very occasional smoker. But when she did smoke, she had used filter cigarettes. In his excitement at the moment he did not consider the possible significance of this fact. He went downstairs again. There he found his brother Sam lying flat on the floor, apparently trying in this way to alleviate the pain in his neck vertebrae. Painfully, he repeated to Patrolman Drenkhan his story of Mari-

lyn's cries for help, his attempt to aid her, and the unknown who had
knocked him unconscious. When Richard Sheppard stooped over his
brother, he saw Sam's sport jacket lying on the floor beside the couch,
badly rumpled. But at the time he barely noticed this. He said: "She's
gone, Sam." And then, while his brother cried: "Oh, my God, no," Richard Sheppard inquired (so Houk later testified) in a low voice: "Did
you have anything to do with this?" Samuel Sheppard answered: "Hell,
no."

That was all Houk heard because Drenkhan took him aside to say that
the case was too big for him; they would have to get help. Police Chief
John Eaton, of Bay Village, and the Coroner of Cuyahoga County were
called. At six twenty Eaton and the third Sheppard brother, Stephen,
arrived simultaneously. Stephen came with an intern from Bay View: he
too had thought medical help would still be possible. When he realized
that there was no life to be saved, he turned his attention to Sam. His
brother was complaining of more and more acute pains in the back of
his neck, but had sufficient grip on himself to enlarge on his previous
account. He and Marilyn had had guests the night before, he said. He
himself had fallen asleep on the couch in the living room, and had heard
the guests dimly, in a doze, leaving the house. Marilyn had also said
good night to him before she went upstairs to the bedroom. After that
he had fallen into a heavy sleep, from which he was roused by cries for
help. In the darkness he rushed upstairs to the bedroom, saw a white
figure, was knocked down, after an indefinite time revived, heard noises
in the house and again saw a massive white form run out of the house
and down to the beach house by the lake. He pursued the unknown,
caught up, but was knocked down a second time, and came to himself
lying partly in the water. Half stunned, he staggered back to the house.
Still dazed, he went up to Marilyn, felt her pulse, realized that he could
feel nothing, and telephoned Houk for help. That was his story. It was
interspersed with complaints about pain and inability to think clearly
or grasp his nightmarish experiences.

Stephen Sheppard had the impression that the unknown's blows had
injured his brother's spinal column, and decided to take him to Bay
View Hospital as quickly as possible. With the intern's help he got Sam
to his feet and half led, half carried him to his station wagon, while
Richard Sheppard woke young Chip and placed him in his wife's care.

Houk, Eaton, and Drenkhan watched this departure without making
any objection. More or less at loose ends, Eaton went down to the beach
to look for clues. Drenkhan meanwhile inspected the ground-floor

rooms. The drawers had been pulled out of the desk in Samuel Sheppard's den. Their contents lay on the floor. Nearby Drenkhan caught sight of a woman's gold wrist watch, the crystal and band stained with blood. All this upheaval seemed to indicate an attempt at burglary, and Drenkhan set about checking doors and windows. But he found no trace of any effort to break in violently.

Whatever police work was done during the first few hours was done unsystematically, in obvious confusion. No one ever succeeded in explaining afterward why Samuel Sheppard's corduroy jacket, which his brother Richard had seen lying crumpled on the floor, appeared neatly folded on the couch by the time the coroner from Cleveland appeared. No one could say whose hand had drawn down Marilyn's pajama top, preserving her modesty and at the same time changing the position of her arms. It proved impossible to account for the cigarette in the toilet bowl, which Richard Sheppard had noticed. It had disappeared forever when Sergeant Hubach of the Bay Village police for unfathomable reasons flushed the toilet.

It was not until eight o'clock that active investigation of the scene of the crime began. Samuel R. Gerber, the coroner, arrived at the Sheppard house. The personality of Gerber and the part he was henceforth to play in the Sheppard affair can be understood only if we know something about the history of criminology and forensic medicine in the United States.

When New York got rid of its coroners in 1918, as we have mentioned, the city was putting the ax to one of the most antiquated institutions in the country. The existence of coroners elected by popular vote, who were not necessarily doctors and who for simplicity's sake were frequently chosen from the ranks of undertakers, was a ridiculous relic of the past. Nevertheless, in the course of several decades only a few other American cities and counties followed New York's example. Samuel R. Gerber's importance and reputation were based on his being one of the relatively few American coroners who were not only physicians but had also endeavored to apply tested principles of forensic medicine and criminology to their work.

On the morning of July 4, 1954, when this short, lean man of fifty-eight with parchment-colored face and grayish-white hair entered the Sheppard house, barely a year had passed since he had achieved one of the great goals of his life. Even before New York erected a modern building for its chief medical examiner, Gerber had persuaded Cuyahoga County to put up a million-dollar building for him on the land of

Western Reserve University. The new County Coroner's Office contained modern mortuaries, autopsy rooms, lecture rooms, and laboratories. In the spring of 1953 Gerber had moved from the old mortuary on Lakeside Avenue, built in 1894 and modeled on an Egyptian tomb, into the handsome and efficient new building.

Gerber had spent only too many years in the impractical old mortuary. He had been County Coroner since 1936, re-elected every four years with astonishing regularity. During his twenty years in office he had introduced a good many innovations, including an accident service and medico-legal evaluation of the causes of accidents by using the latest methods of X-ray technology and color photography. Thanks to him, Cleveland could boast of a toxicological laboratory and apparatus for measuring the alcohol content of the blood of drivers. But along with such matters he was jealous of his right to participate in all investigations of crimes of violence. The laws of Ohio assigned the coroner the duty of investigating the causes of all violent or mysterious deaths. Gerber made the most of that duty.

Yet in spite of Coroner Gerber's zeal, he had quite a few critics. There were people in Cleveland who charged him with putting his fingers into too many pies and using every opportunity for self-advertisement. These persons doubted that his abilities were commensurate with his reputation. The very diversity of his career, from student in Indiana and Ohio, ship surgeon on a South American run, internship and residency in New York, general practitioner and Mayor of Scott, Ohio, physician at the Warrensville Correction Farm, official of the Democratic Party in Cleveland, and a law degree obtained when he was in his fifties—all this tended to cause skepticism. But the careers of other American pioneers in criminology have been similarly colorful; and Gerber's self-promotion could easily be accounted for as a product of the unhealthy situation in which almost every coroner found himself because his office was elective. He was constantly torn between simply doing his job and the necessity of offering the masses visible tokens of success. Only giants could in the long run reconcile these dualities. Probably Gerber fully realized his own lacks in medico-legal and technological matters. At any rate, he had engaged a specialist in pathology, Dr. Lester Adelson, and in toxicology, Dr. Irving Sunshine, for his Coroner's Office. Serological tests were handled by a woman, Mary Cowan, who had been doing such work for the Coroner's Office for more than a decade. But critics maintained that Gerber was inclined to dictate what went on in the laboratory when a spectacular crime was being investigated.

On that morning of July 4 Gerber could not have doubted that the slaying of Marilyn Sheppard was such a spectacular case. Some newspapers even asserted later that he had gone over the heads of the Bay Village police in sending two members of the Cleveland homicide squad whom he knew well, Detectives Robert Schottke and Patrick Gareau, to the scene. Be that as it may, when he entered the Sheppard house, Gerber gave the impression of a "compact bundle of nervous energy." It was in keeping with his high-keyed temperament that he spent only a few minutes in the murder room; he confirmed the fact of Marilyn Sheppard's death and decided that it had probably taken place between three and four o'clock in the morning. Then he asked Houk and Eaton to describe the course of events. When he heard of Samuel Sheppard's removal from the scene, and Richard Sheppard's curious question to his brother, he promptly conceived the idea that Samuel Sheppard might indeed have committed the murder and that the Sheppard family were trying to snatch a possible murderer out of his, the coroner's, grasp.

Together with Eaton, Gerber drove to Bay View Hospital. When he arrived, Samuel Sheppard was just being wheeled to his bed from the X-ray room. Gerber behaved with his wonted courtesy, but was clearly annoyed at Sheppard's having been taken to the hospital without his permission. Richard Sheppard explained that his brother had at least a compression of a cervical vertebra, and it had been the obvious thing to take him to their own hospital. This explanation did not satisfy Gerber, who did not have the impression that Samuel Sheppard was a very sick man. He was even less satisfied with what Sheppard, who seemed recovered, had to tell him about the events of the night. Sheppard's explanations were essentially the same as those he had given before. Their very vagueness was still the same. In vain did Gerber try to elicit a better description of the mysterious "white form" Sheppard had bumped into. He finally insisted that all the clothes Sheppard had last worn be turned over to him, and expressed wonderment when he was given only trousers, shorts, socks, and shoes. Sheppard said he had had on only a T-shirt and did not know what had happened to it. He must have lost it at some time during the night, but did not know when, where, or how.

Gerber observed what seemed to be a bloodstain on the knee of Sheppard's still wet trousers. He asked about this. Sheppard said that it must have come from his contact with the bloodstained bed when he tried to discover whether Marilyn was still alive. This explanation sounded logical enough. Nevertheless, Gerber returned to the Sheppard house disgruntled and full of mistrust.

At the house he found Detectives Schottke and Gareau, and Michael S. Grabowski, a fingerprint specialist from Cleveland. Grabowski vainly searched the house for fingerprints, and deepened Gerber's suspicions by remarking that it looked almost as though all fingerprints in the house had been carefully wiped away.

Grabowski did not even find the trace of a fingerprint on the telephone or on Sheppard's medical bag. On the other hand, there were slight scratches on various objects which Grabowski thought might have come from hard rubbing with cloth or light sandpapering. (Twenty days later just a single thumbprint of Samuel Sheppard's was found on the headboard of his wife's bed. But no significance could be attached to this since no one knew how old the print was; Sheppard might have made it while bidding his wife good night in the days before the murder.)

Schottke had searched the house in vain for traces of violent entry and was now busy questioning the curiosity-seekers, who had meanwhile assembled, in an effort to find witnesses who might have made any observations during the night. Gareau, with the same purpose in mind, was driving from neighbor to neighbor. But during the whole of the twelve hours no one had noticed anything unusual. People recalled having seen light in the Sheppard house until late at night. But that could not be considered unusual; the light in question was in a small upstairs dressing room on the street side of the house. The Sheppards were in the habit of letting this light burn whenever Samuel Sheppard was not in his bedroom. Whenever he left the house to make a night call, this light would burn until he returned home and went to bed.

At least some of Sheppard's statements about the preceding evening and night were checked and confirmed. A neighboring couple, Nancy and Don Ahern, had had dinner with the Sheppards. They had spent the evening talking and watching television. After a while Sheppard had complained of drowsiness and fallen asleep on the couch. He was sound asleep when the Aherns said good night to Marilyn Sheppard at twelve thirty and left the house by the door facing the highway. Both Aherns declared that Sam and Marilyn had been distinctly affectionate to one another in the course of the evening; they had sat close together in a single chair. Moreover, Nancy Ahern gave the surprising information that Marilyn had recently learned that she was going to have a second child.

Such details seemed to argue against the suspicion that had formed in Gerber, and that Gerber had communicated to the Cleveland detectives.

But soon Gareau and Schottke heard rumors and hints that changed the picture. Until July 3 Dr. Lester Hoverston—a former classmate of Sheppard who had shifted about from one medical post to another, without much luck—had been staying with the Sheppards as a house guest. This was not his first visit, and it was an open secret that Hoverston had a yen for Marilyn. On the other hand, there was a woman named Susan Hayes who until February 1954 had been a laboratory technician at Bay View Hospital and had since taken a job in Los Angeles. Several witnesses asserted that since 1952 she had been Sam Sheppard's mistress and that Sheppard had recently met her in Los Angeles. There were women patients of Sheppard's who spoke of petting in cars with the doctor. He had pleaded the excuse that since the birth of Chip his wife had been neurotic about sex and had avoided sexual relations with him.

Meanwhile a car had arrived to take the body to Gerber's office for autopsy. Gerber supervised. When Marilyn Sheppard was lifted out of the bed, Gerber noticed two small white splinters lying on the blood-soaked mattress. They proved to be bits of teeth. Since rigor mortis made it difficult to open the murdered woman's mouth and determine whether the fragments came from her teeth, Gerber put the particles aside for later examination. In the course of his further inspection of the bed, he lifted the pillow, which was covered with spatter spots and splashes of blood. On the underside was a huge bloodstain. This stain consisted of several broken surfaces, as though the blood, before it reached the pillow, had run over some intricately shaped object that had been lying on the pillow. In any case, the moment he saw that curious shape Gerber had an idea that became an obsession with him. He believed the pillow held the bloody imprint of a pincerlike or clamp-like surgical instrument which had served as a murder weapon, or at any rate played some part in the murder. He never explained precisely what kind of surgical instrument it was or could have been. The instrument remained a product of his imagination—which for the purposes of scientific criminology is one of the most dangerous items of all. How dangerous was made plain by the attitudes of Schottke and Gareau. These detectives looked upon Gerber as an authority, and the phrase "surgical instrument" could not but establish in their minds a direct connection between the murder and Samuel Sheppard, who as a surgeon was the owner of numerous "surgical instruments."

With these observations, Gerber contented himself. He looked for no further clues in the room where Marilyn Sheppard had been killed. He was standing in the midst of a welter of bloodstains which would have impelled any experienced serologist or medico-legal expert to attempt a reconstruction of the crime. The dead woman's bed was covered with bloodstains and spatters of the most varied types; the other bed in the room was also marked with blood. Even more information could have been gathered from numerous blood spatters on the walls of the room, in which the beds stood north-south. Both the north wall and the south wall of the room showed blood spatters which could have led to deductions on the direction and speed of impact. The great mass of the bloodstains were concentrated on the south and west walls. Any bloodstain expert with a minimum of experience should have noticed that the corner where the south and west walls met was free of blood, as though a screen—or a figure standing there—had caught all blood spattered in this direction.

Gerber paid no attention to these clues. Instead, he put full emphasis on the idea of the surgical instrument. When Schottke reported what he had learned about Sheppard's love affairs, the case against the doctor gained ground. Did not the existence of a mistress represent a motive for murder? With his wife out of the way, Sheppard would be able to live with Susan Hayes. Perhaps he had killed Marilyn in an access of hatred, then clumsily tried to make the place look as if a burglary had been attempted, and invented the wild story of the unknown figure who had knocked him out. Perhaps he had never been hit at all but had gone to the lake to wash his bloodstained trousers and weight his blood-stained T-shirt with a stone before throwing it into the water.

Gerber urged Schottke and Gareau to hold back no longer, but to subject Sheppard to hard questioning, without any interference from the clannish family. If he were to be caught in his lies, the police would have to act quickly. Gerber personally would lead a search of the house, and if necessary the surrounding land, for a surgical instrument that might have served as the murder weapon.

At eleven o'clock that morning, Schottke and Gareau entered Sheppard's room at the hospital. Sheppard was wearing a temporary bandage around his neck. Once again he repeated his story. Now he thought he recalled that he had already been inside the doorway of the bedroom when he was struck a stunning blow from the side. He thought there could have been two intruders, because as he collapsed he also heard the sound of the blows raining down upon Marilyn. Schottke asked why Sheppard had not switched on the light when he rushed to the aid of his wife. Sheppard did not know. He had blindly followed the screams. Besides, there might have been a light on in the dressing room. After a number of other questions Schottke abruptly asked whether Sheppard had relations with other women. Sheppard's reply was an unequivocal "no." Knowing what he did, Schottke took this denial for a lie—and if Sheppard lied about this, he might well be lying about other things as well.

Irritated at the way the Sheppard brothers kept coming into the room and interrupting, the detectives left the hospital. They arrived back at the house just after an important discovery had been made. The murder instrument had not been found, but a green bag had been. This bag ordinarily lay in the desk in Sheppard's den and contained keys and some tools for the motorboat he owned jointly with Mayor Houk. Now it also held a bloodstained wrist watch that had stopped at four fifteen, a fraternity ring of Sheppard's college days, and a keyring on a chain which the doctor had been carrying in his trousers pocket. The green bag was taken as evidence that Sheppard himself had tried after the murder to pretend that there had been a burglary. As Gerber saw it, he must have put the watch, ring, and keyring into the bag and thrown it away so that he could assert that the intruders who had killed his wife had stolen these objects while he was unconscious. The fact that the watch had stopped at four fifteen was regarded by Gerber as confirmation of his verdict that Marilyn's death had taken place between three and four o'clock. He wanted to know what Sheppard had been doing (assuming that he had really been knocked down near the water at this time) in the interval between his return to consciousness and his call to Houk, which had been at least an hour. His theory was that Sheppard had used this time to think out his story. Moreover, the coroner quickly convinced Schottke and Gareau that such had been the case.

For the second time during this hectic morning the two detectives drove over to Bay View Hospital. This time their first question to Sheppard was: What had he done during the time after he regained consciousness on the shore of the lake? Sheppard replied that he had returned to the house, had looked for his wife, had wandered around stunned, until he recalled Houk's telephone number. Schottke asked: Had all this taken a full hour? Sheppard did not know. Neither did he know how long he had lain unconscious on the beach, in the shallow water. Schottke commented that a normal person would have drowned if he had lain in the water any length of time. Sheppard replied that some natural instinct must have kept his head above water.

The next question was: How had the green bag come to be on the grounds? Sheppard tried to recall. But he could not. Now Gareau asked for an explanation of the blood on Sheppard's wrist watch. Sheppard said the watch could have been stained while he was feeling for Marilyn's pulse. And what, Schottke asked, could explain the fact that Sheppard's dog had not barked when strangers broke into the house? Sheppard could at first suggest no explanation, but after some seemingly strenuous thought offered what sounded like an unusual idea. There was one possible explanation for the dog's silence, he said—that the intruder or intruders might be known to the dog as friends or acquaintances who had been in the house often before. But this possibility seemed so monstrous to Sheppard that he refused to name anyone he knew whom he thought capable of the murder.

All of Sheppard's replies seemed to the two detectives vague and implausible. As he had done during the first interrogation, Schottke abruptly changed the subject. This time he asked pointedly: Was there any employee of Bay View Hospital whom Sheppard had made his mistress, and had he visited her recently in Los Angeles? Sheppard denied this so firmly that Schottke told him to his face: "I don't know what my partner thinks, but I think you killed your wife." Sheppard for the first time tried to sit up, and with his face twisted by pain retorted: "Don't be ridiculous. I have devoted my life to saving lives. I love my wife."

But these were wasted words. The detectives once more returned to the Sheppard house and discussed the situation with Gerber.

The coroner's suspicions had now reached such a pitch that he assumed Sheppard must be pretending injuries, and that his brothers were collaborating in this fraud. He asked Dr. Richard Hexter, general practitioner in Bay Village, to go to the hospital and check on Sheppard's state. Hexter found that no one placed obstacles in the way of his examining Sheppard. But he ignored the diagnostic views of Sheppard's brothers and confined himself to a superficial examination. Although he observed the absence of several reflexes—sure signs of neurological disturbances—he reported to Gerber that he had not found a seriously injured man. He thought it possible that Sheppard's bruises were self-inflicted. Just what impelled Hexter to make this indubitably shallow judgment was never adequately explained, but his report in any case corroborated Gerber's theory.

The coroner recommended that Sheppard's hospital room be placed under police guard, and that the murder house be sealed, with only the police allowed to enter. Inwardly certain that he was on the trail of Marilyn Sheppard's murderer, Gerber returned to Cleveland. He turned Sheppard's and Marilyn's bloodstained wrist watches over to his serological assistant, Mary Cowan. She was asked to determine the blood groups of the stains, and to compare these with the blood group of the murdered woman, which would be determined from her blood after autopsy. This was the second instance in which Gerber concerned himself with blood clues. But this directive was just as puzzling as his previous imaginative conclusion that a spatter of blood represented a surgical instrument, and as his disregard of the numerous other blood spots in the room. Given the quantities of blood all around the dead woman and on the bed, it was logical that both watches should be stained with Marilyn Sheppard's blood. The same was true for the stain on Sheppard's trousers. Gerber's procedure showed what a limited view he had of the possibilities of forensic blood technology.

18

On July 5 a medley of police officials assembled in Bay Village. In addition to Eaton and his men of the Bay Village police, there were Schottke and Gareau from Cleveland, detectives of the Cuyahoga County police, including their chief, Rossbach, and men from the office of Frank T. Cullitan, the prosecutor of Cuyahoga County. But Gerber, openly or not, remained the motive force behind the investigation. Since Eaton was highly skeptical of Sheppard's guilt, and since the Bay Village police resented interference from Cleveland, Schottke and Gareau were more or less pushed out. They had no valid reason for further investigation in Bay Village. On the other hand Gerber, as the coroner responsible for the case, enjoyed full jurisdiction. He acted accordingly, and did not fail to air his mind to the reporters of the Cleveland newspapers, who first went to him for information as a matter of routine.

Gerber's assistant, Deputy Coroner Dr. Lester Adelson, had performed the autopsy of Marilyn Sheppard on July 4. He had confirmed the fact that she was pregnant, and had determined that no less than thirty-five wounds had been inflicted. Most of these were on the face, but there were some on the back of the neck and on her hands, with which she had tried to fend off the murderous blows. From the type and shape of the head wounds, Adelson had not been able to conclude anything as to the nature of the murder weapon. For lack of any evidence to the contrary, therefore, Gerber held fast to his idea of a surgical instrument.

Gerber had the pillow, with the bloodstains which he believed to show the imprint of that unspecified surgical instrument, color-photographed to preserve its appearance.

Marilyn Sheppard's blood group was determined from a specimen of blood taken from her heart. She proved to have had Blood Group O with an M factor. Miss Cowan found herself unable to determine the group of the bloodstain on the left knee of Sheppard's trousers. She reported that the stain did not provide enough material for a grouping. In testing the stains on the two wrist watches she came to a strange result (and one that suggests her lack of experience). The bloodstains reacted to an anti-M serum in the Holzer test, thus testifying to the presence of the M factor which had also been in the dead woman's blood. But in the easier task of determining the over-all group, Miss Cowan failed. The absorption of anti-A and anti-B appeared to be so uncertain that she finally declared herself unable to state whether or not the blood belonged to Group O. Thus the bloodstain analysis had proved totally valueless.

Gerber, however, continued his investigation of Samuel Sheppard and the rest of the Sheppard family. The Sheppards, after the tumultuous events of the first days, promptly engaged one of the most distinguished criminal lawyers of Cleveland, William J. Corrigan, to act as their adviser.

Corrigan recommended that they refuse to let the police interrogate Sam further because of the danger to his health. Chief Eaton and the Bay Village police were inclined to go along—the elderly Eaton was prepared to believe that Sheppard's injuries were serious. He was particularly impressed by the diagnosis of a respected independent neurologist from Cleveland, Dr. Charles Elkins, who spoke of a spinal injury. Moreover, the nurses in charge of Sheppard after he entered the hospital stated that his hands and feet looked like those of a person who has lain in water a long time.

But such evidence cut no ice with Gerber. On July 6 and 7 he demanded that the Sheppards allow him and the police free access to Samuel Sheppard's bedside. When Marilyn Sheppard was buried on July 7, and Sheppard appeared at the cemetery in a wheel chair, wearing a supporting collar, it became evident that the suspicions of Gerber and the Cleveland detectives were already spreading. Certainly the reporters had been infected. Sheppard's picture was published in some newspapers with dark hints that behind the orthopedic collar a murderer was hiding and mocking laws that applied to every ordinary man. It has always remained a mystery why Corrigan, a lawyer with plenty of experience in dealing with publicity, did not foresee the gathering storm of public ill-will and avert it by conciliatory action. But Corrigan gave a blunt No to Gerber's demand—only to have to yield before Gerber's threat to obtain a warrant for Sam Sheppard's arrest. At this point Corrigan said that Sheppard would accept interrogation by County Deputy Sheriff Carl Rossbach. He ruled out Schottke and Gareau as biased. Later Corrigan declared that he had believed so firmly in Sheppard's innocence and counted so heavily on justice that he did not for a moment think of the way public sentiment could be swung. In any case, it was already too late.

On July 10 Sheppard appeared in Rossbach's office for his first interrogation outside the hospital. He repeated his former account of the murder, without deviating from it an iota. At the same time he repeatedly denied having had relations with other women. But the following day several newspapers published the first references to a Susan Hayes who was Sheppard's mistress. It remained a moot question whether these stories were skillfully planted or whether clever reporters had already tracked down "the other woman." In any case, the stories roused instant animosity toward the man who had concealed his adulteries behind a picture of a happy marriage. Was not such a man capable of murder— murder of his wife and of his unborn child?

Next day Gerber and Mary Cowan went through the Sheppard house for usable blood clues. This time, too, Gerber disregarded the murder room. He concentrated on the stairs, looking for bloodstains on the treads, and drew chalk circles around a large number of suspect spots that presumably formed a "trail" leading from the living room and kitchen into the bedroom. Mary Cowan took samples of these spots and examined them in the laboratory. She succeeded in showing that six spots were from human blood. But once again she did not have enough material, in her opinion, for a blood group determination. Even if the blood group of Marilyn Sheppard had been found, it would still not be clear what significance such tests could have as evidence. Gerber's point, that the murderer had descended the stairs to the kitchen with the murder instrument dripping blood, applied equally to Sheppard or the unknown intruder of Sheppard's story. Nothing in the whole examination of blood connected Sheppard with the murder.

Meanwhile, Schottke made good use of his enforced leisure. With the aid of the police in Los Angeles, he tracked down Susan Hayes and had her interrogated by the prosecutor there. On July 13, the record of the interrogation reached Cleveland. Susan Hayes, described as young, pretty, and well dressed, did not deny that she had been friendly with Sheppard. She also did not deny that she had met him in April in Los Angeles, and had received a watch from him as a gift. But she denied having been his mistress. Upon hearing this, Detective Schottke set out for Los Angeles to "put more pressure" on Miss Hayes.

That same day, July 13, the name of Susan Hayes appeared for the first time in headlines, and three days later Louis B. Seltzer, editor of the Cleveland *Press*, decided that the time had come to voice what was by now a common sentiment. In an editorial headed "The Finger of Suspicion" he spoke of "the tragic mishandling of the Sheppard murder investigation." He deplored the incompetence of the Bay Village police, their fending off assistance from the Cleveland homicide specialists, and their handling of the Sheppards with kid gloves. By July 20 the attacks in the Cleveland *Press* had become virulent. An editorial on the first page carried a five-column heading: "Getting Away with Murder." Below this headline were such statements as: "In the background of this case are friendships, relationships, hired lawyers, a husband who ought to have been subjected instantly to the same third degree to which any other person under similar circumstances is subjected. . . . It's time that somebody smashed into this situation and tore aside this restraining curtain of sham, politeness and hypocrisy and went at the business of solving a murder—and quit this nonsense of artificial politeness that has not been extended to any other murder case in generations."

Frank Story, the Cleveland Police Chief, saw his mandate and offered to take over the investigation of the Sheppard case from the Bay Village authorities. Under the pressure of the publicity campaign, the Bay Village Council accepted the offer.

On July 21 Gerber called an inquest. For six hours he questioned Sheppard, who appeared for the first time without the orthopedic collar. Again Sheppard did not deviate from his previous account. And before a throng of spectators he declared under oath that he knew Susan Hayes but had never had intimate relations with her. Sheppard could explain later that he was trying to protect Miss Hayes from the merciless glare of publicity. His defense lawyer was to point out that Sheppard was entitled to deny a circumstance which he knew would prejudice innumerable women against him. But given the revelations that had already been published in the newspapers, the denial was an act of almost incomprehensible imprudence. It boomeranged against Sheppard during the inquest, even before Schottke had accomplished his purpose in Los Angeles. Among other witnesses, Gerber questioned Nancy Ahern, who had been visiting the Sheppards with her husband on the night of the murder. She repeated her statements about the affectionate conduct of Sheppard and Marilyn. But then Gerber extracted from her statements about matters she had concealed during the initial questionings. She declared that Marilyn Sheppard had known about Sheppard's relationship with Susan Hayes and had long been afraid that the doctor wanted to divorce her.

The inquest ended in a tumultuous scene. Women tried to kiss the coroner, as though he were the stalwart champion of monogamy. The hysteria was beginning.

On July 23 the Cleveland police sent a member of its scientific bureau, Henry E. Dombrowski, to the deserted house. But Dombrowski and his assistant likewise ignored the bloodstains in the murder room. Dombrowski later "explained": "It was our opinion that just from the appearance of the blood in the room it would add nothing to the investigation." With magnifying glass, spotlight, quartz lamp, and luminol spray, Dombrowski detected some sixty blood spots—all on the steps, to which Gerber and Mary Cowan had already turned their attention. More spots glowed under the luminol spray on the way through one door of the living room to the terrace overlooking the lake. But Dombrowski confined himself to luminol and the benzidine test, and no further check was attempted. In only a single case did he bother to prove the human origin of a spot, one which was on the staircase. As for a blood group determination, Dombrowski did not even attempt it. All his work was, therefore, sheer waste. Even if he had established the presence of Group O human blood everywhere, the finding would have been just as meaningless as Mary Cowan's work.

Once again, the many spots on the stairs and paths could indicate either Dr. Sheppard moving through house and garden with an instrument dripping blood, or else the unknown intruder whom Sheppard insisted on, and who could have escaped the same way. Nevertheless, public excitement grew more and more intense, just as it had done after Mary Cowan's blood tests were reported. Bloodstains were taken as synonymous with murder, and they incriminated Sheppard because everyone had already decided that he was the killer.

On July 26 Schottke brought Susan Hayes to Cleveland from Los Angeles. A few months afterward, in a trial that was to startle the world, Miss Hayes was to show remarkable dignity and honesty. But she was not yet steeled to her unfortunate role, and in Los Angeles she had collapsed when Schottke confronted her with the statements of a couple in whose home she had slept with Sheppard. Since adultery was an extraditable offense, she had no choice, and went along to Cleveland. Her resistance broken, on July 26 she signed a statement in which she admitted that she had been intimate with Sheppard from 1952 on. She added, however, that Sheppard had never promised to marry her. She knew quite well that he had only turned to her for the physical love which his wife for some reason denied him. He had repeatedly emphasized that he loved Marilyn Sheppard in a different way and was attached to her. But such distinctions were drowned out by the rising storm of moral outrage.

The Cleveland *Press* stated what had become virtually the general opinion: "Now proved under oath to be a liar, still free to go about his business, shielded by his family, protected by a smart lawyer who has made monkeys of the police . . . Sam Sheppard still hasn't been taken to headquarters."

For four days the authorities conferred on and off. Their problem was whether there was enough evidence to arrest Sheppard. Even now, there was no agreement on Sheppard's guilt. There were too many unexplained factors. Even if Sheppard had considered murdering his wife, would he not, as a doctor, have had at his disposal other methods than this savage, bloody bludgeoning? What connection was there between the proved show of affection of the last evening and the murder early in the morning? Even if it were assumed that Sheppard had deliberately staged the tender episode to serve as an alibi, there remained the problem of reconciling such coolheadedness with the obvious frenzy of the crime. But of course human beings are capable of highly contradictory actions. Who would have suspected the true state of things inside the Sheppard household, when so much of the life of every family in Bay Village took place virtually in public? Was it conceivable that the dead woman had for years withheld herself from her husband, as was asserted, and thereby driven him into adultery? If so, could she have yielded to him again for a while that spring, reasoning that pregnancy would make divorce impossible? Perhaps she had again refused him on the night of the murder because she had reached her goal and was already pregnant. This could have roused Sheppard to disappointed fury and to the frenzy that had led to the murder. Then again, there were rumors that Marilyn Sheppard had had a lover who suited her physically better than her husband. Hence there was another possible theory: that on the night of the murder she confessed to Sheppard (perhaps in revenge for his infidelity) that he was not the father of the child she was expecting. Could Sheppard then have flown into a blind rage and killed her, then come out of his frenzy and invented the preposterous story which he now repeated with unyielding consistency?

All these possibilities were conceivable. But they were all so highly speculative that the hypothesis of Sheppard's innocence should have been given precedence so long as there was not a single shred of evidence linking him with the murder. And where was such evidence to be found?

Nevertheless, on July 30 the authorities of Bay Village succumbed to public pressure. Late that evening police appeared at the elder Dr. Sheppard's house and took Dr. Sam away in handcuffs.

19

Sheppard's lawyer, William J. Corrigan, was an old fighter of the courtrooms, an aggressive not to say bellicose man. Like many lawyers, he knew absolutely nothing of the scientific basis of technical investigations of crimes. Like most of his fellows, he was satisfied with occasional advice from experts in scientific criminology. He loved the dramatic, momentary triumphs that could be had by catching experts and detectives out in trivialities, in errors of logic, improper phraseology. He would come up with technical literature they had not read, minor omissions in a testing procedure—anything that would shake the jury's faith in their accuracy. This alone explains the fact that the lawyer, during the three and a half months preceding the opening of the Sheppard trial on October 18, 1954, never thought of doing anything about the gaps that Gerber and the Cleveland police had left in their examination of the bloodstains. He rightly regarded the bloodstain evidence that Gerber and the Cleveland police laboratory had accumulated as meaningless. He thought that Gerber's description of the murder weapon as a surgical instrument was too fantastic to be believed by anyone. This certainty was strengthened when Gerber failed to find any murder weapon of the sort he had conjectured. But Corrigan committed a crucial mistake in overlooking the susceptibility of jurymen to Gerber's fanciful interpretation of blood clues. He should have tried to find a specialist who could have countered Gerber's flash of inspiration with cogent findings.

Even worse, the lawyer seems never to have thought that the murder room and its unexamined bloodstains might provide evidence valuable to the defense.

To be sure, the murder house on Lake Road had been under police supervision since July 4. It was also true that Sheppard's family was allowed to enter it only a few times, to take out some things belonging to young Chip. But Corrigan made no serious effort to procure access to Sheppard's house for the defense. Just once he requested the prosecutors, John Mahon, Saul Danaceau, and Thomas Parrino, to let him have the keys. But he tamely accepted the refusal of his request. He seems to have made it only for tactical reasons, in order to plead infringement of the rights of the defense in case of appeal. All that he read about the blood-splashed murder room stirred no associations in his mind, gave him no new ideas.

When Common Pleas Judge Edward Blythin—a septuagenarian who seemed rather too fond of equating smooth legal procedure with justice —opened the trial of Samuel Sheppard in Cleveland on the morning of October 18, Corrigan stood empty-handed as far as scientific evidence went. He fought a tenacious, bitter, sometimes savage battle against Thomas Parrino and the jury, five housewives and seven average citizens who lacked all insight into the world of Samuel Sheppard. With rage and scorn Corrigan lit into Gerber's theory of Sheppard's injuries being self-inflicted. He brought a parade of medical technicians to the stand, culminating with Dr. Charles Elkins, the eminent neurologist, who testified to the very real nature of those injuries. Corrigan heaped scorn on Gerber's theory of the imprint of a surgical instrument on the bloodstained pillowcase, which had been brought into the courtroom for the jury to see. He denounced Gerber's tactic of showing colored slides of those same bloodstains, and his repeated references to the surgical instrument whose name or nature, however, he never specified. But rage and scorn proved insufficient to banish the impression made by the bloody pillowcase, and the graphic description of the so-called blood trail which led from the murder room down all the stairs to the ground floor.

Corrigan found some encouragement in the fact that the jury took an unusually long time, from December 19 to 21, to reach its verdict. Even exposed as they had been to the torrent of prejudice, the jurors seemed uncertain. But after they had been out for 102 hours they returned to declare Sheppard guilty of second-degree murder. Thus they saved him from the death sentence, and Judge Blythin sentenced him to life imprisonment.

Two days later, shortly before Christmas, Corrigan for the first time obtained the keys to the Sheppard house, which the prosecution was now willing to surrender. Still smarting from his defeat, he paced through the deserted rooms, ascended the stairs to the upper floor, and entered the room in which Marilyn Sheppard had died. He never said whether the sight of the blood-spattered walls gave him the idea that these stains might well be invaluable clues to what had really happened on the night of the murder. In any case, shortly after the new year, Corrigan turned for help to California. He appealed to a man who had for many years been one of the foremost pioneers of scientific criminology: Dr. Paul Leland Kirk.

20

Kirk (born in Colorado Springs in 1902) had reached the summit of his career in 1954 as Professor of Criminalistics at Berkeley. A student of chemistry and biochemistry, he had won degrees from Ohio State University, the University of Pittsburgh, and the University of California. From 1929 to 1945 he climbed the Berkeley academic ladder, rising from instructor to Professor of Biochemistry, with time out during the war years when he served on the Manhattan Project in plutonium research. He was a sound scientist whose interest in his field had been stimulated by contact with a small group of people at Berkeley who were endeavoring to establish scientific criminology as an academic discipline.

The history of this group went back to the First World War, when August Vollmer, a remarkable personality who had risen from mailman to Police Chief of Berkeley, for the first time applied scientific methods to police investigations. He set up a tiny laboratory in a back room of his office. His enthusiasm was communicated to Alexander Kidd, Professor of Law at the University, and Karl Schmidt, Chairman of the Division of Biochemistry and Kirk's teacher. This small group was joined by Edgar O. Heinrich, who ran a private laboratory in which he undertook all sorts of criminalistic investigations, from toxicology to handwriting studies.

Vollmer was a restless soul who moved here and there across the continent. For a long time he served as Professor of Police Administration at the University of Chicago. But eventually he returned to Berkeley, where in the thirties he headed the first university institute for criminology and criminalistics. Later his pupil, O. W. Wilson, succeeded him as head of this institute. Until 1948 the institute lacked any definite status or proper budget. The war paralyzed all work. But between 1948 and 1950 John Holmstrom took up the task and established an official School of Criminology at the University of California. Paul Leland Kirk became head of the criminalistics department.

Kirk was a practical man rather than a theoretician. As early as 1934 he had concerned himself with the application of biochemistry to criminological questions. The number of his studies ran into the thousands. His comprehensive book, *Crime Investigation, Physical Evidence and the Police Laboratory*, was regarded as one of the few standard texts in the field. He had also dealt with questions of blood testing for many years. He and his pupils published innumerable studies on investigation of blood clues and blood group determinations.

Kirk received Corrigan's request for aid with no great surprise. He was familiar with the many deficiencies in criminalistic-serological investigations in the country. He offered to go to Bay Village and see for himself whether at this late date—eight months after the crime—any conclusions could still be drawn from the bloodstains. On January 22 he arrived in Cleveland, where for all the usual short-livedness of sensations everyone was still talking about the Sheppard case. The suicide of Sheppard's mother on January 7, the death of his father barely a week later, and the public appearances of Sam Sheppard himself—briefly released to attend the funerals—had kept the drama very much alive.

After Kirk finished his first inspection of the murder house, he voiced his regret that everything which was now being asked of him had not been requested in July 1954. He could only write a "postscript" on matters which eight months earlier would have provided important evidence for or against Sheppard. Nevertheless, he decided to remain and conduct a detailed examination of all clues. The prosecution did not hinder Kirk from inspecting all the "exhibits" submitted at the trial, such as the much-discussed pillowcase, the watches, and Sheppard's trousers. Still rejoicing in their triumph, they could not imagine that Kirk would be able to turn up anything new.

Kirk returned to Berkeley loaded down with photographs, sketches, and exhibits. A few months later, in April 1955, he sent the results of his investigation to Cleveland. His report was a bulky document with numerous appendices, annotated photographs, diagrams, and laboratory data.

Kirk had concentrated most of his attention on the murder room, applying to the existing bloodstains the tried and true methods of determining the point of origin, distribution, and impact velocities of splashed blood. Back in Berkeley he had constructed a kind of model of the room, with movable walls, in which he had carried out extensive experiments. An artificial head made of various plastics was subjected to blows from a large number of possible weapons. What type of bludgeon would produce injuries such as Marilyn Sheppard had suffered? Another series of experiments showed how blood would be distributed by different types of blows. The walls of the mock-up room were covered with paper which was removed and studied after each experiment.

In the end, from the experiments and reconstruction of the height, direction, and impact velocity of the bloodspots in the Sheppard bedroom, Kirk arrived at a highly interesting picture. A heavy flashlight when used as a weapon produced wounds which strikingly resembled the lesions on Marilyn Sheppard's head. The two beds were separated by a night table and stood with their heads to the south wall. The door into the room was likewise on the south wall, to the right of the dead woman's bed. It had been open at the time of the murder. Close to it in the east wall was a door leading to a wardrobe; this door had been closed at the time of the crime. All the blood spots on the north wall, where the spattering was heaviest, on the west wall (which had fewer spots because of the greater distance), and on Sheppard's unused bed, could be traced back to their point of origin on Marilyn's bed. They had been caused by the numerous blows upon the head, which gushed more and more blood. The spots on the north and east walls were of two kinds which differed distinctly in shape. Some came directly from Marilyn Sheppard's head wounds. Others had been cast from the bloody murder weapon as it was swung forward to strike (toward the south wall and head of the bed) and on the back strokes (toward the east wall, which ran parallel to the bed) as the weapon was raised for another blow. The ceiling showed no trace of blood. From that Kirk concluded that the blows had not been delivered vertically, but rather horizontally. Various experiments confirmed this conclusion. Finally, he came across a spot of a third type on the wardrobe door. This was a spot that had not been spattered or thrown from the weapon, but produced by direct contact with a bloody object or a bleeding wound.

The only area on the bedroom walls which was completely free of blood spatters was at the corner where the east and north walls met. Along the north wall this clear area extended about two feet, along the east wall about four feet. Since there were splashes of blood all around, there was only one explanation for this phenomenon. The body of the killer must have intercepted the blood that spattered in this direction. The murderer must therefore have stood beside the victim's bed, or half kneeling on it, back to the foot of the bed, left side toward the east wall and the door of the wardrobe.

Close examination of the bloodstains on Marilyn Sheppard's bed also led Kirk to significant discoveries. On the sheet on the right side of the bed were some smear spots which differed from the other blood-stains. These were not spatters, drips, or spurts of blood that had been soaked up by the cloth. The spots were smeared in streaks. They were situated precisely where the killer must have propped a knee in order to be in the position required by the interception pattern on the walls. From this point, and the height and direction of the blows, a further conclusion had to be drawn: the murderer must have wielded the weapon with the left hand—must, that is, have been lefthanded or ambidextrous. Sheppard was definitely not either.

The second conclusion of the study was that the murderer must have been completely splashed with blood. Even though Sheppard's T-shirt had vanished on the night of the murder, his trousers and shoes remained. It was improbable that the water could have cleaned his trousers completely. Had that been so, then the large spot, partly hemolyzed by the effect of water, would also have been washed away. On the other hand, there was a confirmation of Sheppard's statement that the blood-stain on his trousers had come about when, soaked from being in the lake, he had staggered upstairs, stepped over to his dead wife's bed, and felt her pulse. For there was only one small area of blood on the entire bed which likewise showed signs of hemolysis (dissolution of hemoglobin under the influence of water) like the stain on Sheppard's trousers. This area was about halfway up the bed, on the outer rim, precisely where Sheppard's knee could have touched when he stepped up to the bed.

Another clue caused Kirk to make further experiments, in order to clarify the order of events. In Cleveland he had inspected the fragments of teeth found in the bed and later identified as chips from Marilyn Sheppard's incisors. The prosecution had contented itself with the explanation that blows on the face had broken the teeth. During his stay in Cleveland Kirk had argued that the type of break was conceivable only if Marilyn Sheppard, frantically defending herself, had bitten hard on some object which had then been violently pulled away from between her teeth. After many experiments with dentures Kirk found that pulling fingers or hands violently away produced just such fragmented teeth as were found in Marilyn Sheppard's mouth. This led Kirk to a further conclusion which at first seemed to verge dangerously upon pure speculation. He asked himself: Could the bloody contact spot on the wardrobe door have come from the murderer, who might have been trying to silence the struggling victim with his right hand and been bitten badly in the process?

If this were the case, Sheppard could not be the murderer, for his hands had shown no trace of injury. To reinforce this hypothesis, Kirk attempted to determine the blood group of the "contact" stain, so that he could compare it with the group of the stains which were indubitably from Marilyn Sheppard's blood. His aim was to demonstrate a difference between the contact stain and the other stains, and to show that this contact stain had been produced by a third person, rather than by the uninjured Sam Sheppard or the blood of Marilyn Sheppard. In spite of the age of the spots, Kirk succeeded in obtaining the group. His careful procedures and the excellent state of preservation of the stains made this possible. The findings, however, were of little value. Both the absorption and the Lattes tests showed the stains as belonging to Group O. An attempt to determine blood factors failed. The age of the spots proved an insuperable obstacle.

In preparing extracts from the various bloodstains, Kirk had nonetheless noticed that the spots that were certainly from Marilyn Sheppard's blood dissolved quickly and promptly produced strong agglutinations. The same was true for Sheppard's blood. The contact spot on the wardrobe door, however, dissolved slowly, and the agglutination was much slower and more uncertain.

Japanese investigators of the war and postwar years had made a number of novel studies of Group O blood. The literature contained articles by Furuhata, Murakami, Makkawa, and Tokugavo, all of whom had been experimenting along lines pioneered by their fellow countryman Hihino as far back as 1935. On the basis of distinct differences in the type of agglutination Hihino had proposed dividing Group O blood into several subgroups (like the subgroups A_1, A_2). The most recent work in the field was Furuhata's, who in 1952 pointed out that three subgroups of Group O could be distinguished with certainty. Kirk had made several attempts to duplicate these findings. Nevertheless, he was somewhat exceeding his authority when he capped this section of his report with the sentence: "These differences are considered to constitute confirmatory evidence that the blood on the large spot [on the door] had a different individual origin from most of the blood in the bedroom." He may have been right in his belief that this blood spot pointed to the presence of an unknown third person; but he was also crossing the boundary of certainties and exposing himself to possible attacks which could endanger the value of his work as a whole.

Finally Kirk extended his researches to the pillowcase and its alleged impression of a surgical instrument. Both sides of the pillow were heavily spotted or stained with blood. From this it was evident that the pillow had changed position during the struggle between the murderer and his victim. Either Marilyn Sheppard had tried at some point to use the pillow to fend off the blows, or else the killer had tried to press it against her face to smother her screams. It seemed probable that the pillow had been doubled over in the course of the struggle. If a similar pillow were taken, stained with blood, and folded in this manner, blood impressions were produced which because of their symmetry might easily look as if they had been made by a double-pronged instrument.

Finally there remained the blood spots on the stairs, which led from the bedroom to the living room and from there to the lake terrace—the spots which, meaningless though they were, had so deeply impressed the jurors. Kirk undertook a series of additional experiments to determine whether the killer could have caused these stains. He found that such spots could indeed have fallen from a bloodstained weapon. But any smooth weapon, however blood-soaked, was quickly divested of the blood clinging to it; the last drops fell away after only a few yards. Dripping lasted longer the larger the surface of the weapon. Be that as it may, no weapon could have left a blood trail that extended from the murder room to the terrace. Thus the prosecution had been arguing from a series of stains which could not have been caused on the night of the murder, or perhaps were not blood at all.

To sum up Kirk's results: there were a number of factors which raised serious doubts of Sheppard's guilt and pointed up the inadequacy of the scientific investigation of the crime. Moreover, the question inevitably arose: What facts would have come to light if a complete examination of the bloodstains had been carried out immediately after the murder?

Corrigan immediately went to the Court of Appeals for the Eighth District of Ohio with Kirk's affidavit. But hopes that a retrial would be granted on the basis of this new evidence were soon blasted. In his written opinion Judge Julius M. Kovachi expressed respect for Kirk's "high qualities of originality and imagination," but based his rejection on the legalistic thesis that Corrigan had been in no way hindered from undertaking the same researches before the trial, had he seriously intended to do so. Corrigan repeatedly cited the hostility of the prosecution, and the fact that he had been refused the keys to the Sheppard house. Nevertheless, he had not really pressed the point at the time and was being thus penalized for his lack of thoroughness.

In his scrutiny of the scientific aspect of the affidavit, Kovachi spotted the questionable element in Kirk's argument. He obtained the opinion of Dr. Roger W. Marsters, a serologist, who dismissed Kirk's group differentiation procedure as unacceptable. Although in his own affidavit Marsters betrayed the fact that he was a fresh-blood serologist and had no experience in the field of bloodstain investigation, he also happened to be right—from the standpoint of scientific caution.

Thus the one series of bloodstain tests produced by the Sheppard case lost its legal value, and Corrigan helped neither the cause of Sheppard nor that of serology when in the summer of 1958, in the course of further efforts to appeal, he once again tried arguments connected with the blood clues. This time he proceeded from the chance discovery that a filing card on which Mary Cowan had noted the results of her blood group tests in Gerber's laboratory had disappeared from the documents of the trial. It was a filing card dated July 7, 1954, and concerned the blood grouping tests of the stains on Marilyn Sheppard's watch; concerning this, Miss Cowan had testified in court that she had been unable to establish the blood group. The card bore a notation that in the Lattes test blood cells of Groups A and B had shown only slight agglutination —too inconclusively for them to be unequivocally attributed to Group O blood.

For Corrigan, it sufficed that the card contained a reference to A and B cells; without checking with an expert he jumped to the conclusion that the stain must be Blood Group B and therefore represented an unknown third person. He accused Mary Cowan of having concealed or at least obscured this fact, and he charged the prosecution with having suppressed the filing card in question. On the basis of this argument he demanded a new trial. Nothing could have more exposed Corrigan's scientific ignorance; nothing could have been more fatal to an objective evaluation of the Sheppard case than this appeal, which inevitably led straight to a new defeat.

Thus, in an alternation of appeals and rejections of appeals, and in waiting for parole, Samuel Sheppard spent the next nine years in prison. At last, in 1964, a court was found within the intricate machinery of justice which frankly acknowledged the prejudice of the investigation and the trial of 1954, and ordered Sheppard's release.

The prosecution in Cleveland did not give up. In the autumn of 1966 it brought Sheppard to trial once more. But it now faced the difficulty that every prosecutor encounters upon attempting a retrial after so long a time. The testimony of incriminating witnesses no longer carries the weight it did, in view of the inevitable failures of memory. Moreover, the antagonism toward Sheppard had given way to uncertainty or indifference. The defense found it easy to demonstrate that the 1954 trial had advanced inadequate proofs and had been conducted under the pressure of overwhelming public opinion. The jurors could not bring themselves to return a verdict of guilty against Sheppard. They acquitted him, and thus restored him to permanent freedom. But the mystery of the murderer or murderers of Marilyn Sheppard remained unsolved.

The omissions of an inadequate investigation could not be repaired. Out of the many discussions of the case over the years, only one theory emerged which seemed to fit the strange facts of the story. It originated with the Chicago journalist Paul Holmes, who pointed out that Marilyn Sheppard had been beaten with a savagery which, according to old criminological lore, was typical of a woman blind with fury. From a few remarks of Samuel Sheppard's, Holmes deduced that Marilyn Sheppard had had a number of passionate (and married) admirers among her circle. He cited the fact that on the night of the murder the light was burning in the dressing room, the light which normally meant that Dr. Sam was out on call. A lover, not suspecting that Sheppard was asleep in the living room, could have entered the house with a key and gone straight to Marilyn's bedroom. Knowing the man, the family dog did not bark. This time, however, the man had been followed by his wife, whose suspicions had long ago been awakened. She surprised him in the Sheppards' bedroom. The man withdrew to the staircase, but the woman, crazed with hatred, attacked Marilyn Sheppard with the big flashlight she was carrying. Sheppard awoke and rushed up the stairs; the man knocked him down to save his wife from discovery. He sent his wife out of the room after she had come out of her frenzy—possibly he told her to go down to the lakeside, where he would have come by boat. Then he himself fled. When Sheppard followed him, he knocked Sheppard out for the second time and returned to the house, on a sudden inspiration to make it seem that there had been a burglary. Then he left the house for good. Whatever may be thought of this theory, it explained many of the mysteries. Nevertheless, it was only a theory. Although in the second trial the defense dropped dark hints that it knew the names of the possible murderers, at the time of writing no new persons have been indicted in the still unsolved murder of Marilyn Sheppard.

As far as the use of blood clues goes, the Sheppard affair takes its place in a whole gallery of bungles which demonstrated, during the first decade after the Second World War, how much still had to be done to make existing knowledge and existing techniques a part of the arsenal of detectives, and to improve on that knowledge and those techniques.

21

New methods were needed for the determination of human blood where the Uhlenhuth test fell short of perfection. Throughout the world, experimentation continued, and once again French serologists took the lead, especially in the Pasteur Institute. Between 1954 and 1956 J. Duclos and J. Ruffié published several papers on their work in this direction. They drew upon studies in an area of general medical serology which had belatedly attracted an unusual degree of international attention. This was the discovery, mentioned earlier, of the Rhesus factor by Landsteiner and Wiener. Because of the war this 1940 discovery did not reach the world outside America until 1945.

The story of this discovery was as follows: After Landsteiner identified the M factor, he experimented with many animals in order to produce an anti-M serum which could be used to demonstrate the presence of the M factor in human blood. Shortly before the war he and Wiener used Rhesus monkeys in their experiments. It turned out that the blood of these monkeys had a factor that corresponded to the human M. If the blood of Rhesus monkeys were injected into rabbits, the rabbits developed a serum that contained anti-M substances which could be used to determine the presence of the M factor in human blood. But when the serum was actually applied to human blood, it was found to clump red blood cells which contained no M factor as determined by other techniques. There must therefore be a hidden factor in human blood. Landsteiner called this unknown factor the Rhesus or Rh factor.

This discovery might have remained purely academic if Philip Levine had not simultaneously made another observation. In examining the blood serum of a woman who had given birth to a dead infant with completely decomposed blood, he came upon an antibody which he had never previously encountered, or recognized. Wiener showed that the serum of this woman agglutinated samples of human blood of the type that responded to anti-Rhesus serum by clumping. He then raised the question: Was there a connection between the mysterious Rhesus factor —which was found in many persons but not in all, and which apparently was as hereditary as the other blood factors—and the death of the baby? He soon found the answer. If a man with the Rhesus factor (his blood was called Rhesus-positive or Rh_+) had a child by a woman who did not have the factor (that is, was Rhesus-negative or Rh_-), the father passed the Rhesus factor on to the baby. At the same time, however, the mother's blood occasionally produced an antibody to this foreign factor. In the exchange of blood between mother and the growing fetus, these antibodies passed through the placenta into the child's bloodstream and destroyed the blood cells. This phenomenon did not necessarily take place in all pregnancies, but it was strikingly frequent. To make matters worse, the formation of antibodies generally did not take place during a first pregnancy. Anti-Rhesus antibodies developed fully in the mother's blood during second or third pregnancies, as a rule, and led to the deaths of the infants. The only way to save the baby consisted in a total exchange of blood by transfusion. It was therefore vital to determine in time whether anti-Rhesus factors had formed in a mother's blood.

It was relatively simple to show the presence or absence of the Rhesus factor itself. All that was needed was an anti-Rhesus serum. But it proved surprisingly difficult to track down the anti-Rhesus factors that might have formed in a woman's blood serum. If a suspect serum were mixed with Rh_+ test cells, no reaction could be observed, no matter whether or not an anti-Rhesus factor were present. In experimental cases in which it was known that there was an anti-Rhesus factor in the serum, the blood cells—suspended as usual in saline solution—did not agglutinate at all, or agglutinated only in some cases. Something must be hindering the agglutination which under normal conditions took place in the body and caused such dire destruction of cells. American and British scientists invented a wide variety of names for these refractory inhibiting antibodies. Among other things, they called them "blocking anti-Rhesus bodies."

In 1944 Wiener finally succeeded in dealing with these anti-Rhesus bodies by means of a trick. The serum he wanted to test for anti-Rhesus bodies was mixed with Rhesus-positive blood cells in saline solution. After some time Wiener added a different serum which had proved to agglutinate Rh-positive blood cells under normal circumstances. If agglutination now failed, something must have changed in the Rh-positive cells he had added to his serum. This change consisted in a union between the anti-Rhesus bodies in the serum with the cells in the testing fluid—a union without visible agglutination. The anti-Rhesus bodies "blocked" the agglutinating effect of the added serum, and thus betrayed their presence. It soon turned out, however, that once again only some anti-Rhesus factors possessed this blocking effect and could be uncovered by means of Wiener's trick. The majority of anti-Rhesus factors remained hidden.

The war was barely over when three British scientists took the decisive next step. They were R. R. A. Coombs, immunologist at Cambridge University, A. E. Mourant, and R. R. Race. Their procedure, which has become known as the Coombs test, was likewise based on a trick, but it was sufficiently comprehensive to identify all anti-Rhesus factors.

The method was based on the observation that the anti-Rhesus factors contained globulin, a protein component of human blood. If anti-Rhesus factors existed in a suspect blood serum, and if they were mixed with Rh-positive blood cells, they would unite with these cells without betraying their presence by agglutination. There had to be a way, however, to make these antibodies "visible" by identifying the globulin in them. Coombs and his colleagues pursued this matter. They injected human globulin into rabbits. The animals' blood thereupon produced the usual defensive reaction against human globulin. The researchers then had an anti-human globulin serum, now known as Coombs serum. The next step was to add a quantity of Coombs serum to a mixture of Rh-positive blood cells and a suspect but still unknown blood serum. If anti-Rhesus factors were present and had invisibly united with the blood cells, the Coombs serum produced a kind of agglutination of the globulin, thus betraying the presence of the anti-Rhesus factors.

This test also involved a procedure which might surprise those unfamiliar with the recondite world of biochemistry. The test blood cells, after having been mixed with the serum to be tested for a given period of time, had to be "washed" in saline solution, thereby removing the last remains of the serum, and all those components which had not been absorbed by the blood cells. Only then could the tester be sure that the Coombs serum was agglutinating only the globulin which belonged to the anti-Rhesus factors, not to some other protein.

This discovery of Coombs' by no means ended the search for other methods for determining anti-Rhesus factors. As early as 1949 Wiener pointed out that the Coombs serum forfeited its precise effect if the washing process were not carried out with sufficient precision, or if the test materials were contaminated with even the slightest particle of human protein. This phenomenon, Wiener thought, could be turned to use, and could provide another way of testing whether bloodstains came from human blood. One would start with a serum known to contain anti-Rhesus factors. Mixed with a limited quantity of Coombs serum, such serum would produce agglutination of the globulin. Suppose, then, that a portion of the Coombs serum were mixed beforehand with a solution made from a suspect bloodstain. If the bloodstain were of animal origin, the globulin would agglutinate as usual. But if the bloodstain were of human origin, the globulin would not agglutinate, for then the Coombs serum would have been contaminated with human protein, its antibodies would already have been absorbed, and there would be none left over to agglutinate the globulin in the anti-Rhesus factors.

This procedure was somewhat roundabout, and had the disadvantage, as against the Uhlenhuth test, of identifying only human blood, not various species of animal blood. But it surpassed the Uhlenhuth test in sensitivity. Extremely tiny blood spots could be thus identified.

Paul Moureau, Professor of Forensic Medicine at the University of Liège, and his pupil Paul Dodinval, improved the Coombs procedure by combining it with the Holzer method. Before using Coombs serum they measured its titer by a series of dilutions, then measured the drop in its effectiveness after application. This further increased precision of the Coombs method as a test for human blood. As a result of Moreau's work, progressively minded serologists more and more adopted the new test. But even so its application remained limited.

The situation was somewhat different in the field of blood group determination. Here there were innovations in plenty. From the work of Finnish, German, French, and American scientists, a method emerged which at last made possible the identification of Group O blood, which had previously been extremely difficult or impossible to determine in stains.

For decades serologists had wondered whether Group O was really a "negative" characteristic of blood, that is, whether the blood cells contained no agglutinogens. Repeated attempts had been made to obtain an anti-O serum, so that Group O cells could be detected in the same way as A or B cells. These efforts had always failed.

Back in the thirties von Eisler had been experimenting in Vienna with Shiga bacteria (the agents of dysentery). His aim was to find an antiserum against these bacteria. Eventually he obtained a rabbit antiserum effective against Shiga bacteria. But the same serum also agglutinated human blood cells, and moreover (as Landsteiner, Schiff, and Hirszfeld discovered between 1931 and 1938) cells of Group O. In addition, the serum had a certain effect on the cells of Blood Group A_2. Somewhere, therefore, there existed antibodies against Group O characteristics. Six years later, in the aftermath of the Second World War, Morgan and Watkins named this still unknown substance "heterogeneous," or, for short, "anti-H." All the researches on Group O up to 1957 demonstrated only one fact with some clarity: that the group could not be purely "negative" but possessed some kind of agglutinogens of its own.

Just seventy years before, Stillmark and Elfstrand had dealt with the peculiar phenomenon that the seeds of some plants are able to agglutinate blood cells. At that time it had been thought that the plants were in some way poisonous; the term "phytotoxin" was coined. In 1925, however, Fritz Schiff hit on the idea of searching plants systematically for agglutinins which would clump the cells of specific blood groups. These studies were taken up a quarter of a century later by Boyd and by Renkonen. Among 262 species of plants, Boyd found 70 which had the desired characteristics, agglutinating the cells of various blood groups, particularly Group A_1. Renkonen found that the ornamental Scotch laburnum (*Laburnum alpinum*) clumped cells of Group O and also Group A_2.

Within a few years a host of further studies followed. Between 1948 and 1959 twelve plants were found whose seeds had an anti-H effect on blood cells of Group O. The plants ranged from Renkonen's laburnum to the European gorse (*Ulex europaeus*). Their effects were not all the same. But if their peculiarities were known and their side-effect on Blood Group A_2 taken into consideration, they proved excellent for directly determining the presence of Group O in blood and secretory spots of all types. Like anti-A or anti-B serums, they could be used within the framework of the Holzer process.

The discovery of this method remained, however, the single significant success in the development of blood clue determinations. The time for a complete revision of existing methods had not yet come. And in the meanwhile doubt was cast upon the whole technique by a shattering event which mercilessly exposed existing inadequacies. That event was the "Jaccoud affair," which for a long time engaged the attention of all Europe.

22

Plan-les-Ouates was the name of the drab Swiss village in which the Jaccoud affair began late in the evening of May 1, 1958. Situated in a valley at the foot of the French Alps, Plan-les-Ouates is only five miles from the center of Geneva. Diverging from the main highway where it reached the village was a branch road called Chemin des Voirets. At the end of this road was a house bearing the number 27. In it lived Charles Zumbach, a dealer in agricultural machinery, his wife Marie, and his twenty-seven-year-old son André.

At 10:58 P.M. the Geneva police station received a call from a Madame Bouchardy, a neighbor of the Zumbachs, who reported that a murder had just taken place at No. 27. The policemen dispatched to the scene were met by a distraught woman bleeding from a shoulder wound. She was Marie Zumbach. She stood helplessly in her son André's room beside the body of her husband outstretched on the floor.

Before an ambulance took Marie Zumbach to a Geneva hospital, she gave a rather confused account of what had happened. About ten fifty she had come home from a woman's club meeting in a car driven by a woman of her acquaintance. As she entered the house, she heard shots and cries for help from her son's room. She thought she had heard three shots. She had opened the door of the room and seen a stranger "of alarming appearance," a pistol in his hand. Terrified, she had fled back through the front hall and into the garden. The stranger had followed her, shot at her, and struck her in the shoulder. Either because he was out of ammunition or for some other reason, he did not fire again. He ran back into the house, and a little later came out again. Ignoring the woman, who cowered in the shadow of the house, he swung up on a bicycle that stood by the garden gate. Peddling vigorously, he vanished in the darkness.

Marie Zumbach had suffered such intense shock that she was unable to give an exact description of the unknown man and his bicycle. She described him in vague terms—"over thirty" and "very tall"; the bicycle was "of a dark color." She could not say exactly how many shots she had heard and how many of them had actually been fired at her.

Despite the presence of so many international organizations in the city, the canton of Geneva maintained only a small police force. Capital crimes were not too common. The city of Geneva itself was in many respects caught up in a patriarchal conservatism strongly at odds with the international spirit that had come in with the establishment of the League of Nations. That spirit rarely penetrated the walls of resistance erected by the old Geneva families against foreign ideas and newfangled ways. This limited view—as many observers called it—had according to these same observers colored the police system and kept it in a state of backwardness.

Be that as it may, the murder of Charles Zumbach stirred up not only the officials of the Geneva Sûreté, but also the Chief of Police, Charles Knecht, Examining Magistrate P. Moriaud, and the Prosecutor-General of Geneva, Charles Cornu, a man of seventy. These one by one appeared at Plan-les-Ouates and intervened in the investigation. Knecht at once instituted police checks in the area between Geneva and the French border in order to catch any suspicious-looking bicyclists. Professor François Naville, the seventy-five-year-old Director of the venerable and outmoded Institute of Legal Medicine of Geneva, was sent for. Officials of the Geneva Identification Service (modeled on the French system) began inspecting the scene of the crime.

The dead man, dressed in trousers, an unbuttoned jacket, and a blood-soaked shirt, lay between the door, a wicker armchair, an overturned wooden chair, and his son André's grand piano. The carpet was thrown back. Zumbach's left slipper lay beside his hip. Four cartridge shells which the murderer had evidently fired from a .25-caliber pistol were strewn over the floor. An unfired cartridge was found in the middle of the room. Another empty cartridge turned up near the steps leading from the garden to the front door. It probably came from the shot that had been fired at Marie Zumbach. Neither windows nor doors were damaged. This seemed to rule out forcible entry. In the room where the dead man lay a closet had been opened and ransacked. But in the nearby kitchen an untouched wallet was found, containing 171 francs. It seemed likely that the murderer had been looking for a particular object. Across the street from the house one of the policemen discovered a dark button which seemed to have been ripped off or have fallen from a coat. It was so clean that it could not have been lying there long. The threads still clinging to the button indicated that it had come from a dark-blue article of clothing.

When Professor Naville arrived at the house, he contented himself with certifying death and making a rather superficial inspection of the corpse. He found that the murdered man had received a sizable number of both bullet and stab wounds in his chest. The body was taken to the Institute of Legal Medicine for autopsy. When it was undressed a bullet fell out of the clothing. The clothes themselves were turned over to the Identification Service. Naville and his assistant, Dr. Herrman, then set about making a closer examination of the wounds and determining the cause of death.

Meanwhile Examining Magistrate Moriaud and Chief of Police Knecht, who had no clue at all to the criminal, sought out the dead man's son, André, who was associated with the Geneva radio station as musical director. He was found at the broadcasting offices and asked to go to Plan-les-Ouates, where Moriaud and Knecht at once bombarded him with questions. They wanted to know chiefly whether his father had had any enemies who might be considered potential murderers.

André, a good-looking, dark-haired young man, replied that his father had led a peaceful, unexceptionable life. André could recall only one quarrel, and that was with a man named Clot who rented the garage belonging to the Zumbach house. Charles Zumbach had once found burglar's tools in this garage. There had been reports of some burglaries in Geneva at the time and he had had angry words with Clot about the tools. But the quarrel had hardly been serious enough to have led to a murderous attack.

Moriaud had Clot questioned and his alibi checked. Since André could name no other personal enemies of his father, Moriaud finally asked whether André himself had enemies who might have been looking for some possession in his room. André Zumbach made the following statement for the record: "I have learned that Mademoiselle Linda Baud, the secretary of the Director of Radio Geneva, had a liaison with a lawyer in our city, Monsieur Pierre Jaccoud. I myself had friendly relations with Mademoiselle Baud, and she went out to dine with me several times, but also with other employees of the radio station. Gradually I learned that she wanted to break completely with Jaccoud. I believe that she had probably given him to understand that my relations with her were more intimate than they really were. It is therefore possible that Jaccoud was or is jealous of me. I have several times received anonymous telephone calls, especially yesterday evening. In addition, in August or September 1957 I was sent two letters signed 'Simone B.' which called my attention to Mademoiselle Baud's loose morals. They contained three photographs of Mademoiselle Baud completely naked. To my mind, only Jaccoud could have taken these photographs. Finally, some time in 1957 he requested a meeting with me. We had a talk in his car. Jaccoud wanted to know whether I intended to marry Mademoiselle Baud. I answered negatively, but without disabusing him of his evident belief in the intimacy of my relations with her. Jaccoud did not threaten me. But he was very cold. Is it possible that I prompted him to a murder which was really directed at me?"

What led André Zumbach to drag the name of Pierre Jaccoud so quickly into the case has never been clarified. There were malicious tongues that called him a scheming careerist who had been treated condescendingly by Jaccoud, and who knew that Jaccoud as a member of the Administrative Board of Radio Geneva could put a spoke in his wheel.

Jaccoud was one of the most distinguished and sought-after lawyers in Geneva. He played an important part in political and public life. Even if we ignore the exaggerations and inventions spawned by the many newsmen who descended on Geneva in the course of the Jaccoud affair, the fact remains that here was a successful, prosperous, and influential person. Jaccoud was in his late forties. His father André Jaccoud, who had immigrated to Geneva from Savoy, had worked his way up from minor assistant in a lawyer's office to head of his own legal firm. After passing the bar examination brilliantly, Pierre Jaccoud had entered his father's firm. He helped his father, a victim of Parkinson's disease, to make the difficult journeys to the courtroom, and after his father's death in 1941 he had himself taken over the firm. In the course of time he had carved out his own kingdom in Geneva, small but significant for that city. He was possessed of a brilliant mind, a seemingly inexhaustible capacity for hard work, and an extraordinary body of knowledge, particularly in the field of commercial law. These qualities, together with a sharp and occasionally merciless gift for argument, had made him the legal adviser to many Swiss and foreign persons, businesses, and industrial corporations. His office on the Rue de la Corrvaterie was a meeting place for influential men. As representative of the dominant Radical Party in the "Grand Council of the Republic and of the Canton of Geneva," and as a member of numerous committees and organizations, he enjoyed the admiration of his adherents and inspired fear among his opponents. Of medium height, by no means handsome, Jaccoud exerted charm because of his genuine cultivation. He played a considerable part in the city's cultural activities. His family life, centered in an apartment on the quiet, respectable Rue Monnetier, where he lived with his wife Mireille, his son Alain, and his daughters Silviane and Martine, seemed to his friends enviable. Very few persons indeed, including his closest colleagues, knew anything about the drama behind this irreproachable façade.

Prosecutor Cornu, at any rate, knew Jaccoud and his family personally. He had frequently been a guest at his house. Moriaud and Knecht, too, knew Jaccoud as a skillful attorney for the defense. Their instinct was therefore to pooh-pooh Zumbach's allegations. They put the young man through some rather stringent questioning. But Zumbach revealed so many details in the course of this interrogation that the three were left with no choice; they had to move on to the seemingly grotesque and certainly dangerous "Jaccoud terrain." As a first step, they took possession of the photographs of Linda Baud in the nude, and the anonymous letters. Zumbach did not say why he had carefully preserved the pictures and letters for so many months, in spite of his friendship with Linda Baud. He also supplied more stories about Jaccoud's violent jealousy—things he had apparently heard from Miss Baud. In September 1957, it seemed, when Linda Baud was trying to break with her tyrannical lover, Jaccoud had persuaded her to take a drive with him one evening. He had stopped in front of the Zumbach house in Plan-les-Ouates and there blown his horn madly in order to bring André Zumbach out of the house and stage a scene. When no one responded to this provocation, Jaccoud drove on to the bank of the river Arve, took out a pistol and pressed it against the back of Linda's neck. She managed to wrest it from him, hurl it to the ground, and flee. He pursued her in the car. In the end, she only escaped because Jaccoud had an attack of faintness brought on by the excitement. Given such behavior patterns, Zumbach said, Jaccoud in a fit of hatred might very well have come to his house meaning to kill him, and shot his father instead.

Despite these revelations, the prosecutor, the examining magistrate, and the Police Chief felt strong inhibitions against launching an investigation of Jaccoud. Next day they followed up the trail of Clot. This seemed all the more logical since Professor Naville had meanwhile sent in his autopsy report. Naville had found four bullet wounds. One bullet had struck the aorta and caused the death. In addition the body had three stab wounds in the upper abdomen and chest, and a smaller stab wound in the back, near the left kidney. One puncture had struck the liver. Naville observed that the wounds on the front of the body had been caused by a dagger or knife. He attributed the puncture in the back to some other thin weapon.

These data suggested that several killers had been present. Moreover, it seemed doubtful that a man of no special physical strength, like Jaccoud, should have wielded three different weapons to kill an old man whom he did not know. Clot was interrogated several times. When it developed that he actually had connections with a gang of burglars, and especially with a man named Reymond, the homes of Clot and his cohorts were searched. The gang consisted of former members of the French Foreign Legion. Numerous pistols and knives were confiscated, but none of them fitted the categories of weapons that had killed Charles Zumbach. Clot and all the members of the gang had alibis which seemed to rule out their participation in the murder. Still some detectives obstinately argued that killing by firearms and dagger together exactly followed the Foreign Legion's formula for *combat rapproché*. They insisted that the killer must be sought among members or former members of the Legion. But they could discover no clues that led anywhere.

In the face of these failures, Knecht decided to take up the matter of Jaccoud after all. On May 3 he went in person to call on Linda Baud at her parents' apartment, 14 Boulevard du Pont d'Arve. As yet he was still highly skeptical and correspondingly cautious. Linda Baud proved to be a young woman of about thirty-five, slim, dark-haired, and well dressed. Prompted by his sense of caution, Knecht spoke of suspicions which had been raised against Jaccoud. He did not mention the nude photos or the anonymous letters, and affirmed that he personally considered any suspicion of Jaccoud absurd. But for the sake of an orderly investigation, he would like to ask a few questions. Linda Baud, for her part, quickly sensed where this might lead. With horror, she foresaw the scandal in the offing, and more and more restricted her answers to what was literally being asked her.

Nevertheless, Knecht learned that she had in fact been Jaccoud's mistress since October 1948. He learned furthermore that the relationship had begun breaking up about a year and a half earlier, for various reasons, and had practically ceased at the end of 1957. She also admitted that during the period of disengagement she had met André Zumbach. Out of a feeling of loneliness she had seen a good deal of him, but their relationship had remained strictly a friendship. She admitted that Jaccoud had at one time suspected an intimacy and shown signs of jealousy of Zumbach. Such was approximately the outcome of Knecht's first, semiprivate conversation with Linda Baud. What he did not learn, because she was saying the minimum, was that she had given up all connection with Zumbach for months and had recently struck up a relationship with a third man, so that Jaccoud's jealousy, from any normal point of view, would hardly be directed against André Zumbach.

The authorities were still reluctant to go after Jaccoud. A series of chance events, however, pushed them on. One such chance was the appearance of Mrs. Jaccoud at police headquarters on May 9, where she had come to pay a petty fine for a traffic accident for which she had been held responsible. The accident had occurred at 7 P.M. on May 1, that is, on the day of the murder. Knecht chatted with her and discovered from the unsuspecting woman that her husband had not come home to supper on the evening of May 1 (allegedly because of a meeting), and had in fact arrived home around eleven forty-five—approximately one hour after the murder of Charles Zumbach. This fact constituted some incriminating evidence against Jaccoud, and when in the following days all the checking of the Reymond gang seemed to lead to nothing, Examining Magistrate Moriaud decided on an official interrogation of Linda Baud. Police Chief Knecht himself brought her to Moriaud's office on May 19. But the Linda Baud whom the Examining Magistrate questioned was by now quite a different person from the woman Knecht had spoken to.

Shortly after her talk with Knecht, André Zumbach had telephoned her and asked her, in the event that she were questioned, not to betray the fact that their relationship had briefly been intimate as well as friendly. He explained that he was intending to marry and that he had already been engaged to the young lady in question at the time he was seeing Linda Baud. He could not afford any trouble with his future wife. At the same time he informed her, to her horror, that he possessed nude photos of her and anonymous letters from Jaccoud, and that his suspicions of Jaccoud were well founded. He promised Linda Baud to give her the pictures, but in the course of another telephone call had admitted that he had already turned them over to the police. If her first interview had frightened Linda Baud into a kind of frozen helplessness, she was now in a state close to hysteria. When Moriaud questioned her, she was confused, agitated, unable to muster defensive arguments. Although she attempted several times to point out the lack of any motive for Jaccoud and the incompatibility of his character with murder, she revealed more than she had originally intended. She exposed to view another aspect of Jaccoud, known only to her: the suffering and warped being hidden behind the enviable façade of a forceful, successful man.

We may presume that behind the fronts of morality and virtue Geneva has as many "liaisons" of upright citizens as has any other city in the world. But we may doubt that there are many such marked by so much psychological torment as the Jaccoud-Baud love affair which had begun in October 1948 after a dinner of the Administrative Board of Radio Geneva. Outwardly, to be sure, it was the all too familiar story of a man in his forties recognizing, amid the routine of work and marriage, how quickly his life is running away, and plunging into an affair with a young woman as if she were a fountain of youth. And yet everything was in fact different, because Jaccoud could not be equated with thousands of other men.

When he met Linda Baud—he over forty, she in her middle twenties —he had long ago begun paying the price for his rapid career. The chief source of his triumphs, his remarkably sensitive, intuitive mind and an equally sensitive nervous system constantly operating at high tension, had demanded of him the same price that other exceptional people pay for talent and success. For a long time Jaccoud had been tormented by a variety of illnesses, stomach complaints, neuralgias, cardiac disturbances, blood pressure disorders, tendency to fainting fits, and insomnia. His nervous system took its toll for being overtaxed; he suffered from frequent depressions and spells of despair.

It was later asserted that Jaccoud had never before experienced genuine, passionate love. When he fell—or rather plummeted—in love with Linda Baud in 1948, he saw in her depths, significance, a complexity which less perceptive minds would never have seen. Hundreds of love letters bore witness to this. Whether Linda Baud spiritually and intellectually justified such passion is another matter. At any rate, Jaccoud had found in her not only a mistress but a person who seemed to be receptive to his interests, his views, his whole world. He had tried to shape her according to his ideas, and undoubtedly he had to a considerable degree formed her. And in return he had received love—not only lovemaking. But for all his happiness or satisfaction, the psychological burden had increased. He was incapable of following the way of less complicated natures, of regarding an affair as an affair and dropping or changing the bedmate as soon as she collided with ordinary life and career. At the same time he no longer had strength enough to choose the alternative solution, the break with his family and public acknowledgment of his mistress, with all the concomitants—to be pilloried, at least temporarily, by the upholders of morality, and to risk the ruin of his professional life and career.

Since he had found real love in Linda Baud, he had apparently never heard from her the extortionist demand that he must marry her or she would leave him. But he was too sensitive not to know that even the greatest love on the part of a young woman must eventually wear out if it is lived in a vacuum. Eight years had been filled with clandestine meetings in restaurants, brief hours of lovemaking in a rented room in the Plainpalais quarter of Geneva, an eternal game of hide-and-seek and constant fear of running into acquaintances every time the pair went to the theater. They had been truly together only on brief vacation trips, and even then he had been haunted by the fear that he would be recognized by someone from Geneva. He had known that her love was bound to perish unless he decided wholly for her someday. But the more conscious he became of the weakness and hopelessness of his position, the more stubbornly he resisted seeing the dénouement when it actually came upon him, at the end of 1957. There are those who may judge Linda Baud harshly, while others may say that she acted in a way natural to a woman approaching her middle thirties. The vision of the future that oppresses single women, the fear of missing forever all chance of marriage and of being left alone one day, had come upon her in full force. She had succumbed to a law that kills love in almost every woman, unless she is altogether extraordinary. Love cannot survive too many sacrifices, too much loss of dignity, too much concealment. In the course of 1957 Linda Baud realized that her attachment to Jaccoud was not what it used to be. Nowadays she only accepted or sought his presence because she was afraid of being alone. She wondered whether she had been taken up with him for too long, so that she was no longer capable of another relationship and would thus be doomed to ultimate solitude.

While she was psychologically freeing herself, Jaccoud's determination to keep her grew all the stronger. In earlier years he had thought of suicide in moments of depression. Now he threatened to kill himself if she left him. He bombarded her with letters, telephone calls, flowers. He offered to divorce his wife and marry her, but immediately afterward demonstrated that he was too caught up in his social and family ties actually to take a step in that direction. She had felt that her own emotions were moving into a new stage—Jaccoud's pleas and threats of suicide stirred in her only a new and dismal feeling of pity, but not love. She too had been weak and vacillating when she started an affair with André Zumbach. By the summer of 1957 the affair had reached its last stage—the stage that Moriaud wanted most to hear about.

Was it true that Jaccoud had learned of her affair with Zumbach? Was it true that Jaccoud had told her he might accept losing her to another man, but only to a man who was his equal, not to such an "insignificant person" as André Zumbach? Had Jaccoud run into the two of them at the theater and openly displayed his contempt of Zumbach? Had he also obtained samples of Zumbach's handwriting and had it analyzed in order to demonstrate to Linda what a third-rater she had got entangled with? And was it true that her friendship with Zumbach had in fact been an intimacy, and that Jaccoud had known this? Was the story about the car, the horn-blowing in front of Zumbach's house true, and had Jaccoud later threatened her with a pistol because of Zumbach? Linda Baud was evasive, but in the end she had to admit that the essential features of these stories were true.

Moriaud showed her the anonymous letters to Zumbach. She read a characterization of herself that could not possibly have come from Jaccoud, if all that she had experienced with him were not deception. Moriaud also did not spare her the flashbulb shots of her naked except for high-heeled shoes. Had Jaccoud taken these pictures? She admitted that he had. Moriaud insisted on an explanation. She replied that Jaccoud had telephoned her in the early summer of 1957 and asked her to come to him. She had done so. In their apartment in Plainpalais, she said, Jaccoud had suddenly drawn a revolver and forced her to undress. He had then taken the pictures, after which she had fled. Days later he had begged her to forget what had happened.

The latter story may have been the truth or it may have been a fiction designed to save her modesty, the pictures actually having been taken under less dramatic circumstances. Moriaud, at any rate, could not help taking it as evidence that Jaccoud had been prone to uncontrolled, violent acts after he became obsessed by jealousy of André Zumbach. This time Linda Baud pointed out (or so she declared later) that her relationship with Zumbach had been over for months, and that Jaccoud knew it. In December 1957 she had also finally broken with Jaccoud. He had offered to divorce his wife so they could marry. This time she had replied that she could not marry him. On May 1, when Charles Zumbach was murdered, Jaccoud no longer had any reason for jealousy of Zumbach, she declared. And he also had no reason to hope for a renewal of their affair—least of all after so inconceivable an act as murder. And, she emphasized, murder was inconceivable for Jaccoud. He was an exceptional human being—he might be at the end of his rope, desperate, unbalanced to the point of making threats, but he was certainly no murderer.

Moriaud, too, probably felt doubts after this interrogation. But matters had by now progressed to such a point that they had acquired their own terrible momentum.

Later that day, May 19, Jaccoud was questioned for the first time. He appeared before Moriaud—self-controlled, relaxed, unconstrained, superior, as Moriaud had always known him to be. He made light of the embarrassment of being questioned by a man fifteen years his junior, and had the air of a person who intends to dispel easily a silly, if troublesome, suspicion. Without demur he admitted that he had sent both the anonymous letters and the nude photos to André Zumbach. In August 1957 a Miss Yolande Neury, who was now living in Paris, had come to his office, referred to a former friendship between her father and Jaccoud, and asked him for help. She had been willing to write the letters at his dictation. Jaccoud did not deny the repulsive aspect of this aberration, but regarded it as something well in the past, an unfortunate human response to a stress situation, which was a source of more anguish to himself personally than to anyone else. He stated that the breach in his relations to Linda Baud now lay a year and a half in the past, and concluded: "I do not understand how I can be suspected in any way of this crime."

Jaccoud's dating of the breach of his relations with Linda Baud struck Moriaud as so conspicuously untrue that he was taken aback. Was it conceivable that a man like Jaccoud, who had taken part in so many trials and knew so well the techniques of cross-examination, could indulge in so crude a lie? Moriaud wanted to know where he had been and what he had been doing at the time of the murder. Jaccoud replied that he had been working in his office and had not come home until around midnight. His wife could certainly testify to that. His assistant, Junod, had been at the office with him. Moriaud asked to be shown his office. They went together, and Junod spontaneously confirmed the fact that Jaccoud had not left the office before eleven o'clock on the night in question. Finally Moriaud asked Jaccoud what weapons he owned. Jaccoud replied that he had his army pistol, of course, a Mauser Parabellum, and in addition a .25-caliber Mauser with a brown butt. The latter was in the office, and Moriaud took possession of it. Jaccoud added that up to a few years ago he had had another pistol, but on his wife's insistence had thrown it into the Rhone; his wife had been afraid that he might use it against himself during one of his spells of depression.

That was the end of the interrogation. Jaccoud's freedom of movement remained unrestricted. He traveled to some bar meetings in Amsterdam and Stockholm. But during his absence Moriaud discovered other circumstances which more and more strengthened his suspicions. On April 28, a few days before the murder, Jaccoud had registered his bicycle with the traffic authorities. Hitherto the bicycle had been standing unused in his garage; now it was given a license number and could henceforth be used in the streets. In addition, Jaccoud's original alibi was upset. His assistant, Junod, retracted his first statement. He had remembered wrong; Jaccoud might have left the office by ten thirty. Detectives undertook test rides to Plan-les-Ouates and found that Jaccoud could have traversed the distance between his office and the Zumbach house in ten minutes, and thus might have committed the crime at ten fifty. One Tinjod, a client of Jaccoud's, had seen the lawyer in front of his office again at eleven thirty. It seemed quite conceivable that Jaccoud could by that time have returned from Plan-les-Ouates. The incriminating factors multiplied when Jaccoud's statements about his weapons were checked. The bullet that had fallen out of Zumbach's clothes during the autopsy could not have been fired by Jaccoud's .25-caliber Mauser, nor by his army pistol. But when both weapons were shown to Linda Baud she said, without realizing the significance of her statement, that the weapon with which Jaccoud had threatened her the previous year, and which he had brandished several times when threatening suicide, was not like these. It had been smaller and had not had a brown butt. What was more, the cleaning woman of Jaccoud's office had seen in his desk drawer a pistol like the one Linda Baud described. Thus it was quite possible that Jaccoud had had another pistol at the time of the murder, used it to commit the murder, and disposed of it afterward.

When Jaccoud returned from Stockholm on June 3, his investigators received something of a jolt. Jaccoud's chestnut-brown hair had turned blond. To friends he explained that the barber in his Stockholm hotel had by accident used a hair dye instead of a hair tonic on him. But Moriaud, who heard of the transformation, thought the matter important enough to make inquiries in Stockholm.

On June 5, while this matter was being looked into, Jaccoud called Prosecutor-General Cornu and said he would like to talk with him. Cornu gave him an appointment. At first Jaccoud seemed as sure of himself as he had during his first interrogation by Moriaud. He averred that he was innocent. But then, with utter abruptness, there appeared the other side of his nature, which Linda Baud had described, and which Cornu himself had not hitherto seen. He warned that he would have to take his own life if his name continued to be brought into the Zumbach affair. When Moriaud asked him to another interrogation two days later, June 7, he actually took a large dose of sleeping pills, although not large enough to have fatal effects. His attempt to hang himself in the Geneva Cantonal Hospital a few hours later also failed. But from this moment on there emerged more and more openly the hitherto concealed, tormented and depressive side of his personality. He refused to answer questions, had failures of memory, or attempted evasions. To an observer with some experience in psychology, none of this behavior was necessarily proof of guilt. On the contrary. If Jaccoud were innocent, unjust charges and the public exposure of his private life would be likely to trigger violent and seemingly incomprehensible reactions in his strained nervous system. Nevertheless, when Moriaud received his report from Stockholm, the scales once more sank in Jaccoud's disfavor.

The barber in Jaccoud's hotel remembered quite well the Swiss who had explicitly asked to have his hair dyed. There was no question at all of a mix-up between hair tonic and hair dye. Moreover, on the day that Jaccoud had this done, French newspapers in Stockholm had reported the Zumbach murder case. Among other details they stated that Frau Zumbach had described the murderer as a man with chestnut-brown hair. Moriaud now wondered whether Jaccoud's bizarre act could have any other meaning than a guilty man's hysterical fear of being given away by his chestnut-brown hair.

As the days passed, Cornu and Moriaud were slowly forming a theory about the crime. They asked themselves: Could it be that Jaccoud had not at all intended to commit a murder out of jealousy? Was it not conceivable that he was merely trying to lay hands on the anonymous letters and pictures, those shaming outgrowths of his jealousy? Perhaps he feared that Zumbach would someday be able to use this evidence against him, with annihilating effect. Had he armed himself with a revolver and knife intending if necessary to force André Zumbach to return the documents? It was conceivable that Charles Zumbach had admitted the visitor in his son's absence, conceivable that he had led Jaccoud into André's room and asked him to wait there for his son. Possibly Jaccoud had used this interval to look for letters and pictures. Caught in the act by Charles Zumbach, he might have been seized with panic and reached first for his pistol and then the dagger in order to wipe out the witness who had surprised him, a lawyer, going through a stranger's drawers. Anything seemed possible when Jaccoud made such a spectacle of himself as he was now doing.

Undoubtedly anything was possible—innocence as well as guilt. Cornu and Moriaud therefore decided on June 16 to make a search of Jaccoud's home. First they descended on his vacation house in Collonges. There, their search proved fruitless. On the drive back to Geneva they resolved to look over Jaccoud's apartment on the Rue Monnetier that very day. Two hours later they were in possession of three objects which henceforth became the focal points of their investigation. These were a coat, a suit, and a curved Moroccan dagger which Jaccoud had long ago brought back from a Mediterranean tour.

The coat was found in a package addressed to the Swiss Red Cross, but not yet mailed. It was a dark-blue gabardine coat of English make, carefully folded. Jaccoud had handed it to his wife with instructions that it be given away. The lowest button of the coat was missing, and Moriaud instantly asked himself whether the button found on the Chemin des Voirets belonged to this coat.

The dark-gray suit had been sent for cleaning on May 12, and since then had hung freshly pressed in Jaccoud's bedroom. Its being sent for cleaning shortly after the murder inevitably aroused Moriaud's suspicions. The Moroccan dagger, finally, was found in a wardrobe. It was in a wooden sheath to which was attached a long, coral-colored carrying cord. This dagger seemed to Cornu highly significant in connection with the stab wounds in Zumbach's body.

He asked Pierre Hegg, the director of the Geneva *laboratoire de police scientifique*, to examine these objects. On June 17 Hegg informed Moriaud that he had subjected the blue coat to a preliminary laboratory inspection. He emphasized that the results could only be considered tentative. But there were indications that the dark button found near the scene of the crime actually came from Jaccoud's blue gabardine coat. Moreover, the coat and suit had spots which might have come from blood. Upon receiving this information, Moriaud had Jaccoud arrested that very day on suspicion of "murder and attempted murder."

23

Later a French journalist described the course of the Jaccoud affair after June 17 as a "bloodstain tragedy or tragicomedy." These phrases miss the point. The second was certainly wrong, in view of the utter seriousness of the affair. But however we may wish to term it, it certainly was an unusual drama of scientific criminology which could be properly understood only against the background of the unsatisfactory status of bloodstain investigation, and some of the peculiarities of the Swiss police laboratory system.

Swiss forensic medicine was a belated offshoot of international legal medicine. Switzerland is a well-ordered country which for many years had far less of a crime problem than the rest of Europe. Hence there was no special demand for the development of advanced criminological techniques, which fact in turn retarded the progress of forensic serology on Swiss soil. Until 1912 there had been no institute of forensic medicine even in Zurich. As late as 1953 the first noted medico-legal specialist in Basel, Salomon Schönberg, had at his disposal only tiny quarters in the physics building of the university, and confined himself to autopsies. The Institute of Forensic Medicine in Bern was largely oriented toward pathology and was by 1958 quite outmoded. The institute in Lausanne was a minor appendage of the Medical School. Its director, Professor Thélin, had concerned himself chiefly with questions of criminological theory. But Geneva's institute was the poorest of all, headed as it was by the aged Naville, who performed autopsies but had long since closed his mind to most aspects of medico-legal progress. At the time of the Jaccoud affair a basic revival and renovation of Swiss forensic medicine was just beginning; it had taken its start in Basel, where Schönberg's successor Jürg, a man of forty-five, was supervising the building of a modern institute.

The effects of this situation on the technique of analyzing bloodstains could have been predicted. As the Jaccoud drama moved into its next phase, Naville had to admit that his institute was not able to carry out a blood typing or blood group study. That sounded almost incredible in the year 1958. But it was a fact that applied not only to Geneva, and furthered the tendency to have bloodstains examined at the blood donor headquarters of the various cantons. The practice seemed reasonable, since these centers had enormous experience with determination of blood groups. It merely overlooked the point that there is a fundamental difference between fresh blood and dried blood determinations.

Pierre Hegg of Geneva was the founder of one of Switzerland's few police laboratories. When on June 16 he was asked to examine the stains on Jaccoud's coat, suit, and dagger, he could not have imagined how deeply he would be drawn into the drama of forensic serology which the Jaccoud case became. Hegg, a slender, dark-haired man in his forties, with a zealot's bony face, was a native of Geneva. He had studied at the Institute for Police Science in Lausanne, established by Reiss and carried on by Marc Bischoff. This Institute, however, could have no great standing in Switzerland or Europe because of its distinctly old-fashioned orientation. Reiss was a convert of the Bertillon school of photography and identification. Marc Bischoff had made his mark in the investigation of document forgeries. Critics had long commented on the lack of practical co-operation with the police, and malicious tongues had it that the students came primarily from overseas, so that they could go back home armed with a Swiss diploma. These criticisms were surely somewhat exaggerated, but it was a fact that the Institute was quite incapable of teaching the enormous amount of material required of scientific criminology in this age of specialization. Accordingly, when Hegg tried to interest the Geneva police in the possibilities of scientific criminology, he had to depend on knowledge acquired by coping with the problems as they came up. Not much support was forthcoming. His laboratory consisted of a single room at 14 Chemin de l'Écu. Mocked by enemies as the "director of a one-man laboratory," he worked for some ten years under altogether inadequate conditions, without trained assistants, without modern equipment. Whenever he needed to use some modern technique—spectroscopy, for example—he had to ask private firms and specialists for help. These conditions were a serious obstacle to effective work. Even those who respected his ultimate purpose felt that he was somewhat of a failure. Years of sluggish resistance and outright opposition had turned him into a soured lone wolf with a tendency to egocentricity and arrogance—so even his well-wishers admitted. Friends and enemies alike regarded him as a pioneer caught in the sometimes tragic dichotomy between aims and dreams on the one hand and the limited possibilities of a small country and canton on the other.

Upon finding the first bloodstains on Jaccoud's blue gabardine coat, Hegg began studying all the objects that had been turned over to him for bloodstains. He was the only person in Geneva who knew how to conduct such an investigation—which proved how much he had taught himself in recent years. With few exceptions the spots and stains could be detected only under strong magnifying glasses. Hegg's detection of them presupposed a careful attention to detail worthy of a Kirk or Martin. Painstakingly Hegg picked out tiny spot after spot, photographed and marked each one by a thread, and determined by means of the hemin reaction, which he had learned to handle, that they were blood spots. On Jaccoud's gabardine coat Hegg found at least ten indubitable bloodstains. They were located chiefly inside, on the lining, in the left pocket, along a seam and near a button close to the left sleeve opening. He also noticed that the lining around the left pocket had been damaged by a sharp object.

In his examination of Jaccoud's suit, Hegg found blood smears especially near the tailor's label and the left inside breast pocket. Similar traces also clung to the left side of the vest. A tiny bloodstain was discovered on the right trouser pocket. All these stains had survived the cleaning. Hegg also received Jaccoud's bicycle for examination. The gear-shift lever, the right handlebar handle, and the left, rear, lower edge of the seat were spattered with extremely small traces of blood. Finally, he found a number of peculiar stains when he examined Jaccoud's Moroccan dagger. While the blade was free of blood, there was a bloodstain in the middle of the haft. The opening of the wooden sheath also showed bloodstains, whereas the inside of the sheath again appeared to be free of blood. It was, however, noticeably damp and displayed fungus growths typical of damp places. While the blade was free of rust, the point where the metal entered the handle showed rust, as though the blade had been washed and some of the water had run down under the handle. The coral-colored carrying cord was also unquestionably bloodstained, although the blood was only the thinnest of films.

It seemed evident that these finds of bloodstains incriminated Jaccoud severely. For Cornu and Moriaud, the results of Hegg's work overnight became central to the case; they regarded Hegg as a key figure who might possibly obtain proofs which all the interrogation of possible witnesses had so far not obtained.

Jaccoud was questioned about the bloodstains. He replied that the blood on his coat must have come from a fall on the stairs of his office which he had had in May or April. But he thought it conceivable that the stains even went back to an automobile accident in the summer of 1957, when the windshield of his car had been shattered. He had touched his coat with bleeding hands, he said. He could offer no explanation of why certain spots on the coat were in particular places. He also attributed the stains on his suit to injuries to his hands. As to the stains on his bicycle, he thought they might have originated on May 11, 1958, during a bicycle tour he had taken with his daughter. He had bent back the chain shield on his wheel, and cut himself. The bloodstains on the dagger and the dagger cord probably occurred at the time of that fall on the office stairs. He had been going through the contents of a cabinet and was taking the dagger home to be kept there. He might have passed blood from his hands to the weapon and cord.

These explanations did not strike the examining magistrate as especially convincing. However, they could be refuted only by firm evidence, that is, by demonstrating that the bloodstains were human and contained the group characteristics of Charles Zumbach's blood.

In 1958 neither Cornu nor Moriaud knew very much about the field of criminalistic serology. In their newborn faith in Hegg, they turned to him again. Hegg took Charles Zumbach's bloodstained shirt to the Geneva blood donation center, where the laboratory technicians agreed to try to make a belated determination of Zumbach's group from the large stains. Whether they told him then that it was hopeless to attempt any determination from the minute spots on Jaccoud's possessions remains unclear, but further developments suggest that they did. Hegg got in touch with the hematologist Dr. Erik Undritz, whom he had consulted, with spectacular success, in an earlier criminal case. Undritz explained that he was on the point of leaving for a meeting of Swiss immunologists in Seelisberg. Nor was he too encouraging when he heard what was wanted of him. Hegg must not cherish any illusions, he said: the one point he could decide was whether the blood in question was human. Perhaps it might make sense for Hegg also to come to the conference. Switzerland's most prominent serologists would be present. Possibly Hegg could ask them for advice about blood group determination.

And so on June 25 Hegg left for Seelisberg, armed with a suitcase containing Jaccoud's coat, wrapped in plastic, the stains carefully marked.

24

Dr. Erik Undritz was at this time fifty-eight years old, a tall, lean man with an intelligent and impressive face under thinning dark hair, and kindly eyes. Much traveled, he was lively of speech and gesture, able to converse in Russian, German, Italian, and French.

Undritz was a Baltic German, born 1901 in Revel, a minister's son. While studying medicine in Dorpat he had come down with tuberculosis of the larynx, and his father sold all his property in order to send the young man, already marked by death, to a sanatorium in the Black Forest in Germany. There he was saved by electric cauterization of the larynx, and returned to his studies, only to be stricken with tuberculosis of the lungs. He went to an Arosa sanatorium, thus for the first time setting foot in Switzerland, where he was later to make his home. During his own slow cure he served as a resident physician at various sanatoria in Arosa, Montana, and Locarno from 1927 to 1938; finally he joined the hematological laboratory of the Sandoz firm in Basel, first as an assistant and subsequently as chief of the hematological laboratory. Many of his scientific publications dealt, naturally, with the problem of tuberculosis. But the major theme of his work was the investigation of the blood and its diseases. As a student he had encountered leukemia in all its hopelessness. He would never forget the first leukemia patient from whom he had taken blood in Dorpat so that he might study its characteristics. His compassion had been deeply stirred by her weary "Your Honor, why are you still tormenting me?" He had then and there determined to get to the bottom of this mysterious disease.

In the summer of 1958 Undritz was one of the leading hematologists of Europe, thanks to his researches into the various types of blood cells and their analogies, his studies of staining techniques. His colored *Sandoz Hematological Plates,* published in 1950, had become standard texts in the field. His interest in animal blood and the skill he had developed at recognizing the different kinds was largely in the nature of an avocation. He had never dreamed that his hobby would one day make him a figure in a sensational murder trial.

On the way to Seelisberg he was beset by conflicting emotions. He knew little about the Jaccoud affair, but he understood that his scientific knowledge was wanted for a criminalistic matter. He felt a strong reluc-

Pamela Coventry whose body was found in a ditch in 1939

Detective in house-to-house search   Leonard Richardson

Hildegard Wassing and Peter Falkenberg

Where the bodies were found

Dr. Otto Martin,
head of the Biological Section
of the
West German
Federal Criminal Office

Dr. Samuel Sheppard
and
Susan Hayes

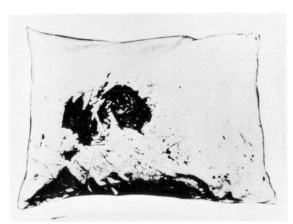

Marilyn Sheppard's
bloodstained pillow

Pierre Jaccoud and Linda Baud

Exhibits in the Jaccoud case

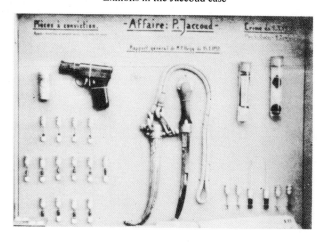

tance to enter this alien world. On the other hand, as a scientist he was tempted by the specific problem. Since his discovery of the stability of leucocytes, he had made many microscopic studies of dried blood. The different shapes of the seven human leucocytes were now so familiar to him that he could recognize them at a glance. He knew only one rare animal, which did not occur in Europe, whose leucocytes might possibly be mistaken for human white blood cells.

Hegg met Undritz in Seelisberg. He showed him the coat, from which some patches of cloth with bloodstains had already been cut out, and Undritz undertook some preliminary studies.

It certainly seems unusual for him to have done such work in a hotel rather than a laboratory. But Undritz was accustomed to working while traveling. Hegg assisted, to the extent of ensuring that no more than half of each individual stain was used, so that there would be enough left for possible control studies. Undritz transferred flakes of blood to his slides, diluting them with blood serum, and staining. He utilized techniques that had long been established by hematologists. One type of white blood cell, the basophile, for example, possessed an attraction for basic stains such as methylene blue. Another type, the eosinophiles, absorbed the stain eosine, which is red. All the nuclei of blood cells likewise absorb basic stains. But there is a powerful nucleic acid present in the nuclei which may shift the blue color somewhat toward red, so that it appears violet. The granula in the protoplasm surrounding the nuclei contain traces of sulphuric acid. This acid absorbs toluidine blue, another dye, and develops an unmistakable red-violet shade. Altogether, the scale of colors for distinguishing the components of blood ranges from blue through blue-gray, yellow, dark-brown, orange, olive-green, and violet to pink and a bright red. The various stains are named after their discoverers—Pappenheim, Graham-Knoll, Lepehne, Feulgen, Hansen—and add up to a system bewildering to the outsider, but one with which Undritz was perfectly familiar.

After examining the first slide prepared from the spots on Jaccoud's coat, Undritz declared: "All the components of the blood are human." Eight more times he made the same announcement. Hegg now pressed him to look into the question of determining the blood group, but Undritz declined, introducing him instead to L. P. Holländer, the distinguished Basel serologist who headed the blood donor center in his city. Holländer, too, refused to attempt a blood group determination; he felt that the quantity of material was insufficient. Hegg then put his request to Dr. Alfred Hässig, head of the laboratory of the Swiss Red

Cross blood donor center in Bern. But even Hässig excused himself from the task. Later it was asserted that the serologists had bowed out because of their reluctance to become involved in the Geneva murder case. Whatever reasons underlay their scruples, Hegg returned to Geneva with only half his mission accomplished.

Back home, he received word from Dr. Fischer, head of the blood donor center in Geneva, that examination of the bloodstains on Zumbach's shirt had yielded the information that Zumbach's blood group had been O. Jaccoud, too, had Group O blood. Blood factors could not be determined. This news was highly significant, though in a totally negative fashion. Any further efforts to determine the grouping of the bloodstains on Jaccoud's coat, suit, dagger, and bicycle would be pointless. If the blood were found to be Group O, it might be either Jaccoud's or Zumbach's; there was no way to refute Jaccoud's contention that the bloodstains came from his own blood. Should the blood be of some other group, it could not be connected at all with the Zumbach murder case. Thus the information practically put an end to the serological investigation, unless something could be done to determine blood factors and thus obtain some differentiation between Jaccoud's and Zumbach's Group O blood. Given the inadequate facilities and the well-known difficulty of determining factors in dried blood, any such effort seemed foredoomed to failure. It remains one of the mysteries of the Jaccoud affair why Hegg did not give up at this point and announce that differentiation of the blood was impossible.

Instead, he got in touch with Undritz once more and arranged another meeting—working session, it was called—with that overworked man, who was rushing back and forth between his laboratory and scientific meetings. This time Hegg brought the Moroccan dagger as well as the other objects.

Undritz did not quite understand why Hegg should want further proof of the presence of human blood. He therefore decided that Hegg's interest might be less in the criminalistic question than in a further verification of the method. He began by making seven solutions of the bloodstains on the carrying cord of the sheath, staining them with Hansen stain. In examining his stained preparations he made his usual pronouncement: "All the leucocytes are those of human blood." Then he gave a start. His eye had caught large, violet, nuclear shapes which by their size and type could not possibly be those of blood. Out of one hundred leucocytes he counted eighteen or nineteen nuclei different from those of blood cells. With mounting excitement he examined other preparations of the same spots, which he treated with Graham-Knoll stain. He observed what he later described as "tissue fragments of an internal organ, a cell aggregate in places well defined with cytoplasm, pigment, and relatively large nucleus, with large, quite visible nucleoles." The finding struck him as improbable, but no matter how carefully he examined the slide, he could not escape the fact: there was no doubt that the cell aggregate consisted of a tiny portion of an internal organ, embedded in human blood. Finally he stained the cells with Lepehne stain for a check; this procedure revealed the large alien cell nuclei—two or three times larger than those of white blood cells—in great numbers. They looked to him like liver cells.

At this moment Undritz knew too little about the details of the Jaccoud case to realize the significance of his observations. But when he had spoken the words "liver cells" and heard of the stab wound that had pierced Zumbach's liver, he became aware, with some anxiety, of the possible connection. Later he reported, with the unconstraint of a man who had hitherto had no dealings with criminology, that he had suddenly thought, horrified: "Why, now, Jaccoud is guilty." He felt as if he had been the witness of a crime. Had Jaccoud's dagger, which lay on the table, penetrated Zumbach's liver and been withdrawn with liver cells still clinging to it, which had then been accidentally wiped off on the cord as the dagger was replaced in its sheath? Further examination of the dagger showed only human blood on the handle. But the liver cells on the cord were undeniably there. When Hegg returned to Geneva and reported this discovery, the men involved in the investigation became convinced that they had closed an important link in the seemingly fantastic chain of evidence against Jaccoud. Only one thing seemed to be lacking: proof that the dagger fitted the stab wounds in Charles Zumbach's body.

A check of Naville's autopsy report revealed that it could be of no help. Nothing in it pointed to the use of a long, curved Moroccan dagger as the murder weapon. On the contrary. Naville's conclusion that two different stabbing weapons had been used rather pointed in the opposite direction. It had earlier been noted, in the course of an inspection of Zumbach's clothes, that there was no hole in the cloth corresponding to the stab wound in Zumbach's back. This curious fact had remained unexplained. Now, after Hegg's return, a new question was raised: If Jaccoud's dagger with its ten-inch blade were the murder weapon, could the wound in Zumbach's back not be an entry wound at all, but mark the spot where the Moroccan dagger had penetrated through the entire chest and come out at the back?

By June 8 the examining magistrate had ruled that Zumbach's body should be exhumed and the wounds once more studied. Hegg, on Moriaud's instructions, telephoned the institutes of forensic medicine in Zurich, Bern, and Basel. He persuaded Chief Assistant Franz of Bern and Professor Im Obersteg of Basel to come to Geneva. On June 12 these two specialists performed a second autopsy on the exhumed body. Their work was considerably hampered by the deterioration of the corpse. But with the aid of X rays they found an additional two bullets that Naville had left in the body. Im Obersteg found that Naville's report had assigned an entry wound in the right side of the dead man's chest to the left side, and a penetration wound through the base of the left lung to the right lung. Franz thought it "convincing" that the Moroccan dagger, because of its curvature, might have made two of these wounds. Im Obersteg was far less positive. He merely refused to exclude Jaccoud's dagger as a possible murder weapon—and no doubt he was right in being so cautious. Forensic specialists have learned that it is always a dubious matter to try to deduce from an exhumed corpse whether some particular weapon has been used. The task is all the more difficult when it is not accompanied by an examination of the clothing for entry wounds. That was not done during the second autopsy because Zumbach's clothes were not placed at the disposal of Franz and Im Obersteg. Since Naville had omitted the accompanying inspection of the clothing, Hegg seemed determined to leave this part of the investigation to a combined group of experts, including himself.

On July 10 Undritz, who up to now had been dealing only with Hegg, received an official assignment from Examining Magistrate Moriaud to collaborate with Hegg on inspection of all pieces of evidence confiscated from Jaccoud. He was to use all the means at his disposal to look for blood spots and above all for traces of liver. The chief purpose of the assignment was to determine whether Jaccoud might have stabbed Zumbach several times with his Moroccan dagger, penetrated his liver, and transferred traces of blood and liver to the weapon and to his clothing. Moriaud also asked whether it would be possible to determine whether the bloodstains were of male or female origin, and furthermore whether their age could be ascertained. In any case, on that July 10 Undritz was irrevocably removed from his ivory tower.

That same day Hegg arrived in Basel with new pieces of evidence, including the handlebars of Jaccoud's bicycle. On July 15 and 26, and on July 31, August 28, September 24–25, October 2, 12, 14, and 24 he had meetings with Undritz. In the course of this series of "working sessions" extending over four months, almost all the bloodstains that Hegg had found were checked and diagnosed as human blood. No more alien cells which could be attributed to an organ of the body turned up during those months. It was as though fate had reserved the crucial surprises for the beginning and end of the studies. For during the last sessions, on October 12 and 14, a second significant find was made. Undritz was studying the small smears of blood that had been found in the left pocket of Jaccoud's coat, and at the opening and on the underside of the left sleeve. In all these places Undritz saw not only evidences of human blood but also "large nuclei with large nucleoles and net-shaped structures which undoubtedly belonged to the cells of internal organs and obviously to liver cells." Here was the same determination as with the stains on the cord of the dagger sheath. To assure himself that the cells were really of the same origin, Undritz made detailed comparative studies of stained slides from the two sources. He found that the organ cells were as like one another as the components of the blood with which they were mixed.

From Undritz' observations a series of conclusions followed, for Hegg and Moriaud. Suppose that after the murder Jaccoud had thrust the dagger, now soiled with blood and particles of liver, point upward into his left coat pocket, where he had also deposited the sheath. Traces of blood and liver might then have been smeared on the sheath cord, the pocket, and the lower end of his sleeve. Afterward he might have washed the dagger, but failed to notice the stains on the cord, the handle, and the coat, because they were so small. The evidence certainly seemed to support this theory.

Zumbach's shirt, pierced and blood-soaked, was taken to Basel for Undritz to check for the same organ cells and blood elements at the spots corresponding to entry wounds. But in this task he failed. He could find no leucocytes or large cell nuclei. He suggested a possible explanation: that before his death Zumbach had broken into a violent sweat, and the sweat had so affected the cellular elements of the blood that they could no longer be brought out by staining. Thus there remained a gap in the chain of evidence between the dagger and the stabbing holes in Zumbach's clothing. But Hegg was so impressed by the discovery of the liver cells that the crucial question of whether the dagger and the liver cells could really be connected unequivocally with the murder and the victim became a bit blurred. He did, to be sure, consider the question of whether cells from a liver would cling to the blade of a dagger and not be wiped off by skin and clothing as the weapon was drawn out of the body. But as was later shown, he contented himself with an explanation which he had not adequately thought out. He noted that the blade of the dagger was slightly chased, and decided that the blood and cells had remained in the grooves of the metal as the weapon was drawn out of Zumbach's body. He overlooked the fact that Zumbach's liver had only been grazed to a depth of about a quarter of an inch and a length of only an inch or two, so that the chased part of the blade could not possibly have reached it.

Meanwhile Undritz, with his blithe unawareness of the techniques and boundaries of forensic medicine, was proceeding along new and hitherto totally unexplored lines to answer the questions regarding the age of the bloodstains and the sex of the person whose blood had caused them. Having succeeded in investigating bloodstains by normal hematological methods, he thought it possible to apply to microscopic smears of dried blood the procedures used in hematology for dealing with the phenomena of aging blood. It was known that certain types of white blood cells, the neutrophiles, the eosinophiles, and the monocytes, contain enzymes which lose their effectiveness as blood ages. The enzymes of monocytes break up in about four weeks. Those of neutrophiles last from eight to twelve months, while the enzymes of eosinophiles may remain stable for as long as five years. Environmental factors, such as dampness or excessive sunlight, can diminish or prolong the period of preservation. Nevertheless, the age of the blood can be gauged, within rough limits. The presence and potency of the enzymes are revealed by the Graham-Knoll stain, which colors the granula in the cell bodies of leucocytes either tan, green, or brown. Since Undritz found no staining whatsoever of the granula in the monocytes, he concluded that the blood spot at the time of his test must be more than four weeks old. The granula in the neutrophiles, however, responded to the stain. This meant that the blood spots must be less than eight months old. The date of Zumbach's murder, May 1, 1958, lay within this time span.

The second hematological principle that Undritz applied to his dried bloodstains concerned the sex determination of the blood. It was based on the findings by two British scientists, Barr and Bertram. Both had discovered in 1945 that the cell nuclei of female blood contain larger quantities of a readily stainable compound, chromatin, than male cell nuclei. In addition curious appendages looking like drumsticks had been found on the leucocytes in female blood. These are extremely rare in male blood. They had in fact been given the name "drumsticks." Smears of fresh blood of unknown origin in which from five to seven leucocytes with drumsticks, out of five hundred, could be detected, might safely be regarded as female. Undritz looked for drumsticks in all the bloodstain solutions he had prepared. Since he observed none, he concluded that the blood on Jaccoud's clothing and dagger was of male origin, and hence could have been Zumbach's.

Toward the end of October Undritz and Hegg drew up their deposition. It was a document that, formally speaking, went far beyond the ordinary expert opinion. Throughout, it bore the impress of Undritz' unusual and in many respects brilliant personality. It was a collection of laboratory results which as a matter of course assumed in the reader the kind of scientific knowledge few besides Undritz possessed. Hegg had made an attempt to sum up the results. Nevertheless, the whole paper remained a curious document. The summary listed the following findings: The bloodstains were from human blood. There was a high degree of probability that the blood was from a man. The stains were more than one month and less than eight months old. Mixed with the blood in various places were cell nuclei that had come from a liver.

By the time Cornu and Moriaud received this opinion, they already had reports on some other technical studies conducted by Hegg. He had borrowed a spectrometer for some of these; others (since there were no facilities for ballistic analysis in Geneva) he had had done in Lyons, France. He himself had undertaken to evaluate the results. Among other items, he had analyzed the button found at the scene of the crime, as well as the fibers clinging to it, and compared these with the buttons and the textile fibers on Jaccoud's coat. His conclusion was that the buttons and fibers were of the same origin. However, the main emphasis rested on the opinion from Basel and the demonstration that liver cells had been mixed with the blood.

The prosecutor and the examining magistrate reconstructed the crime as follows: On the night of May 1, 1958, Jaccoud, dressed in a gray suit and blue gabardine coat, had taken his Moroccan dagger with its sheath and cord and a Mauser pistol, caliber .250, with him. He mounted his bicycle, which he had only recently re-registered, and rode unseen to the Zumbach house in Plan-les-Ouates. There were a number of possible motives. He could have been thinking of belated vengeance upon André Zumbach, whom Jaccoud still blamed for Linda Baud's break with him. He might have intended to recover the nude photographs and letters, if necessary forcing André Zumbach to surrender them. But he found that André Zumbach was not at home. Charles Zumbach led him into his son's room to wait. He used this time to look for documents. Charles Zumbach heard noises and caught him rifling the cupboard. From fear of being exposed as a thief, Jaccoud shot at Zumbach four times. Then Zumbach's wife appeared. Jaccoud pursued her, then heard cries from the dying Zumbach and tore back to the murder room. He thought Zumbach was still alive. Since he had emptied his gun, he wildly stabbed Zumbach, one of the stab wounds piercing Zumbach's liver. Then Jaccoud thrust the dagger, point upward, into the left outside pocket of his coat, where he already had the sheath with its carrying cord. Thus he stained the pocket, sheath, and cord with blood and liver cells. Rushing out of the house, he took his bicycle. Stains from his blood-smeared right hand remained behind on all the places he touched, handle bars, and gearshift lever. A loose button from his coat fell to the ground. Jaccoud rode off. As he rode he became afraid he would lose the dagger and transferred it to the inside left breast pocket of his suit, ripping the pocket and leaving bloodstains. In a garage he cleaned himself up and carefully washed the blade of the dagger, unaware of the spots on the cord. The water ran under the handle of the dagger, producing rust. It also dampened the sheath and left conditions under which mold formed. Jaccoud also overlooked the numerous spots on his clothing and the bicycle which could be seen only under a magnifying glass. He had his coat packed up for the Red Cross and sent his suit to be cleaned in the vain hope that the cleaning would eliminate all remaining spots. He disposed of the pistol but kept the dagger, perhaps because of personal associations.

25

On November 22, 1958, Jaccoud was taken to the Law Courts in Geneva and led to Moriaud's room. Article 148 of the Geneva code of trial procedure provided that the parties—prosecution, defendant, and defense attorneys—must be informed of the results of a preliminary investigation. They can then challenge these results in a *discussion contradictoire*. Thus Jaccoud was informed of the results of the blood stain tests and requested to state his views.

Ever since the first interrogations Jaccoud had more and more taken refuge in an attitude of passive resistance. He was by now only a shadow of his former self, constantly suffering nervous collapses. He barricaded himself behind the statement: "I have been accused of a crime of which I am innocent and with which I have had nothing whatsoever to do. It does not concern me. There is no reason for me to do or to say anything at all."

Such an attitude could have arisen from actual innocence. It could have been a reaction to a truly monstrous, incomprehensible injustice. But it could also have been the stratagem of a guilty man who subsequently regarded his own crime as alien to himself, inconsistent with his whole nature. Given so sensitive a personality as Jaccoud's, there was the possibility that he put the incomprehensible act out of his mind, refused to recognize that it had ever taken place. Nevertheless, now and then there emerged out of Jaccoud's repeated psychic breakdowns some remnants of his clear lawyer's mind. He had engaged three attorneys, Maître A. Dupont-Willemin and Maître R. Nicolet of Geneva, and the most famous although also one of the most controversial lawyers in France during those years, Maître Floriot of Paris.

It was Jaccoud's right, in the course of the *discussion contradictoire*, to request new experts to check the existing opinions on the bloodstains. If Pierre Jaccoud were completely convinced of his innocence, it would have seemed obvious to take this course. But he did not do so. He declared that he would make no further statements during the preliminary investigation. The whole thing was a conspiracy built up of false charges and speculations. He reserved the right to demonstrate his innocence in public during the trial itself. Until then he would have nothing to say.

Cornu was not prepared to take Jaccoud's statement at face value. He suspected that Jaccoud feared more experts would only further incriminate him. On the other hand, he saw the possibility that Jaccoud might present surprise experts during the main trial. Such experts, to be sure, would not themselves have had the chance to examine any single piece of evidence. They could only advance theoretical arguments. But this was to the advantage of Jaccoud, inasmuch as they also would not turn up evidence against him, which might happen if they personally examined the exhibits. Skillfully guided, they might manage to cast doubt on the expert opinions and thus influence the jury in Jaccoud's favor.

Cornu saw only one way to outmaneuver this. He could ask the court to call in experts to check the opinion of Undritz and Hegg and to counter, by the weight of their names, any surprise experts Jaccoud might produce. At this time Cornu had his own grave doubts of the reliability of the bloodstain tests. But since under Geneva law the examining magistrate has the right to inform the public of the course of his investigations, there had been several articles published since November 1958 on the work of Undritz and Hegg. To be sure, little was said in these articles about the actual methods used. But the very circumstance that a fresh-blood hematologist like Undritz had been entrusted with the blood analyses caused a stir among medico-legal specialists of international reputation. From them came the first ominous signs of doubt, in fact of the tempest of outrage that was to burst over the head of Undritz, the outsider, a year later. The prosecution was forced to recognize that Jaccoud's hypothetical surprise experts would in any case be able to advance a highly significant argument: For more than fifty years forensic medicine had unequivocally rejected microscopic study of blood as impossible and unreliable. Such a statement could not fail to make an impression upon the jury.

On January 9, 1959, therefore, Cornu asked Moriaud to consult a team of three new experts who were to look into the methods used by Undritz and Hegg and decree whether they regarded them as "scientifically certain." They were also to repeat the analysis of the bloodstains using "methods generally accepted in forensic medicine." The experts chosen were Paul Moureau of Liège, H. E. Bock of Marburg, and Albert Alder of Aarau. The choice showed that French-Swiss reservations about Germans and German Swiss had yielded to the pressure of events. Moreover, this time Moriaud left nothing to Hegg and nothing to chance, but accepted good advice.

Paul Moureau of Liège, a slightly built, impulsive man in his fifties, with a mobile, furrowed face, was by 1959 one of the most noted medico-legal men in Europe. He had begun specializing in criminal matters at the age of thirty-two. His particular field was serology, and he was among the few who had taken up the Coombs test as a new technique for determining the presence of human blood. If there were anyone in Europe who was in a position to check Undritz' opinion by acknowledged biological methods, such as the Uhlenhuth and Coombs tests, it was Moureau. Someone had apparently pointed out to Examining Magistrate Moriaud that even if Undritz' identification of liver cells were correct, there was no proof that the cells came from a human being. No means were available for distinguishing microscopically between human and animal liver. Hence it was essential to obtain corroboration of the opinion that the bloodstains in which the liver cells were embedded actually came from a human being.

Professor H. E. Bock was a specialist in internal medicine at the University of Marburg. He had for some time been applying a new method of diagnosis for diseases of the liver. It consisted in thrusting a "punch" through the abdominal wall into a patient's liver, pricking out a tiny piece of liver, and studying the cells. Having examined liver cells of countless patients, he surely would be able to say whether Undritz was right about having detected such cells.

Professor Albert Alder was a hematologist. He was fully familiar with the entire field of hematology, and among other matters had dealt with the aging of leucocytes.

All three met with Undritz and Hegg on the morning of April 27, 1959, in the Anatomical Institute in Basel. From the very start Undritz was made to feel his temerity in having ventured into the sacred precincts of criminalistic serology. Moureau as yet had no clear notion of what Undritz had actually done. For him, too, microscopic study of blood to determine its type was something that had been given up as a bad job fifty years ago, and his attitude toward Undritz was correspondingly chilly. Alder knew Undritz well from many meetings of hematologists, but he took his assignment very seriously and was likewise reserved. The most open-minded of the three seemed to be Professor Bock, who was filled with curiosity concerning this new development in criminology: the recognition of liver cells on a murder weapon.

Coolly, the three men listened to Hegg's account of the general situation. Then they inspected the various exhibits, and Undritz lectured on his work. Moureau smiled. The enthusiasm with which Undritz described his procedures, quite forgetful of the bias of his hearers, made him think that this was an engaging but scientifically irresponsible idealist. Toward noon Moureau indicated that he wished to confer alone with Bock and Alder. In the course of this discussion Moureau bluntly declared that in view of the minute quantity of blood in the stains, only one technique would do for determining the type of blood: the Coombs test. He did not conceal his astonishment that this method, or at least the capillary form of the Uhlenhuth test, had not been attempted from the start. Was there really no one in Geneva who knew how to carry out these elementary tests? Was it possible that bloodstain studies had been placed in the hands of an inexperienced outsider like Undritz? With the others' permission, he would telephone his assistant, Dr. Dodinval, to come to Basel with the necessary apparatus, serums, and test blood cells.

The others agreed, and Moureau arranged for Dodinval to take the train which would bring him in early next morning. Undritz and Hegg were called in again that afternoon. The atmosphere was still strained. Alder virtually subjected Undritz to an examination. He presented him with blood smears which showed leucocytes from blood samples of different ages. Alder's mistrustful attitude began abating, however, when Undritz was able to give the correct ages of the samples and infallibly distinguished human blood from that of various animals in another set of samples. Bock proceeded in similar fashion with preparations of cells with which liver cells had been mixed. The general reserve vanished entirely when Undritz again came through with perfect scores. Alder and Bock asked to see how Undritz prepared his slides. From that moment on, the meeting became a lecture demonstration, with the experts as eager pupils. Alder's and Bock's interest and respect were in the end transmitted to Moureau. Hesitantly, then unreservedly, he too acknowledged Undritz was right: his slides did indeed reveal the typical forms of leucocytes. Undritz pointed out the human neutrophiles with their one to four segments; the eosinophiles with two segments and round granula in the cell body; the lymphocytes with only scattered, delicately bluish granular formations; the very small basophiles; the monocytes with their globular nuclei, and the unnucleated blood platelets. Contrasted with these were the slides of a wide variety of animal blood cells, with all their different peculiarities. By the time Undritz reached those slides in which he purported to find liver cells, the three experts had in principle accepted his method. Bock gave his opinion. On the basis of his own experience, he agreed that the cells must be those of liver. Late that afternoon the session ended in general agreement, which each of the three experts expressed in terms of his own temperament:

Alder: "Yes, I too can only confirm that what you have done is quite right."

Bock: "Undritz, what you have done is absolutely sound."

Moureau: *"C'était merveilleux!"*

For the record, Alder, Bock, and Moureau noted: "We herewith corroborate the conclusions of the experts Undritz and Hegg. . . . The morphological studies have yielded results which permit the conclusion, with a probability verging on certainty, that human blood is present."

They chose this phraseology not because they retained any doubts, but in deference to the well-known fact that no new scientific procedure could be considered absolutely certain until it had been tested many times. As for the liver cells, Alder and Bock testified: "On the basis of experience with liver puncture procedures . . . the experts are convinced that these elements are cells from the liver."

Moureau bade them good night, saying: "If we have judged the type of blood correctly, 'Coombs' will provide confirmation tomorrow." Moureau, Alder, Bock, Undritz, and Hegg were up early and meeting again by seven forty-five next morning. Dodinval had arrived, bringing the test tubes Moureau needed for the Coombs test. He had also brought a Coombs serum prepared in Liège, an anti-Rhesus serum from a patient in a Liège hospital, blood cells of Group O with Rhesus factor from the blood center in Liège, and a horse serum for control purposes. Moureau was aware that the long train ride might have affected the blood cells. But he assumed that these effects would be negligible, and since Switzerland could not provide the necessary materials for the test, there seemed to be no choice.

Dodinval began by picking out, with magnifying glass, the largest remaining bloodstains on the coat. He cut a piece of cloth from the coat and labeled it sample 1. Then, for purposes of comparison, he cut a piece of cloth free of blood, and labeled this sample 2. A piece of lining from the back of the coat, with blood on it, made sample 3. A piece of lining without blood was sample 4. Since the bloodstains from Zumbach's shirt indubitably came from human blood, a stained piece of this shirt was prepared as sample 5. And since the authorities had had the shirt treated with a moth repellant named Trix, to preserve it, Dodinval took a sample of the shirt itself, without bloodstain, as a control specimen. Finally Dodinval set aside some of his horse serum as samples 7 and 8. After these elaborate preparations, the Coombs test for human blood could begin.

This test, as has been mentioned, grew out of the experience gathered by serologists in their efforts to identify the dangerous anti-Rhesus factors in the blood of pregnant women. The first step was to mix the blood cells of Group O human blood known to carry the Rhesus factor with the serum of the woman. This mixture was then placed in a warming oven and kept at blood temperature for some time. Then Coombs rabbit anti-globulin serum was added to it. If there were anti-Rhesus factors in the woman's blood, the Rhesus-positive Group O blood cells absorbed the globulin in the anti-Rhesus factors and clumped. In other words, the Coombs serum agglutinated this globulin. If the anti-Rhesus factor was absent, no agglutination took place.

The application of this test to criminalistic serology was founded on the discovery that Coombs serum diminished in potency if, before the test, it came into contact with the slightest quantities of human blood or protein. Known Rhesus-positive blood cells of Group O were therefore mixed with a serum known to contain anti-Rhesus factors. If fully potent Coombs serum were now added, agglutination of the cells followed. But if the Coombs serum had previously been mixed with a solution from a bloodstain, two things might happen. If the stain contained human blood, the Coombs serum was weakened and the agglutination reaction correspondingly diminished or obliterated. If no human blood were present, the Coombs serum retained its full potency and the agglutination took place.

In order to make the test more precise Moureau, as we have seen, had combined the method of the Holzer test with the Coombs test. He prepared series of dilutions of the Coombs serum. Then he determined the degree of dilution to which the serum retained its capacity to agglutinate Rh-positive Group O blood corpuscles which had been mixed with anti-Rhesus serum. For control, he then added Coombs serum to a sample of animal blood. Since animal blood proteins in no way diminished the potency of the serum, agglutination took place. Only then did Moureau mix additional serum with the bloodstain to be tested, and with the cloth from which it was taken. Once again a dilution series with Coombs serums was set up. The standard was that the titer must be lowered by at least three stages for the bloodstain to be certainly identified as human. The degree to which the base material affected the test also had to be determined.

This was the technique Moureau followed on the morning of April 28.

The Rhesus-positive Group O cells were "washed" three times and mixed with anti-Rhesus serum. From 9:30 to 11:30 A.M. Dodinval kept this mixture in the warming oven. Then the cells were washed once more, and only then suspended in 5 per cent saline solution. Coombs serum was distributed among ten test tubes in increasing dilutions: 1:4, 1:8, 1:16, 1:32, 1:64, 1:128, 1:256, 1:512. When the dilutions were applied to the test mixture, it was found that the serum retained an agglutinating effect up to a dilution of 1:256. Eight more sets of dilutions were then prepared and tested with horse serum—that is, animal protein. It was determined that the animal protein did not diminish their potency. Shortly after one o'clock Moureau began checking those samples of serum which had been mixed with bloodstains from Jaccoud's coat. Ten minutes later he had the first results. The titer of the serum diminished from 1:256 to 1:64, that is by two stages. Thus there were indications that the bloodstain contained human blood, but not proof. Two hours later, when Dodinval checked the samples of unstained cloth from the coat, the titer of the Coombs serum diminished from 1:256 to 1:128, that is by one degree. Since this degree had to be taken into the reckoning, the bloodstain had lowered the titer only by a single degree. This was regarded as too little for certainty. A feeling of uneasiness spread through the group of men. It disappeared, however, when Moureau checked the bloodstain on the lining of Jaccoud's coat and the samples of unstained lining. It quickly turned out that the lining itself produced virtually no loss of titer in the Coombs serum. At 1:256 there was just a slight weakening, which at best could be regarded as half a degree. On the other hand, the serum brought into contact with the bloodstain dropped down to 1:64, and even at 1:32 only a feeble agglutinating effect could be detected. This was a drop in titer of three full degrees, which was regarded as sufficient proof of the presence of human blood.

All the rest was only a postlude. By six thirty that evening the last experiments were completed, and Moureau noted: "The spot on the lining of the gabardine coat is a spot of human blood. . . . The spot on the gabardine coat is probably of human origin. The smallness of the spot explains why our conclusion cannot be put more categorically."

Moureau must have realized at this moment that his conclusions were the most definite that could be obtained. Jaccoud's defense attorneys could, of course, contend that the bloodstain on the lining of Jaccoud's coat might indeed be from human blood, but that this was no proof that the other stains, especially the stain in the coat pocket and on the cord of the dagger, the one that contained the liver cells, likewise came from human blood. There was nothing to be done about such an argument. The failure of the test on the cloth of the coat indicated to Moureau that any tests with the other even smaller stains had no prospect of success. By now, however, he was so firmly convinced of the reliability of Undritz' work that he considered the single successful test sufficient.

A few weeks later Moureau, Bock, and Alder summed up the results of their work as follows: "We uphold the careful and conscientious investigation by the scientific experts Undritz and Hegg.

"We have demonstrated with certainty the presence of human bloodstains, mixed with cells which are not blood cells, these latter cells being from certain internal organs."

Of course the critics were right in later pointing out that this final statement should have been somewhat qualified, in view of the above-mentioned empirical principle. A single positive check and partial confirmation of a new procedure is insufficient to make this procedure the basis for a legal decision. But Cornu and Moriaud regarded this report as so definite that they no longer had the slightest doubts about charging Jaccoud with murder. Moriaud wanted only one further point checked. Even if the existence of human blood and liver cells had now been determined beyond the shadow of a doubt, as far as he was concerned, he still wondered whether the dagger could have removed such cells from Zumbach's body. Hegg's theory of the grooved blade did not seem to him quite convincing. Consequently, many subsequent experiments were carried out in Marburg, Basel, Liège, and Geneva. Hegg himself obtained liver from a slaughterhouse and made experiments with stabbing it, but did not succeed in reproducing the conditions of the murder, so that his work came to nothing. Undritz, however, hit on a plausible point. When in his research he made spot slides, using finely drawn glass rods, a large number of liver cells always remained clinging to his rod if the liver had previously been drained of blood. Zumbach had been bled by the shot which struck his aorta, and it was in this condition that the dagger had struck his liver. On the basis of his own experience with glass rods Undritz believed that even a completely smooth knife blade injuring a liver drained of its blood would have emerged with liver cells clinging to it. To prove his contention, Undritz undertook experiments with anesthetized monkeys whose aorta was opened so that they died of internal hemorrhage. He then drove a smooth stabbing instrument through a double layer of woolen cloth, cotton cloth, and the animal's skin into the bloodless liver, and drew it out again. Whole groups of liver cells clung to the blade.

This experiment removed the prosecution's last doubts. Seemingly no further attention was paid to the question of the presence or absence of liver cells at the sites of the stab holes in the clothing. As it turned out later, there was room for doubt on this matter, just as there was as to whether Jaccoud's dagger had really been the murder weapon. Moriaud, however, contented himself with the affidavit of Dr. Franz, with the cautious language of Im Obersteg, and above all with Hegg's statement in the "grand general deposition" in which he declared the curved dagger to be the murder weapon, supporting his opinion with the results of his own experiments.

On November 2 Cornu read the indictment to the Geneva arraignment court, which is the equivalent of the American grand jury. Jaccoud, leaning on the arm of a doctor, cried out despairingly: "Everything that has been done against me is nothing but a miserable infamy. I have affirmed my innocence. I shall continue to affirm it to the end of my days. . . . To the end of my days I shall continue to protest against this miscarriage of justice." On January 18, 1960, the trial of Pierre Jaccoud began in the Geneva Law Courts, under Presiding Judge Barde. The jury consisted of four housewives, a working woman, a jeweler, civil servants, artisans, and workingmen. Geneva's trial of the century had begun.

26

From the start the case rested on circumstantial evidence. Against a wall and on a table, neatly arranged by Hegg, all the prosecution's exhibits were laid out, from the bicycle to the coat, from the lost button to the dagger. For all the parade of witnesses who testified from January 18 to February 4, none of them offered anything new, no new alibi, no tangible defense for Jaccoud, but also no new and convincing incriminating evidence. No one had seen Jaccoud riding to the scene of the crime or back from it; no one could suggest a believable motive for the wanton murder Jaccoud was alleged to have committed. On the other hand, there were many elements in the prosecution's reconstruction of the crime that could not help raising doubts in the minds of unprejudiced observers. Was it really conceivable that a man of Jaccoud's type, armed with a pistol and a clumsy dagger, should have ridden on his bicycle to Plan-les-Ouates in the darkness? Was it conceivable that Jaccoud should have set out to take vengeance on a man who was no longer even the lover of his lost mistress, or to force him to give up incriminating documents? Was it conceivable that he should have struck down the old man, whom he had never met before, in such a brutal manner—or that he had diabolically decided to commit the kind of murder which would shift suspicion to Foreign Legionnaires?

Anything is possible in this world. The demons that inhabit a spiritually and physically racked human being can drive him to the wildest, the most incongruous of actions. But the doubts remained. All the more dramatically, therefore, those carefully arranged technical and scientific exhibits, which the participants in the trial saw every single day, moved into the foreground.

Between January 27 and January 29 Hegg, Undritz, Moureau, Alder, and Bock appeared in court, along with Naville, Franz, and Im Obersteg, to describe the structure of evidence which they had built or helped to build. For Jaccoud and his defense attorneys it must have been clear that the case rested almost entirely on the bloodstain analyses and on the assumption of the dagger's having been the murder weapon. The defense thought it was well armed. As surprise experts it had obtained the services of four medico-legal specialists and serologists who, the defense lawyers hoped, would be able to shake the foundations of Undritz' work. They, too, had had to go beyond the borders of Switzerland to find their experts in forensic medicine. Jaccoud's chief defender, Floriot, had called upon two Frenchmen. The first of these was Dr. Roger le Breton of Paris. Le Breton, a short man with a ready tongue, in his forties, could boast of considerable experience in the field of classical serological methods of investigation, and he had taken part in many criminal cases. But he was also one of those people who from egotism or ambition are sometimes drawn into undertakings for which they are inadequately prepared. The second defense expert was a man calculated to inspire respect by reason of his age: Professor Maurice Muller, Director of the Institute for Legal and Social Medicine in Lille. It was he who in 1946 had taken the first steps to improve the Uhlenhuth test. Muller was beyond ambition and vanity; he was firmly convinced, however, that forensic serology must be protected from the invasion of outsiders like Undritz.

Jaccoud's Geneva lawyer, Raymond Nicolet, had also combed the field for experts and had obtained the support of two Austrians. They were Professor Anton Werkgartner, the head of the Institute of Forensic Medicine in Graz, and his assistant Wolfgang Maresch. Werkgartner, like Muller, was a man in his sixties, a tall, white-haired, impressive figure. He was a representative of the famous Vienna school, and had done a great deal to develop Austrian forensic medicine. Way back in the twenties he had recognized the importance of blood group determinations for criminalistics and jurisprudence. Among other achievements, he had devised the micro-methods which allowed the Uhlenhuth test to be applied to extremely small bloodstains. His notable example had largely influenced Maresch, thirty years his junior, to devote himself to serological work.

None of these four experts was a hematologist or had any experience in the field of hematology comparable to Undritz', Alder's, or Bock's. Whether old or young, all the defense experts were so committed to the traditional school of medico-legal serology, with its blanket edict against microscopic blood type determinations, that they never thought to make a detailed study of this new microscopic technique. The defense had provided them with the first opinion of Hegg and Undritz, dated October 31, 1958, which, as we know, gave no very clear picture of the methods employed. From it, one might easily assume that Undritz had taken up the long-discredited microscopic methods of determining blood type. They thought that Undritz, as a hematologist, had stepped innocently into the field of criminalistics and committed the fateful error of treating bloodstains like fresh blood. They knew nothing about the surprise Undritz himself had felt on discovering that the leucocytes in dried blood could be brought out by proper staining and recognized. None of them had seen the photographs of Undritz' slides, let alone the slides themselves. Finally, none of them had a chance to test the procedure in practice. They rushed more or less unprepared into the defensive struggle. Yet at the beginning Floriot, who had a weakness for rhetoric, proclaimed that he would shoot Undritz down like a burning airplane.

On January 27 Undritz and Hegg, and later Moureau, Alder, and Bock, presented the results of their work to the court. It then became apparent how difficult, if not impossible, it was for simple jurors, as well as one-sidedly educated lawyers and judges, to understand the scientific questions at issue. The colored photographs of blood smears which Undritz projected onto a screen must have looked to jurors and jurists like novel textile patterns. That one group of pictures showed neutrophiles or neutrocytes, another liver cells, was a matter to be taken on faith. They believed or did not believe according to whether the scientists radiated an aura of reliability. Men like Undritz, Alder, Bock, and Moureau certainly had this aura.

Nevertheless, Floriot seemed convinced that his victory would be easy. Undritz' photographs were still in the projector when Floriot— dressed in a French advocate's robe and wearing the cross of the Legion of Honor—launched his first attack. He had a pile of ponderous books in front of him. "I see then," he said, "that you have applied the microscopic method." If he understood the procedure correctly, Undritz had scraped off bits of bloodstains and mixed them with serum to convert them to a condition once again like liquid blood. Was that correct?

"Yes," Undritz replied, "we carried out our analysis by adding human serum to the stains."

"Splendid," Floriot continued, "but then I must unfortunately inform you that all books on forensic medicine agree in stating that this method leads to gross errors and that it has therefore been discarded."

Undritz revealed the hematologist's unfamiliarity with the literature of forensic medicine by answering: "I should be very glad to see these interesting books."

Floriot replied sarcastically that it would be a pleasure to provide Undritz with them. Had Undritz never read the writings of Professor Derobert, one of the most celebrated holders of the Chair of Forensic Medicine in Paris? Here is what Derobert had to say in his textbook, *La Pratique médico-légale,* published in 1938, about microscopic investigation of blood. He read aloud: "The human or animal origin of blood cannot be determined by microscopic examination. In consideration of the extreme change of shape of the components of blood during the drying process, measurement of the red blood cells is an illusion."

If Undritz was unfamiliar with Derobert, Floriot continued, perhaps he was aware of Derobert's famous colleagues Thoinot and Balthazard. He had before him Thoinot's *Précis de médecine légale.* The book had appeared in Paris as long ago as 1913, but he did not think that red blood cells had changed since 1913. Thoinot stated distinctly: "Red blood cells can never be completely regenerated and are therefore usually distorted. . . . For that reason this procedure has been altogether abandoned." As for Balthazard— Floriot picked up the next book. In 1943 Balthazard had made the annihilating statement: "Although it is easy, so long as a spot is fresh, to distinguish the blood of mammals and birds . . . differentiating the blood of various mammals causes great difficulties. There are three procedures for this. One is based on measuring the average diameter of the red blood cells. . . . But modern research on the changes in the dimensions of the red blood cells . . . has led to total rejection of this procedure."

Floriot tossed Balthazard's work to the table and opened another book, by Professor Simonin. Simonin regarded microscopic examination of blood as so absurd that he did not even mention it seriously. "And this method," Floriot histrionically flung his words at Undritz, "which all experts have unequivocally condemned for fifty years as wrong and unreliable, is the method you have applied. That is the method which has led to Jaccoud's indictment for murder."

Floriot's attack was rhetorically effective, but a waste of good ammunition on the wrong target. If Floriot and his colleagues had taken the trouble to study Undritz' work, they would have realized that Undritz had based his conclusions on white blood cells; the red blood cells were altogether subsidiary in his studies.

Undritz therefore had a fairly easy time answering this volley, and earned applause when he declared, with the staunch faith of a discoverer, that he had not read the authorities in forensic medicine, but that their remarks on microscopic studies of blood belonged in a museum. Floriot obviously did not understand Undritz' reply. He merely realized that he had somehow been worsted, and retreated behind the assertion that experts for the defense would follow him, men who knew more about this field.

Next morning, January 28, the first of Floriot's experts, Le Breton, took the stand. After his defeat the day before, Floriot is said to have planned Le Breton's tactics more carefully. The idea was for Le Breton to take the stand, vehemently attack Undritz and the other experts for two hours, and sow distrust and confusion among the jurors. Then he was to leave, on the pretext that he had to take a plane to Paris for his afternoon lecture. He would thus avoid a possibly dangerous exchange with Undritz and the other prosecution experts.

Carrying a suitcase full of photographs and photographic slides, Le Breton entered the room, a small, rather stocky figure. He solemnly greeted the presiding judge and the jurors. Looking directly at Moureau, Alder, and Bock, he intoned: "You have been called to lend the weight of your names to a method. This method, I contend, is full of perils when it is applied to forensic medicine. I have come to Geneva to point out these perils to you, lest errors cause a miscarriage of justice."

These were portentous words, and Le Breton enjoyed the close attention of the entire courtroom. For all his tendency toward theatricality, he undeniably possessed the gift of expressing himself in a way that laymen could understand. He painted a broad picture of the tried and true methods of testing bloodstains. He even managed to explain the involutions of the Coombs test, which was really a feat. Only then did he proceed to the case at hand. In a loud, strong voice he declared that it filled him with alarm to learn that out of thirty bloodstains, only one had been proved to contain human blood by the Coombs test, which was itself a very new technique and by no means foolproof. The Coombs test had not, he emphasized, shown human blood in any of the other stains, and particularly not in those alleged to be mixed with liver cells. Thus the whole structure of the prosecution rested solely on Undritz' method. "I have been working with all these questions for twenty years," Le Breton told the jurors, "and they are so difficult and so fraught with responsibility that one seldom attains complete certainty. Do you have complete certainty when you form a judgment on the basis of a process that is not yet one year old and that, apparently, only one man can carry out? Have you the right to construct a verdict on such data? Even if the procedure should prove a valid one, it must first be tested for a long time before a human being can be condemned on the basis of it."

Here was the crucial point of the whole bloodstain question. Le Breton might have driven it home to the jurors, had he only taken a bit more time for this part of his argument. Instead, he rushed on to what was perhaps more emotionally satisfying to him: a full-scale demonstration of Undritz' methods and results. These were, he said, the dangerous escapades of a hematologist in forensic medicine, and as such absolutely nonsensical.

Ignorant, perhaps, of Floriot's misadventure of the preceding day, Le Breton began by quoting the experts in forensic medicine whom Floriot had already cited. He next presented his own transparencies of animal and human blood, in order to show that microscopic discrimination was impossible. This, too, was ill-advised since even the jurors could perceive that these pictures would not bear comparison with Undritz' clean photographs. They were simply poor, and moreover showed a lack of skill in the hematological technique of staining. But Le Breton seemed totally undaunted. He went on to disparage the use of natural blood plasma in the preparation of Undritz' suspensions. Undritz might very well have introduced the human blood cells he had discovered under the microscope with this very plasma. "My specialty is forensic medicine," he concluded dramatically, "but I am also a hematologist. . . . Monsieur Undritz is a hematologist. I shudder to think that he is preparing medico-legal depositions, You, ladies and gentlemen, are here to fulfill the duties of free citizens in a free democracy. . . . It is the duty of a good judge to doubt when doubt is called for."

This was imprudent and improper interference, on the part of a foreigner, with Geneva justice. Nevertheless, Le Breton might still have escaped the final débâcle if the prearranged plan had gone through. Le

Breton turned to the presiding judge and said that he was finished with his testimony and had time at most to answer a few questions; his plane for Paris was leaving at eleven and would not wait for him. He was visibly unnerved when Judge Barde replied that it was impossible, he could not be allowed to depart without a detailed discussion with Undritz or Moureau. Le Breton threw a look of appeal to Floriot, and declared that his future career was in danger if he did not arrive in Paris on time. Judge Barde refused to be impressed; he ordered a private plane held in readiness to take Le Breton back to Paris. Thus Le Breton was forced to enter into the discussion which was to be his undoing. When Undritz and Moureau set forth the real principle of Undritz' work, he had to admit after a brief debate that he had not grasped these principles. But he would not yet surrender. Instead, he raised the question of whether leucocytes could be distinguished in bloodstains. From his suitcase he produced a book which he passed around, explaining that this book contained colored prints of microscope slides on which leucocytes could be recognized. Let the Undritz photographs be compared with the excellent pictures in this book, and it would be evident how little they meant.

The courtroom rocked with laughter when Moureau called Le Breton's attention to the fact that the book in his hands had been written by Undritz, it being no other than the *Sandoz Hematological Plates*. Le Breton had failed to notice the author. From this point on the arrogant expert exposed more and more of his inadequacies. He had to admit that he was unfamiliar with differences between human and animal leucocytes. He asserted that the leucocytes in Undritz' pictures could not be recognized as leucocytes because the granula in their cell bodies could not be completely counted. He obviously did not know that in some circumstances hematologists count the segments of the nuclei, not the granula. He took refuge behind the assertion that he could not see neutrophiles in Undritz' photographs because the granula were not visible. Apparently he was unaware that staining with hematoxylin Hansen-Biebrich scarlet dye, which had been used in the blood smear in question, did not stain the granula of neutrophiles; it served exclusively to make the nuclei visible. Again, he was apparently unaware that neutrophiles could be recognized in spite of this. They could not be mistaken for eosinophiles because with this type of staining the latter turned bright red. In the end, Le Breton did only disservice to the cause of Jaccoud.

Despite the sorry showing his experts had made so far, Floriot continued to bring on his cast. Maurice Muller avoided, with the dignity of age, all boastfulness and ill-considered detraction of the opponents. But he too, experienced though he was in forensic medicine and serology, proved to lack the knowledge of hematology so vital in this case. He sounded impressive when he stated: "Dr. Undritz is a hematologist of international reputation. . . . But it is my duty to declare that hematology, which deals with fresh blood, stands worlds apart from forensic medicine, which concerns itself with bloodstains that have been subjected to the altering effects of air, light, heat, and cold." But Muller too had not seen a single one of Undritz' slides in their original state. He pronounced dogmas; when asked whether he had undertaken any practical tests, he was forced to say that he had not. And his guarded statement that he could not recognize liver cells with absolute certainty in Undritz' photographs was overwhelmed by Alder's unequivocal reply: "When I see a canary, I say: 'That is a canary.' When I see a different bird, I say: 'That is a different bird.' As far as these cells are concerned, it is the same thing." Muller also sacrificed much of his credibility when he raised the question of the dagger. This question might well have been more central than the whole matter of bloodstains and liver cells: for it was open to doubt whether a dagger of this size and shape could possibly have been the murder weapon. But Muller did not succeed in making the cogent points, and seemed only to be caviling again.

Anton Werkgartner and Wolfgang Maresch of Graz had no greater success. They too were inadequately prepared, and neither Werkgartner's dignity nor Maresch's sprightliness could save them from the consequences. Werkgartner stated: "When we stabbed the liver of a human corpse, we brought to light only three liver cells. Liver cells are as difficult to find as oranges in the forests of the Vosges Mountains." It was a striking image, which even a court interpreter could translate into forceful French. But the metaphor rebounded against him when Undritz, Bock, Alder, and Moureau showed, by means of Undritz' photographs and their numerous experiments, that stab wounds in the liver drained of blood brought out so many cells that they "piled up like oranges in a Sicilian orange grove." Undritz, who until this point had preserved his composure and courtesy, burst out angrily against people who would pass judgment on matters they did not understand.

By the time the session of January 28 was nearing its end, Floriot had to recognize that the attempt to discredit the blood tests had failed. Whatever the jurors may actually have understood about the details of the scientific explanations, one thing had not escaped them: Undritz,

Moureau, and the other prosecution experts had done practical work, while the defense had offered only theories. The jury therefore inclined to trust Undritz, Moureau, Alder, and Bock where scientific views collided, even though the dissension among the experts may have left some doubts in the minds of one or another of them.

Six days later they found Jaccoud guilty, not of murder but of manslaughter. The court sentenced him to seven years in the penitentiary. Verdict and sentence were clearly a compromise that revealed a degree of uncertainty. The intriguing question was what link in the chain of circumstantial evidence had aroused this uncertainty.

According to what leaked through to the public, the jurors had been least troubled by the proofs based on the bloodstains. These had been accepted. Most of the skepticism centered around the questions of motive and the reconstruction of the crime, even after Cornu's last eloquent appeal to the jury: "You must answer the question of Jaccoud's guilt with a strong yes. This coward who murdered an old man one spring evening must receive his punishment!"

27

Causes célèbres have frequently shaken the fundamentals of criminology, but few cases have had so powerful an effect as that of Jaccoud. The simple jurors may have taken the bloodstain analyses on faith, but for the experts there was too much that was new and controversial about those techniques for the findings to go unchallenged.

Every professional had to face certain questions. Had the structure of forensic serology so many weak spots? Were the traditional methods so superannuated that blood tests of this importance could fall into the hands of an outsider, even one so gifted in his own field? And just what value should be attached to that outsider's work? Were the attacks by Le Breton, Muller, Werkgartner, and Maresch valid or not? Would Undritz' work, if carefully investigated, fall apart or would it prove a real innovation with promise for the future?

Even before the serologists began wrestling with these questions on their own, they were drawn into a crusade. A group in Bern denounced the Jaccoud case as another Dreyfus affair. A Bernese doctor named Sutermeister, a fanatic by nature, took the lead in this campaign, and began collecting money and evidence to force a review of the verdict. Sutermeister was filled with the zeal of an inveterate reformer, and moreover was convinced that Jaccoud had been made the victim of sinister political intrigues. Of necessity, a large part of his campaign was directed against Undritz and Hegg. Letters, inquiries, requests for statements, were sent to medico-legal experts and serologists in Europe and America. One went to Wiener in New York, another to Coombs in Cambridge. Sutermeister himself set out on a journey to collect indictments of Undritz and his work. No sooner would he receive a statement from one or another scientist than he would transform the most cautious remarks into a denunciation, which he then spread abroad in a series of highly unsound articles, pamphlets, and letters. In letters to Undritz, for example, he wrote: "If what internationally known cytologists say about your liver cells is confirmed, you must be prepared to be sued by Jaccoud to the tune of at least a million francs for damages. . . . There is only one way to avoid this disaster: to withdraw your deposition before the review begins." Or: "I should alert you to the fact that we have confidential evidence that the whole Jaccoud affair was a frame-up. You know, too, that the Coombs test was . . . falsified." Or: "Your liver cells . . . are in fact quite certainly salami cells from sandwiches, since Jaccoud took the coat with him in his car and used it as a picnic blanket. . . . If you are really a scientist, you yourself should join us in demanding the review. It will be a world-wide scandal." To Alder he wrote: "After having completed my European tour of prominent cytologists in Germany, England, France, and Austria, and everywhere aroused nothing but amusement in regard to Undritz' 'liver cells,' I should like to ask you . . . the questions which should have been asked in court." Here there followed an assortment of random questions. "Moreover, we have long known the real murderer. . . . I am writing this to you not as an emotional appeal, but because the Supreme Court has a ruling to the effect that an expert who does not rescind an opinion recognized as false before the resumption of the trial can . . . be punished with imprisonment of up to five years. We will show no more mercy to the experts than you showed to Jaccoud."

Thanks to Sutermeister's fanaticism, at any rate, enough funds were collected for the case to be placed in the hands of sound Bernese and Genevan lawyers, Horace Mastronardi and Roland Steiner. But Sutermeister's excesses also tended to frighten away respectable medico-legal specialists and serologists who otherwise might have consented to check the blood test methods that had been applied in the Jaccoud case. Perhaps Sutermeister would have failed completely on this score had not Le Breton still been smarting from the defeat at Geneva. He was now haunting every congress on forensic medicine hoping to persuade his colleagues to pronounce a condemnation of Undritz. Maresch, too, was calling for a check of Undritz' methods in order to vindicate the points he and Werkgartner had raised at Geneva. Moreover, all scientific societies are prone to condemn the work of outsiders. Thus the ground was favorable for a general denunciation of Undritz.

But it soon turned out that the integrity of scientists was more powerful than their emotions. At the medico-legal congress in Graz in October 1960, and at the Congress of International Forensic Medicine in Vienna, no condemnation of Undritz was forthcoming. Italian scientists who had tried out Undritz' method of microscopic blood testing offered a cautious confirmation of his work. They regarded the differentiation of leucocytes as no illusion. They concluded, however, that the method, because of its dependence on special knowledge of hematology, could not be accorded "the value of a standard method for the general diagnosis of bloodstains."

In May 1962 Jaccoud's defense attorneys asked Professor of Pathology Rüttner of Zurich University to check Undritz' slides. But Rüttner's report was hardly any comfort to them. "The cells shown in Geneva do look like liver cells," it concluded. "It may be added that . . . it is impossible to prove that they are not liver cells. Dried liver cells, as has been shown in our own experiments, last for months and can be recognized by Undritz' method."

Thus the first outcry had given way to sober consideration. Undritz' method of microscopic examination of blood was indeed something new, not to be equated with the procedures that had been abandoned around the turn of the century. This did not alter the fundamental principle that single tests of a new method could not be sufficient for legal certainty.

From 1961–62 on, new methods of determining type and group of blood spread from England, Sweden, and France over Europe and the world. Perhaps it was not by accident that Maurice Muller in Lille and Wolfgang Maresch (by now Werkgartner's successor as Professor of Forensic Medicine in Graz) made decisive contributions toward preparing the way for these new methods, which bore the mysterious-sounding names "Ouchterlony" and "Mixed Agglutination." Their development undoubtedly marked as significant an advance in the history of serology as had the discovery and dissemination of the Uhlenhuth, Lattes, and Holzer tests.

28

From 1961 to 1965 there were many cases which lent themselves to the new techniques. Among these was a crime that took place in the tiny South German village of Reichelshofen on May 10, 1962. At the intersection of two highways lay the humble property of a cooper named Friedrich Lindörfer, an equally humble man in his late fifties. The ground floor of the house consisted of a kitchen, living room, and bedroom, a narrow threshing room, and, on the side toward the courtyard, Lindörfer's workshop and a barn with attached pigsty. Lindörfer himself lived on the ground floor with his wife Elis and two grown sons who worked at outside jobs. Upstairs were three more rooms and an attic. The doors of the rooms opened onto a small landing reached by a staircase from the front hall. One of these upper rooms was occupied by Lindörfer's daughter Erika, her husband and small children. The other two were less heavily used, belonging as they did to Lina Lindörfer, the cooper's unmarried fifty-two-year-old sister, a seamstress afflicted from birth with a disease of the hip joint. Lindörfer had been the eldest son, and when he took over the property from his parents he had promised to leave the upper floor to his invalid sister for her lifetime.

On the evening of May 11 Anna Eckel, a friend of Lina Lindörfer's, came to the house to help with some sewing. To her surprise she found the door to Lina's combined living room and kitchen slightly ajar. The part of the lock in the door jamb was wrenched from the wood, as though someone had forced his way in. The room was empty, as was the bedroom. This was all the more surprising since unfinished sewing and a cold meal were on the table, and Lina Lindörfer was noted for her compulsive neatness.

Anna Eckel was still standing at the door when Friedrich Lindörfer in his workclothes came up the stairs and gave her so sour a look that she did not dare to ask about Lina. She went to an acquaintance in the house next door. The neighbor was also well aware that Lina never left her apartment without cleaning up, and always pinned a note to the door saying when she would be back. She had not noticed Lina going out. Later, curiosity impelled her to go across to the Lindörfer house. She asked Lindörfer if he knew where his sister was, and what had happened to the lock on her door.

The cooper seemed altogether surprised. He went up to examine the lock and insisted that the door had been properly locked until Anna Eckel arrived. She alone could have broken it. Lina had left the house about two o'clock and got into a car with someone he did not know—he had happened to step out of the workshop just in time to see her leave. That was all he knew, and it was none of his affair. Everyone knew Lina was hell-bent on finding herself a husband. She'd spent money enough on letters to *Heim und Welt* (a weekly noted for its lonely-hearts advertisements). Maybe she'd got someone on her hook and had gone off to "try him out."

Possibly the affair would have gone unnoticed for a long time if Anna Eckel had not heard what Lindörfer had said about the lock. She took offense. On May 21 she appeared at the nearest station of the Bavarian State Police in Rothenburg and made a complaint against Lindörfer for slander. Police Sergeant Pfliegl heard her, and then set out for Reichelshofen. He was quite familiar with the Lindörfer place. Lina Lindörfer herself had frequently appealed for police protection, claiming that her brother and his family were persecuting her. They wanted to drive her out, she had said, in order to have more room for themselves. Pfliegl had found that there was in fact a great deal of friction in the confined quarters of the cooper's house. Lindörfer and his family were dreadfully crowded. On the other hand, Lina was quarrelsome and noted for her sharp tongue—a spiteful, unhappy old maid. That, at any rate, was the neighbors' view of her, while Lindörfer was generally regarded as a sound, hard-working, thrifty man. As far as the State Police station in Rothenburg was concerned, the Lindörfer ménage was like several dozen others, subject to the same problems and the same bickerings.

When Pfliegl arrived in Reichelshofen, Lindörfer was diligently pounding away at his barrels. He repeated what he had already told the neighbor woman and complained about "these womenfolk who make nothing but trouble." Pfliegl inspected the door and decided to forget the matter until Lina Lindörfer returned. It was June 3 before he learned that Lina's apartment was still standing empty. Once again he drove out to Reichelshofen. And this time he also inspected Lina's room. Its untidiness, to be sure, struck him as strange. But he contented himself with asking Friedrich Lindörfer to write to all their relatives and find out whether Lina was with any of them. Another week passed. Finally, on June 11, the State Police filed a missing-persons notice with the Bavarian State Criminal Office in Munich. Shortly afterward, however, a family in the village of Steinsfeld reported that they had seen Lina at a church fair, so the missing-persons notice was withdrawn. The police in Rothenburg were still inclined not to take the affair seriously. But when the Steinsfeld family on July 4 discovered that the woman they thought was Lina was someone else, a second missing-persons notice was sent to Munich. A day later the police received orders to check whether Lina Lindörfer had taken a sizable sum of money with her on her trip. On July 6 several policemen made the first thorough search of her rooms. They opened a money-box containing savings bank books amounting to about 13,000 marks, and 234 marks in cash. No money had been withdrawn from the savings accounts for a long time. It seemed peculiar that Lina Lindörfer should have left home leaving most of her money behind. At last, on July 9, the criminal division of the Bavarian State Police in Ansbach took over the case. Inspector Heberger was assigned to it.

Heberger and two other detectives, Klug and Burckert, first undertook the usual steps in such cases. They questioned everyone in Reichelshofen itself, beginning with the Lindörfers and going on to the people for whom Lina had sewed. No one had seen her since May 10. Heberger, too, at first accepted the probability that the old maid had gone traveling. If thoughts of a crime ever entered his mind, he assumed that it had taken place during her travels. The Bavarian State Criminal Office sent bulletins to the central offices for missing persons in the other states of West Germany. Newspapers in the whole region of Central Franconia published search notices. The name and description of Lina Lindörfer appeared in the "wanted" and "sought" list put out by the German Federal Police. On July 19 a teletype message went out to all police headquarters in the German Federal Republic. Swiftly, the search widened. The police appropriated all of Lina Lindörfer's back issues of the newspaper *Heim und Welt* and drew up a list of all the ads the spinster had underlined. The addresses of the applicants were obtained from the newspaper, and cautious inquiries were made in their home towns. The neighborhood of Reichelshofen was searched by squads of police with dogs. The idea that Lina Lindörfer might have been killed by the stranger with whom she had driven away, and her body thrown into the water somewhere near Reichelshofen, finally led to a search of streams and lakes with rubber boats and divers. But all this massive effort came to nothing.

Around this time a suspicion began to grow in Heberger, although at first he felt it to be absurd. When he carefully considered the various statements of the inhabitants of Reichelshofen, he realized that there were some which cast a somewhat sinister light on the situation of the spinster within the family. Her sisters, who occasionally came home for a visit, commented that their brother Friedrich had wanted to obtain possession of Lina's rooms at all costs. Since he barely made enough to live on with his cooper's work and tiny farmstead, he feared he would have to pay Lina off to leave if she did not go voluntarily. He had therefore tried to oust her by making life as unpleasant as possible for her. He had resorted to such tricks as locking up the woodshed, so that she could not get wood, putting her bicycle out in the rain, and taking over her patch of garden. He had been heard to utter threats, such as: "When the time comes, I'll get you out. You'll be glad to go." Among Lina Lindörfer's papers Heberger found notes she had made recording the quarrels with her brother. Among them were such items as: "February 5, 1960. He said . . . he'll knock out all my teeth." Or: "March 5, 1961 . . . wants to throw out my things." Was it possible that the search operation throughout West Germany came to nothing because the secret of Lina's disappearance was to be sought not far away, but in the Lindörfer house itself? Was it conceivable that the stunted, rather shy, awkward cooper knew the answer to the mystery?

Heberger once more looked through the statements by Lindörfer, his wife, his sons, and the neighbors about Lina's departure. No one but Lindörfer had seen Lina leave. Everybody merely repeated what Lindörfer himself had told them at various times. And Heberger stumbled upon a good many contradictions. The cooper had told Police Sergeant Pfliegl that he could not describe the stranger or the car in which Lina had departed. But in the succeeding days he had given many descriptions. In one story the car had stood by the brewery, in another on the road to Adelshofen, then on the road to Endsee, then in front of the smithy, finally at the intersection of a small street called Kappelweg. According to one account, the stranger had driven off in a gray car; another person had heard it was green, still another said he had heard the car was yellow. Lina was in one version dressed in gray, without her coat, but in another account was wearing a light-colored coat, with a kerchief on her head.

Of course it was conceivable that Lindörfer with his limited mentality had muddled the story. But it was equally possible that he had been telling a lie from the first, and had gone on lying, forgetting what he had told the person before. Was it possible that Lina Lindörfer had never left the house? Could the cooper have done away with his sister whom he could not manage to drive out of the house?

Heberger had the remains of food in Lina Lindörfer's kitchen sent to the technical section of the Bavarian State Criminal Office in Munich. He asked for a toxicological study. But none of the known poisons were found. Heberger then searched the apartment for signs of a struggle, and looked particularly hard for traces of blood. But he and his men had neither the means nor the experience to conduct a really systematic investigation. To be sure, the police noticed several dark spots that could be blood on the lid of a well shaft. The stained bits of wood were cut out. A pair of Lindörfer's work trousers and shoes also seemed suspicious. On July 21 Heberger had the linoleum removed from the floor of Lina's apartment. All these materials were sent to Munich. But blood was nowhere found. Heberger and his men even moved Lindörfer's entire dung heap, in the vague hope of finding some trace of malefaction, but this labor, too, proved vain. At the end of July the search around the Lindörfer property was abandoned and the police once again concentrated on the possibility that Lina might have vanished or been killed somewhere outside of Reichelshofen.

Only when week after week had passed without results did Heberger return to his alternate theory. On August 23, a whole month later, he and his men descended once again on the grim old house at the intersection of the highways. Heberger was again looking for blood. He had with him an analysis lamp whose usefulness for the purpose had long been disputed. For the first time it seemed to him that he could detect a trace of nervousness beneath Lindörfer's stolid manner. But after hours of going about with their lamp, the detectives found no suspicious traces.

Lina Lindörfer was not the only person who had vanished without a trace in West Germany. Tens of thousands of persons were constantly disappearing in the same manner. In reaction to the excessive regimentation of the Nazi era, the Germans with characteristic lack of insight had swung far in the opposite direction and were now committed to exaggerated freedom and the abolition of as much control as possible. There were innumerable gaps in the system of registration and search; various people found those gaps only too convenient. The Federal Republic had become a favorite asylum for international criminals. The situation was pungently described by a French gang leader: "The best place to hide out is in a country with a guilty conscience." Was there any chance that Heberger's search for the missing Lina Lindörfer would succeed, with so little to go by and the odds against it so great? For several days he was ready to give up on this case. But he kept remembering that trace of nervousness Lindörfer had shown during that last visit. Could it mean that the house did in fact conceal traces of a dreadful secret, which would require a much more systematic search to uncover? At this point Heberger recalled a recent lecture he had heard by an assistant of the Erlangen Institute of Forensic Medicine, on modern methods for detecting blood. The speaker, Dr. Lothar Lautenbach, had argued that the search for bloodstains ought to be set up as a special discipline involving direct collaboration between detectives and scientists.

On August 27 Heberger decided to telephone the Institute of Forensic Medicine in Erlangen and ask for help. If the people there could send a serologist to Reichelshofen, he would try to obtain a search warrant from the state prosecutor's office allowing him to go through the cooper's house from cellar to roof. If this search proved vain, he would have to give up.

29

The Institute of Forensic Medicine and Criminalistics in Erlangen had taken the lead in Germany in trying out the Ouchterlony test and the Mixed Agglutination test.

In September 1958, when the Jaccoud affair was running its course, Maurice Muller had addressed a congress of medico-legal experts in Zurich on "Identification of Biological Products by Immunochemical Methods." He gave the first complete account of the technique by which the Swedish scientist A. Ouchterlony of Göteborg had succeeded in demonstrating the presence of human or animal protein in bloodstains with far greater certitude than ever before, and in overcoming the problems still besetting the Uhlenhuth test. His method was so simple that one had to wonder why it was not discovered sooner. Readers of Swedish scientific journals could have read of his experiments with agar-agar, a gelatinlike material from certain seaweeds (known simply as agar

213

gel), as early as 1949. But eight years passed before Muller and several other French scientists made use of these experiments. Maurice Muller was the first to alert European serologists to Ouchterlony's work. But general interest was not aroused until Ouchterlony's articles on allergy research appeared in a major New York journal.

Ouchterlony had hit on the idea of employing agar gel as a kind of clarifying buffer between the bloodstain solutions and the corresponding anti-serums. He placed agar gel in a warm, fluid state on a small plate of glass. After cooling, a layer of gelatin about a tenth of an inch thick has formed on the plate. With a round metal cylinder one quarter inch in diameter holes are punched in this layer. One hole is made in the center, with four more grouped around it each at a distance of one half inch from the central hole. In order to test a bloodstain for its human or animal origin, a solution of the stain is dropped into the center hole. It does not matter whether or not the solution is clear. The surrounding holes are filled with a variety of anti-serums, both anti-human and anti-animal. If the agar gel plate is placed in a moist chamber at 98 degrees Fahrenheit for twenty-four to thirty-six hours, plainly visible lines form between the central opening and the hole which contains the anti-serum to the type of blood in that opening. The protein precipitation in the gel makes these lines so obvious that there is no danger of misinterpretation. The method can be reversed, with an anti-serum in the central hole, this form of the experiment permitting a larger number of tests to be carried out at once. A control solution for the anti-serum, containing the type of blood it should be effective against, and in addition a solution of the bloodstain to be tested and a solution of the underlying material can be placed in the outside holes. The test takes longer than the Uhlenhuth test, but it is more precise and not subject to defects. Uriel, Scheidegger, and Grabar of the Pasteur Institute showed that the precipitation lines in the agar gel could be stained and then photographed, thus serving as indestructible evidence.

About the same time other French scientists, Hartmann and Toilliez, developed a technique for applying the Ouchterlony test to extremely minute bloodstains. Instead of a glass plate they used the slide of a microscope for the whole test; the punched holes were of a diameter of only one sixteenth of an inch. Extremely small stains and quantities of serum sufficed to make the protein precipitation visible. Serologists who had been troubled by the limits of the Uhlenhuth reaction and had therefore taken up the complicated Coombs test turned with relief to "the Ouchterlony." Its sensitivity was not less than that of the Coombs test, and the advantages in ease and sureness were enormous.

An even speedier new method had been developed. In 1960 the periodical *Nature* published two papers by Stuart S. Kind, Principal Scientific Officer of the Department of Biology at the Home Office Forensic Science Laboratory in Harrogate, England, on a hitherto unknown method for determining blood groups in stains, which he called the Mixed Agglutination method. A year later another paper on the same subject followed. Its author was none other than R. R. A. Coombs of Cambridge, collaborating with Barbara Dodd of the Department of Forensic Medicine at London Hospital Medical College. This paper bore the title "Possible Application of the Principle of Mixed Agglutination in the Identification of Blood Stains," and was concerned with a method of blood grouping likewise founded on the Mixed Agglutination technique.

In order to understand this technique, we must return to 1939. At that time Alexander S. Wiener and his associate Herrman in New York had carried out experiments with the agent of pneumonia, pneumococcus Type 14. In the course of their work they made a curious observation. These pneumococci, which according to accepted ideas had no relationship to human blood groups, absorbed human anti-A and anti-B serums in exactly the same way as blood cells of Groups A and B did their respective serums. Even more interesting was the following circumstance: pneumococci were mixed with anti-A serum and absorbed the anti-A substance in this serum. If the same pneumococci were then mixed with A cells, the cells were nevertheless agglutinated. In other words, the anti-A or anti-B substances in human blood serum seemed to have the capacity for double absorption or, chemically speaking, for forming bonds to two substances. They could serve as links between bacterial cells and blood cells, if the bacterial cells contained the same group factor as the blood cells. The Second World War had prevented further work in this direction, so that Wiener's first suggestion was not implemented by practical work.

In 1955–56 Coombs hit upon the same phenomenon. He had been working with skin transplantation. There were frequently difficulties in the adaptation of the transplanted skin which was used to cover skin defects. It occurred to Coombs to study whether the epidermal cells might not also contain grouping substances which perhaps interfered with healing. In the course of the work he and his colleagues Bedford and Rouillard hit on the discovery that Wiener had made in 1939. Like pneumococci, skin cells also possessed blood group characteristics corresponding to the blood group of the person concerned. According to their blood grouping they absorbed the antibodies of anti-A or anti-B serums, and these in turn formed bonds with the corresponding red blood cells and agglutinated them. It was as though the antibodies possessed two arms, one of which clung to the skin cell and the other to the blood cell. In order to determine what group a skin cell belonged to, it sufficed to mix it with anti-A and anti-B serum. After waiting for absorption of the antibody, the superfluous serum was removed and blood cells of known group were added. Depending on whether A or B cells were agglutinated, the skin cell contained A or B blood group characteristics. Coombs dubbed this curious process "Mixed Agglutination," and pointed out that it might well have applications to criminalistic serology.

This hint was disregarded until Stuart S. Kind took it up in 1960. It occurred to Kind to treat dried flakes or particles of blood which were firmly united with cloth as if they were unknown cells. He analyzed them for blood grouping in the way that Coombs had done for skin cells. At first Kind was interested only in finding out whether the process was possible at all. If so, the rather elaborate procedure associated with the Holzer absorption test could be avoided. It would no longer be necessary to determine whether the effectiveness of anti-A or anti-B serum had been diminished. It would suffice to add the serums to unknown particles of blood, wait for the absorption, and then test with known blood cells to see which were agglutinated. If A, then the unknown blood group was A; if B, the unknown group was B. If both were absorbed and agglutinated, the blood group would be AB.

Kind's method was to place fibers of bloodstained clothing in the wells of dimpled slides. These he treated with boiling "McIlvaine buffer," a solution of chemicals which fixed the forms of the cells. As in the Holzer test, he added anti-A and anti-B serums and let them absorb for two or three hours. Then he washed away the excess serum with saline solution and added his test blood cells. Under the microscope he looked for agglutination. Once he had perfected this technique, Kind obtained a hundred artificially dried samples of blood from the Regional Blood Transfusion Laboratory in Sheffield and demonstrated that his method was extremely reliable.

When Barbara Dodd took up the same method a year later, she had a further aim in mind. The Mixed Agglutination procedure struck her as a promising approach to stains too small to be investigated by any of the existing techniques, even those visible only under the microscope. From bloodstains on cloth she teased out single textile fibers no longer than eight one-thousandth of an inch. These tiny fibers provided a firm support for the equally tiny quantity of blood that clung to them. In order to increase the firmness, Barbara Dodd treated the fibers with acetic acid and crystal violet. She succeeded in washing her specimens with rabbit serum neutralized by heating, in order to remove the surplus fixing chemicals. Then she added anti-A and anti-B serums, each in the minute quantity of four one-thousandth of an inch. She waited up to twenty-four hours, then washed away the surplus serum and carried out the last step of adding known blood cells. She was able to observe agglutination or non-agglutination under a phase contrast microscope; with magnifications of from one hundred to four hundred the slightest details could be discerned. By this technique she succeeded in obtaining a blood group determination from stains which contained barely 1 milligram (one thirty-thousandth of an inch) of dried blood. In Group O stains she also obtained a reading by using anti-H solution from the plant *Ulex europaeus*.

Barbara Dodd's experiments were of great interest to another woman chemist at Scotland Yard's Metropolitan Police Laboratory. Miss Pereira was a practical laboratory worker, and she therefore sought methods that would yield dependable results with a minimum of complicated laboratory procedure. She set about rationalizing the method of Kind and Dodd. She found that a number of the steps were superfluous, in particular the treatment with fixing chemicals. Ultimately, she had reduced the whole process to a series of simple steps that could be performed directly in dimpled slides. First she placed a tiny bloodstained thread into one cavity of a slide. An unstained control thread was placed alongside it, in another dimpled slide. At once she added a drop of anti-A and anti-B serums. Then the thread was teased out into fibers under the liquid. After an hour the serum was removed with pipettes and the fibers were washed three or four times with drops of saline solution. Very fine pipettes had to be used to avoid sucking up the fibers along with the solution. A single drop of a suspension of known red blood cells in a solution of bovine albumen was added. The slides were placed in a high humidity chamber at 125 degrees Fahrenheit for ten minutes. After cooling, they were allowed to stand for two hours. They could then be examined under a microscope for agglutination. It was always thrilling to see how the test cells clung to the fibers as if attracted by a magnet. In her report Miss Pereira commented: "We have tested the method with stains of A, A_2, B, AB, A_2B and O blood with admirable results. We have also examined the MN groups and obtained clear-cut differentiation. . . . Of the Rhesus factors D can be detected. . . . Work . . . is progressing with these and other systems. It may be pointed out that the method works satisfactorily for saliva and semen as well as blood. . . . This method will not completely supersede the classical method. But in cases where the quantity of blood is too small for complete examination by the classical method . . . the proposed method should be adopted."

In August 1962 the Mixed Agglutination test was well on its way to acceptance by all the serological laboratories of the world. In Europe the Hungarian scientist Budvary had subjected it to careful study and published a favorable opinion on it. Maresch likewise hailed it. He pointed out that the usefulness of the technique was by no means limited to bloodstains on fibers. All other bloodstains, whether found on automobile paint, glass, paper, or other surfaces, could be transferred to a fiber support by wiping them onto tiny particles of linen on a glass rod. Difficulties were found only with bloodstains on nylon fibers. Because of its smoothness, the nylon did not hold the stain, and the test cells were not attracted to it.

As it happened, the Erlangen Institute was trying out the Mixed Agglutination test at the very time that Detective Sergeant Heberger telephoned for assistance on August 27. Its director, Emil Weinig, was only too happy to participate in a case that might prove the value of close collaboration between the investigating detective and serologists at the scene of a crime. He therefore deputized his assistant Lautenbach to go to Reichelshofen as soon as a search warrant was obtained. He also recommended to Heberger that provision should be made for conducting the search at night as well as by day. If it should prove necessary to search sizable areas for bloodstains, it would probably be essential to use the chemiluminescence technique, which depended on darkness.

30

Shortly after eight o'clock in the evening on August 29, Lautenbach and an Institute technician, equipped with every possible device for finding bloodstains, arrived in Reichelshofen. Lautenbach was a slight, dark-haired man in his thirties, who had come to West Germany from

Thuringia (in East Germany) in 1953 to study medicine. During his internship at the Surgical Clinic in Erlangen he had helped out at autopsies in order to earn money, and in this way had "fallen into" forensic medicine. His doctoral thesis dealt with the transformations of metallic poisons in cadavers, and this largely unexplored territory continued to fascinate him. But in addition he had made a thorough study of all the subjects that fell within Weinig's province, from autopsy and general investigation of clues to forensic serology.

Darkness was falling when Heberger and his men arrived at the cooper's house. This time they were accompanied by the District Attorney. That the District Attorney wanted to see for himself how a search for bloodstains was conducted had its significance. It indicated how little had been done in this respect, as late as 1962, in the more remote regions of the German Federal Republic.

Lindörfer opened the door, and he became extremely wrought up when he was handed the search warrant. He quickly regained his self-control, however, and assumed his usual attitude of indifference. In the street the inhabitants of Reichelshofen gathered, and for the first time began grumbling about the police who apparently had nothing better to do than to go on endlessly pestering peaceful citizens.

In this atmosphere Lautenbach and the assistant set to work with a small luminol spray apparatus and a flashlight. Lautenbach quickly realized, from his general impression of the house, that the most he could hope for, this first time, was a general survey. As experience had taught him, he concentrated on surfaces and objects which were most frequently touched and therefore most likely to show imprints of bloody hands: doors, door jambs, latches, stair railings, sink faucets. In addition he tried surfaces and objects over which a murdered person might have been dragged, or on which blood could have fallen during a struggle: steps, areas of the floor, thresholds. Working in the darkness was toilsome, and a long time passed without result. At last a few light-blue glowing spots appeared, typical of the luminol process. They showed at several places on the coping of the well, which was situated in a shed next to Lindörfer's workshop, and also on a faucet in the kitchen and on the latch of the door leading from the kitchen to the front hall. Except for this, nothing was discovered on the ground floor.

The group proceeded upstairs. The steps themselves appeared to be free of bloodstains. But that might not mean anything; the paint on the stairs looked so new that they might have been repainted recently. Lindörfer's wife, when questioned, stated that she herself had painted the stairs and the wall of the stairwell, after May and on her husband's instructions. She seemed unaware that her reply might sound incriminating. The search on the upper story produced no clues at first. Walls, doors, floors, and drains in the missing woman's room remained "mute" wherever the spray of luminol touched them—until a spot on a hitherto disregarded door showed up. It was the door to the left of Lina Lindörfer's kitchen door, and led into the attic.

On that door jamb, at a height of about twenty-eight inches, a small streak suddenly glowed. There were more luminescent spots on the inside edge of the door frame. When Lautenbach opened the door wide and sprayed the interior of the attic, several areas and dots glowed bright blue. Involuntarily, the District Attorney and Heberger stepped closer. Could this be the clue? Had their previous searches of the apartment been in vain because Lina Lindörfer had been made away with in this part of the house?

By the light of the flashlight the attic presented a scene of incredible confusion, a clutter of boxes, chests, and all manner of junk. Lautenbach's jet of spray fell on one of the floorboards between the door and the other end of the attic, where a ladderlike stairway ascended to the space under the rafters. A glowing area sixteen inches long and five inches wide appeared on the floor. Given the reliability of luminol spray, it was a fair assumption that this floorboard had been stained with blood. This was not yet a certainty, but it was enough to justify concentrated work in the attic. Smaller bluish spots glistened on the floorboards to the left and right of the glowing area. Lautenbach circled them with chalk. He had the larger board carefully removed and wrapped up, along with the dirt from the cracks between the boards. The spots on the door jamb which showed a luminescent reaction were removed with a plane.

The attic was long and narrow. To the left of the door an old wardrobe hulked, stuffed full of clothing, rags, pulp magazines, cheap novels. Against the far wall stood two old chests. Next to them, in the corner under the staircase to the upper attic, stood a wooden bucket and a pile of charcoal briquettes. The chests were surrounded by battered pots, miscellaneous boxes, laths, corrugated cardboard, and old shoes. In the small space to the right of the door there was a crude sink, its drain running out to the roof gutter. At the foot of the steps stood a rough chest which served as a coalbox.

The night was by now far advanced, and it seemed hopeless to go through all the junk in the attic piece by piece. Lautenbach therefore had to content himself with searching in the immediate vicinity of the stains he had already found. A glow showed on some of the forward pieces of the pile of charcoal briquettes. Other spots gleamed on the steps, up to a height of twenty-eight inches. A piece of corrugated cardboard on the chest showed luminescent patches. The briquettes, the cardboard, an ax, and a shoe tree stained with brownish spots were put aside.

After many hours the first search came to an end. Lautenbach drove back to Erlangen with the material he had collected, to test for blood, and then for species, group, and eventually age and quantity. On August 31 and September 1 he sent his first results to Ansbach. All the stains were just barely analyzable. The board must have been washed so thoroughly that it was difficult even to determine the species of the blood. Tiny usable specimens were obtained only by cutting into the grain channels of the rough wood. The stains on the briquettes were more evident. The spots on the door jamb were just barely identifiable. Those on the corrugated paper were somewhat clearer. Nevertheless, it had proved possible to demonstrate that all the stains were from blood, and the Ouchterlony test had shown that everywhere, even in the heavily scrubbed floorboard, as well as on the briquettes and the cardboard, the blood was human. To make certain, Lautenbach had used a number of different anti-human serums, some German and some from the Pasteur Institute in France. The reaction to human blood was unquestionable. The agar gel plates were available for proof.

Lautenbach informed Heberger that he would now attempt to determine the blood group, but that on the basis of previous experience reliable results were unlikely. However, he said, he would also try a new English technique which was noted for sensitivity. He was referring to the Mixed Agglutination test.

Lautenbach concentrated his efforts at first on the stains on the briquettes and the cardboard. The floorboard itself seemed hopeless, but he hoped that the dirt from the cracks might yield a few particles of blood large enough for a successful grouping test. This would require painstaking examination, so he put the board aside for the time being. His attempts to group the blood on the cardboard, using the Lattes and Holzer tests, failed. Lautenbach then attempted to extract the blood from the briquettes with the aid of filter paper, thus separating it from the charcoal dust. He subjected the precipitate of blood on the filter paper to both the Lattes and the Holzer tests. But there was no convincing result. Some of the reactions in the Lattes test at best suggested that he might be dealing with Group O. He went on to the Mixed Agglutination test, on which his last hope was based, only to encounter a streak of bad luck. A fiber with a particle of blood had adhered to a briquette, but it proved to be of synthetic cloth, precisely the kind of fiber that resisted this test. He then repeated the test with tiny particles of filter paper. This time the obtained several agglutinations with test cells of Group A, showing that the blood on the briquettes belonged to Group A. But when, for verification, he inspected other particles of the filter paper and found that Group B test cells also produced a trace of agglutination, he decided that he must reject the results. Apparently there was some disturbing factor in the charcoal dust. He informed Heberger that it was highly probable the blood belonged to Group A, but that he had not yet succeeded in proving it. He planned to make further studies. Meanwhile he proposed that Heberger undertake the followings steps: 1. Could he find out whether Lina Lindörfer had ever been treated in a hospital and whether her blood group had been determined? 2. Were any pieces of her unwashed underclothing around which would make it possible to determine her blood group from her physiological secretions?

Within two days Heberger had underclothing to send to Lautenbach. At the same time a detective learned that Lina Lindörfer had been treated at the Surgical Clinic of the University in Erlangen. The case history could at first not be found. But on September 4 it was recovered from the files. It contained a notation: Blood Group A. By this time, however, Lautenbach had already studied the underclothing. The missing woman proved to be a "secretor" whose secretions showed Group A. On September 5 Lautenbach sent this information to Heberger and suggested that another search for bloodstains be undertaken, and that this time not a single object in the attic be disregarded. He himself was about to leave on a journey but would resume the work as soon as he was back.

Lautenbach took it for granted that the matter would be pursued. But on his return to Erlangen he learned to his astonishment that the District Attorney's office had abandoned further investigations in Reichelshofen as hopeless. Lautenbach inquired, and found out what had happened during his absence. Troubled and uncertain, unfamiliar as he was with the problems of investigating bloodstains, the District Attorney had asked to see again the board that had shown such a strong reaction to the luminol spray. He wanted to determine for himself that there was blood on this floorboard. Since Lautenbach was away, one of his younger associates had inadequately carried out a benzidine test for blood and obtained no reaction. Probably he had been looking for an excuse for his own incompetence—at any rate he had told the District Attorney that the stains might not be from blood but from urine. This remark had naturally increased the District Attorney's uncertainty and led him to call off the investigation.

Probably the matter would have rested there forever and the fate of Lina Lindörfer would never have been explained, had it not been for chance. A few months later a young detective, familiar with modern principles, was transferred from Munich to Ansbach. This man was Inspector Valentin Freund. The first thing he did in his new post was to study the files of unsolved crimes. In the spring of 1963 he came upon the Lindörfer file, got in touch with Lautenbach, and personally took charge of the mysterious affair.

On April 9, 1963, Freund went to Reichelshofen to look over the terrain. The inhabitants of the house, who had long since decided that the matter was settled, received him with anything but friendliness. Lindörfer was plainly frightened, so much so that for a moment he was incapable of speech, but he calmed down as quickly as he had done in the past. Freund wanted to have a look at the attic and Lina's apartment. It seemed that the cooper and his family had made many changes there. A large number of objects, listed in the records of previous searches, were now missing. The briquettes and the wooden bucket were no longer to be seen. Some of the junk had been moved. But Freund noticed a pair of woman's black oxfords which showed brownish discolorations on the inside and the edge of the soles. He took possession of them. In Ansbach he studied photographs of the attic that had been taken on August 29, 1962. The shoes showed up in these pictures; they had formerly stood in front of the first chest below the staircase. On April 9 the shoes were taken to Erlangen.

Lautenbach first determined the presence of blood. Then he found that the blood was human. Finally he examined the blood by the Mixed Agglutination procedure. He let the anti-A and anti-B serums work for fifteen and a half hours to obtain the most dependable results. Three times he came to identical conclusions: the blood belonged to Group A —Lina Lindörfer's group.

From then on Freund refused to be discouraged either by the skepticism of the District Attorney's office or the open hostility of the people of Reichelshofen. On April 16, 17, and 22 he again looked around Lindörfer's property and sent Lautenbach a cleaning rag which he thought might provide significant clues. He also sent the drain from the sink and samples of mud from the roof gutter because he assumed that bloody water from the washing of the floor might have been poured into the sink. On May 7 he finally prevailed on the authorities to issue another search warrant. On May 8 he and Lautenbach undertook another intensive search for stains.

This time Lautenbach brought with him an automatic spray pistol, which permitted a finer diffusion of the luminol spray. With it he discovered many more bloodstains on the floorboards. They were all grouped around the area where the large floorboard had been removed already. This was where most of the blood must have been spilled. The spray revealed otherwise invisible drip stains on a cardboard carton which in August had stood beside the shoes in front of the chest. It also showed up many spatter stains on the coalbox, which stood to the right of the door between stairs and sink. No less than twenty spatter stains showed on the front of the box, with a number of other stains on its side.

Lautenbach was conscious of how much these stains would be able to tell if they proved to be human blood, and, what was more, Group A blood. Careful inspection indicated the direction from which they had spattered, so that it would be easy to determine what part of the attic had been the scene of a bloody struggle.

Lautenbach hurried back to Erlangen. His tests of the sink drain and guttering mud proved a disappointment. No liquids containing blood had been poured out through them. But this disappointment could be dismissed, for all the other stains—on the floor, on the cardboard carton, and on the coalbox—showed up in the Ouchterlony test as human blood. The microscopic spatters on the coal chest were too small to be grouped even by the Mixed Agglutination method. Lautenbach therefore concentrated on the center of the area where he thought most of the blood had probably been spilled. He fetched out the floorboard which had been set aside in August and looked for usable flakes of blood in the cracks of the board and in the smudge of dirt along the edges. Finally, at the end of the board that had been nearest the pile of briquettes, he found what he needed. Again he used filter paper to draw tiny particles of blood away from the dirt, so that he could prepare his solutions. A day later he no longer had any doubts. The blood on the board had come from a person with Group A blood—Lina Lindörfer's group.

Matters had reached this point when Freund proposed that they make a wooden model of the attic and mark all the bloodstains that had been found in it. His idea was that this model would help to convince the District Attorney that the attic concealed the secret of Lina Lindörfer's disappearance. Lautenbach, on the other hand, considered the model an excellent means for attempting a reconstruction of the assumed crime.

He measured the existing spatter stains one by one to determine the direction of impact. The bloodstains on the side of the coalbox must have come from a bloody object with a small surface, or from a wound; they must have been hurled at the box from a height of between twenty-eight and thirty-two inches and from a distance of about sixteen inches. The twenty spatter marks on the front of the same chest, on the other hand, came from a larger bloody surface or a wound about twenty inches from the chest and twelve inches above the floor. It had been spattered horizontally against the wall of the box. The stains on the shoes and the carton, both of which stood more than six feet from the coalbox, had been dripped from a height of between twenty and forty inches. The whole bloodstain pattern suggested a struggle or "killing in violent movement" which had ended on the floor near the wide, blood-soaked floorboard. In this last phase the blood must have spattered on the briquettes.

Freund and Lautenbach spent two weeks marking in all the stains on the model. Those whose species and blood group had been determined were designated in red, all the others, simply known to be blood, in orange. The red marks comprised the great majority. They proved that at any rate a person with Blood Group A must have been severely wounded in that attic.

On June 15 Freund asked the District Attorney's office for a warrant to arrest Lindörfer. He had to produce the model and make a most urgent plea before the warrant was issued on June 19. On June 22, shortly after 9 A.M., Lindörfer was at last arrested and taken to a police car through a cordon of indignant neighbors. As he left the house he swore that he was innocent. Thereafter he did not speak another word. In jail he ate lunch with visible appetite and took a sound afternoon nap. When Freund heard of this, he was for the first time assailed by doubts. Was such conduct possible in a guilty man? he asked himself. What was going on behind Lindörfer's expressionless face? Was he innocent, or so dull-witted, so emotionally impoverished, that no inner stirrings ever showed in his exterior?

Freund began his first interrogation on the afternoon of June 22, and continued it with interruptions throughout June 23. He set forth to Lindörfer all the results of the investigation, all the contradictions— in vain. Lindörfer went on stolidly insisting that Lina had left the house with a stranger. By evening of June 23 the District Attorney, partly with resignation and partly with a sense of having been proved right after all, declared: "If Lindörfer doesn't confess tomorrow, we'll have to release him."

Still Freund did not give up. He had kept back what he felt to be his strongest card: the model of the bloodstained attic. Experience told him that he had to wait for the moment in which a small crack appeared in the man's armor, which had shielded him so long against the eruption of inner tensions, guilt feelings, or fear. He knew how suddenly that could happen in these simple natures. Consequently, he began the interrogation patiently, tenaciously, utilizing every contradiction in Lindörfer's replies and again and again posing the same question: "What has happened to your sister? She cannot have driven away. She never left your house."

Shortly after eleven fifteen in the morning, Lindörfer was still saying: "It's God's truth that Lina drove off. I don't doubt that she'll turn up." But he added a curious sentence in a low murmur: "It will come to light, everything does." Freund pricked up his ears. A few seconds later Lindörfer bowed his head and broke into a low sobbing. Silently, Freund placed the model of the attic on the table, so that Lindörfer would find himself confronting the scene as soon as he looked up. When Lindörfer raised his eyes, he stared horror-stricken at the model. His sobbing became violent, and at the same time his surrender began— step by step, still reluctantly, but at last in a torrent. "I never wanted to harm her," he began. One revealing phrase followed after another, interrupted repeatedly by sobbing, often confused. Bit by bit, jerkily, a picture of the truth emerged; it was evident that even this slow, dull fellow was suffering the torments of conscience. "I didn't mean to . . . Nobody knows, nobody else knows about it. I swear, nobody at home knows. . . . She isn't in the woods, nor at home, nor anywhere on my land. . . . But it's right—your model there is right—she fell right by the briquettes."

That was how the confession began, a story so frightful that Lindörfer could only bring it out a fragment at a time, among disguising lies or embroideries, as though he feared to hear the unspeakable horror from his own lips.

According to Lindörfer's initial confession, what had happened on

May 10, 1962, was this: At noon, when his sons and son-in-law were on their way back to work and his wife and daughter were out digging the garden, Friedrich Lindörfer went upstairs to ask his sister to do some work in the garden too. She had several vegetable beds there, and he wanted her to attend to them. He called her name in the hall, knocked, and entered her kitchen. Lina was standing at the table, ironing; she said she had no time for the garden now. Her refusal instantly kindled her brother's smoldering hatred. She had no time for the garden but she had plenty of time to write anonymous letters, he snarled at her. He was alluding to anonymous letters in which a neighboring woman was accused of adultery. The villagers had decided that Lina was the author of these letters.

Lina called her brother a scoundrel. At that he leaped at her and struck her in the face. She raised her iron and pursued him as he retreated back into the hall. There he wrested the iron from her and lifted it to strike her with it. She in turn retreated through the open door to the attic, continuing to abuse him. He threw the iron at her and struck her on the side of the head. She fell back onto the floor and lay near the briquettes, dead. When Lindörfer "awoke from his fury" and realized what had happened, he ran downstairs and locked the front door. Then he rushed upstairs again, wrapped his dead sister in an old coat that hung in the attic, and dragged her down the stairs to the barn. He hid her in a heap of straw and sawdust beside the pigsty. He washed the blood from his shoes, hands, and leather apron with cold water. Then he wiped up the floor. He removed the briquettes which he saw stained with blood and burned them. By the time his wife and daughter returned home, "the worst" was done and everything cleaned or hidden so well that neither noticed anything. He waited until next day and finally used the evening hours to drive out to a field a quarter of a mile away and bury the body there.

Lautenbach, who was informed at once of Lindörfer's confession, declared that the details were untrue. According to the bloodstain patterns, Lina Lindörfer could not have been killed in the manner described. There must have been a struggle in the attic, and she must have received several blows from the murder weapon. Experience showed that an initial wound seldom caused spatters of blood unless an artery were struck. Only more blows upon an already bloodstained wound could have produced the spatters that Lautenbach had found on the coalbox.

Again the model stood on the table as Freund once again interrogated Lindörfer to extract the whole truth. For two days Lindörfer resisted.

Then he came around: "All right, Inspector, since you know the whole story, I might as well admit it." His first account had been somewhat simplified. After striking Lina in the face, he had been driven out of the room by her. She had locked the door behind him. In fury he had braced himself against the door and broken in. Only then had his sister reached for the iron to defend herself. He had retreated to the hall. But then he had caught hold of Lina. They struggled. He forced her into the attic. Then he wrested the iron from her and brought it down on her head. She had collapsed between the coalbox and the stairs, but half kneeling and still clinging to him until he struck her head with the iron again. Then she had fallen to the floor and lain with her head close to the briquettes. There she had bled heavily. He had wrapped her head in a jacket to catch the blood and dragged her to the left so that she could not be seen as soon as the door was opened. That was how the blood had fallen upon the box, the shoes, and the corrugated paper. All the rest, Lindörfer concluded, was as he had told it.

Only after the police had dug in the field and found no trace of the body did Lindörfer release the next bits of frightful data. He admitted that he had not buried the dead woman, but chopped up her body in the barn, using his ax, while the family was away from home. First he claimed that he had burned the body piece by piece in his workshop stove. Lautenbach examined the corner of the barn where Lindörfer said he had performed the frightful work of mutilation. He found bloodstains. Behind the stove he discovered tiny fragments of bone which, when ground to a dust, showed up in the Ouchterlony test as of human origin. But he held that it would have been impossible for Lindörfer to have burned the body in the small fire of the stove. At this point Lindörfer told the rest of the gruesome tale. That's right, it had been impossible to burn the body, although he had tried. He had finally boiled it in the large kettle in which he heated water for cleaning his neighbors' cider barrels. Then he had stripped the flesh from the bones and burned those. The remains he had put into paper bags and taken to the woods near Reichelshofen. "It takes nerves," he said. "You have to be real coldblooded." A little later he added: "You'd never believe what a man is capable of—what you can bring yourself to do. . . . But then I went to bed just like I do every day." He had emptied the water used for the boiling partly into the canal, partly by the hedge in his garden. Some fat was still clinging to the leaves of the hedge when the police first called at his house, but no one had noticed. Finally, he had taken some of the ashes from his sister's bones to the cemetery and buried them in his mother's grave. He said: "I had a feeling that I must do that."

Later he had gone into Lina's room and taken possession of her identity card, since that might have betrayed the fact that she had not left home. At this time he had also taken some cash. But most of all he had used every free moment from then on, day after day, to clean the attic, the stairs, the barn, and his workshop, scrubbing everything with soapy water and a stout brush. He had poured the stained water into the canal so that there would be no trace of it in the drains. He had washed the walls in the barn and workshop several times and put the bloody sawdust in the manure. Then he had had his wife paint the front stairs and the wall in the front hall. Finally he had seen no further trace of blood. He had been firmly convinced that no one would ever be able to find any evidence against him. He had even cleaned and scoured where he saw no blood, but only thought there might be. "I was sure nothing could ever be found," he said, half boastful and half querulous. "I wasn't worried at all when the police searched the house and took the floorboard out. I wasn't even worried when you came, Inspector Freund. I thought: They don't really think so themselves. I didn't believe the police knew anything till I saw the model. Because I'd cleaned up there all over again. I didn't see any bloodstains and still I scrubbed. . . ."

The confessions went on into early July. It was late in the summer before Lautenbach, together with detectives, visited the places in the woods where Lindörfer had hidden the last vestiges of his crime. Lautenbach found numerous splinters of human bone which confirmed the confession. He also found burned particles of bone shallowly buried at one spot above the grave of Lindörfer's mother. On the other hand, the murder instrument—the iron—was never found. But it was no longer needed to complete the picture of the crime and to corroborate the confessions which Lindörfer had concluded with the words: "Now I can go to communion with a clear conscience."

Five months later, when Lindörfer stood in the dock at Ansbach, charged with manslaughter, the many spectators stared at him with repugnance and horror. Perhaps a few of those present guessed at some of the elemental powers which lurk everywhere beneath the surface of life (not only in the character of this defendant) and which had driven Lindörfer, out of avarice and the crowded conditions of his home, into an act which inexorably forced him into greater and greater horrors. Sentenced to eight years in the penitentiary, he showed no signs of remorse; apparently he felt that he had salved his conscience with his confession.

As Lindörfer was led out of the courtroom, it was amply clear that the scientific side of this case would remain a noteworthy achievement of serology. It dramatized all that forensic serology was capable of after sixty years of development. Above all, it pointed up what could be done when scientists and police worked closely together.

II

Clues in the Dust:

Forensic Chemistry and Biology

1

In December 1887 the readers of *Beeton's Christmas Annual* of London were introduced to Sherlock Holmes, the most famous detective in history, and Dr. Watson, Holmes's faithful companion and chronicler of his feats, his theories, and his methods.

The fact that Sherlock Holmes made his appearance in the same year that Alphonse Bertillon, the founder of scientific criminology in Paris, climbed the first crucial rungs of the ladder to world fame, may at first glance seem to be a matter of chance. Arthur Conan Doyle, a twenty-seven-year-old physician who used the long intervals between patients to write magazine stories, did not know Bertillon, nor could he boast of any relations to Scotland Yard. Nevertheless, the real phenomenon of Bertillon and the new turn he gave criminology sprang from the same root as the literary career of Sherlock Holmes.

What was involved was the fundamental belief of the late nineteenth century that all of life's problems could be solved by precise thinking, precise scholarly deductions, and scientific knowledge. The young Bertillon had absorbed this doctrine in his parental home with its strong scientific tradition. When in 1879, during his first year as an assistant clerk in Paris police headquarters, he made some suggestions for identifying criminals by means of physical measurements, he was only exemplifying this spirit and applying these principles. Arthur Conan Doyle imbibed the same philosophy during his medical studies in Edinburgh, which he began in 1876. During the years in which Bertillon was developing his science of anthropometry, Arthur Conan Doyle's hero, Sherlock Holmes, was sketching the outlines of another branch of criminology which was to become part and parcel of detective work, along with Bertillon's system, fingerprinting, forensic medicine, toxicology, ballistics, and serology. For Sherlock Holmes was the harbinger of a kind of criminological investigation which did not fit into any of these special disciplines, and which ultimately far surpassed them in range. What Holmes did was to avail himself of all the chemical, biological, physical, and technological methods which were springing up at the turn of the century.

In 1893, at the time that Conan Doyle—by now out of ideas and sick of the whole thing—sent his hero Sherlock Holmes plunging to his death in the gorge of Reichenbach, a book appeared in Germany which was a far cry from literary fancies and nevertheless gave substance to the ideas and methods of the early Sherlock Holmes. It was a scholarly book on crime and the law bearing the sober title, *Handbuch für Untersuchungsrichter* ("Manual for Examining Magistrates"—ultimately published in English under the title of *Criminal Investigation*). The author, Hans Gross, was himself an examining magistrate in Graz, Austria: a practical man rather than a theoretician, who in the course of his daily work kept a sharp eye out for new paths for criminal investigation and paid close attention to the currents of science. It is not known whether he had ever read the Sherlock Holmes stories. The likelihood is that quite independently and by quite other ways he arrived at ideas similar to those of Conan Doyle.

You had only to open Gross's book to see the dawning of a new age. Of course he strongly advocated anthropometry, forensic medicine, toxicology, ballistics, and serology. But in addition he had a number of chapters dealing with matters that had never been considered in a work on criminology. Some of the chapter headings were: "Employment of the Microscopist," "Employment of the Chemist," "Employment of the Physicist," "Employment of the Mineralogist, Zoologist, and Botanist." The subtitles indicated the kind of employment Gross had in mind: "Hair, Dust, Dirt on Shoes, Spots on Clothing." His chapter on the employment of the microscopist began: "Advanced though the construction of microscopes is today, and much as science can accomplish with this admirable artifact, the criminologist has as yet scarcely drawn upon the art of the microscopist. Studies of blood, determination of semen spots, and comparison of hairs is virtually all that the microscopist has to do for the criminologist. Other investigations occur only exceptionally, although there are innumerable cases in which the microscopist could provide vital information and perhaps clarify insoluble problems." The same was true, Gross held, of chemistry, physics, biology, and technology. Each of his chapters was an appeal to examining magistrates (his term for criminologists) to avail themselves of the potentialities of science and technology far more than they had so far done. The book was full of sentences such as: "Dirt on shoes can often tell us more about where the wearer of those shoes had last been than toilsome inquiries."

When Gross published the first edition of his book in 1893, he himself scarcely dared to hope that it would be reprinted. But the second edition came out within a year. In four years there was a third; two years later the fourth edition appeared—an unusual record for a textbook of this sort. Did this mean that the time was ripe for the realization of Conan Doyle's dreams and Hans Gross's matter-of-fact exhortations?

It seemed so. A rather significant answer to this question came when the fifth edition of the "Manual for Examining Magistrates" was published in 1907. It came from a remote area of Southwest Germany, where quiet villages and hamlets lay scattered among fields, hills, and woods in the vicinity of the city of Kaiserslautern. Altogether, the region seemed anything but the background for a *cause célèbre*. Nevertheless, a crime committed on a wooded hill near the village of Falkenstein became the crime of the year. What made it noteworthy was not any special external circumstances, not the unusualness or prominence of victim or murderer, but solely the fact that a little soil on a pair of shoes exposed the criminal.

2

A picture taken in January 1908 of a certain Margarethe Filbert of Eschau showed, despite all the "artistic" retouching by the Kaiserslautern photographer, an unattractive, flat-chested woman of about thirty wearing an elaborately crinolined skirt, a beruffled shirtwaist, and a huge hat. Without a family, without a husband and with no prospects of finding one, she worked in the town of Rockenhausen, running the household of an architect named Seeberger and consoling herself by buying clothes which might give her the appearance of a lady in the eyes of the simpler neighbors.

Thursday, May 28, 1908, was Ascension Day, and Margarethe Filbert had the afternoon off. She decided to take the train to Winnweiler, the next sizable hamlet, and walk home from there. The way led through Falkenstein Valley to the village and the ruined castle of Falkenstein, then by paths through fields and woods to Rockenhausen. But she did not reappear at the architect's in time for the evening meal, or even the next morning. When she was still absent by the evening of May 29, her employer informed the Royal Bavarian Police Brigade in Rockenhausen, and next morning at eight o'clock Patrolmen Ott and Kall set out to look for Margarethe. In Falkenstein they found two persons who said they had seen her. In the upper part of the village a farmer named Philipp Schlicher recalled having met "a skinny woman" about three o'clock in the afternoon; she had asked him the way to Rockenhausen. Schlicher's daughter, Anna, had seen the woman picking flowers in a sloping meadow nearer Rockenhausen about 3:30 P.M.; Anna recalled that she had been holding a parasol over her head, against the sun. This meant that Margarethe Filbert must have disappeared somewhere between Falkenstein and Rockenhausen. Ott and Kall tramped all possible paths in that direction, but in vain. Back in Rockenhausen, they organized a search in which all the police and many of the villagers took part. The woods were combed. About the middle of the afternoon a boy reported finding the dead body of the missing woman in the section of the state forest known as Schelmenkopf. Ott and Kall rushed to the spot. They found Margarethe Filbert surrounded by a crowd of the curious; the woman's skirt had been thrown back over her head and the naked lower part of her body was covered with leaves.

A messenger was sent to the Police Chief, Sergeant Mühlbauer, and the district court officials in Winnweiler. They passed the news on to District Attorney Sohn of Kaiserslautern, and by seven o'clock Sohn, District Judge Hofbauer, and a physician, Dr. Hennig, met at Schelmenkopf to inspect the scene of the crime. Sohn had only recently read Gross's "Manual for Examining Magistrates," and he had brought along not only the doctor but also a forester named Hummel as an expert on the woods. Sergeant Mühlbauer of Falkenstein led the party through the forest.

At eight o'clock they reached the spot, where a throng still lingered and several policemen stood guard over the body. Margarethe Filbert lay on a slight incline about a hundred and fifty feet below the forest path she must have taken—close to a small, deserted hunting lodge. She lay on her back, slightly to one side, her left leg bent, her right leg outstretched. Her black stockings and shoes were untouched. Her skirt and petticoat also were undamaged, only turned up—the light brown skirt pulled way up, a russet petticoat reaching to her shoulders. Mühlbauer lifted the dead woman's raised skirt and found that her head was missing. It had been severed from the neck apparently with a knife. The striped blue and white blouse alone was soaked with blood from the terrible neck wound, but otherwise there was no sign of injury or soil on her body. The leather glove was still firmly on her right hand, while the left glove had been nearly pulled off, as though the murderer had been looking for rings. Pocketbook, hat, jacket, and parasol were missing, and Sohn could not decide whether he was confronted with a sex crime or robbery. According to her employer, Margarethe never carried more than one or two marks with her. Had someone been misled by her fine dress into thinking she might have larger sums or jewelry on her person?

Darkness descended so quickly that Sohn gave up the inspection for the present and had two horse blankets laid over the body. Next morning the commission assembled again at six o'clock, this time reinforced by Heinrich Börtzel, a local photographer. Since there was no trained police photographer available, Börtzel was asked to take a few pictures while Sohn, Hofbauer, Hummel, and the doctor carefully looked over the scene and the body once more. They found clinging to the fingers, above the torn glove, hairs of different colors, and they folded them into a sheet of document paper. They went down on their knees to study the ground, since Sohn suspected that Margarethe Filbert's clothing had gone upward only because she had been dragged by the feet from the actual site of the murder to the place where she now lay. Hummel, the forester, could find no trail of a dragged body, but he did find leaves from the hairy hawthorn, and a bilberry leaf clinging to her skirt. There were hawthorn bushes growing a few feet away, but they were not the hairy kind. Hummel, who knew every inch of the woods, pointed out that hairy hawthorns and bilberries grew about a hundred and forty feet farther up the slope, right near the footpath. Sohn sent two policemen up to look for bloodstains and the missing head. Then he had the body taken by cart to the town hall in Falkenstein. Meanwhile the district court physician, Dr. Zahn, had arrived there. Assisted by the barbersurgeon Müller (for the "menial tasks"), he performed the autopsy.

He concluded that the murderer had first strangled his victim and then beheaded her. Since Zahn could not decide whether or not there had been a sexual attack, Hofbauer had the genital organs sent to the Medical Committee of Würzburg University, which at this time had no institute of forensic medicine. Margarethe Filbert's clothes were packed in an old chest, loaded on a hay wagon, and sent to the courthouse at Winnweiler. Meanwhile, the police discovered bloodstains that had soaked into the ground above the path; they also came upon hairy hawthorn and bilberry bushes. But all efforts to find the missing head and the dead woman's possessions, especially her pocketbook, proved fruitless.

Before Sohn and Hofbauer left Falkenstein, they instructed Corporal Schmidt of Winnweiler to check on all convicts and "other suspicious persons." Schmidt "knew his people," as he assured the District Attorney, and he made forays on a number of workmen and day laborers with records of morals offenses, to search their apartments or rooms. But all of them had good alibis. Either a cow had calved and they had been in the barn attending to her on the afternoon in question, or they had been seen in reputable company. The corporal finally went to the Mayor of Falkenstein, Peter Fischer, to inquire into other possible suspects. Fischer had no hesitation about naming one. If the crime had not been committed by some outsider, he said, there was only one person in the village capable of it: a factory worker named Andreas Schlicher. Fischer's incontrovertible reasoning was: "Because the man was once charged with poaching and because he hasn't the best of reputations."

Andreas Schlicher was known to the police corporal; he had for years been under suspicion of poaching, but had never been caught. Schlicher was, to quote Schmidt's report, "forty years old, Protestant, married, father of five children." He owned a wretched little farm consisting of a few widely scattered fields and depended for most of his income on his job in the Gienant Copper Plant. He was head over heels in debt, and reputed to be coarse, violent, and quick-tempered. The only difficulty was that there were a dozen men like him in Falkenstein alone, also given to violence, also suspected of poaching. But the Mayor pointed out that one of Schlicher's fields lay right along the path that Margarethe Filbert must have taken. That clinched it for the corporal; accompanied by the Mayor, he went to Schlicher's farm. They found Schlicher in the cow stable right behind the kitchen, while his wife was at table with the children in the front room. Schlicher, a stocky man with black, close-cropped hair, a clipped brown mustache, and yellowed teeth with many gaps, growled about being disturbed at work. But he willingly enough gave an account of his activities on the day of the murder. Since it was a holiday, he had put on his Sunday suit and shoes about one o'clock in the afternoon and gone to visit his fields on the Herzberg hill, going in turn to each of his strips in the areas known as Dreimorgen, Schinderborn, Herzenthal, and Hinterm Hahn. He had looked to see how his crops were doing and by three or three-thirty had been back home again. His neighbor Philippine Fluhr had seen him coming home, he said. After that he had not left the house. As for Margarethe Filbert, he had never met the woman. In fact he had not heard of the murder until Friday night, May 29.

Schmidt asked whether he had not also gone to his field at Schelmenkopf. Schlicher replied with an unequivocal "No." His wife Karoline shrugged her shoulders to all of Schmidt's questions. She was by nature close-mouthed, and the jog-trot of her life, from work and making ends meet, rough copulation and births, had not made her any more talkative. She did not even look up from her bowl. Only after many questions did she growl that "if he says he was home on Ascension Day afternoon, he must have been."

Schmidt asked to see Schlicher's hands and arm. No scratch or bruise was to be seen. He took possession of Schlicher's Sunday clothes. In the report he sent the district court in Winnweiler he noted: "There was not the slightest trace of blood on any of the clothes. Schlicher also owns two knives, one with a fixed and one with a movable blade, on which there were likewise no detectable bloodstains."

In the afternoon Schmidt paid a call on the neighbor, Philippine Fluhr. He noticed that the young woman first checked to see whether her house was under observation from the Schlichers' before she answered. Then she confirmed the fact that she had seen Schlicher on the afternoon in question, when he stood in front of his door in his gray Sunday jacket. She had noticed nothing unusual about him. Her conduct was curious and anxious to the last—but all the same, an alibi was an alibi. Ill-humored by now, Schmidt set out again. This time he stopped at the tavern in Falkenstein, Zum Wilden Jäger, to ask the tavernkeeper Heinrich Fischer if he had noticed anything unusual. Fischer waited until several patrons had left the tavern before he confided to the policeman that he too regarded Andreas Schlicher as the murderer. Only a few hours ago one of his patrons, Hermann Klein, had recounted that some time ago Schlicher had tried to persuade him to join in a holdup of an old man. When Schmidt pressed the tavernkeeper for more information, Fischer referred him to a small farmer named Martin Fischer. Martin Fischer would tell him that Andreas Schlicher was lying when he said he had not left his house again on the afternoon of Ascension Day. He had come out of the woods between eight and ten o'clock and slipped into the village from up on the hill. But perhaps Martin Fischer wouldn't talk because everyone in the village was afraid and would keep his mouth shut as long as Schlicher was at liberty.

This was the first time anyone had spoken of the villagers' fear of the man. But from then on Schmidt encountered this fear everywhere he went. When he called on Martin Fischer, the man escaped him by slipping out of the house by the back door. At this same time Ott and Kall were still searching the slope of Schelmenkopf. They had a blood-hound with them and dragged ponds and dug for the head in innumerable places. But their only find up to the evening of June 1 was a tiny fragment of flesh with some hairs attached to it; they believed this might have come from the dead woman's head. On June 2 Schmidt found a single witness who was willing to make a statement: a Frau Zabaroff of Imsbach, who had been gathering moss in the woods on May 28. Toward five o'clock in the afternoon she had heard cries for help from the direction of Schlicher's field along the path to Rockenhausen. That was all Schmidt could get out of anyone. For all his efforts, he came up against a wall of fear.

Meanwhile District Attorney Sohn in Kaiserslautern was trying to find a chemist or "microscopist" who might tell him something about the origin of the hairs found in the dead woman's hand, and of the small piece of flesh. The district court physician would not undertake the task. The doctors in Würzburg also refused; they merely informed Sohn that they could find nothing indicating "sexual abuse" of Margarethe Filbert. This negative finding gave some weight to the hints about Schlicher's interest in robbery, but was otherwise of little aid.

On June 3 Sohn was leafing through his copy of the "Manual for Examining Magistrates," hoping for light. Suddenly a newspaper clipping dropped into his hand; he must have tucked it in the book several years before. It was an article from a Frankfurt newspaper reporting that a Frankfurt commercial chemist, Dr. Georg Popp, had solved several crimes in an unprecedented way. He had photographed fingerprints that the criminals had left on the clothing of their victims. Moreover, in the case of a sex crime he had found conclusive evidence against the assailant solely by examining the dirt on a handkerchief.

That very afternoon Sohn telegraphed Frankfurt and heard from

Georg Popp himself that he "actually existed and was looking forward to hearing more." The District Attorney thereupon had not only the hair and piece of flesh, but all the clothing that had been on Margarethe Filbert, packed up and sent to Frankfurt. He asked Dr. Popp to examine all the objects microscopically and in particular to let him know whether "bloody fingerprints" could be found on the clothing which might be compared with the fingerprints of a possible culprit. His letter concluded with a plea that would strike later generations as touchingly ingenuous: "In that case I beg to be informed by what procedure fingerprints can best be taken from such persons."

3

At the time Sohn's package arrived in Frankfurt, Georg Popp was forty-seven years old and the moving spirit of the Popp-Becker Chemico-technical and Hygienic Institute. Anyone who set out to study the letter-head of this estimable outfit had a task before him. The Institute was everything from an "Independent Public Chemical Laboratory for Food Studies" to a "Government-franchised Expert for Mineral Water Plants"; it was an "Agricultural Experimental and Control Station," an "Institute for Industrial Bacteriology," and an "Experimental Laboratory for Technical Aspects of Fire." In small type one line announced: "Section for Technical Investigations of Crime, Handwriting Analysis, and Microscopy."

Son of a Frankfurt tailor who had prospered by creating a fashion house, Popp had studied chemistry in Marburg, Leipzig, and Heidelberg under such famous men as Bunsen and Treadwell. After a short interlude in Wiesbaden he had founded his own laboratory in 1889 and eventually had an organization employing between twenty and thirty men.

An imposing figure with dueling scars to testify to his membership in a student fraternity, Popp had from the first too much enterprise and imagination to be content with the routine of a consultant laboratory. His marriage to Jennie Zinn, the daughter of a wickerware manufacturer who had made his fortune in New York, gave him the means to indulge in a variety of experiments. Not all of them were successful. But setbacks did not discourage him or suppress that love for the new which in 1900 led him to follow in the footsteps of Paul Jeserich and Hans Gross. One day a Frankfurt examining magistrate who had read Hans Gross's manual inquired whether Popp would have a look at some spots on a suspect's trousers. That one assignment had been enough to arouse in him a true passion for criminalistics. He had begun with serological and toxicological investigations and then, when the first news of finger-printing arrived from England shortly after the turn of the century, had plunged into dactyloscopy. At a time when various German police forces were still busy introducing Bertillon's physical measurements as the basis for their files, Popp had already reached the conclusion that only fingerprinting had any prospects. Concurrently he had turned to photography. He had become a diligent student of all the photographic methods that Bertillon and his disciple Reiss in Lausanne were recom-mending. In 1904 he had helped catch three murderers by photographic preservation of fingerprints. The first two, Stafforst and Gross, had murdered a Frankfurt piano dealer named Lichtenstein in his shop. They left behind a fingerprint on a sheet of paper and the imprint of an index finger on their victim's collar. A few months later, in November 1904, the minister of Heldenbergen in Hesse had been killed. Popp's contri-bution to the Stafforst-Gross trial had won him so much prestige that a rich Frankfurt manufacturer put his automobile at the chemist's dis-posal, so that he could be driven to the scenes of crimes. In this second case, Popp provided the examining magistrate with a color photograph of the knife that had been used in the murder. A finger mark, where the blade had been wiped, could be seen clearly in the photograph. Since butchers were wont to wipe their knives in this way, Popp sug-gested that the police look in the ranks of butchers for the killer. In addition he photographed the imprint of a right hand with an index finger that had been lopped off at the tip. Within a short time these clues led to the arrest and conviction of a butcher from Darmstadt.

But Popp sensed that there were other, still untried applications of the sciences to criminalistics. In October 1904 the District Attorney's office in Freiburg im Breisgau had asked him to come to Wildthal, where a seamstress named Eva Disch had been found in a bean field strangled with her own blue and red scarf. The only clue the murderer had left was a filthy handkerchief. Under the microscope Popp saw blue and red silk threads on this handkerchief, corresponding in appearance and color to the scarf. Moreover, the nasal mucus clinging to the cloth con-tained particles of snuff, also bits of coal, grains of sand, and crystals of hornblende. The police began to suspect a former Foreign Legionnaire named Karl Laubach who was employed in a gasworks, also did part-time work at a gravel pit, and was known to take snuff. When the man was arrested, Popp continued his microscopic studies. Under Laubach's fingernails he found a collection of coal dust, sand grains, and hornblende crystals. Above all, the microscope revealed red and blue silk threads exactly like the fibers in the victim's scarf. Finally, Popp noted spots of soil at the bottoms of Laubach's trousers. There was yellow loam, as well as a light-gray, muddy layer which crusted the loam here and there. Popp determined the kind and quantity of quartz grains and the components of crystals and vegetation in the layer of mud, and obtained samples of soil from the spot where Eva Disch had been found. Comparing, he came to the conclusion that the loam clinging to Laubach's trousers corresponded with the soil from the scene of the crime. The gray, muddy crusts contained an unusual admixture of crushed mica and particles of coal. The same components were found in samples taken from the path leading from the scene of the crime to Laubach's home. From this Popp concluded that Laubach had smeared his trousers with the loam while committing the crime, then walked home along the muddy path. When Laubach, who at first denied everything, finally admitted that Popp was right, the Frankfurt newspapers hailed the feat of detection under headings such as "The Microscope as Detective." That same year Popp was asked to address an association of independent public chemists of Germany, as well as the distinguished Senckenberg Society. In two remarkable lectures he made a profession of faith in the potentialities of chemistry, mineralogy, and botany as scientific auxiliaries to criminology.

By the time the appeal for help came from District Attorney Sohn, Popp had assembled a private criminological museum whose like could scarcely be found among the police forces of major cities. Several rooms on the ground floor of his house had been set aside for the display of photographs, objects, and microscopic slides which had played an important part in the solution of criminal cases.

Popp was speedier than the District Attorney could have hoped. By the next day he reported that the hair on the gloves was woman's hair, possibly from the victim herself. The hair on the pieces of flesh was animal's hair, probably that of a mole. His own feeling was that this find had nothing whatsoever to do with the murder, but he would check this by subjecting the flesh to an Uhlenhuth test to see whether it contained animal or human protein. He had found no fingerprints of any kind on the dead woman's clothing, but a great many horsehairs. As the

District Attorney noted in the margin (a reflection of Popp's accuracy), these last must have belonged to the horse blankets spread over the body the first night.

The report to Kaiserslautern was still on the way when Sohn received an anonymous letter from Falkenstein, forwarded to him by the district court in Winnweiler. Long, rambling, semi-illiterate, the letter stated that the whole village believed Andreas Schlicher guilty of the murder but that people were afraid and unwilling to accuse him.

On June 4 Sohn telephoned orders to have Schlicher arrested and taken to the Winnweiler jail. District Judge Hofbauer was instructed to search Schlicher's property for the second time. The police came to Falkenstein heavily armed, but Schlicher surrendered meekly enough, saying: "I can go along quietly, I didn't kill the woman." Hofbauer and Schmidt remained behind to search the crowded hovel with its many odd nooks and corners. They clambered through an opening in the kitchen leading to the cellar, rummaged through the shed and the oven, and went up a steep stairway to the bedroom. There Hofbauer once again looked over the clothes which Schmidt had examined a few days before. But he noticed nothing unusual. The same was true for Schlicher's Sunday shoes, which stood on the clothes chest. Hofbauer could only confirm the statement Corporal Schmidt had made on May 31: "In the course of the major search of the premises no traces of the crime . . . could be found."

In Kaiserslautern Court Counselor Seeberger was appointed examining magistrate for the case. When he interrogated Schlicher for the first time on June 5, he heard the same story that Schmidt had already heard: of Schlicher's visiting his fields in the vicinities of Dreimorgen, Schinderborn, Herzenthal, and Hinterm Hahn between one and four o'clock in the afternoon. Schlicher reiterated that he had not set foot in the vicinity of the state forest, had never seen Margarethe Filbert, and had not left his house after four o'clock in the afternoon. All questions proved in vain. The swarthy, black-haired man stuck to his story. The formal record contained the statement: "I deny the charge of murdering Margarethe Filbert of Rockenhausen. . . . I deny that I ever engaged in poaching." Seeberger could not make up his mind. In the afternoon he finally went to Falkenstein himself to take a look at Schlicher's house. Karoline Schlicher received him with hostile curtness, and Seeberger reported: "The accused's wife would not condescend to answer the questions put to her." For the third time Schlicher's clothes were examined. But Seeberger, too, concluded that there was nothing about the clothes worth noting. He did observe that the shoes were not quite clean—there was a small amount of earth on one of the soles—but since he saw no blood and considered the earth totally unimportant, he put the shoes back on the chest. He took back with him only a torn work smock spattered with some reddish-brown spots he thought might be blood.

Meanwhile Popp had completed his analysis of the piece of flesh. It unquestionably came from an animal. This negative result and the meagerness of the material he had so far received served as a challenge to his active temperament. Learning from the newspapers that Schlicher had been arrested, he came forward with a number of suggestions. He wrote to Kaiserslautern asking that Schlicher's clothes be sent to him so that he could search for clues. He also asked that Schlicher's fingernails be cut, or at least that the dirt from under the fingernails be sent to him. Sohn promptly passed Popp's letter on to Seeberger. But unlike Sohn, Seeberger was not a convert of Hans Gross. Having "seen for himself," he was firmly convinced that any further examination of Schlicher's clothes would be absolutely useless. However, the proposal to examine the dirt from Schlicher's fingernails struck him as reasonable, since some clue might be found pointing to a struggle between Schlicher and the victim.

On June 9 Popp reported that he had found traces of human blood under the fingernails. He took this opportunity to revert to Schlicher's clothing, and again asked permission to examine it. Sohn, however, took Seeberger's word for it that the clothes had already been sufficiently looked into. But the discovery of human blood under the fingernails prompted him to go personally to Falkenstein once more, accompanied this time by the examining magistrate, Forester Hummel, and ten policemen. On June 10 the search for the head and missing possessions of Margarethe Filbert was extended to all the woods southwest of Schelmenkopf and Herzenthal. When the afternoon brought a pouring rain, and nothing had yet been found, hopes began to fail. At this point it occurred to the forester to lead the searchers to the ruined castle of Falkenstein. The ruin was often used as a hiding place by poachers, he remarked. Perhaps the head could be found there.

The group combed the bushes and heaps of stone and rubble around the castle. Twilight was already falling when the party, carrying lanterns, penetrated into the underground vaults. There, too, nothing was found at first, although the policemen probed every pile of rubble. At last they climbed through a hole on the north side into a dungeonlike cellar. Here, after cursory shoveling, a leather strap turned up. It belonged to a rust-stained hunting rifle. Underneath lay a tin box of shells and a bundle consisting of a pair of damp brown man's trousers wrapped in a woman's blouse.

With the feeling that they were at last on the trail of something, Sohn and Seeberger took the finds to Kaiserslautern. Since the blouse had not belonged to Margarethe Filbert, however, they saw no connection between the finds and the murder. But they might have found some evidence of Schlicher's poaching. In the early morning hours of June 11 they studied the blouse and trousers by daylight, concluded that there were no stains on either, and sent both articles to the police in Rockenhausen with instructions to find out whether the trousers belonged to Schlicher and the blouse to his wife. In examining the rifle, Sohn once more consulted Gross's book. Since he knew no expert on guns, he again turned to Popp, whose impatience had meanwhile grown. Popp took the next train to Kaiserslautern. Unfortunately, Sohn was busy in court, so he was received by only Seeberger.

Popp quickly turned his attention to the shotgun shells that had been in the tin box. The shells were closed with rounds of cardboard that obviously had been cut out of a picture postcard with writing on it. Popp asked to see Schlicher's signature at the bottom of the minutes of several interrogations, and fancied that the handwriting coincided with that on the bits of postcard. He therefore proposed that a search be made of Schlicher's house for postcards. There was the possibility, he pointed out, that remains of the card from which the circles had been cut out could be found. He then once more brought up the subject of clues on Schlicher's clothing, and particularly asked about the trousers and blouse. Seeberger turned frosty. He had ascertained that there was no blood or any other kind of clue on these articles, he said. Further investigation was unnecessary. Popp replied that there were clues which only a specialist could see with a microscope. Seeberger felt that his professional acumen was being called into question. He replied sharply that the blouse and trousers were in Rockenhausen by now and not available. He gave Popp only the smock which had aroused his suspicions and was hardly pleased when Popp declared that the red spots Seeberger had taken for blood were nothing but rust. By now completely antagonized, Seeberger haughtily refused to give Popp any details on the previous investigations.

Disheartened by Seeberger's ignorance and lack of co-operation, Popp returned to Frankfurt. He scarcely felt any better about the case when, a week later, a small package arrived containing all the paper the police had been able to scare up on Schlicher's farm. Included was a card Schlicher had addressed to his father years before. It had several rounds of cardboard cut out of it, and the holes exactly fitted the bits of cardboard plugging the shells.

This proof that Schlicher was connected with the gun in the ruined castle certainly had bearing on the question of his poaching. But it cast no new light on the murder and did not divert Popp from his concern with Schlicher's clothing. He saw no way, however, to force the authorities to turn the clothes over to him.

Meanwhile, back in Falkenstein Patrolman Kall found out that the blouse belonged to Karoline Schlicher, while the trousers had been made in Würzweiler for Andreas Schlicher by the tailor Jakob Thom. The tailor pointed out the name "Schlicher" penciled on the inside of a seam—a notation that Seeberger had overlooked. Seeberger now concentrated on getting Schlicher into court on a charge of poaching. His aim was to put the man out of circulation by a longish term in jail, during which time some new data might come to light. With this in mind, he had reported the murder to the Bavarian and Hessian police authorities and asked for word of tramps and "other suspicious persons" who might have been in the vicinity of Falkenstein on Ascension Day or who had turned up with any of Margarethe Filbert's possessions.

On the question of poaching he scored a success. Early in July Corporal Schmidt succeeded in drawing so tight a ring around two other men suspected of poaching, Joseph Wildling and Philipp Demmerle, that they betrayed Schlicher in order to save their own skins. But nothing new was learned about the murder.

At the end of July District Attorney Sohn lost patience and took the unusual step of turning to the neighboring Grand Duchy of Hesse for help, asking for the services of a trained detective. The Hessian Attorney General's office dispatched Detective Inspector Daniel from Darmstadt to Kaiserslautern. Daniel took collaboration with Popp for granted, and at once shipped off Schlicher's trousers to be properly analyzed. He followed this up with another search of the Schlicher house and confiscated all Schlicher's clothes, including his Sunday shoes. Within three days Popp was able to report that both knees, where Seeberger and the police had noticed nothing, were "smeared with human blood." In addition he detected on the trouser cuffs a dried, greenish film of what looked like excrement. Under the microscope it proved to consist largely of oat beards. Popp decided that it was "in all probability from horse manure." By August 9 he was studying the other confiscated clothes and shoes and could soon report that the Sunday jacket which Schlicher had worn on Ascension Day showed numerous spatters of human blood. Obvious attempts had been made to wash away the larger spatters.

But the most exciting specimen was the shoes. On August 22 Popp wrote to Kaiserslautern: "The shanks of both shoes show traces of animal excrement, overlaid in places with muddy gray soil, such as might have come from a rain-wet path. Examination of this excrement . . . likewise showed oat beards; both in color, appearance, and microscopic composition the picture is the same as the findings of excrement on the accused's trousers."

At this point, Popp asked for Margarethe Filbert's shoes, to check whether she too had come into contact with horse manure. This might prove that Schlicher and the murdered woman had met at the same spot. The shoes reached him by return mail, for Seeberger by now took a keen interest in the microscopic studies. The victim's shoes proved a disappointment, however. They showed no trace of horse manure; there was only a slight encrustation of soil containing scales from the buds of beech trees, a token that it had come from a forest path.

At last, on August 24, Popp learned from Inspector Daniel that Andreas Schlicher had from the beginning denied having set foot on his field near the place where the dead woman was found. Popp at once saw an opportunity here. "Since Schlicher denies having been at the place where the body was found and at the presumptive scene of the crime," he wrote, "this assertion might possibly be checked by comparison of the soil found on the boots he wore that day. . . . We might therefore compare his boots with samples of soil from these places, as well as considering the soil from the fields he allegedly visited and the path he allegedly took. Possibly there will be important similarities or dissimilarities. . . . I therefore recommend that the samples of soil from the shoes not be removed, but left for me to remove during my studies, so that the succession of layers and the characteristic stratification may be as far as possible recorded photographically. It would be useful if I myself could collect the necessary soil samples."

Just at this point Inspector Daniel fell ill and took a sick leave, so it was September 21 before he met Popp in Falkenstein. For an entire day the two tramped over the paths and fields that Schlicher allegedly had visited on Ascension Day, as well as the field near the scene of the crime and the path that led from there to Falkenstein. Everywhere, they took small shovelfuls of soil, which they deposited in boxes. Before dusk they also climbed up to the ruined castle to take samples of its soil and stone. Two days later Popp began on a series of laboratory tests which occupied him and an associate, the Frankfurt geologist Fischer, for more than two months. They did not complete their work until November 23, 1908.

From the viewpoint of later times, Popp's method of examining soil samples may have been defective in some respects. Nevertheless, it contained almost all the basic elements of future procedures. It started from the premise that the soil is a living organism undergoing constant changes which are influenced by mineralogical developments and weather, by the addition of vegetable and animal deposits, and by the activity of soil microbes.

The soil that Popp and Daniel had taken from Schlicher's home property and the village street was distinguished by a noticeable content of greenish goose droppings. The soil from Schlicher's fields in the areas called Schinderborn, Herzenthal, and Hinterm Hahn was on the average very dark and heavily mixed with broken-down bits of porphyry rocks, as well as particles of milk-quartz and mica. The vegetable components were root fibers, weathered straw, and occasional bits of leaves.

The soil of Schlicher's field near the scene of the crime proved to be of very different composition. It was a reddish, sandy earth—a decomposition product of red sandstone mixed with splintery quartz granules, a few scales of mica, and a large amount of ferriferous red clay. The admixture of vegetable matter was very low. But it was interesting to note that the soil from the path leading from Schlicher's field to the forest, and the soil from the scene of the crime and the site where the body had lain, was composed of the same basic substances, although because of the trees it also contained a high percentage of decaying beech leaves. No less interesting was the fact that there was no horse manure on any of the other fields and paths, but there was some on the path leading to the scene of the crime. The manure had been leached by rain, and the oat beards that Popp had noticed in his first study of Schlicher's shoes also appeared in quantity in these soil samples.

Last of all came the soil from the ruined castle. It too showed unmistakable individuality. Large quantities of dark coal particles were present. But the decisive characteristic was its content of brick dust and bits of mortar from crumbling walls.

These differences among the soils provided the basis for the comparative studies that Popp had in mind. Nevertheless, the trickiest part of the job still lay ahead, for Popp remembered what a minuscule amount of soil had been clinging to the shoes, and worried about whether there was enough for his purposes. The problem was to reconstruct the last walks Schlicher had taken in those shoes. Fortunately, close inspection of the encrustations revealed a strikingly reddish coloration which raised Popp's hopes, for it resembled the color of the soil from the scene of the crime. The heavier fragments of earth stuck between the heels and the shanks seemed composed of several separate strata of soil. Popp tried carefully moistening them, then slicing through them with a razor blade, all the way down to the leather. After several attempts he succeeded in obtaining neat slices which showed crosssections of the different strata. The lowest layer, closest to the leather, proved to be earth mixed with goose droppings, such as Popp had found on Schlicher's home property and on the village street in Falkenstein. There followed a layer containing bits of grass which might have come from a path through a meadow which led from Falkenstein to Schlicher's field near the scene of the crime. Next came several thin layers of sandy red earth mixed with splintery quartz granules in red clay, scales of mica, darker bits of humus, and leaf-bud scales of beech. These layers corresponded perfectly with the soil from the scene of the crime.

The outermost layer, Popp found, consisted of earth mixed with carbon and crumbs of brick and mortar from the ruined castle.

For safety's sake Popp cut other segments, but no matter how carefully he looked, nowhere did he find particles of porphyry, the characteristic element in the soil of Schlicher's other fields. Instead, he made a surprising discovery. In order to separate plant components from the soil, he suspended several of his slices in a little water. In the course of this work he came upon tiny fibrous elements in the red strata that presumably came from the scene of the crime. These proved to be threads of wool and cotton one thirty-second to one eighth of an inch long. Some of the fibers seemed purple, but the majority were a reddish brown. Recalling the color of Margarethe Filbert's skirt and petticoat, Popp asked that these articles be sent to him from Kaiserslautern. As soon as they arrived, he examined the fabric. The skirt was made of light-brown wool, but the cloth of the petticoat was a mixture of light-brown cotton and reddish-brown threads of wool. Under the microscope, these last looked identical with the fibers embedded in the soil on Schlicher's shoes. To prove that they were, Popp hit on the idea of using spectrophotometric analysis, which had shown its worth in demonstrating hemoglobin content in bloodstains and was being used more and more frequently in research and industry to identify the chemical components of unknown compounds and to distinguish dyes. It had been found that the absorption bands of the spectra appeared at different wave lengths depending on the type of dye or chemical examined. Popp narrowed the aperture of his spectrophotometer so that each fiber under study filled it completely. In order to obtain standards for comparison, he tested woolen fibers from the petticoat and the skirt. The dye of the woolen fibers showed absorption bands in the wave-length regions of 400–550, 570–580, 650–700, and 700–750 millimicrons. The absorption bands of the petticoat fibers lay in the wave-length regions of 400–450, 490–550, 650–700, 700–780 millimicrons. The reddish-brown fibers from the mud of the shoes showed absorption bands in precisely the same regions.

Still not satisfied, Popp subjected the fibers to various chemical tests, all of which yielded the same result. The fibers were clearly the same. All this meant that on that fateful Thursday Schlicher could not possibly have been at his other fields, as he maintained, because no traces of their soils were found on his shoes. Rather, he must have walked along the village street and taken a meadow path to his field near the scene of the crime, then gone on to the actual crime site itself. Probably, when the victim's skirt turned up as the result of his dragging her by her feet, he had stepped on part of the petticoat, a few of whose fibers had adhered to the soil on his shoes. Later he must have gone up to the ruined castle to hide his bloodstained trousers.

When District Attorney Sohn and Counselor Seeberger received Popp's comprehensive report on December 1, 1908, their last doubts of Schlicher's guilt vanished. Schlicher, however, continued his denials, apparently not understanding the importance of the soil clues. When he finally realized what they signified, he offered alibis which displayed a considerable degree of cunning. He now remembered that he had worn the shoes again on Saturday, two days after the murder, when he went along with other sensation-seekers across his meadow to see the corpse in the forest. He had come close to the dead woman and stepped on her petticoat, he said. But there were plenty of witnesses who could testify that he had neither worn his Sunday shoes nor gone anywhere near the dead woman. Among these witnesses was his own wife. Unaware of Popp's researches, she stubbornly stuck to the statement she had made from the start, that she had cleaned her husband's shoes on the evening of Ascension Day and that they had not been used since. Schlicher went on denying the crime when his trial began in the district court of Kaiserslautern, and still denied it after he had been convicted and sentenced to death. Only when he learned that his sentence had been commuted to life imprisonment did he meet the state halfway. "The chemist was right, what he said about the way I went," he admitted.

He had indeed taken the path from the village to his field by way of the state forest and had come across Margarethe Filbert by accident. Reasoning that anyone so well dressed must have a large sum of money with her, he had strangled her. When he realized the pointlessness of the crime, he took revenge on the corpse by hacking its head off. He then buried the head under a large heap of stones near some bilberry and hawthorn shrubs. Later he had cleaned his clothes in a pond and sneaked home without being seen. There he changed his trousers, which were soaked through from the washing. He did not bother changing his jacket, since the small wet spots where he had washed away some blood had quickly dried. But the trousers, he thought, might give him away. He had therefore wrapped them in an old blouse belonging to his wife and hidden them in the ruined castle that evening.

Not until ten years later, in 1918, did Popp publish an account of the Schlicher affair in which he described the part played by the soil sample studies. The article appeared in the *Archiv für Kriminologie*, the journal founded by the late Hans Gross as a forum for his ideas. By this time Popp's reputation was so great that he was invited to lecture on scientific criminology at the University of Frankfurt, and five years later was granted an honorary professorship. But gratifying though these honors were for Popp, more important was the fact that he no longer stood alone. His example had been heeded and his approach was being carried over to a number of fields. The first of these was the field of hair studies, which received enormous impetus from certain events in Paris in 1909.

4

Working-class Paris was enjoying itself one warm Sunday in mid-July 1909, only a few days after the national holiday, when news of a mysterious crime swept down the boulevards and found its way into the narrowest streets and alleys of the Eleventh Arrondissement.

The starting point of it all was No. 1 Boulevard Voltaire, the ground floor of which was occupied by the Café Bardin. Business was humming during the noon hour. The Bardins, husband and wife, and their staff were scurrying between kitchen, pantry, and the filled tables. The wall clock behind the cash register read almost twelve thirty when Backert the waiter went over to Madame Bardin, who was tending the till. "There's someone screaming upstairs," he said. "You can hear it in the pantry."

Madame Bardin looked up briefly from her reckoning. What was so unusual about that? she demanded. Hadn't they heard that kind of noise before issuing from Monsieur Albert's apartment, quite often at noontime? They were enjoying themselves up there and Mademoiselle Germaine was not stingy with her cries of passion.

Backert returned to his task of collecting bottles and glasses. But with each trip to the pantry he stopped a moment to listen to the racket from upstairs. Just above were the combined office and living quarters of Albert Oursel, a thirty-five-year-old bachelor who ran an employment bureau for domestic servants. For the past year he had been living with a young Breton girl, Germaine Bichon, who was ostensibly his maid, but whose relations with her employer were certainly no secret to the people in the café below. Those relations took a highly audible form, and ever since Backert had come to work here he had often had occasion to listen to the cries and gasps of the couple upstairs, who seemed to have a decided preference for the daytime hours for this form of recreation. Monsieur Albert, as he was generally known in the house, was otherwise a gentleman of regular habits. It was his custom, for instance, to leave Paris every Saturday and visit his mother in Flint-sur-Seine, returning on Monday morning. His little mistress stayed alone in the apartment over the weekend. Backert was fairly sure that he had seen Monsieur Albert leave the house the day before, at the usual time and carrying his usual black valise. But he might have been mistaken. Perhaps he had come back a day earlier, and the two were celebrating their reunion in their customary fashion. Perhaps Mademoiselle Germaine was entertaining someone else. In any case, what went on up there was no affair of his.

The sounds had died away by now and the waiter turned his thoughts from other people's sex lives, for the activity inside the restaurant was now at its height. It was all he could do to keep up with the rush. He was back in the pantry at one ten, washing a batch of glasses, when he felt something warm fall on his head. He assumed it was water splashing up from the sink, but almost at once he felt another such heavy drop, this time on his forehead. He reached up his hand to wipe it off, and received a third drop on his bare forearm. It was a viscous red fluid. The waiter threw a quick look up at the ceiling and saw a reddish spot spreading over the dirty gray of the plaster. He instantly recalled the screams from above, tore into the restaurant, and cried out to the *patron:* "It's raining blood from Monsieur Albert's apartment."

Bardin went to the pantry to see for himself, then ran to the porter's lodge at the entrance of the building. He found Concierge Dumont and his wife and blurted out what had happened, while he stared up at the windows above the café's awning. Oursel's quarters formed a kind of foreign body within the building. Being, as it was, a professional apartment, it had a separate entrance to the right of the café and was reached by its own staircase. The passageway to the waiting rooms and office was closed by an iron gate after business hours. Oursel's living quarters lay behind the office, and could be reached only by passing through it.

The concierge shook the gate, but it was locked. He ran back to the courtyard of the building and up the main stairway. The apartment was not accessible from it, but there was a transom leading into one of the rear waiting rooms. By whom or why this transom had been built the concierge himself did not know. He shook it, but it too was firmly locked. He returned to the front of the building and, with the help of a ladder, climbed up on the café awning in order to inspect Oursel's apartment through the windows. The first window was that of the office, the next that of the dining room. Looking in, Dumont noticed nothing abnormal. But when he reached the bedroom window, he saw a disheveled bed and a scattering of woman's clothing. The mirrored wardrobe had been broken open and evidently rummaged through.

The concierge scrambled down from the awning and made for the police station of the La Folie-Méricourt district. On the way he met Patrolman Lepinay, whom he led back to the building. They carried the ladder into the courtyard and, smashing the pane of a waiting-room window, entered the apartment. They found the first and second waiting rooms untouched, but when they passed beyond them into the living quarters, they came to a halt. On the stone floor of the kitchen lay a female body, half naked. She lay on her back, dressed only in a chemise and red wrapper, her bare legs spread wide apart. Around her head a large red pool seeped over the floor. The beaten face was unrecognizable, but Dumont had no doubt that the dead girl was Germaine Bichon.

As people began to stream out of the neighboring cafés and congregate around the building, Lepinay sent word to the detective for the Eleventh Arrondissement, Inspector Carpin. Carpin came at once, to be followed soon after by Examining Magistrate Warrin, substituting for Magistrate Hastrong whose case this would have been—Hastrong was out of the city this weekend. In the meanwhile Carpin had managed to open the iron gate, so that the apartment could be entered in the usual manner.

Germaine Bichon must have been surprised by her assailant in the dining room. The table was set and a sausage lay on the plate, one end of it already eaten. A stained napkin was on the floor, as though Germaine Bichon had dropped it when she saw the murderer. Hairpins and combs were scattered all the way to the kitchen. From this Carpin concluded that a struggle had begun in the dining room and continued to the kitchen. There bloodstains indicated that the girl had been forced to the floor and savagely beaten. There was no weapon in sight, but when the inspector entered the bedroom, he saw a hatchet on a chair. It had obviously been washed, for it was still wet. Carpin assumed that it must be the murder instrument, and that the murderer had also used it to break open the wardrobe. The entire contents of the wardrobe had been hurled to the floor. Since the strongbox in the office had also been forced, it seemed evident that the murderer had been looking for money. Oursel's secretary-desk had also been broken open. But either the criminal had regarded its contents as unimportant or for some reason had not had time to look through all the drawers and pigeonholes. The sparse personal correspondence had been left undisturbed and bore no relation to the case—with one exception. Among the letters was a note written in a clumsy hand. It read: "Dear sir, this letter is written by your little 'Lolotte' who in a year has become your sweetheart. I want this letter to be a reminder to you of the year we have had together. You are thirty-four years old, I am seventeen. There have daily been more joys than sorrows. . . . These months have passed like a day. You have been like a father to me. I love you beyond reason. I feel as if I were your daughter. . . ."

There the note broke off. If it were a declaration of love from the dead girl to Albert Oursel, it suggested the possibility of a crime of jealousy. Had some passionate admirer forced himself upon the girl in Oursel's absence? Had he killed her because she had repulsed him? But would a man in such a situation look for money? Or had some second lover, whom Germaine received when Oursel was away, tried to use the opportunity to rob the office, and had Germaine made an attempt to stop him?

Then, again, the murderer might have been some unknown burglar who was aware of Oursel's departure but had not counted on finding his mistress there on a Sunday. One argument against that possibility was the fact that the apartment showed not the slightest trace of forcible entry. The gate had been locked. None of the windows was damaged. But when Carpin came to the transom between two waiting rooms, he had a surprise. Under the rather high transom stood a chair. The bolt of the transom, which opened only from inside, was not shot. Concierge Dumont was called at once. He stared at Carpin in consternation. He could swear that the transom had been firmly bolted when he had shaken it violently after first being called between one ten and one twenty. It was absolutely out of the question that it could have been open at that time. Therefore it must have been opened between the time he tried it and the time he returned with the patrolman, Lepinay. Had the unknown murderer escaped through this transom while the concierge was going to the police? Could Oursel or Germaine have neglected to slide the bolt, thus allowing a burglar to climb in, lock the transom behind him, commit murder and robbery, and then wait coolly for the concierge to go away before escaping? Then again, there was the possibility that Germaine Bichon might have admitted another lover through the transom. But in that case he would have had to pass by the concierge's lodge, both on entering and on leaving after the murder.

Warrin asked whether anyone had been watching the entrance while Dumont was going for the police. When he heard that Madame Dumont had been in the lodge, he sent for her. Had she noticed anything unusual at the time in question? Madame Dumont was quite definite in her answer. She had not. Except that shortly before her husband came back with Lepinay, a woman she did not know had rapped at her window. When she opened her door, the woman had said: "I wanted to see Adèle the nursemaid who lives on the fourth floor, but she doesn't seem to be home. Will you be so kind as to tell her that Angèle was here?" The concierge attributed no importance to the incident. There was always a good deal of visiting among nursemaids and servants on Sundays. Warrin too dismissed the episode. He had the entire building searched from attic to cellar, but without result. The questioning of all the tenants in the building, the neighbors, and the patrons of the café also came to nothing. No one had been seen leaving the house during the critical interval between twelve thirty and one thirty. Warrin felt distinctly relieved when he heard that Octave Hamard, the chief of the Sûreté, had arrived to look into things himself.

Meanwhile the crowd around No. 1 Boulevard Voltaire had grown so large that the police had to open a lane for the chief and some of his officials to enter the building. Hamard moved with the briskness of a man who thoroughly knew his business. There had scarcely been a capital crime in the past two decades which he had not handled personally. After leaving the army in 1888 and joining the Paris police force, he had risen swiftly, so that by 1902 he was already head of the Sûreté. Here, he sensed, was another sensational case the solving of which would be a personal triumph. Of course he was somewhat shorthanded at the moment owing to the holiday and the summery weather. Even the Medical Examiner, Dr. Victor Balthazard, was out of town and would not be back until evening. Still, there was enough that he could do right now. Above all he wanted to find out something about the curious ménage of Albert Oursel. Inspectors Sablon and Darnal were to canvass the tenants of the house for information. He was waiting to hear what new facts came to light when the café proprietor sent up some interesting witnesses in the form of two nursemaids named Elaine and Suzanne, and an older woman named Madame Dumouchet. All three had been supposed to meet the dead girl that afternoon in Bardin's café.

The two girls proved to be chance acquaintances of Germaine's. They were terribly shocked at what had happened. Moreover, they knew very little about Germaine, whose stories about herself had tended to be fantastic. Nevertheless, Hamard was able to glean a few details that somewhat illuminated the dead girl's past. She had actually been barely sixteen, and came from Chauvey, in the Loire-Inférieure Département. She was one of many children and had come to Paris a year and a half earlier to escape from her drunkard of a father. She had met the two girls on the street and struck up a sort of friendship with them. At first she had given out that Oursel was her uncle, and later she pretended that he was going to marry her. The girls noticed that she had changed somewhat in the past few months, and suspected that she had "got herself knocked up," possibly by Oursel. At any rate she had complained once or twice that Oursel "wanted to get rid of her." A little while ago she had left the apartment and taken a job as a maid with an Italian who lived in the neighborhood. The very first night he had made her his mistress, and a few days later had beaten her so badly that she fled back to Oursel. Oursel had taken her in, but said he was keeping her only out of pity, until he found another post for her.

Madame Dumouchet proved to be an elderly cleaning woman who had come in every day since May to do up Oursel's office. She also was too staggered by the tragedy to be disposed to gossip. But Hamard soon noted that, like many servants who had spent their lives working for a variety of families, she was a good psychologist and a keen observer. She confirmed the fact that the relationship between Oursel and the dead girl had been deteriorating for some time. In her opinion Germaine had all along been "better in bed than as a housekeeper" and found it perfectly understandable that Oursel should have wanted to send her packing. But Oursel, in Madame Dumouchet's view, was something of a mother's boy and too weak to act decisively. He had let things ride, though Germaine was by now a burden to him. It was true that the girl was pregnant, perhaps by Oursel. In fact, she may have tried to make it happen. But possibly it was some other man, because she had had various affairs in the past few months, in order to make Oursel jealous. Oursel, however, had remained unmoved. She had also liked to write love letters to her protector, the kind a girl might write who'd gone to school only to the age of twelve. On being shown the letter found in Oursel's desk, the cleaning woman said it must have been written by Germaine and no one else.

Hamard inquired whether Germaine might have let other lovers into the apartment when Oursel was away, perhaps the various men she'd taken up with. But Madame Dumouchet replied with an unequivocal "Never." The girl used to tell her all her troubles and had confided, among other things, that she always felt afraid when she was left alone in the big empty apartment. She always locked the doors between the rooms, and even pushed furniture up against them. When she met people, it was always in some lively place outside the house, and she would go to see her lovers in their own quarters. To be sure, Madame Dumouchet had been working at the office for only the past three months, but she was quite certain that Germaine must have acted this way all along. If Hamard wanted to learn more about the situation, he would do well to ask the cleaning woman who had been her predecessor on the job. She, too, had probably been Germaine's confidante and could tell a tale. The woman's name was Rosella, and she lived somewhere in the Saint-Ambroise quarter. Her exact address Madame Dumouchet did not know, but Madame Dessignol would surely know it.

Who was Madame Dessignol? Hamard asked. Oh, that was Oursel's assistant and receptionist. During business hours she sat at the entrance to the waiting rooms and screened the clients. The only way to the apartment also led past Madame Dessignol. She was probably the last person to have seen Germaine Bichon alive, since she worked until

seven o'clock every evening and was responsible for locking both entrance doors, the downstairs door and the upstairs door, before she
went home. On Saturdays, too, she stayed until seven after Oursel left
for the country. Aside from Oursel, only Madame Dessignol and Germaine Bichon had keys to the office and the apartment.

When Hamard asked about the relationship between the receptionist
and the dead girl, the cleaning woman hesitated. Then she replied that
Madame Dessignol was always polite and obliging, but was no friend of
Germaine Bichon. She herself was only in her late twenties, and was
said to have an eye on Oursel.

It was approaching 6:30 P.M. by this time, and Patrolman Lepinay
reported that Dr. Balthazard had just driven up and was making his way
through the throng of the curious to the house. A moment later Balthazard's athletic figure appeared in the doorway at the top of the stairs. He
was then thirty-seven years old, a good decade away from the time when
he would come into his full glory. In 1909 he still stood in the shadow of
Professor Thoinot, who held the Chair of Forensic Medicine at the Sor-
bonne previously occupied by the celebrated Ambroise Tardieu and
Paul Camille Hippolyte Brouardel. Thoinot was scarcely of their caliber, and had already exposed his incompetence in the case of the dangerous child-murderer, Jeanne Weber. Balthazard may have felt it an odd
coincidence that he was here, in his professional capacity, for he had
been born on the same Boulevard Voltaire, where his father also had
owned a café. His youthful interests had turned toward mathematics
and technology, and he had been graduated from the noted École Poly-
technique. In 1893, with his characteristic versatility and thirst for
experience, he had switched to a military career. As an artillery officer
he had begun studying medicine, and he had spent some years exploring
the new field of radium research. In 1904, when he turned to forensic
medicine, he could draw upon a fund of medical knowledge such as few
of his contemporaries possessed. He had at once begun to extend the
range of forensic medicine. He was one of the first to propose using the
microscope to connect bullets removed from bodies with the barrels of
the weapons that might have fired them. He had also, together with
Marcelle Lambert, his assistant and later his wife, learned to read valuable lessons from the study of hairs found at the scenes of crimes or accidents.

Without the slightest trace of emotion, Balthazard entered the
kitchen and knelt beside the dead girl. The pronounced coldness which
in later years earned him the reputation of being rude and brutal sprang

in part from his complete concentration upon the matter at hand, but it was also partly a defense against his innate sensitivity. He was only too well aware of this trait and kept it severely in check. With the swiftness of experience, he gave a preliminary estimate of the time of death as "between 12 and 2 P.M." He pointed out the discolorations of the skin on wrists and throat which suggested a violent struggle. Death had been caused by multiple crushing blows upon the skull. He estimated the number of blows at thirty to forty; the strokes had apparently been delivered indiscriminately with the blunt and the sharp edge of the hatchet. He pushed Germaine Bichon's chemise up above her firm breasts and diagnosed a pregnancy of perhaps five months. Then he suddenly paused and stooped lower over the girl's left hand, which lay outstretched. After a moment, he raised the body slightly, so that the right hand was also visible.

The fingers of both hands were clenched. Balthazard did not have to open them to see the clumps of hair, ranging in color from blonde to light brown, encrusted with blood, protruding between the fingers. He took some from each hand, asked for a sheet of white paper, laid the hairs on it, went to the dining-room window, and studied his find— closely watched by Hamard and Warrin. Ignoring the crowd below, who recognized him and stared up at him, he completed his examination and turned toward the kitchen again. The body could be taken to the morgue, he said, but no one must touch the hands. Had anything interesting come to light as yet? Hamard replied, with that reserve toward medico-legal experts which he had had ever since the Jeanne Weber affair, that they were still working in the dark unless Balthazard himself could tell them something. Balthazard replied coldly that he was not yet in a position to do so, but he had one suggestion which might save the detectives superfluous work. They would be well advised not to waste time looking for a murderer—what they had to find was a murderess. His evidence was the hair lying on the paper. He would have more to say after he had examined it in his laboratory.

5

The use of hair as a clue to a murder was scarcely new. In 1689 one Madame de Mazel, a propertied widow, had been found stabbed in Paris under strange circumstances. Police Lieutenant Deffita noted three hairs in one of her hands and concluded that she had pulled them from her murderer's head. That was as far as he could go, however, for on consulting several wigmakers he was informed that they could not tell whether the hairs were of human or animal origin.

Except for a few experiments by the French scientists Ollivier and Orfila, systematic microscopic studies of hair began only after 1857. In that year J. L. Lassaigne's essay, *De l'Examen physique des poils et des cheveux* appeared in the *Annales d'hygiène publique*. Twelve years later a German, Dr. Pfaff, brought out a book entitled "Human Hair in Its Physiological, Pathological, and Forensic Significance." He deplored how little had been done in this field, since, as he put it, "precise knowledge of the characteristic differences of hair is essential to the forensic physician and the detective, inasmuch as hairs can often furnish the most important clues for the solving of crimes." Pfaff attempted the first full description of the different forms of hairs upon the human body, from the hair of the head to the pubic hair, supplementing his descriptions by numerous drawings. Unfortunately he named characteristics which were for the most part not sustained by subsequent research. But despite its errors, his book also contained fundamental insights which remain valid a century later. This was particularly true in his distinction between animal and human hair. He testified in a number of trials involving sodomy, and was able to prove the presence of horse and dog hairs on the trousers of the suspects. To this extent, at any rate, hair analysis was on a sound basis.

By the time of the murder of Germaine Bichon, hair analysis had become the hobby of a growing number of medico-legal specialists. The famous *Textbook of Legal Medicine* by Eduard von Hofmann, the founder of the Vienna school of forensic medicine, published at the turn of the century, contained a special chapter on "Examination of Hair." By the summer of 1909 certain ruling principles had become well established. It was well known that the hair of both man and animals consists of three parts: the root, the shaft, and the tip. The main part of the hair, the shaft, is composed of three layers: the cuticle, the cortex, and the medulla. The cuticle is the outer skin of the hair. It is formed by scales of epidermis laid one over another like roofing tiles. Underneath is the cortex, composed of long horny cells in which light-gray, deep-yellow, light-brown, dark-brown, or black pigments are distributed, giving the hair its coloring. Between these cells are spaces filled with air. The medulla is the core of the hair and in man is often absent or present only in segments. In any case the medulla is composed of small cells punctuated with large air spaces which under the microscope appear black by transmitted light, silvery by incident light. This presence of air in the medulla was an obstacle to microscopic analysis. It often caused the formation of a meaningless black streak which for a long time was thought to be a dark pigment. Up to 1909 no method was known for "de-aerating" the medulla so that its cellular structure could be studied in every case.

Proceeding from this knowledge, scientists had discovered that there were radical differences between the cuticle of animal hair and that of human hair. In animals, the scaly cuticle cells were not only larger but also more irregular. For many species of animals characteristic shapes had been determined. There were also typical differences in the thickness of the cuticle and the medulla. Not every species of animal hair had been studied, but enough to indicate that the medulla in animal hair was consistently heavier than that of human hair. There could be considerable variety in the cellular structure of the medulla. The hair of some animals had round medullar cells, while others had oval, ring-, or basket-shaped cells arranged in neat rows. Some animals had thicker medullas, composed of several such layers of cells side by side or forming, as in rabbits and hares, spirals. Distinguishing animal from human hair was therefore a fairly routine matter and presented no difficulties if enough hairs were available for study.

Beyond this basic distinction, however, there were various other complexes of questions. If hair had been established as human, was it male or female? What kind of hair was it: from the head, the beard, the pubic region? Since at this period most women wore their hair long, the hair of a woman's head could fairly easily be distinguished by its length and the divided tips which came from frequent brushing. Male hair from the head was characterized by relative shortness and ends clipped by scissors. Freshly cut hair shows blunt, sharp-edged ends which begin to round off after two days and after about a month are fully rounded. The fact that even clipped hair will fray at the ends after prolonged brushing was an additional complication.

As for the other hair of the human body, hair from the beard was easiest to recognize as to its gender. In the course of decades it had been found that the hair of the beard has a wider diameter than any other hair. It averages 0.005 to 0.006 inches as against an average diameter of 0.002 to 0.003 inches for hair from the head. It was virtually impossible to distinguish between male and female hair from other parts of the body. For a time it was thought that female pubic hair averaged 0.006 inches, male pubic hair only 0.004 inches. But then it was discovered that all these measurements are subject to extraordinary variation, and that even single hairs show different diameters if measured at different points.

Some distinction proved possible by examination of the roots. The roots of pubic or armpit hair are short and plump. They are wider than long, unlike the hair of the head and beard, where the roots are always longer than wide. Again much depended on the amount of hair available for study.

There was less difficulty determining whether hair had been pulled, fallen out, been cut or otherwise done violence to. The German scientists Oesterlen and Georg Puppe had endeavored to arrive at reliable rules. Fallen hair can be recognized by its root, which has been expelled from the sheath in which it normally sits. In such case the roots show as dried and shrunken. When hair is pulled out, the roots are damp, bulbous, and open at the bottom. Hair that has been ripped has first been stretched to the limits of its elasticity. The broken ends show a curious curl. No doubt with more research in this department, a great many more interesting facts would come to light, but they were not especially to the point. For criminological purposes, what mattered was some way of proving that particular human hairs, found on the victim of a murder, an assault, a rape, a burglary, or a traffic accident, came from a particular human being, the culprit.

Until the seventies physicians were fairly bold in judging whether or not hair belonged to a given suspect. They would go on the basis of color, cuticle pattern, thickness of the hair, and thickness of the medulla. But as early as 1879 we find Virchow using extremely cautious phraseology in a deposition: "The appearance of the hair is such that it is not inconsistent with having come from the accused." Hair, he went on to say, was never so typical that the scientist could indubitably assert it had to come from the head of the accused.

Ever since Virchow's pronouncement, many attempts had been made to find those qualities in human hair which would allow the forensic scientist to rule that certain hairs came from certain heads or from certain parts of the body of a certain person. But it seemed that nothing could be made of even the most complete correspondences in thickness of hair shaft, type and distribution of medulla, pattern of the cuticle, and shape of root and tip. The trouble was that all these qualities varied enormously in hairs taken from the head of one and the same person. Even the color of hair was by no means uniform in individuals. Only the conjunction of many variously pigmented hairs created the general impression of hair color as blond, black, brown, light-brown, or dark-brown. How treacherous color comparisons could be had been exposed shortly after the turn of the century in the case of Therese Pucher, the victim of a murder in Austria. Three hairs clutched in the murdered woman's hand were compared with the hair of a suspect, and were judged to have come from the suspect's beard. The investigator based his conclusion on the fact that the three hairs showed light-pigmented segments alternating in a curious fashion with dark-pigmented sections. The same phenomenon was found in all hairs taken for purposes of comparison. Nevertheless the investigator was careful to end his report with the following reminder: "Conclusions of identity cannot be drawn with absolute certainty on the basis of comparison of hairs in this case any more than in similar cases." In the end, the suspect was proved innocent: another man confessed to the crime.

Thus even the most remarkable agreement in color distribution did not suffice to prove identity of hair if only individual hairs were available for study. Hence it was suggested that only comparison of larger tufts of hair could be relied on; statistical averages could then be checked against each other. In 1902 a German doctor named Haase compared tufts of hair from the head of a murdered man with tufts of hair found in the trouser pocket of a suspect. Haase determined what percentage of the hairs contained medullas and what percentage had no medullas. His conclusion that the two tufts corresponded and that the man was therefore the culprit was subsequently supported by other means. Nevertheless, the method had grave disadvantages. It was toilsome, roundabout, and called for the greatest care in every individual case. Something quicker and surer was needed.

A better index seemed to be those qualities which came about as the result of outside influences. These included the coating of typical kinds of dirt on particular parts of the hair, or the effects of artificial curling or dyeing. After the turn of the century many studies were undertaken in Germany, France, Austria, and Italy on hair dyes that contained silver, manganese, iron, bismuth, and calcium salts. Chemical methods for demonstrating the presence of such substances were developed. But in spite of all efforts, the identification of particular hairs and proof of their origin from particular persons still remained, in 1909, a dubious affair. About all that could be done was to find gross disparities which would rule out certain persons and save detectives the trouble of following false trails.

6

That, in general, was the foundation that Balthazard had to build on when, on the morning of July 19, 1909, in the Paris morgue, he set about examining the wisps of hair clutched in the hands of Germaine Bichon.

The preceding examination of the body had confirmed the conclusions Balthazard had reached in his first quick survey. He counted nine wounds from blows with the blade of the hatchet and forty-eight administered with the back of it. The autopsy proper, which could hardly throw any light on the course of the crime, was postponed until the following day. Balthazard wanted to give all his attention to the finds of hair. If he could prove that the hair was indeed that of a woman, and not that of the victim herself, he would have data of overwhelming importance.

At eleven o'clock in the morning Balthazard and Marcelle Lambert freed the hairs from the dead girl's fingers and placed them in bowls of soda solution to free them of dirt and blood. These bowls were taken to the pathology laboratory. At two in the afternoon Marcelle Lambert washed each individual hair in alcohol. The hairs were then removed to a glass plate coated with gelatin and each fastened down with Canada balsam. At the end of the elaborate procedure, Balthazard had several dozen hairs whose length he measured. The shortest were fifteen centimeters long (six inches), while most of the others were much longer. This provided a good basis (in those days) for identifying the hair as a woman's. Microscopic study showed the familiar characteristics of human hair: smooth cuticle and a weak, absent, or interrupted medulla. The ends of all the hairs were uncut and showed the frayed tips typical of woman's hair. Careful examination of the root ends showed that with few exceptions the hairs had been pulled out or torn off. Along with hairs whose roots were moist and plump there were others with dried roots which had been on the point of falling out naturally. The other hairs had obviously been torn off close to the root. The typical marks of such tears could be detected: the narrowed medulla, caused by stretching, the greater separation between the ends of the cuticle scales, and the "undulations" at the torn ends. Finally, Balthazard determined the diameter of each individual hair at various points and calculated the average thickness. He found that the diameter of all hairs *except a single one* ranged from 0.0024 to 0.0032 inches, giving an average of 0.0028 inches. The one hair that did not fit into this pattern had the unusual thickness of 0.004 inches, so that it could scarcely have come from the same head as the other hairs. When Balthazard tried to determine the coloration, he came upon another striking difference between this one hair and all the others. Observed with the naked eye, the tuft of hairs appeared light-brown to blond. Microscopic study showed a mixture of brown and blond pigments, with the blond so prominent in a bunch of hairs that it seemed reasonable to postulate the head as a whole being blond. The one hair of unusually large diameter, however, also proved to be an exception in coloring. It was a vigorous chestnut brown approaching black.

In the course of the afternoon Balthazard and his assistant returned to the morgue to begin the second part of their study, comparison with Germaine Bichon's own hair. Obtaining sample hairs from various parts of the head was in itself a problem because of the many wounds. In the laboratory the cleansing procedures and other preparations were repeated. When Balthazard finally began measuring the thickness of the hair, he found at once that it was unusual. The minimal values were in the range of 0.003 inches, the maximal as much as 0.005 inches. Thus there was such a distinct difference from the tuft of hair found between the fingers that Balthazard felt entitled to exclude Germaine herself as the source of the latter. On the other hand, the one hair in the clump that had an average thickness of 0.004 inches accorded perfectly with the general character of Germaine Bichon's hair. Her hair color was chestnut brown veering toward black. Thus Balthazard was able to sum up his conclusions as follows: The hair found between Germaine Bichon's fingers had come from a woman and, with the exception of a single hair from the victim's own head, undoubtedly could be ascribed to the murderess.

Toward five in the afternoon he sent his deposition to Examining Magistrate Warrin. He stated that he was prepared at any time to compare the hair of possible female suspects with the hair found on the body. In view of the difficulties of such studies, however, he would have to insist on carrying through the necessary procedures himself.

Sûreté chief Hamard had by no means ignored Balthazard's remark the night before, however bizarre it had sounded. He had before him the record of a careful interrogation of the concierge, Madame Dumont, about the unknown woman who had passed by her lodge shortly after the discovery of the murder and had given her name as "Angèle." The concierge's memory was not especially good. Nevertheless she had been able to state that the stranger was tall, rather corpulent, and between thirty-five and forty. She had apparently been a woman with a rather ordinary, puffy face, wearing a black kerchief, black bodice, and a black-and-white dotted skirt, such as servants often wore in those days. Most of her hair had been hidden under the kerchief, but the concierge thought it had been light-brown to blond. Inquiries among all the families in the building threw more suspicion on this unknown woman, since none of the nursemaids had a friend named Angèle. Nevertheless, unless the woman had hit on a right name by sheer luck, she must have known her way about the house, for there was a maid named Adèle actually working for a family on the third floor.

Hamard had also questioned Oursel's receptionist, Madame Dessignol, as soon as she appeared at 1 Boulevard Voltaire. She was about thirty, an undistinctive pale-blond, thin, pug-nosed creature. Hamard could only feel that the cleaning woman, Madame Dumouchet, had summed her up correctly. In spite of the shocking murder in her employer's apartment, Suzanne Dessignol remained quite composed, indeed rather cold, and exhibited a kind of calculating obligingness. She stated that she had last seen Germaine on Saturday, the day before the murder. She herself had left the office earlier than usual because of the holiday, and since Germaine wanted to shop, they had gone out together. She and Germaine had walked together as far as the Place de la République. After a while Germaine had left, saying that she wanted to be back home before dark. This, Suzanne Dessignol said, was the last time she had been with the dead girl. She did not know whether Germaine might actually have lingered in the Place de la République to talk with admirers and perhaps take them back home with her under cover of darkness. As for money, there had been only seven francs in the cash drawer and thirty francs in Oursel's desk. Both sums had been stolen. She could not state whether anything had been stolen from the wardrobe in the bedroom. With pronounced emphasis—a shade too pronounced—she declared that she had never paid any attention to Oursel's apartment, and had certainly never set foot in his bedroom. She had uttered the word "bedroom" in so contemptuous a tone that Hamard had drawn a red line under these passages in the record. He had likewise underlined her reference to the possibility that Germaine might have taken home a chance acquaintance on Saturday night. Recalling the cleaning woman's statement that Germaine would never have admitted a stranger to the apartment, Hamard deliberately raised the question once more, asking Suzanne Dessignol whether she thought it possible that Germaine might have admitted an unknown admirer on Saturday night. Suzanne replied that she did not know, since she had never been in Oursel's rooms in the evening. (At this point in the record Hamard again underscored the statement in red and added a marginal comment: "Suppressed desires?") The receptionist added that she did not want to say anything bad about the dead, but with such primitive, sensual creatures, who slept with their fathers and brothers when they were only children, anything was conceivable. ("Hate? Jealousy?" Hamard noted in the margin.) Finally Hamard asked Suzanne what she had been doing on Sunday. She replied that she had gone for a walk and, as Hamard noted, could cite no witnesses to confirm her story.

On the whole, Hamard felt distinctly suspicious of the receptionist. Only too often he had seen unprepossessing female employees cherishing a hidden and therefore all the more ardent passion for their employers, and hating rivals to the point of murder. Could it be that Suzanne Dessignol would necessarily have come to terms with Oursel's affairs "away from home," but had regarded Germaine, half her age and physically far more attractive, as an intruder into her own "realm"? Had she decided that the girl had been hanging around far too long? Or perhaps, out of devotion mixed with egotism, she had decided to liberate Oursel from the jade who had become a nuisance to him. In that case she might have used her key to enter the apartment at night, hidden there all night, and attacked Germaine when she got up toward noon and opened the barricaded bedroom door. She might then have escaped through the transom, with which she would have been thoroughly familiar. Hamard noted these possibilities on the record of the interrogation, and ordered his men to look into the receptionist's affairs and to check her statements about the day of the murder.

Meanwhile, Albert Oursel had returned from Flint-sur-Seine. Two detectives met him at the Saint-Lazare station and took him to Hamard at once. Hamard was a systematic man, and he meant to pursue all possibilities. His knowledge of human nature suggested to him that it was far from improbable that Germaine might have been murdered by her employer. How many men there were of Oursel's type, too weak to break with a troublesome pregnant mistress, to whom murder seemed the easiest way out. Oursel might have utilized his usual weekend visit to his mother merely as an alibi; he could have returned to Paris unnoticed, committed the murder, given the rooms the appearance of burglary, and then returned to Flint-sur-Seine.

Oursel proved to be an unimpressive, nervous fellow with sparse hair and a well-curled mustache. Although he had learned of the terrible event while still in Flint-sur-Seine, he seemed pale and distraught. He admitted that Germaine had been his mistress for a year. It had happened the way such things always happened. She had turned up at his office accompanied by her sister, to apply for a position—wearing a thin summer dress, her youthful breasts pushing out her blouse. Oursel swore he had not known that she was barely fifteen years old. In any case, she had seemed to him the embodiment of voluptuousness. Since he needed a housekeeper at the time anyhow, he had hired her—"crazy with lust"—although she knew hardly anything about housekeeping. For two days she had slept in his waiting room; then he had taken her to his bed, and she had not disappointed him. He had spent five or six wild months with her. When he had had enough, he told her that she must take another job, and he had found several and offered them to her. He had been too good-natured to drive her out of his apartment. He admitted that she had become a nuisance because she was so attached to him. He admitted that she wrote him letters when he ignored her and did not talk with her. He also admitted that she had tried to make him jealous. After being cornered by Hamard, he finally admitted that he knew about the baby; Germaine had tried to use her pregnancy to put "a little pressure" on him. But he swore that he was not the father. He was "careful about such things" and avoided complications. When he began to gather from Hamard's questions that the Sûreté chief suspected him of murder, he lost his composure. But after a while he got a grip on himself and enumerated the various points of his alibi: his departure from Paris on Saturday afternoon, arrival at his mother's, coffee in the afternoon, an evening with the mayor and the doctor of Flint-sur-Seine, Sunday morning in church, Sunday dinner with the schoolmaster, a three-hour bicycle ride with a friend, a game of cards with the schoolmaster in the evening.

Hamard noted down every single point and ordered the police to make inquiries in Flint-sur-Seine, checking every detail. He then went to the apartment with Oursel to determine what had been stolen. Except for the thirty-seven francs from the cash drawer and the secretary-desk, nothing but a Russian gold ruble worth forty francs and a gold watch chain had vanished. All in all the loot seemed too petty, as Oursel had to admit, to justify a murder; it looked rather like an attempt to divert suspicion toward an imaginary burglar. Oursel could not suggest anyone who might have killed Germaine. Nor could he explain how a stranger—except for himself and Suzanne Dessignol—could have entered the apartment. All these circumstances steadily increased Hamard's suspicions of Oursel. But at four o'clock in the afternoon these suspicions collapsed like a house of cards. Oursel's alibi was unshakable. The police reported that he had been seen so frequently from Saturday afternoon to Monday morning in Flint-sur-Seine that he could not possibly have been in Paris for so much as a second.

Though Hamard had given priority to the interrogations of Madame Dumont, Suzanne Dessignol, and Albert Oursel, he had also sent detectives out to comb the entire La Folie-Méricourt quarter for possible witnesses. He hoped to locate some of the dead girl's acquaintances, especially the men with whom she was reputed to have slept. From Suzanne Dessignol they also obtained the full name and address of the cleaning woman who had been Madame Dumouchet's predecessor: Rosella Rousseau, 56 Boulevard Belleville. Finally, the detectives queried the servants and nursemaids in the quarter. The results of their day were scanty.

A visit to the home of Rosella Rousseau revealed the fact that the former cleaning woman lived with a nail-maker named Martin and was called "Madame Martin" in the neighborhood. No one was at home, and the detectives left a summons for Rosella Rousseau to present herself at the Saint-Ambroise police headquarters. Of Germaine's multitudinous lovers, only one was found: a traveling salesman named Pierre Maçon, who testified that he had had the briefest of flings with the girl some six months earlier. After an acquaintance of barely an hour, she had gone to his room, had intercourse, and afterward asked him, in payment, to write a love letter for her to Oursel. Maçon had taken the request as a joke, had not seen his little bedmate again, and had been in Lille during the previous weekend.

The systematic questioning of servants did, however, yield one interesting item. A nursemaid named Emilie Griffat told a curious story. She reported being accosted by a woman in the vicinity of the Place de la République, who asked her to accompany her to the Oursel employment agency. She wanted to ask for some money that was owing her there, and needed a witness. The nursemaid had refused. She described the stranger as about forty years old, inconspicuously dressed, puffy of face, her hair between light-brown and blond. Later a detective came upon another maid named Lucille who told a similar story. A woman had stopped her on the Boulevard Voltaire, asked whether she knew Albert Oursel, and requested her to go with her to the office as a witness. Lucille, too, had refused. As far as she could recall, the stranger had introduced herself as Madame Bosch. She had been of medium height, with a florid face, and had worn a gray dress with a gray camisole. Her hair was light-brown or blond.

These two reports were lying on Hamard's desk when Balthazard's findings were brought to him at five o'clock. Hamard was irritated by the failures of the first day's work, and skimmed through Balthazard's report in a mood of considerable annoyance. But when he came to the statement that the hairs found in Germaine Bichon's hand had been, with one exception, of light-brown to blond color, he laid the report down and checked the interviews with the nursemaids. Then he turned to the record of the concierge's description of the unknown "Angèle." After considering the matter for a moment, he ordered Detective Dol to center his attention on a search for "Angèle" and the woman who had accosted the nursemaids. The next step was to have Suzanne Dessignol brought to Balthazard's laboratory—for hair comparisons.

7

Before Balthazard proceeded to the autopsy of Germaine Bichon on Tuesday, July 20, he examined Suzanne Dessignol's hair. The receptionist allowed him to cut various locks off without the slightest show of emotion on her part. Coolly, with a touch of mockery, she said good-by and left Balthazard and Marcelle Lambert to their work.

Under the microscope all the samples of Suzanne Dessignol's hair proved to be remarkably homogeneous. Every hair was pale blond and without any shadings or interspersion of darker pigments. In color, there was no relation to the tuft of light-brown-blond hair clutched in the dead girl's fingers. The thickness of the hair also differed markedly. Suzanne Dessignol's hair was remarkably fine; its average diameter did not exceed 0.0024 inches.

Hamard might have been discouraged had the report reached him half an hour earlier. But as it happened, Suzanne Dessignol no longer concerned him. When Balthazard's report came in, he had just finished reading the record of the interview with Rosella Rousseau made by a detective from the Saint-Ambroise headquarters. The content seemed totally uninteresting. To be sure, Rosella Rousseau had also been a confidante of Germaine Bichon, but the woman seemed so stupid that the detective had got nothing out of her that Hamard did not already know. In fact, Hamard had been on the point of laying the record aside when his eyes chanced to fall on the personal data: Louise Rosella Rousseau, divorced, formerly Madame *Bosch*. Wasn't that the name used by the unknown woman when she had introduced herself to the nursemaid Lucille and asked the girl to accompany her to Oursel? What was more, Hamard had received several new reports of the same nature. An unknown middle-aged woman had spoken to two more nursemaids on July 10, in a café on the Boulevard Voltaire, asking them to accompany her to Oursel's. The woman had not given her name in this case, and the girls were not able to describe her well. But it seemed likely that the same person was involved in all four incidents.

Hamard gave orders for Rosella Rousseau to be brought to him that afternoon, and arranged for the four nursemaids to be waiting in an adjoining room, as well as Madame Dumont, the concierge. Possibly, Hamard remarked to Examining Magistrate Hastrong, he was acting only on a hunch. Still, it was conceivable that Rosella Rousseau for some undetermined reason had been trying to get into Oursel's apartment, that she had killed Germaine Bichon for an equally unknown reason and had escaped from the building by pretending to be "Angèle."

At three o'clock in the afternoon Rosella Rousseau was brought into Hamard's office. She was a slovenly-looking creature with drooping breasts, bloated belly, and ravaged face expressing a curious compound of sensuality, evil, and motherliness. She seemed unperturbed. Hamard threw a searching glance at her unkempt hair. It was indubitably light-brown, with blond strands, as unsavory as the rest of her person.

Asked for an account of her life, she poured out with prolix incoherence the kind of sordid history only too common in the French metropolis: a proletarian childhood, seduction at eleven, marriage at twenty; her husband, Jean Bosch, a workman with a weakness for drink; the birth and death of her only child; Bosch's rapid sinking into alcoholism; quarrels, beatings, and separation; a period as a factory worker; finally in 1905 meeting with Henri Martin, the nail-maker, whose wife had left him and who was living alone with one child. The two now lived together at 56 Boulevard Belleville. From time to time she hired out as a cleaning woman to earn a few francs.

She declared that she had left Oursel because she had been unable to stand looking on at his conduct toward a "simple girl of the people." It soon was clear to Hamard that Rosella Rousseau, though talkative enough, had none of Madame Dumouchet's talent for observation. As soon as anything was said about the murder the woman broke into violent sobbing: she had loved "that poor thing Germaine like a mother." Asked who in her opinion could have killed the girl, she replied that it could only have been someone who had the key, for how else could the person have got into the apartment? At this point Hamard attempted a ruse by asking whether after quitting her job she had ever been in the apartment and whether she knew a nursemaid named Adèle in the building. But Rosella Rousseau seemed neither confused nor alarmed. No, she replied, she had never been back there. And no, she did not know any Adèle. Did she know any of the other nursemaids of the neighborhood and had she talked with them? She said she had not. On what terms had she parted from Oursel? Had they quarreled? Oh, she said, she had simply not gone back there. Had Oursel owed her any wages? No, why should he have? She had worked by the day and he had paid her every day.

Hamard opened the door and ushered in the four maids. He asked Rosella Rousseau whether she knew these girls. Had she ever met them? Once again the woman showed no signs of embarrassment. She had never seen them before, she declared. The girls claimed, Hamard explained, that she had accosted each of them on the street or in a café and asked them to accompany her to Oursel. Rosella Rousseau replied that she could not imagine what ever gave the girls such an idea. They must be mistaking her for someone else. Hamard insisted: Wasn't her name also Bosch? A Madame Bosch had spoken to the girls, and had looked just like her. "There are thousands of Bosches in Paris," the woman replied, and thousands that looked like her. Besides, she always gave her name as Madame Martin.

At this point Hamard broke off the interrogation to have a private word with the nursemaids. But he had to swallow a disappointment. Only one of them would hazard that Rosella Rousseau was the woman who had spoken to her, and even she was quite uncertain. There were so many women that age who looked as gray and downtrodden. Returning to his office, he found Rosella Rousseau sitting with her face in her hands, weeping piteously. Could the inspector really think, she sobbed, that she could have wanted to harm Germaine Bichon, who had been like a child to her?

Hamard asked where she had been the previous Sunday. At that she stopped sobbing, and seemed to be thinking hard. On Sunday morning, she painfully remembered, she had gone to Neuilly to find out the address of an uncle. She had returned at dinnertime, one o'clock, and had stayed home with Martin and the child. Then she had not been on the Boulevard Voltaire around two o'clock? Hamard insisted. No, not at all.

Hamard had the concierge brought in and asked Rosella Rousseau whether she knew Madame Dumont. Not really, the woman replied. She had seen her once or twice, but since Oursel's apartment had its own entrance, she had not had much to do with her. Then she had not come up to the concierge's lodge at about one thirty on Sunday and spoken to her?—No, she had been at home taking an afternoon nap with Martin. Hamard took the concierge aside in the adjoining room, and had a second disappointment. Madame Dumont was flustered and uncertain. There were similarities, certainly, but "Angèle" had been dressed differently—in particular she had worn a black kerchief on her head.

At four o'clock Hamard dismissed Rosella Rousseau. But he did so with mixed feelings. He had nothing in the way of substantial evidence against her, and he found himself unable to conceive of a motive that would have made her kill Germaine Bichon. Nevertheless, he felt profoundly suspicious of the woman. Confrontations, as he knew by long experience, could be extremely misleading. He therefore ordered his men to look more deeply into the life of Rosella Rousseau and Martin, to check where they had been on Sunday, and to determine whether either of the two had attempted to pawn a ruble or a gold watch chain.

He had no sooner issued this order than he received a startling communication from Balthazard. Shortly before noon Balthazard had carried out the autopsy of Germaine Bichon. In the handling of the body, he had come upon a small, hard object caught in the tangles of the hair which had so far escaped detection. Balthazard sent along the object; it was a small silver brooch of the kind women used to pin their blouses. If the brooch had not belonged to Germaine Bichon, it certainly would support Balthazard's theory that the killer had been a woman. Hamard sent Inspector Dol racing over to 1 Boulevard Voltaire with the brooch, and Dol returned with word that nobody had ever seen Germaine Bichon wearing such a pin.

Meanwhile the murder had become the sensation of the day in Paris. Everybody was talking about it. Journalists sharpened their wits on the riddle of how the killer could have entered the locked apartment. The wildest rumors circulated about the mysterious "Angèle," who had been quickly dubbed "the blond woman." But the conception of a murderess was still far from the popular mind—any woman involved was thought to be an accomplice to the crime. Hamard drove his men furiously. By Wednesday afternoon Inspector Dol presented his summary, and Hamard at last had the feeling that he was on the right track in investigating Rosella Rousseau.

There could be no doubt that Rosella Rousseau had lied about her activities on Sunday. The wine dealer Vigouroux, who was the manager of 56 Boulevard Belleville, reported that Martin and his mistress had been owing their rent for months. He termed Martin a weak man who was glad to have the woman about so that she could care for the child. But the old bag had scarcely made her way by honest toil before she found a home with Martin; actually, she had knocked about in many beds until no one would have her any more. She took good care of the child. But otherwise she kept Martin from his work and was always nagging to be taken out to country inns for a good time. She was deeply in debt in all the cafés of the neighborhood, and was always up to small tricks to get money. On the Saturday before the murder, Vigouroux had sent "the Martins" an ultimatum about the rent. On Sunday morning at eleven o'clock Martin had pleaded for time, saying that his "wife" was on her way to get money and would settle what they owed as soon as she returned. About four o'clock in the afternoon Martin and Rosella turned up in Vigouroux's café. She was excited, paid part of the debt, and drank several glasses of white wine. At six o'clock both of them had left to go to a peddler named Hablutzel, to whom they wanted to sell something.

Hablutzel was tracked down on the Rue des Couronnes. At first he claimed that he did not know the Martins, but at last he admitted that "Madame Martin" had come to see him last Sunday afternoon to sell a coin that she "had found in the street." He had sent her to another buyer. He said he did not know whether the coin was a gold ruble. Hablutzel's daughter had accompanied "Madame Martin" to the store-keeper Lavergnas. But Lavergnas had not taken the coin, either. An unknown lady who happened to be in his store bought it for thirty-five francs, he said. Allegedly no one knew who this lady was or where she lived. Hamard pressed his men to track down the unknown buyer because he felt certain that the coin must be the stolen ruble. All Wednesday a large force of detectives worked on the problem—but in vain. The woman could not be found. Once again, a promising trail was leading nowhere.

By now, however, nothing could shake Hamard's feeling that he was on the murderer's track. On the morning of July 22 he had Henri Martin brought to him directly from the nail factory where he worked. But it was soon apparent that this man was so entirely subject to the will of his mistress that nothing of value could be got out of him. Martin repeated Rosella Rousseau's story of their Sunday. He held to it even when Hamard confronted him with the statements of the building manager, the peddler, and Lavergnas. Shown the silver brooch that had been found in Germaine's hair, he swore he had never seen it before. Impatiently, Hamard dismissed him, and sent Inspectors Sablon and Darnal to Boulevard Belleville with orders to collect Rosella Rousseau with all the summer dresses and black kerchiefs she possessed, and bring her to headquarters. He was toying with the idea of another confrontation with the concierge, and for this purpose wanted to dress Rosella as "Angèle" had allegedly been dressed, in a kerchief and a black-and-white dotted skirt. But Rosella Rousseau claimed she owned only a gray dress and gray kerchief, and nothing else was found in her wardrobe.

Hamard therefore abandoned the idea of a confrontation and limited himself to a new interrogation. This was a long one, lasting from eleven o'clock in the morning until four in the afternoon. Once again Rosella Rousseau was talkative, occasionally excited, but quickly composing herself, and unshakable in her story. She had never seen the brooch. She had nothing to do with the murder of Germaine Bichon. The building manager, the peddler, and the storekeeper were liars. So it went, hour after hour. At last, about three o'clock, she surprisingly made a concession which revealed depths of cunning. She admitted that she had lied about her doings on Sunday. But she had lied only because she wanted to conceal a small theft. On Saturday she had gone to a relative of hers, Carpentier, in Neuilly, to borrow money from him. He had put her up overnight, but refused her request for money. On Sunday, while he was asleep, she had stolen a hundred francs and a gold piece from him. With that, she had returned to Paris, paid her rent, and sold the gold piece.

Hamard had her story checked at once. He found out that Carpentier actually existed, but was so senile that he could not even say whether or not he had received a visit from Rosella Rousseau.

Nevertheless, Hamard now believed he had sufficient grounds to ask Examining Magistrate Hastrong to make a thorough search of the Martin home. Balthazard, he said, should accompany the detectives. They were to look for hidden dresses belonging to Rosella Rousseau, and to check these for bloodstains. Balthazard was also to examine Rosella Rousseau's hair and compare it with the hair found on the body of Germaine Bichon.

Shortly after eight o'clock that evening, Rosella Rousseau was taken back to her home by two detectives. When Hastrong, Hamard, and Balthazard drove up in a second carriage, the rumor spread that the murderer of Germaine Bichon had been found; and within minutes a crowd (the *Petit Parisien* put it at more than three hundred persons) assembled in front of 56 Boulevard Belleville. While several detectives went through the apartment, Balthazard went into the bedroom with Rosella Rousseau, had her let down her hair, and set about examining it under a special magnifying glass. Later he wrote: "Her hair was generally of a light, chestnut-brown color. There were, however, also a number of lighter, almost blond tresses, especially at the front of the hair and along the temples." The similarity of this to the hair from the dead girl's fingers was highly encouraging. He took samples from various parts of the woman's head, especially from the front and the temples.

About this same time Inspector Dol found some hidden clothes in a chest—a dotted skirt, a black bodice, a black kerchief. These, Hastrong ruled, were to be examined by Balthazard for bloodstains. Rosella Rousseau was to be arrested and taken to the Saint-Lazare prison. When several detectives left the house with the arrested woman between them, the vengeful instincts of the masses discharged in savage vituperation and calls for death to the murderess, although there was as yet no proof whatsoever that she had had any part in the crime.

Despite the lateness of the hour, Balthazard eagerly returned to the laboratory and carried out the comparison of the hair that same evening. He measured the diameter of the hair samples as usual. The average was 0.0028 inches, corresponding precisely to the measurements of the hair found with Germaine. But that did not mean much. In comparing colors, he concluded that the hair found on the body, with its typical predominance of blond as against brown elements, must have come from the front of Rosella Rousseau's head, if at all. But that was a probability, not a proof. When, however, he studied the roots of the hair, and in particular the torn ends, he began to wonder whether Germaine Bichon had not gripped and finally torn out a whole tuft of hair all together. This suggested to him examining the brow and temple region of Rosella Rousseau's head to see whether there were not, at one definite spot, empty and damaged follicles and the stubs of broken hairs which could be fitted to the hairs that had been found. If this could be done, it would represent absolute proof that the hair found clutched in the fingers of the murder victim was Rosella Rousseau's.

Early Friday morning Balthazard received authorization to examine the arrested woman once more. He found her considerably changed by her first night in prison, tired and apathetic. Without a word, without even realizing what was happening, she permitted Balthazard to proceed with his work. Balthazard subsequently described his findings: "When we . . . examined the region of the left temple, we determined . . . that in this area there were a number of hairs torn off about one sixteenth of an inch above their roots. In addition we found several root glands emptied of their contents. . . . Approximately twenty hairs had been pulled out in this way. This observation permitted us . . . to come to the certain conclusion that the hairs of Madame Bosch found in the hands of Germaine Bichon had been pulled out in the course of the struggle."

Before delivering his report Balthazard examined the items of clothing, but he discovered that they had been cleaned with great care. Only on the lower part of the skirt did he find tiny traces of bloodstains. Since it was impossible to determine the origin of the blood (the Uhlenhuth reaction was not applied in France until 1912), these bloodstains were valueless. The useful evidence remained the results of the hair comparisons.

Hamard, too, was conscious of the importance of this finding. In the afternoon he had Rosella Rousseau brought to his office from the Saint-Lazare prison. For several hours he subjected her to a merciless interrogation. In the course of it, as a newspaper account expressed it, the hair "from the bloody hands of the dead girl became uncanny props that exerted a ghostly influence on the mind of the obstinate but somewhat superstitious prisoner." Late in the afternoon she suddenly broke into sobs and cried out: "All right, I did, I did kill Germaine Bichon. I'll tell you the whole story."

Her confession began: "Because I was so worried about my debts I thought of getting money . . . out of Oursel. I thought Monsieur Oursel was rich. I knew he went away every Saturday . . . leaving Germaine alone. So I thought I'd get into the office with the help of the nursemaids. I wanted to hide there. But the girls I asked wouldn't come along. So I decided to act alone. Saturday afternoon I went to the house, went upstairs, and when the receptionist's attention was elsewhere for a moment, I slipped into the first waiting room. . . . That's the room where the transom opens on the stairwell and where there's a bed closet. I shut myself in there and waited. . . ."

From her hiding place Rosella Rousseau heard the receptionist leave the house with Germaine, locking the doors. Now the way was clear for her to look for money. But at the same time she was gripped by the fear that Germaine might come back at any moment. And so she missed her first chance. She heard Germaine return to the apartment and lock the door to dining room and bedroom. At this point she realized that Oursel had probably locked up his money in the wardrobe, and that she could no longer get into the bedroom. She decided to wait until Germaine opened the doors again in the morning. In this way she spent a sleepless night. It was nearly noon before Germaine got up, unlocked the bedroom door, and came out in her dressing gown to prepare a meal for herself.

"I stealthily left my hiding place and crept into the dining room, where I suddenly stood in front of the astonished Germaine. She leapt to her feet crying, 'Where did you come from?' But without answering, I threw myself on her." Hair flying, the two women struggled until Germaine escaped into the kitchen. There the girl allegedly reached for the hatchet. Rosella wrested it from her and knocked Germaine to the ground. Then she blindly struck her until the girl's cries subsided to feeble groans. She listened to see whether anyone in the house had heard Germaine's screams for help. When everything remained quiet, she washed her clothes and the hatchet, and opened the cashbox and the secretary-desk. Disappointed at how little she found, she broke open the wardrobe. Her disappointment grew when she found only the gold ruble and the watch chain. Then she heard noises from below and from the direction of the waiting room, and became afraid that people were going to investigate. Since she assumed that they would look in the stairway first, she climbed on a chair, opened the transom to the stairwell, and listened. All was still, so she decided that the noises in the café must have been due to something else. She took Germaine's house key, opened the upper door, descended the steps, opened and closed the iron gate, and stepped out onto the street unobserved in the initial confusion. There it suddenly occurred to her to go to the concierge's lodge and by inventing "Angèle" get away without leaving any suspicious trail behind. She had come home safely and told Martin the same story about robbing a relative that she had also told Hamard.

The story of her escape sounded so implausible that it remained a question whether she had not after all left through the transom and, since in that case she had to pass the concierge's lodge, hit on the "Angèle" notion. But Rosella Rousseau insisted on her tale when she repeated her confession to Examining Magistrate Hastrong at five thirty that same afternoon. In February 1910, seven months later, she denied these confessions in court, and resorted to the assertion so familiar to every criminologist that the confessions had been extorted from her. Unimpressed, the jury pronounced her guilty, and on February 8, 1910, she heard herself sentenced to death.

Within the framework of forensic biology, the case of Germaine Bichon has a double significance. It supplied Balthazard himself with a vital stimulus and encouragement to further studies of hair, the fruit of which was *Le Poil de l'homme et des animaux* ("The Hair of Men and Animals") written in collaboration with Marcelle Lambert. This book, published in 1910, remained for at least fifteen years the fundamental guide to criminalistic investigation of hair. For scientific criminology in general, the Bichon affair became a prime example of the fact that hair comparison, fraught as it was with so much uncertainty, could—given careful work—be of crucial value. Clearly, it was a technique worth pursuing and perfecting.

8

In the very year that Balthazard's study of hair was published and Rosella Rousseau was condemned to death, a young scientist in Lyons realized a dream which had preoccupied him for years. His name was Edmond Locard and he was a native Lyonnais. Thirty-three years old at this time, he was a trim, graceful man with a dark mustache, an aquiline nose, and eyes gleaming with vitality.

A pupil of Alexandre Lacassagne, Professor of Pathology and Forensic Medicine at the University of Lyons, Locard too had grown up in the era in which Alphonse Bertillon was laying foundations for scientific criminology. His teacher, Lacassagne, was one of the two dominant figures (the other being Brouardel) of French forensic medicine before the turn of the century. At one time a military doctor in French North Africa, Lacassagne had studied tattooings among the soldiers and the rabble of the Algerian Casbah. He had thus ventured into that borderline realm in which medicine, crime, and the law met. In 1880 he had taken over the direction of the Lyons Institute of Forensic Medicine. Thanks to his vast medical and biological knowledge, his intellectual vitality, and his lively imagination, he had become virtually the "king" of forensic medicine in southern France. In 1889 he had used novel techniques of bone study, dental comparison, and other methods to identify the body of the Parisian bailiff Gouffé, who had been murdered and sent in a trunk to Lyons. This case had won him fame, and made him a still stronger champion of the collaboration of natural science and criminology. Although he was one of the few persons in the world who felt friendly toward Bertillon, he soon recognized Bertillon's limitations. He himself looked for a wider scope for scientific criminology than the founder, Bertillon. He had encouraged some of his students to make studies on clues that few or no criminologists had hitherto considered. Thus, he had proposed the idea that the dust on clothing, or on people's ears, noses, and fingernails, could provide information on the occupations and whereabouts of suspects. In line with this, his pupil Émile Villebrun had drawn up whole lists of the microscopic particles that could be found under human fingernails.

Locard, too, had been spurred to look beyond the contemporary borders of forensic medicine and Bertillon's concept of scientific criminology. Later, more or less by chance, Locard had read French translations of the *Adventures of Sherlock Holmes*, and parts of Hans Gross's great book. The idea that every culprit, whether thief, burglar, traffic offender, or murderer, came into contact at the scene of his act with some particles of dust, appealed especially to Locard's lively imagination. As much as twenty years later he was to write in the introduction to a comprehensive text on criminalistic investigation of dust:

"A spot of mud on a shoe or a pair of trousers tells Sherlock Holmes at once which part of London a visitor has just passed through, or what course he has taken within the environs of the town. A spot of clay or chalk will be from Horsham. A particular reddish street mud is found only at the entrance to the post office on Wigmore Street. We may wonder whether—even with the genius of a Sherlock Holmes—we do not risk grave errors if we attempt to make such diagnoses from a distance. But in these books we at least find a hint of the direction we ought to take. We would do well to read over such stories as 'A Study in Scarlet' and 'The Sign of the Four.' . . . When we reflect on the matter, we are startled that we should have been so tardy at carrying out so simple an idea: gathering the dust from an article of clothing and discovering from it which objects the suspected person brushed past and touched. For the microscopically finest particles that cover our clothing and our bodies are the mute witnesses to each of our movements and encounters."

The question of trace clues so occupied Locard's mind that he went off on a "smallish world tour" to study what was being done in this field. He visited Bertillon in Paris. He went to Lausanne, Rome, Berlin, Brussels, and finally to New York and Chicago. But what he found was disappointing. Bertillon had not advanced a step beyond his anthropometry and *portrait parlé*. His occasional efforts to deduce what tools had been used to break open doors from the scars on the wood, or to take the prints of shoes or feet, let alone some of his more unfortunate excursions into graphology, were not of the sort calculated to turn an anthropometric and photographic identification service into a laboratory capable of scientific criminology. Wherever the police themselves were doing what passed for scientific work, their interest was in identification; the great issue seemed to be whether *bertillonage* should be replaced by fingerprinting.

Edmond Locard returned to Lyons quite downcast, but with a vision burning in his mind. He was possessed by the idea of building up genuine laboratories within the police force which could investigate those clues that needed to be studied scientifically, the sort of clues that figured in the fictions of Conan Doyle and in the doctrines of Hans Gross. In an article Locard wrote after his return he spoke of a new "police science," for which no generally accepted principles had yet been laid down. But it was already clear, he declared, that every useful procedure of the natural sciences must be applied to criminal investigation. Such work was an art, he said, the goal of which was to achieve more and more independence of forensic medicine and ordinary chemistry.

In Lyons, however, he encountered total indifference. In spite of Bertillon, the French criminal police force, especially outside Paris, was still largely dominated by men of the old "empirical school." In the provinces, police power was almost entirely in the hands of the prefects of the *départements* and the mayors of towns. To be sure, the Sûreté Nationale, which was separate from the Parisian police and directly subordinate to the Minister of the Interior, had been intervening more and more in crime control throughout France. Faced with the problem of roving gangs of criminals, it had created the Brigade Mobile, a force of mobile detectives. The Sûreté was also taking over criminological work in the large cities. But for most police officials, the measuring procedures of anthropometry seemed science enough. Only by the full use of personal connections was Locard able to prevail on the prefects of the Rhone Département in Lyons to grant him two attic rooms in the Law Courts, and two Sûreté officials as assistants. This was in the summer of 1910, and was the small beginning of what was later to be known as the Lyons Police Laboratory. Its entrance was on a narrow side street, around the corner from the huge stone block of the Palais de Justice with its solemn Corinthian colonnades and its two majestic stone staircases leading down from the main entrance to the embankment of the Rhone. The laboratory was reached through a gloomy entrance hall from which one corridor led to the prison and a dirt-stained door into the dusty caves of the archives. Every day Locard climbed the steep winding staircase leading to his laboratory four floors up. Twenty years later, when he already enjoyed world fame, he was still working up there—in somewhat larger quarters, but still under the most primitive of conditions, the heating consisting of wretched coal stoves which constantly deposited new layers of soot on the cracked walls.

These dreary surroundings did not prevent Locard from realizing his dream. He was also responsible for the police's anthropometrical work, which took up hours of his day. As he went through the form of taking the measurements of all new prisoners, he was aware that the whole procedure was pointless because fingerprinting was marching forward invincibly from triumph to triumph. All this considerably curtailed the time he would gladly have devoted to other studies, above all the investigation of dusts. Nevertheless, he had his lucky moments. The years 1911 and 1912 presented him with several criminal cases which seemed made to order to prove his theory of the usefulness of dust deposits for establishing links between crimes and culprits.

First there was the case of the counterfeiters. The Sûreté had for some time been vainly trying to track down the source of a flood of false franc coins. Informers had repeatedly given the police the names of three men: Brun, Ceresk, and Latour. But it proved impossible to show a connection between these men and the counterfeit money, or to locate the men's workshop. Experts had merely determined that the false coins contained antimony, tin, and lead. Locard, hearing of the case, proposed to the detective in charge, Inspector Corin, that the clothing of the three suspects be sent to him. Corin hesitated, not understanding the point of Locard's suggestion, but after repeated requests finally sent him the clothes of one suspect. Locard examined all the pockets under a magnifying glass and with a fine pincers removed every metallic particle he found. Then he brushed out the sleeves over glossy white paper. From the dust, which showed up plainly against the paper, he again sorted out the metallic particles, and obtained instructions from the Lyons chemists Meunier and Griguard on the accepted methods for determining the presence of antimony, tin, and lead. After a brief period of testing, lens-shaped crystals, frequently grouped in threes, appeared, the typical signs of antimony. Immediately afterward, he tested his solution for tin. Treated with rubidium chloride, the unmistakable octohedral and tetrahedral crystals of rubidium chlorostannate appeared. Lead was similarly revealed by the formation of oblong prismatic plates with irregular voids.

At this point Inspector Corin turned the clothing of the remaining suspects over to Dr. Locard, who seemed to possess almost preternatural powers of detection. With clothes the men had been wearing in the course of their felonious employment, Locard obtained similar results. Since none of the suspects could account for the presence of the metallic particles on his clothes, all three were arrested and soon afterward confessed to counterfeiting.

The detectives who had participated in the case were so dumfounded that henceforth they went of their own accord to Locard's attic laboratory whenever they encountered seemingly insoluble problems. One such was the case of Émile Gourbin, a Lyonnese bank clerk, who had come under suspicion of killing a girl named Marie Latelle in a fit of jealousy. Marie was found dead in her parents' home; the culprit had apparently left no clues at all. All that was known was that the murder must have taken place before midnight.

Gourbin's courting of the girl was well known. He was arrested, but produced an alibi. He had spent the night in question, he alleged, with friends in a country house called La Terre several miles from Marie Latelle's home. The local police made inquiries. Gourbin's friends confirmed his statement. They had sat up playing cards until late at night. Gourbin had not left the house, and all of them had gone to bed after one o'clock in the morning, by which time Marie Latelle was already dead.

The investigation seemed to bog down at this point. But the examining magistrate had heard of Locard's work and appealed to him for help. Locard examined the dead girl at the morgue and found distinct marks of strangulation on her throat. Then he went to Gourbin's cell and scraped the dirt from under the man's fingernails. He placed it in envelopes and began the work of sorting it out on a sheet of shiny white paper. He found a large number of epithelial cells in the form of transparent flakes. These might well have come from Marie Latelle's neck, but not necessarily, since Gourbin could have scratched them from his own skin. Locard noticed, however, that the flakes were covered with a curious pink dust. Under high magnification most of these dust particles appeared as polygonal crystalline grains. None were rounded. Their diameter varied between 0.0001 and 0.0004 inches. These were the characteristics of rice starch. After Locard had also found the particles to contain bismuth, magnesium stearate, zinc oxide, and a reddish iron oxide pigment, Venetian red, he asked the police to bring him all the cosmetics from the dead girl's room. Among these was a box of pink face powder which her mother said the girl had used daily. It proved to be a special preparation made by a Lyons druggist, and consisted of rice powder and the chemicals that Locard had found under Gourbin's fingernails. A few decades later, when facial powder was mass produced, such evidence would have been valueless, but in 1912 it was enough to discountenance Gourbin. He made a full confession, describing how he had concocted his alibi by advancing the wall clock in his friends' house so that it read one o'clock when it was actually only eleven thirty. Shortly before midnight he had met his sweetheart; she had refused to marry him and thus shattered the plans he had been basing on her dowry. In a violent rage, he had strangled her, he said. Actually, his careful tinkering with the clock provided good evidence for premeditated murder.

It was understandable that after solving this case Locard swiftly acquired something of the reputation of a "wizard" that Georg Popp enjoyed in Germany. With the ample support he now received, he was able to launch on a large-scale scientific study of dust which was to be a lasting contribution to criminology. During the war much of his time was taken up with graphological and cipher studies for the French armed forces. Nevertheless, between 1912 and 1920 he completed a work of encyclopedic scope. His starting point was the motto of the famous German chemist Liebig: "Dust contains in small all the things that surround us." Locard studied the deposits on clothes, shoes, hats and hatbands, hair, ear and nasal orifices, tools, fabrics of all kinds, furniture, rugs, windows and window sills, streets, gardens, factories and workshops. There is, in fact, nothing organic or inorganic in the world which cannot be found drifting about in the form of dust, which sooner or later comes into contact with human beings, animals, or objects. "The task," Locard wrote, "is to find out what the state of the matter was before it passed into the pulverized condition. The powdered form results in the destruction of the original appearance which in general permits us to determine what objects are through our senses or by the use of our instruments. On the other hand, the transformation does not go so far that the objects are reduced to their ultimate elements, to molecules or atoms. . . . It therefore follows that the dust still contains distinctive characteristics which permit us to determine its origin."

During the years he was engaged in his first experiments Locard had at his disposal only a microscope, a small spectrometer, and the techniques of chemical analysis. Even in the latter field he was severely restricted, for the methods of microanalysis were still to come. These had their beginnings in 1910, when Pregl, the Austrian Nobel Prize winner, reduced the accepted minimum amounts of one hundred milligrams of material to a single milligram (one thirty thousandth of one ounce) by using extremely tiny test tubes, crucibles, and pipettes. Locard was also unacquainted with the spot test technique devised by Fritz Feigl, in which a single drop of an unknown material on filter paper or in dimpled glass plates could be analyzed by the addition of equally tiny quantities of chemical reagents. The extraordinary refinements of spectroanalysis, of ultraviolet, infrared, and X-ray spectroscopy, which were to loom so large in the scientific developments of future decades, were only in their inception. Even the criminalistic usefulness of ultraviolet light (which Robert Wood of Johns Hopkins University first demonstrated to the members of the American National Academy in August 1902) had not yet been realized. Locard therefore had all the more reason to feel gratified when in 1920 he looked at the endless list of types of dust and dust components which he had managed to identify and study. It included a fantastic array of dust from the organic and mineral realms: slag, plaster of Paris, sand, coke, coal of all kinds, and innumerable metallic dusts, from iron and aluminum, copper and tin down to particles of rare strontium compounds. The list further contained dusts of vegetable origin, from every kind of leaf, from plant and flower seeds, and above all pollens, which Locard for the first time took heed of for criminological purposes. Then there were the dusts of disintegrated plants, the remains of stems, barks, roots, branches, as well as countless drugs and drug powders. He studied the dustlike particles of textile fibers, rugs, upholstery, cotton, linen, hemp, jute, calico, coconut fiber, the remains of wood and paper. All of it could be and was classified.

With tenacious labor Locard had mastered all the microscopic and analytical methods belonging to organic and inorganic chemistry, botany, and zoology, adapting them to the problem of differentiating components of dust. He had worked out a regular system by which dust clues could be obtained and sorted before being subjected to microscopic and chemical tests. Hans Gross's "Manual for Examining Magistrates" had recommended that the clothes of a suspect be placed in a clean white sack and beaten until the dust from the clothing had collected in the sack. This procedure seemed to Locard too crude. He preferred to examine every part of an article of clothing with the magnifying glass, to search for clinging particles. The location of particular particles of dust on clothing might have important bearing on the case, he pointed out. He would then remove the bits of dust with pincers or absorbent cotton and place them in carefully labeled envelopes. Particles that adhered firmly he would scratch off onto plates of glass or clean watch crystals. He handled pockets with special care, never turning them inside out and beating out their contents. Instead, he removed the pockets completely at the seams and only then studied what was in them. His practice with shoes corresponded to Popp's. He had had a case in which a man betrayed his walk to a mill and back on a damp day by a layer of flour between the deposit strata of soil from the path to the mill and the way back. He therefore laid special stress on preserving the various layers of dirt that accumulated on shoes in their proper order. Once he had obtained the dust or dirt, he spread it out on white or black paper. He then extracted the parts of easily recognizable character. In order to separate some of the metallic traces from the rest of the dust, he used magnets. For microscopic sorting of the finest particles he constructed a graphoscope. This was a microscope that could be made to scan large surfaces of dust-covered paper, thus allowing every square inch of these surfaces to be studied.

By the time Edmond Locard's work had come this far, in 1920, he was no longer alone in the field of dust research. Influenced by the reports from Lyons and by Hans Gross's book, several other young men had taken up this new field and made their mark in it. In 1920 a Dutch technical journal published a rather special article. Its author was J. C. van Ledden-Hulsebosch, a young Amsterdam chemist who was well on the way to becoming for Holland what Popp was for Germany and Locard for France. He was born into a family of pharmacists who generation after generation had plied their trade in the same narrow, picturesque, old brick building. Legend has it that his father examined his own excrement day after day for thirty years in order to learn the secrets of metabolism. The son had inherited this scientific curiosity and analytical talent but transferred his passion to criminology. He too realized that criminalistic science must go far beyond the existing limits. Inspired by Locard's work with dust, he plunged into similar studies and soon developed ideas of his own. The above-mentioned article, published in March 1920, described some of his innovations:

"It is not always so easy to collect the small particles which may represent vitally important evidence when studied scientifically. If it is a question of material that might be found in the clothing of a suspected person, I collect what I need with the aid of an instrument that consists simply of an altered hair-drier. Where the air is ordinarily . . . sucked into the apparatus, I have installed a . . . funnel, and where the apparatus normally blows out the air it has sucked in, I have attached a filter opening into a cotton bag. Plugged into any ordinary electric outlet, this little vacuum cleaner draws the particles from the fabric into the small cotton bags. These are then cut open, and everything that has been removed from the clothes in this modern way lies spread out before me ready for microscopic examination."

Filled with the pride of an inventor, Ledden-Hulsebosch did not know that far across the Atlantic an American had already hit on the same idea. In Berkeley, California, that unique center of developing American criminalistics, the chemist Dr. Albert Schneider had also embarked on dust studies. Since the vacuum cleaner was an Anglo-American invention (the first vacuum cleaner was patented in 1901), Schneider had the apparatus ready to hand. He had used a vacuum cleaner back in 1916 to collect dust from suspect clothes, and five months after van Ledden-Hulsebosch he published an article, "Police Microscopy," giving a detailed account of this new technique.

During this period a third young chemist was at work providing a scientific foundation for the study of dust clues. His name was August Brüning, and the scene of his activities was Berlin.

Brüning was born on a farm in Westphalia in 1879. When he was twelve his father gave him his first camera, and thereby aroused a passion for photography which became the basis of his work in criminology. After attending school in Münster, Westphalia, he was a pharmacist's apprentice for a time. In 1898 he went to Zurich, and later to Geneva, continuing to study pharmacology and botany. Restive, full of curiosity, he moved on to Freiburg in the Black Forest, completed his university work there, discovered that pharmacology was too humdrum for one of his temperament, and in 1901 began postgraduate study of chemistry in the laboratories of two Freiburg professors, Killiani and Authenrieth.

Authenrieth was a toxicologist who was often called upon to serve as an expert in criminal cases. Through him, Brüning began to be intrigued by criminology. One case in particular captured his imagination. A servant girl in a Black Forest village was accused, in the high-flown language of the day, of "having disposed of the fruit of her womb." Authenrieth was given the girl's dress spattered with some vomit, and asked to determine the type of abortifacient used. He quickly discovered that the girl had eaten the tips of some twigs of the poisonous savin (*Juniperus sabina*). What is more, he found the vomit contained a special type of plant parasite. Authenrieth next established that in the garden of the girl's place of work there were savin bushes rife with this parasite. The neatness of this scientific proof, complete with its own check, made a strong impression on Brüning.

Two years later, in October 1904, he was present at the Freiburg trial of Karl Laubach and witnessed Georg Popp's sensational presentation of the evidence in particles of soil. Authenrieth, who was going to confer with Popp, took his young assistant along to meet the great man, and Brüning's choice of career was sealed. He was firmly resolved to become a "clue hunter" himself. After putting in some years on the chemistry of foods, he received an invitation from Popp to join him in Frankfurt. In 1910 he entered Popp's laboratory, spent two years there learning all he could about the techniques of tracking down clues, and in 1912 moved on to Berlin. After some months of dealing with poison cases and anonymous letters Brüning had the chance to try his wings at his first criminal case involving dust clues.

He had already shown what he could do in June 1913 when he brought to bear his talents as a chemist in a safecracking case. Such cases were common enough in Berlin to figure in the daily work of the criminal police. A common tool of the burglars was a "nibbler," a heavy kind of pliers with which one "nibbled away" at cheap safes. Brüning discovered microscopic traces of metal and paint on such instruments which corresponded with the material on several cracked safes. This correspondence led to the conviction, greatly to their surprise, of a whole gang of burglars.

Several months later he made an even greater coup which put an end to the career of the Berlin fence Paul Markowitz. Markowitz was suspected of having staged a particularly clever series of burglaries, but nothing could be pinned on him. In October 1913 in the vicinity of Alexanderplatz a robbery occurred in which the thieves gained access to a safe by cutting a hole through the floor of the apartment above. The safe itself was a cheap model built of thin walls of sheet metal. The space between these walls was filled with an insulating material supposed to protect the papers inside the safe in case of fire. This insulation was made of lignite ashes, some of which had come out and fallen on the floor during the burglary.

As soon as the robbery was discovered, Detective Inspector Müller rushed to Markowitz' house and inspected every room with care. But as in all previous cases of the sort, he could find no trace of the loot. By chance, however, he happened to notice Markowitz' shoes. He observed a curious rim of dust between sole and upper which reminded him of the lignite ashes. Remembering Brüning's previous analyses of metallic dusts, Müller confiscated the shoes and took them to Brüning's laboratory.

Brüning set to work at once. With a fine brush he transferred the light-colored dust to dark glazed paper. Under the microscope he quickly discovered that it was indeed lignite ash. He asked Müller to obtain the clothes Markowitz had worn the previous evening. Markowitz, still unsuspecting, handed over the garments with a stream of sarcastic remarks, and Brüning proceeded to brush them out by Gross's method. He collected so large a quantity of dust in a paper bag that it was easy to show its identity with lignite ash. This, however, did not yet constitute substantial evidence. Markowitz could always counter that he had come into contact with lignite ash on some other occasion. Brüning therefore looked for some characteristic correspondences between the dust on the shoes and clothing and the ashes from the cracked safe. He took samples from the safe and found the ashes contained skeletons of heavily silicified plant cells which had remained intact through the burning of the lignite. Under the microscope the shapes of the former cells could be distinctly perceived, and their structure and size were identical with similar cells in the ashes on Markowitz' clothing.

With Paul Markowitz' stunned and furious confession, Brüning's confidence in his methods was confirmed. Military duties during the First World War interrupted his work, but he was back at it in the very first postwar months, and overwhelmed with new tasks. The universal shortages of the time led to a host of thefts such as Germany had never experienced before. Berlin, especially, became a center for robbers who hit on the idea of stealing the valuable copper and bronze wires of telegraph and telephone lines. "Specialists" with climbing shoes mounted the telegraph poles at night, cut down hundreds of yards of wire, rolled it up and vanished noiselessly in the darkness on their bicycles. They took their loot to a constantly changing series of hiding places known only to the fences. For months the Berlin police labored in vain on such cases, until in a chance search of a shack they came upon a knapsack containing a large roll of copper wire. The owner of the shack, a postal worker named Hermann Schalluk, denied knowing anything about the contents of the knapsack. He said it belonged to an unknown tramp whom he had put up for a night out of pity and who had asked him to keep the knapsack for him. But Schalluk's hands struck the police as suspiciously black. They therefore decided to take the man to Brüning's office on Alexanderplatz. Brüning found that the blackening came from particles of dust that had accumulated in the ridges of the skin. He washed Schalluk's hands in hot, dilute hydrochloric acid, and the hands instantly became clean. But when Brüning evaporated the acid in a porcelain bowl, he obtained a yellow-green precipitate containing almost pure copper chloride. Confronted with this fact, Schalluk had the presence of mind to explain that he had opened the knapsack out of curiosity and handled the roll of wire. Brüning, convinced that the man was lying, looked for some way to trap him. He telephoned the postal authorities and learned that the wooden telegraph poles were soaked in copper sulfate. He therefore made Schalluk remove his trousers. Under the microscope he discovered along the part of the trouser legs that covered the inner thigh particles of wood. He collected these particles, soaked them in a solution of ammonium nitrate, and heated them until they turned to ashes. A chemical reaction quickly revealed the presence of copper from the copper sulfate with which the wood of the poles had been impregnated. Soon afterward Schalluk confessed that he had stolen the wire the previous night. From then on, the testing of clothing of wire thieves became a part of the daily routine in Alexanderplatz.

In 1923 Brüning for the first time published an account of his experience with trace element studies, entitled: "Contributions to the Conviction of Criminals by Demonstration of Key Elements on Their Bodies and Their Clothing." He thus introduced the concept of key elements into the investigation of dusts and other traces. "In geology," he wrote, "fossils . . . which occur in a specific stratum of the earth's crust . . . are termed key fossils and regarded as characteristic of the stratum. If such key fossils are found in a hitherto unknown rock, the specialist can tell at once . . . what stratum the rock belongs to. Similarly, the microscopist and chemist can deduce from certain finds on the clothing and body of a person his occupation and whether he has come into contact with certain objects. . . . Thus the chemist can assist . . . the criminologist, the key elements serving as criminalistic guides."

When Brüning wrote these lines, he was still only at the beginning of his long career. But like Locard and van Ledden-Hulsebosch, he was convinced that the method of trace-element investigation should be applied in all attempts to solve crimes. And the time was indeed ripe. That became apparent as the result of a *cause célèbre* which stirred up Paris for many months during 1924, and which like the Bichon case was destined to occupy a conspicuous place in the annals of scientific criminology.

9

Like many other cases, the Boulay-Teissier affair began with a package and an unknown corpse. It started in the Bois de Boulogne on the morning of June 8, 1924, near the narrow Allée des Réservoirs which wound from the Allée de l'Hippodrome through the woods toward the Longchamps tower. It was a Sunday, and Antoine Courtin, a locksmith of Neuilly, was bicycling innocently along the *allée* about six thirty in the morning. Suddenly he caught sight of a large package lying under a bush about twenty feet from his path. He stopped, pushed his wheel across the grass, observed a hand and two feet protruding from the package, jumped onto his bicycle again, and pedaled off at high speed to report the matter to one of the park attendants, named Thory.

In half an hour Chief Inspector Bethuel was on the scene, accompanied by several policemen. Bethuel opened the bundle, which consisted of an old sheet. He saw the corpse of a man between sixty and seventy, who had apparently died of several head injuries. The corpse wore a white shirt with purple stripes, celluloid collar, black tie, gray trousers, dark socks and high laced shoes. His jacket, a navy-blue vest, and a white straw hat lay rolled up beside the body. Bethuel took note of a number of smaller details, in particular a hernia truss with a brand mark, *As,* and a button tab on the shirt imprinted 4644,37 C.P.B./CX 1723. He noted that the dead man's pockets had been emptied. A few bits of coal, however, were clinging to the lining of the left trouser pocket. Parts of the shirt also looked as if they had been in contact with coal, so that Bethuel thought the body might have lain in a coal cellar before it was deposited in the Bois de Boulogne. Since he observed no tracks of an automobile or carriage near the scene, he had the body taken to the Paris morgue and consigned to the medical examiner, Dr. Paul. He ordered Inspectors Bertin and Bonardi to make inquiries among the park attendants and other persons who were in the park daily. He himself returned to his office to check missing-persons reports, among which he found several that fitted the corpse. The closest seemed to him that of a man who had been missing since May 30. His name was Louis Boulay; he was seventy years old and lived with his wife at 20 Rue de Bassano. For the past seventeen years he had been working as a general factotum in the office of Berner & Nielsen, 24 Rue de Milan, a firm selling materials for paper manufacture. He had left the office at 9:30 A.M. on May 30 to go to the post office, where he was to mail some letters and buy 150 francs' worth of stamps. In addition to the 150 francs he carried an unknown sum in his own wallet, a platinum watch chain, and a gold watch. Every one of the letters Boulay had had with him had reached the addressees. He must therefore have discharged his duties at the post office. But that was the last that had been seen of him. Bethuel sent a detective to the Rue de Bassano to ask Madame Boulay to come to the morgue for possible identification of her husband.

At the same time Dr. Charles Paul was on his way to the morgue. Paul had begun his work in Paris in 1905, almost concurrently with Balthazard, but he had not chosen an academic career. Born in Boulogne-sur-Mer in 1879, the son of a lawyer, he had contented himself with the practical work of a medical examiner. In his youth he had been a cyclist, tennis player, and golfer. In later years an amusing spherical figure with a pink face and pink bald pate, he was yet so vain that, by the time he was sixty, he refused to give his date of birth even in court. He yearly averaged between two and four thousand autopsies, which he performed with the practiced motions of an automaton, yet with something of a flourish. On the other hand, the police could be sure that at any time of day, any day of the week he would put in an appearance at the scene of a crime or at the morgue. Never to neglect his work formed part of his fame and of his vanity. When he died thirty-six years later it was said that he had two hundred thousand autopsies to his credit, although he himself had always coquettishly maintained that he no more counted autopsies than a waiter the number of ducks he had carved in a lifetime.

Although it was a Sunday, Paul proceeded without delay to the postmortem on the corpse from the Bois de Boulogne. He determined that the man had died from several blows on the head. The murder weapon must have been a clublike instrument, possibly a piece of wood. He estimated, in his typical free-and-easy way, that the man had been dead for fifteen to twenty days. This observation disturbed Inspector Bethuel. If Paul was right, the body could not be that of Louis Boulay, who had been missing only since May 30, nine days ago. He was therefore impatient for the return of the detective whom he had sent to the Rue de Bassano. But the man came back with word that Madame Boulay, fleeing the loneliness of her apartment, had left town to stay with her children; she would not be back until the following day. Bethuel therefore had to contain himself until Monday morning, when the distraught old woman appeared at the morgue, identified the dead man as her husband, Louis Boulay—and incidentally demonstrated that Dr. Paul's estimates could err.

In the course of the morning Examining Magistrate Jousselin took over the case and ordered Chief Inspector Riboulet to work on it. Riboulet belonged to one of those special brigades that had been established by Chief of Police Céleste Hennion in 1913. A man of ideas, Hennion—the first real policeman who had risen to the rank of Prefect of Police—had created these special brigades to aid the various precincts throughout the city. From their headquarters on the Quai des Orfèvres they operated wherever they were needed. Riboulet belonged to the First Brigade, which dealt with capital crimes. However, another personage immediately intervened in the investigation: Gaston Edmond Bayle, Alphonse Bertillon's successor as head of the Police Identification Service (which in another of his reforms Céleste Hennion had merged with the Paris Sûreté). As it happened, Bayle was no run-of-the-mill official, but a stellar figure in scientific criminology.

On February 13, 1914, Alphonse Bertillon, suffering from pernicious anemia and toward the end totally blind, had died. As his life drew to a close he had been haunted by the nightmare that anthropometry, the heart of his lifework, would be replaced by fingerprinting. He had doggedly fended off the development of a fingerprinting system in France, since it would soon supplant his own circumstantial procedure. Everywhere he had scented traitors who were only waiting for his death to desert to the camp of dactyloscopy. Hence he had allowed no one of stature among the men around him, and consequently no one who might have given a new stamp to the Identification Service. As a result, Bertillon was succeeded only by a temporary director, his mediocre, colorless associate of many years, David, who had neither the will nor the knowledge to switch to fingerprinting and to develop the identification service into a scientific laboratory. Possibly an abler person would have been brought in, if Céleste Hennion had not himself been replaced as Prefect of Police, in favor of a more military-minded official. The advance of the German armies on Paris, and the memory of 1870, had aroused the ominous possibility that the entire Parisian police force might have to assume military functions. By the time the danger was over, the need for reforms in the Identification Service had been forgotten. However, it was due precisely to the military influence that on January 1, 1915, a hitherto unknown chemist and physicist, Edmond Bayle, was brought into Bertillon's antiquated rooms, ostensibly as David's assistant and deputy, in reality as the embodiment of a spirit of renewal.

Bayle had been born in Paris in 1879, had studied chemistry and physics, and worked for a considerable time at the Pasteur Institute. Before he entered the police headquarters, he had been an official chemist for the state railroad. Somewhere along the way he had looked into the question of secret writing and ways to bring it out by chemical methods. Since the French military intelligence service was preparing to enlist the Identification Service for tasks of its own, Bayle was installed as a specialist on secret writing. But in the course of his contact with the police Bayle—like Locard and Brüning—succumbed to the fascination of scientific criminology. He saw especially what part could be assigned to chemistry. By the time the war was over, Bayle had more or less eclipsed David and had begun determinedly to call Chief of Police Raux's attention to Locard's successful work in Lyons. Bayle, then forty years of age, somewhat puny and insignificant to look at, with gold pince-nez glasses, was actually a person of great energy and ambition. He waited restlessly for three years until on September 1, 1921, David was pensioned off and he himself was appointed chief. He at once began making up for lost time, and by 1924 he had established a scientific laboratory provided with the kind of modern equipment available in Lyons or Berlin.

Since his days at the Pasteur Institute Bayle had kept abreast of the rapid progress in spectral analysis, not only of visible light but also of spectral lines produced by a variety of chemical substances in regions of the spectrum not visible to the human eye. The limits of the visible spectrum are defined by certain wave lengths of light rays, which are sometimes measured by a unit of length named after the Swedish physicist

Angström, which is one one hundred-millionth of a centimeter, or four one-billionth of an inch.

The visible spectrum extends from red through orange, yellow, green, blue, and indigo to violet. Red rays barely within the limits of visibility have a wave length of 8000 angstroms. All waves of greater length are invisible; they lie "beyond the red," and are called infrared rays. At the other end of the visible spectrum barely recognizable violet rays have a wave length of about 4000 angstroms. All rays with shorter wave lengths are likewise invisible and are called ultraviolet rays. The spectral lines in these regions can be photographed, even though they cannot be seen with the naked eye; and at the time Bayle took office the study of these invisible rays was in full swing and year after year provided new knowledge which, he saw, could be used for the determination of unknown substances, in other words, for criminalistic clues. Bayle proposed to introduce spectral analysis into criminology to a degree hitherto inconceivable.

In addition, Bayle had been following the work of a German scientist, Gustav Kögel, who was concerned with the luminescent effects of ultraviolet rays. He had discovered that these possessed peculiar characteristics when they were isolated from other light rays and directed at various objects. They caused many materials to luminesce, or even to phosphoresce—that is, to continue to glow after the irradiation with ultraviolet light had ceased. Colors which seem alike in normal light may glow in different hues under ultraviolet light, depending on their chemical composition. Zinc white, for example, shows up as a yellowish green; lithopone white glows a sulfurous yellow; lead white a yellow brown. Types of paper which seem alike under the microscope will or will not show the phenomenon of luminescence, according to their composition. Kögel was prompted to study palimpsests, ancient manuscripts written over a second time by medieval monks in order to save parchment. The monks had erased the original writing with water and sand, thus destroying numerous important documents of antiquity. Under ultraviolet illumination the original text of the palimpsests became readable once more.

In 1919 Kögel had written an article for Hans Gross's *Archiv für Kriminologie* suggesting that his discovery be exploited for criminalistic investigations, and Bayle had at once taken up this suggestion. Bayle had applied the technique to a Rembrandt painting whose genuineness some experts were calling into question. Under ultraviolet illumination the invisible lines of Rembrandt's signature fluoresced brilliantly. Spots

on materials which might not appear under normal illumination immediately became visible when subjected to ultraviolet radiation. Even
various types of flour dust could be distinguished by the different colors
they showed under ultraviolet light.

Bayle also quickly seized upon the procedure which has become enormously important in science and industry under the name of spectrophotometry. It was based on the fact that the intensity of light passed
through chemical substances changes. It is weakened differently and
characteristically for each type of material. Paints and dyes in particular
display characteristics which cannot be detected by any other method.
The importance of such a technique for criminology was obvious.

Versatile and ambitious, Bayle had already acquired an unusual degree of experience and some remarkable technical aids during his first
five years at the Identification Service. On that morning of June 9, 1924,
when he intervened in the Boulay affair, he went straight to the morgue
to examine the body of Boulay for possible clues. While Dr. Paul stood
smoking at the other table as he performed one of his routine autopsies
on a clochard found dead during the night, Bayle and an assistant
looked down at the skinny body of Louis Boulay and the heap of clothing lying beside it. Bayle quickly saw that there were no clues to be
found on the body, and turned his attention to Boulay's hair, which
seemed to him unusually dirty. Under his magnifying glass he noticed
tiny fragments of a wide variety of substances: grains of coal, sharp-
edged particles of stone, grains of sand, sawdust, and a scrap of tan
cardboard no more than a sixteenth of an inch long. With tweezers,
Bayle plucked every single particle out of the hair and packed the different kinds separately in envelopes. He wrapped up Boulay's clothing and
the sheet in which the body had been wrapped—packing each item
separately. With these materials he returned to his laboratory, where he
spread all the exhibits out on a large table covered with white paper. He
examined the sheet first; there were soil and grass clinging to it, but
these materials came from the Bois de Boulogne and thus had no further
importance. Then he began on Boulay's shirt. It was blackened in several places, as Bethuel had already observed, and the blackening material proved to be very fine coal dust. Oddly enough, there was not the
slightest trace of sand or sawdust on the shirt. But as Bayle examined
each square inch of the shirt, he suddenly paused over two spots. He
found two dead, colorless insects such as inhabit only lightless rooms.
In the course of his subsequent examination of Boulay's trousers, he
found on the back of the waistband particles of coal, sand, and sawdust

—exactly the same as the materials in the hair. Similar particles were also clinging to the shoes and the jacket, although there were very few on the latter. The vest and hat, on the other hand, were like the shirt completely free of sawdust and sand.

After having made careful notes on all this, Bayle proceeded to the next step. He brushed each article of clothing until he was sure he had removed all significant particles of dust. Inspection of this dust revealed more clues. Most of them were further particles of coal, sawdust, and sand, and again these were missing from the shirt, vest, and hat. In the dust of trousers and shirt, however, there were two green woolen fibers and some curious flakes of a red substance averaging 0.020 inch in diameter.

By this time the evening was well advanced, and Bayle delivered to Riboulet a preliminary report which merely served to confirm Bethuel's guess that the dead man had probably lain in a cellar before being taken to the Bois de Boulogne. The colorless insects bore witness to that. But after all there were innumerable cellars, dark rooms, sheds, and caves in the vicinity of Paris. And if a cellar had been the scene of the murder or a temporary hiding place for the body, what kind of cellar had it been? Were there any special signs that would distinguish this cellar from thousands of others? Bayle assured Riboulet that he was only at the beginning of his work in this respect, and that he would carry out a large number of tests in the hope of being able to supply Riboulet with better leads.

10

Riboulet and his men attacked the major questions which loom large at the beginning of every crime investigation. They began with the dead man's widow, and with the firm of Berner & Nielsen, for which Boulay had worked for so many years. None of them thought that they would be at the case for nearly five months before they would even begin to approach their goal. Madame Boulay proved to be a dull-witted woman who had gone about her housework and never given much thought to her husband's doings. According to her account, he had left home daily, except Sundays, at ten minutes to five and betaken himself to the George V Métro station. From there he rode to his place of work, and returned in the evening at seven o'clock. He took his meals in restaurants. At home he had never spoken about the details of his work.

Riboulet and Inspectors Leroy and Coste questioned everyone connected with the firm of Berner & Nielsen. Everywhere they heard the same story of a decent old fellow who did his duties conscientiously and whose cruel end seemed wholly mysterious. Monsieur Nielsen himself stated that Boulay had never carried large sums of money which might have attracted a robber. The firm conducted its business mostly with checks. It was true that Boulay had been supposed to fetch ten thousand francs in cash from the bank for the payroll on the afternoon of May 30, but this sum had not been withdrawn. Thus the murder had taken place before he reached the bank. There was not a single indication of anything amiss in the colorless picture of a clerk of irreproachable traits: reliable, good-humored, honest, hard-working, no drinker, not the slave of any passion.

It was several days before a faint ray of light illuminated the darkness. Riboulet personally inspected Boulay's desk off in a corner of the office. Lifting a cushion which lay on the old man's chair, he discovered underneath a newspaper which proved to be an issue of a tip sheet for horse races, dated May 27. The names of two horses were underlined in red pencil, Libre Pirate and Star Sapphire. At this point the head clerk, Ihlen, recalled that Boulay had occasionally talked about the horses and placed bets of five or ten francs. But since everybody occasionally bet such small sums, the head clerk had merely smiled at the old man's small pleasures. He did not see that there could be any connection between these petty bets and his death. Riboulet, who had had some experience with the peculiar permutations of the passion for gambling, took a different view and followed up the trail which had so surprisingly been revealed.

He conferred with Inspector Martin of the gambling brigade and combed night clubs, bars, and cafés, especially along the Rue d'Amsterdam and in the vicinity of the Saint-Lazare station, where bookmakers, their runners, and bettors met to carry out their more or less secret transactions: placing bets, exchanging odds lists, collecting stakes, and paying out winnings. Riboulet and his men went from place to place with a photograph of Boulay, and two weeks after the discovery of the body they chalked up their first success. In a drab bar near the railroad station the owner, Carole Petri, recognized the picture. She was sure the dead man must be the same as one of her customers, "Père Louis." The old man used to turn up there quite regularly to talk about the horses.

He would meet others like him who also wanted to try their luck on the races without going out to Longchamps or Auteuil, and who placed their bets not with the franchised bookmakers, but with the hordes of runners who might or might not be honest. During the following ten days Riboulet collected a number of similar statements from petits bourgeois, artisans, or pensioners in the parts of town where Boulay mostly did his errands. Many persons had known him as "Père Louis." They had taken his advice and also let him place bets for them. They did not know his real name—but they had found that he seemed to take great pleasure in the races and that he punctually paid off all winnings. No one had ever bothered about what he did with the list of names and stakes. They were all convinced that he was honest, that he could be trusted with any sum. His knowledge of horses came, they believed, from someone named Baron d'Alméda, whose coat of arms was on a watch that Boulay frequently showed people—a gift from the Baron. But that was the only detail about his life that he had ever given to his cronies and clients. Many of them had wondered at not having seen Père Louis since May 30, but it had occurred to no one that he might have embezzled bets. They had assumed that he must be sick.

Now Riboulet had at least some glimmerings of a motive for the murder. Had one or another of the unsavory hangers-on in racing circles known about Boulay's double life and waited for a day when he had a large sum of bets on his person? Had he been lured into some ambush, murdered, robbed, and the body hidden in a dark shed or cellar until it was convenient to dump it in the Bois? Riboulet's tentative theory seemed confirmed when he learned that the two horses whose names Boulay had underlined in red, Libre Pirate and Star Sapphire, had won on May 28, at odds of 8 to 1 and 13 to 1. If Boulay had bet on these horses, he might well have been carrying sizable winnings which could tempt a murderer.

Aided by Martin, the Chief Inspector began a new series of inquiries. There were many small bookmakers with whom Boulay might have worked. Riboulet and his men tramped from one more or less shabby office to the next. None of the bookies had known Père Louis. At any rate, they all denied having seen him or done business with him. But there were also hundreds of illegal, shady bookmakers who took bets in kitchens and cafés. Many of them had had previous brushes with the law and were therefore known to the gambling brigade. Riboulet could scarcely expect any of them to admit voluntarily that he had placed bets for the murdered man—that would be self-incrimination. Nevertheless, he saw no other way to approach the case. It would be necessary to check all such individuals, at least in the quarters where the dead man had worked. A small gambler like Boulay might well have entrusted his money to such a kitchen bookmaker and received the winnings from Libre Pirate and Star Sapphire through him. If the intermediary could be found, something at least would be learned of how Boulay had spent his last hours. But the Chief Inspector encountered one disappointment after another. Even illegal bookmakers who kept records and bought their freedom from the law by giving information to the gambling brigade seemed unable to help.

By the second half of July Riboulet was beginning to wonder whether he should not give up the hunt. At this point Bayle delivered the report on his thorough examination. It had taken such a relatively long time, he explained, because his work was frequently interrupted by other studies already in progress, by the necessity for testifying in court, by the fact that he performed most of the tests himself, and by the thoroughness with which he had proceeded.

Bayle had begun with more exact analyses of his sundry specimens: the particles of coal and sand, the fragments of stone, the sawdust, the bit of cardboard, the insects, the green fibers, and the particles of red paint. To find out what type of coal he was dealing with, he went back to the well-known fact that various kinds of coal have different densities. The density of an unknown substance can be determined by introducing it into a test tube containing successive layers of liquids of known density; in addition to their differing densities, the liquids do not mix. The unknown element then sinks until it reaches the layer corresponding to its own density. Bayle followed this procedure and floated the coal particles in the liquid. They all sank to the level marked 1.5 on his tube—the density of anthracite.

Bayle was well aware that not all sand is the same. Under the microscope he found that the particles of sand in the present case were a mixture of quartz and silicates. He also analyzed the fragments of stone. They came from a grindstone such as is generally used for sharpening tools. The type of wood from which the sawdust had come seemed to be a more difficult problem. By 1924 criminalists had had some experience in determining the nature of tiny particles of wood, but the matter had not been investigated with nearly the care later to be devoted to it. It was, however, established that the structure of wood could be determined from powdery particles just as well as from cross sections and longitudinal sections of large pieces, if the proper microscopic technique was employed. Crude distinctions between oak and pine were possible simply on the basis of the different colors (dark-brown as against a yellow or light-brown). For more precise distinctions it was necessary to prepare sections of the dustlike particles, then study the structure of the wood under the microscope. Bayle therefore embedded the sawdust in paraffin and used a microtome to cut sections, which he then examined under high magnification. In some of the particles he could make out the typical channels or pores of oak wood, in others the "pits" in the cells of coniferous wood. Looking even closer, Bayle found "frost pores in the junctions of the medullary rays." He recognized these as typical of the common pine. Thus he determined that the sawdust was a mixture of pine and oak.

The tiny piece of yellow cardboard gave him more trouble. Under the microscope he teased the fragment and examined the individual fibers. They proved to be long, thin fibers with jagged cells in between, indicating that the cellulose from which the cardboard was made had been straw and not wood, jute, cotton, linen, or hemp. Bayle undertook several microchemical analyses, in the course of which he added to his test material on microscope slides tiny quantities of phloroglucinol in dilute hydrochloric acid. A reddish color appeared, indicating a cheap material from which the woody parts of the straw cellulose had not been removed.

The two colorless insects proved to be a beetle (Anophthalmus) and a crustacean, both lacking eyes, as is often the case with creatures that live in total darkness.

The green fibers, with scalelike, notched cuticles, showed the typical structure of wool.

Finally Bayle attempted to determine the nature and origin of the two translucent red particles found in the dust on Boulay's trousers. As soon as they were exposed to ultraviolet radiation, they fluoresced brightly. He proceeded to measurements with the spectrophotometer. The particles were splinters of a fade-resistant pigment, rhodamine.

With all these results in hand, Bayle could now say that the dead man had been kept in a totally dark room, probably a cellar in which there was sawdust composed of oak and pine, anthracite coal, quartz sand, particles of a grindstone, insects, some green woolen material, and possibly wood that had been painted with a rhodamine pigmented paint. Could he add any more details that would help to identify the place? Bayle decided to cut out parts of the clothing, soak them in sterile water, centrifuge the solution, and see whether he could find microorganisms.

After he had done so, he found that there were microscopic fungi on the jacket, vest, and straw hat. Microorganisms were likewise found on the shirt, trousers, and tie, but these were not the same type as on the other articles. In order to determine what they were, Bayle made flat-dish cultures, which he kept in an incubator for a while. He found that the organisms on the jacket, vest, and hat were yeasts *(Saccharomyces cerevisiae)* characteristic of places where wine is stored in barrels. The microbes on the shirt, trousers, and tie, however, were the sort of diplococci generally found in damp cellars. Bayle was now certain that the crime had been committed in a cellar, or that at any rate the body had lain in a cellar in which all of the elements he had found must have been present. Moreover, this cellar must contain several sections, since the jacket, vest, and hat had obviously been kept in a different part of it from the corpse itself.

Receiving this report, Riboulet studied it for some time with the disappointment of the professional detective who could not see what good such information might be to him. Was he to search all the cellars in Paris, and crawl through thousands of dark holes and caves? But then he realized that at least he had here an approach for checking on the legal or illegal bookmakers whom he had been questioning for weeks. Was there any one among them who customarily received his customers in a cellar, had an apartment in a cellar, or at the least had access to cellars?

Thus there began the second phase of his investigation, which for the next several months did not take him a single step forward. He was very near to giving up hope when in the middle of November a man named Berger, an employee of Berner & Nielsen, unexpectedly called on him. Berger began with the usual apology: he did not know whether what he had to tell Riboulet was of any importance. But a few days ago he had recalled an incident of the past May. At that time a certain Pierre Boulet had been living at 24 Rue de Milan, above the offices of Berner & Nielsen. Boulet's name closely resembled Boulay's, and one May morning he had found in his mailbox a letter addressed to Boulay. On opening it inadvertently, he had found a mysterious message: "Come to see me. The jockey has a tip." When Boulet passed the letter on to Boulay, the old man had remarked: "Oh, it's from . . ." Berger did not quite recall the name, but he thought it had sounded like Tessier. When he had remembered this incident a few days ago, he had spoken about it with Ihlen, the head clerk, who for his part then recalled something similar. During a casual conversation Boulay had once spoken about betting on horses and mentioned that he used to place his bets with someone named Tessier—"or some name like that"—who lived on the Rue Mogador but that he now went to another bookie.

Riboulet dashed over to the Rue de Milan and checked with Ihlen, who confirmed the conversation and the name. When Riboulet, hoping to find out a little more about this Monsieur Tessier who had suddenly erupted into the case, mentioned that the murder had probably taken place in a cellar, he scored one of those lucky hits that belong among the unforgettable moments of every detective's life. For Ihlen now remembered another detail. Boulay had explained his desertion of the "man named Tessier or Teissier" by remarking: "At the Rue Mogador they take care of you in a cellar, and I don't like that. . . !" He had added that henceforth he was going to take his bets to the bookmaker in the Rue de la Chaussée d'Antin.

Barely half an hour later Riboulet found that a concierge named Lazare Teissier, 30 Rue Mogador, was one of those illegal bookmakers with a police record who had been asked about Boulay at the beginning of the investigation. The previous November Teissier had been caught with his pockets full of betting lists, and been arrested by Inspector Martin. When Riboulet's men went to see him in connection with the Boulay case, he said that he used to see Père Louis but had not seen him for some time because he had given up handling bets since his arrest. He had sent Boulay to another bookmaker, a concierge named Desibour, he said, on the Rue de la Chaussée d'Antin. The detectives had believed Teissier and had gone to see Desibour, who, however, denied ever having taken bets. To be sure, he had long been under suspicion, but there had never been any sound evidence against him.

On the morning of November 20 Riboulet had Desibour and his wife brought in, and he profited by the occasion to have his men search the cellar of 56 Rue de la Chaussée d'Antin in their absence. Riboulet tried bluffing. He gave the Desibours the impression that he had witnesses who could swear that Desibour had received Boulay on May 30 and taken betting lists from him. Desibour, who did not want to be suspected of murder, preferred to admit his illegal occupation. He confessed that old Boulay had frequently given him betting lists because he had been having increasing difficulties about settling up with Teissier, who had long been his bookmaker. It was true, he admitted, that Boulay had been at the Rue de la Chaussée d'Antin on the morning he disappeared, May 30. The old man had brought several betting lists, but had left at once without saying where he was going. That was all he knew, Desibour swore. That had been his last meeting with Boulay, and he had nothing to do with his death.

Meanwhile Riboulet received word that his detectives had found nothing in the cellars under Desibour's apartment which would accord with Bayle's observations. He therefore released the Desibours and trained his sights on Lazare Teissier.

Having been engaged in the affair for so many months now, Riboulet saw no need for acting hastily. Instead, he studied the records of the gambling brigade while having his detectives and informers concentrate on the concierge at 30 Rue Mogador. He was convinced that this approach would yield something this time if the informers were given a particular man to work on. And he was not mistaken. By November 28 he had obtained information on Teissier that added up to a portrait of a highly dubious character. The man was fifty-three, had been living with his wife on the Rue Mogador for twenty years as concierge. But during the same period he had held numerous other jobs: as an office messenger, timekeeper, waiter. The reason for this double employment was not hard to discover. He had long been deeply in debt: his passion for horse racing led him to bet almost daily, and he usually lost. As a bookmaker he was notably dishonest. He falsified betting lists, kept winnings, and invented excuses to deceive his clients. Several times he had claimed that his wallet had been stolen with all the winnings in it. At the end of May his creditors had pressed him so hard that he even begged servant girls in the building to lend him small sums. Customers whom he had cheated reported that they used to be led into a cellar at 30 Rue Mogador to do their betting. But black as this picture was, Riboulet's men did not have a single witness to relations between Teissier and Boulay. No one had ever seen the dead man calling on Teissier. No one had seen him with Teissier or even near the house on May 30 or later.

Yet Riboulet's mind continued to play over the situation. If it were true that Boulay had bet heavily on Libre Pirate and Star Sapphire, and if it were assumed that he had placed the bets with Teissier, Boulay would have gone to Teissier on May 30 to collect his winnings. Was it not conceivable that under the pressure of his creditors Teissier had kept this sum and used it for himself? It was conceivable that the two men had quarreled, that Boulay had demanded his money and threatened to denounce Teissier to the police, until at last Teissier silenced him.

The only way to answer these questions lay in an investigation of the cellar at the Rue Mogador. On November 28 Riboulet reported to the chief of his brigade, Faralicq, and to Examining Magistrate Jousselin. He proposed that Teissier be formally interrogated, that Teissier's apartment and the cellar of his building be thoroughly searched, and that Bayle conduct the scientific part of this search. On the morning of November 29 Bayle received word to hold himself in readiness for the following afternoon.

11

Toward one o'clock in the afternoon Jousselin, Faralicq, Riboulet, and Bayle met in front of the concierge's lodge at 30 Rue Mogador. By that time the examining magistrate had completed an interrogation of Teissier that had lasted for several hours. He came out of it with the impression that he was dealing either with an innocent man or with one of the most cynical and hypocritical murderers he had ever met.

Teissier had amiably admitted that he had known Boulay and taken bets from him until November 1923. He'd always regarded the old man as a friend. As for the cellar, it was possible that he had chatted with Boulay in one of the cellars of the building on occasion, while he was attending to the furnace. But since November, when he'd given up keeping book, Père Louis hadn't come to see him.

Now Lazare Teissier stood in the vestibule of the building among the police officials. Aside from a certain flush to his complexion, nothing about him betrayed nervousness. His detachable collar was white as a lily, his tie impeccably knotted. A pair of genteel gold pince-nez perched on his nose. Only his big red ears slightly marred the portrait of a respectable citizen. When he was questioned, he replied with a friendly smile. Calmly, deliberately, he led the officials down to the cellar by way of a narrow stone staircase adjacent to the door to his apartment. In a niche in the wall hung the keys to the cellars of two buildings, No. 15 and No. 30; these were the only two to which he had access, Teissier declared.

When Bayle entered the cellar of No. 15, which Teissier called his

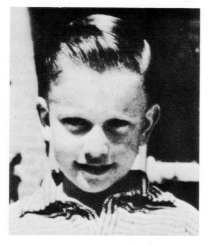

Graeme Thorne

Stephen Leslie Bradley

Graeme's way to school

Stephen Leslie Bradley's house and garden

Albert Guay and his wife Rita   Albert Guay after his arrest

Marie-Ange Robitaille

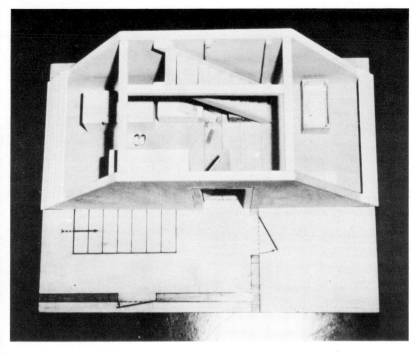

Wooden model of the attic in the Lindörfer case, with all bloodstains marked in color

Friedrich Lindörfer

The serologist **R. R. A. Coombs**

Schematic representations of the principle of mixed agglutination, discovered by Coombs in 1955-56 and described on pages 215, 216. LEFT, epidermal cells: figs. 1 and 2, before treatment with anti-A serum; figs. 3 and 4, after treatment with anti-A serum and washing; figs. 5 and 6, after addition of blood cells and centrifuging. RIGHT, bloodstained textile fibers submitted to the same treatment. Upper row shows mixed agglutination, lower row no mixed agglutination.

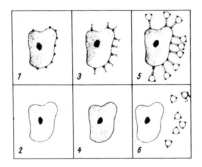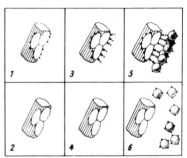

Photomicrographs show tiny bloodstained fibers.
The clumping of Group A test blood cells can be observed on the right

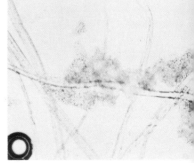

private cellar, he had the impression that this place was not dark enough to explain the presence of the eyeless insects which he had found on the dead man's shirt. A ventilated shaft led to the courtyard. It was closed with a sheet of metal, but there were innumerable holes in the metal, which admitted ample light. This was hardly the natural habitat for Anophthalmus beetles. On the other hand, the floor was covered with a mixture of sawdust, coal, and other dust. Otherwise, there were only empty boxes and a pyramidal coalbin nearly five feet high. One of the slanting sides could be opened. The interior walls were black with coal dust. The bin was empty except for a few pieces of coal.

Bayle was too self-possessed to betray the disappointment he was feeling. But disappointment changed to excitement as soon as he entered the second cellar, No. 30. Here was the boiler for the central heating of a firm that occupied one of the upper floors of the building. Teissier explained that it was his job to take care of this boiler; that was why he had the key to the cellar. This room, too, was fairly light. But Bayle instantly spotted many details that fitted in with his investigation. The floor had apparently not been cleaned for years. Layers of dirt were piled atop one another. In this dirt there were large quantities of coal particles, sand, and sawdust. In the middle of the room lay a large wooden board that had been partly sawed up, probably for kindling. It was painted red—and the color strikingly reminded Bayle of the rhodamine that he had discovered by spectrophotometry. The sawdust was sprinkled with many other paint flakes of the same color.

Near the entrance stood a chest containing pieces of cardboard, some of which had fallen on the floor and mingled with the general litter. The tan color of the cardboard corresponded to the color of the scrap of cardboard from Boulay's clothing.

At the same time Riboulet made another find. Behind an empty crate, among old newspapers, he picked up some papers which proved to be betting lists—and lists, moreover, that had been written out after November 1923, apparently refuting Teissier's claim that he had kept away from bookmaking since his arrest. But Teissier declared with his agreeable smile that all this was scrap paper which had been given to him to start the fires. Since the lists were not written in Teissier's handwriting, there seemed no way to use them as evidence against him, hardly credible though his story sounded.

Bayle was totally engrossed in his own work. He poured sample after sample of dust into white bags, wrapped up the red-painted wood, the other red particles, and pieces of the tan cardboard. Then he turned

toward the cellar stairs to look for clues there. Now, at three thirty in the afternoon, the examining magistrate had both cellars sealed and took Teissier back to his office for further questioning. Bayle was to examine the samples he had taken so far, and report the results to him as quickly as possible.

Bayle's tests were to take several days, but by that evening he transmitted a preliminary report to Jousselin in which he stated that the red paint on the board in the cellar corresponded with the flakes of paint he had found on Boulay's clothing. The sand from the cellar of No. 30 likewise consisted of quartz and silicates, and the coal dust was also anthracite. The bits of tan cardboard were of the same type as the cardboard from the cellar. On the strength of this, Teissier was placed under arrest. By December 2, Bayle had completed his analyses. They showed that the sawdust from the cellar of No. 30 likewise consisted of a mixture of oak and pine wood. Bayle asked that the search of the cellar be continued.

During this same period Riboulet labored mightily to track down further evidence against Teissier, who had been shaken neither by his arrest nor by Jousselin's daily interrogations. Riboulet made inquiries among the tenants of the building, among the neighbors, among acquaintances and relatives of Teissier. He also questioned Teissier's wife. But it seemed as if no one had any inkling of Teissier's secret activities. Riboulet did, however, pry out of a brother-in-law, a restaurateur confusingly named Tissier, the story that at the end of May the concierge had asked him for a loan of 12,500 francs, threatening that he would "otherwise have to jump into the Seine." This bit of information only supplemented the existing statements about Teissier's money troubles. It did seem interesting, however, that a second brother-in-law of Teissier's worked as a cab driver and seemed so nervous during the interrogation that Riboulet began to think he might have helped to transport the dead man on the night of June 7. Some witnesses testified that Teissier had frequently hung around the Place Budapest during the summer; that was an area where many taxicabs stood around while their drivers spent hours in the bars, so that their cars could have been borrowed unnoticed for a short time. It also seemed noteworthy that Teissier's wife displayed a peculiarly obstinate silence, as though she had something to conceal. She declared that Teissier never left the house after nine o'clock at night, and that he had slept right beside her all night on June 7.

The examining magistrate therefore authorized a second search of

the cellar, as requested by Bayle. All through the morning of December 3 Bayle went over the place with two assistants. This time the stairs were illuminated with a strong acetylene lamp, and within a short time a large patch on the side wall, about two and a half feet high, was discovered. An attempt had been made to cover up something with gray paint. But the work had been done so clumsily that a round spot and several spatters remained visible. A benzidine test suggested that the substance was probably blood. After each of the steps had been examined individually, Bayle, stooping down with his magnifying glass, detected at the foot of the stairs an unmistakable encrustation of blood, in which a hair was embedded.

When the inspection of the stairs was completed, Bayle set about searching for small beetles and microorganisms. The brightness of the cellar, which seemed incompatible with his finding of the Anophthalmus on Boulay's clothing, had occupied his thoughts constantly during the previous days. He saw only one possible explanation for this contradiction: the large coalbin in the cellar of No. 15. But no matter how much he hunted, he nowhere found any trace of an insect. There was, however, a certain dampness on the floor of the bin which made him think of the fungi cultures he had obtained from Boulay's clothes. Bayle wondered whether the coalbin might have served as a hiding place for the body for a while. Had Boulay been felled in the course of a quarrel in the cellar of No. 30 and so come into contact with the dust from the floor of that cellar? Had he staggered to his feet, perhaps, and tried to escape up the cellar stairs? Had he then been killed on the stairs and removed to the coalbin in Teissier's own cellar? In order to examine the bin more closely for bloodstains and fungi, Bayle ordered a wagon and had the bin taken apart and transported to the Identification Service.

As soon as the examining magistrate heard of Bayle's finding of bloodstains on the steps, he resumed his interrogation of Teissier. But Teissier had explanations ready to hand. He spoke of a cat that had recently had kittens on the stairs, and about the numerous baskets of soiled wash that the women of the building carried into the cellar, brushing along the walls. Bayle refuted these excuses by demonstrating that the stains were from human blood, and that there were no vaginal epithelia to be found in the stains. The latter fact did not absolutely exclude the possibility that some of the stains might have come from soiled women's underclothes, he stressed. But the presence of blood spatters did. Such spatters could never have come from washing that brushed along the cellar wall. Moreover the hair in the bloodstain at the foot of the stairs corresponded in all details with Louis Boulay's hair.

Significant as these bloodstains were, however, Bayle himself was possessed by the idea that the conclusive evidence would come from his studies of the dust, the fungi, and the insects. He asked Jousselin for a third chance to look through the cellars. This time he went in the evening. Again aided by two inspectors, and armed with sieves, he sifted the layers of dust, looking for insects dead or alive, native to the place or chance wayfarers. But again the search was in vain until, combing through the sand and anthracite dust, one of the detectives turned up the lower, torn end of a Métro ticket. This find would have been of no importance if the little scrap of paper had not borne the imprint *George V*—the very Métro station from which poor old Boulay had set out every morning. The search was continued late into the night in the hope that the rest of the ticket would be found, with its date. But after a few hours the task had to be abandoned.

Bayle spent the next morning carefully examining the coalbin, which now took up a large part of his laboratory. But all attempts to find bloodstains or remains of insects on the black walls proved fruitless. Finally Bayle transferred parts of the damp coating at the bottom of the bin to culture dishes and placed these in the incubator. Just as he closed the door of the incubator, a detective rushed in with the exciting news that a third cellar had been found in the Rue Mogador; the keys were in Teissier's possession and he had hitherto concealed the existence of this room. A tenant of the house by the name of Fidler had come back from a trip on the morning of December 4, had heard of Teissier's arrest, and had gone to Riboulet with the following information. Teissier had borrowed 2000 francs from him during April and promised to pay it back by May 31. He had in fact paid the debt with only a few days' delay, on June 4. Fidler also recalled that early in June he had complained to Teissier about a sweetish odor coming from the small cellar compartment directly under the stairs. This cellar belonged to Fidler, but he never used it. Teissier, who had the key, told Fidler that the smell came from a damaged drainpipe.

As soon as he heard this, Bayle rushed over to the Rue Mogador. There he found Jousselin and several detectives. They descended the winding staircase into the cellar, whose ceiling was formed by the steps themselves. When Bayle opened the door, he found what he had so long been looking for in vain: a totally dark cave, without a ray of light in it, covered with coal dust, large enough to hold the body of a man. The light of a flashlight immediately fell upon three tiny, colorless insects clinging to a dusty wall. Bayle crawled into the chamber and collected insects, samples of the coal dust, and a damp, musty coating from the floor which smelled as if the small room had occasionally been used as a wine cellar. Then he proceeded to study every square inch of the room. He found several green fibers, sand, and small fragments of stone. The job took enormous pains and patience, but Bayle stayed at it until he had obtained every encrustation that might possibly be from blood. With these he sped back to his laboratory.

Discoveries followed hard upon one another. The encrustations proved in fact to be human blood, the coal dust anthracite, the particles of stone parts of a grindstone identical with the kind he had found in the murdered man's hair. The green fibers were wool and with a single exception corresponded exactly in color to the green fibers he had brushed from Boulay's shirt. The tiny insects were the blind beetles of the genus *Anophthalmus,* the microorganisms the *Diplococcus pneumoniae* that had been found on Louis Boulay's shirt and trousers.

Could there be any further doubt that the murdered man had been hidden in this pitch-dark chamber whose keys Teissier had concealed, with good reason? If there were any further problems for the detectives, for Bayle there was only one: the presence of yeast fungi on Boulay's jacket, vest, and hat. But this last mystery was solved on the morning of December 6. The fungi cultures from the coalbin grew in Bayle's flat dishes. They proved to be *Saccharomyces cerevisiae,* the same yeast fungi that had been found on the jacket, vest, and hat. Bayle was now convinced that these clothes had been kept separately in the coalbin while the dead man himself had lain in the den under the stairs.

Galvanized by Bayle's report, Jousselin, Riboulet, and a number of other detectives descended upon the Rue Mogador. In addition to the cellars, they now searched every corner of Teissier's apartment. The apartment yielded a green woolen jersey whose fibers corresponded to the green fibers Bayle had found on Boulay. This was something, but not much. On the other hand, the search in the cellar of No. 30 was a resounding success. Filthy from head to foot, their lungs choked with dust, Inspectors Leroy and Coste went on sifting the dirt for hours. Their efforts were rewarded by three more scraps of the Métro ticket. The whole ticket was put together out of the four fragments. Its upper end, torn into two halves, carried the notation: 151-24-05. This signified the 151st day of the year 1924, 5 o'clock in the morning. That was May 30, 1924, the day Boulay vanished, and the very time he entered the Métro each morning.

12

A year later, on December 13, 1925, Lazare Teissier was sentenced to ten years in the penitentiary for manslaughter. Throughout the trial the concierge had preserved his composure and his smile, and had refused to confess. Nor had Riboulet succeeded in the course of that year in obtaining any further evidence or witnesses to the details of the crime, or to the transfer of the body of Louis Boulay to the Bois de Boulogne. As a result, Bayle's scientific work and his "analysis from dust" had loomed so large in the evidence that the case gave rise to a bitter but fruitless discussion with advocates of the "old school" of criminology, who held that the murderer would have been located and convicted without all this scientific folderol. Bayle himself provided the only possible answer to this contention when he wrote in his personal account of the case:

"Our work proved that the victim was killed in a cellar and that his body was concealed there for a while. . . . It told us nothing about the actual circumstances of his death. Was the murder planned or was it the outcome of a momentary emotion? Were the blows administered with the deliberate intention of murdering him? Was there an accomplice in this cellar and did he play an important or only a secondary part? The missing answers could only have been supplied by human witnesses. . . . The truth always lies between the new theories which press forward too quickly and the routinization which is too fixed and immobile. No matter what scientific advances we make in the future, the laboratory alone will never solve criminological problems, nor can that be its task. But many matters will remain unclarified unless the laboratory is called upon for assistance. . . . It is my opinion that the laboratory will yet have great tasks to accomplish, whose results cannot yet be foreseen."

The Boulay-Teissier case became a historic *cause célèbre* illustrating the development of dust analysis in many of its facets. Bayle himself, however, was not destined to witness this development for more than half a decade. Those were five years of growing successes, growing acknowledgment, remarkable triumphs. In the end Bayle did not escape the vanity that so easily follows from success. He did not escape the mannerisms of the successful in his court appearances, nor did he escape an occasional error when he "pressed forward too quickly," not practicing the salutary skepticism which later generations were to feel toward procedures that were not yet fully established. The Paris newspaper *Excelsior* seems to have characterized him accurately when it wrote:

"He . . . spoke of nothing but his reactions, his tests, his reagents, his fingerprint stories, his examinations of dust. He moved in the world of the most minute minutiae. . . . For him neither dirt nor cleanliness existed. For him there was only one thing: material for investigation and incorruptible analysis. . . . It sometimes happened that a defendant attempted to pin him down: 'Well then, this man was the killer!' Bayle would reply: 'I don't know that. It is not my affair to determine that. But the shoes which stand here as Exhibit number 930 MO are stained with soil that comes from the garden of the plot on 17 Rue So-and-so.' The lawyer Campinchi once exclaimed angrily: 'Ah, Monsieur Bayle, you know everything. One might compare you to a god descended to earth to incarnate our infallible science. You have never erred. . . .' Bayle replied, and no remark was more typical of him: 'Certainly I have erred. But not today.' "

This was Bayle at the end of the twenties, shortly before he met his end by a blow of fate unique in the history of criminological science. On the evening of September 15, 1929, Edmond Locard came from Lyons and paid a visit to Bayle in his laboratory. Locard described the incident several decades later in his memoirs, and the story may be slightly colored by his fondness for anecdote and a slight hostility toward this Paris star who had risen so quickly. As Locard recalled it, a poor madman, one of those creatures who frequently molested the police with their requests, had forced his way in to see Bayle during Locard's visit and was bothering him with confused jabber. Bayle lost patience and snarled: "You are crazy, Monsieur. I cannot waste my time on nuts. You belong in an insane asylum." The visitor slunk away with the expression of a whipped dog on his face. Locard, however, wondered what would have happened if the fellow had been a malicious rather than a harmless mental patient. Abruptly he said: "Bayle, you are going to be murdered. . . ." Bayle laughed self-confidently. . . . So much for Locard's memoirs.

Next day, September 16, 1929, at ten o'clock in the morning, three revolver shots rang out in the Galérie de la Présidence in the Paris Palais de Justice. Inspectors Guérin and Ristori, who were on duty in the building, rushed out and saw a frail little figure lying on the stairs going up to the Identification Service. Blood was pouring from one eye and a wound in the chest. When they came closer, they saw that it was Bayle, dead. A street cleaner pointed out the assassin, who was trying to escape. When they pursued and caught up with him, he surrendered without resistance. Taken before Examining Magistrate Benoit, he declared: "Yes, I was the one who shot Monsieur Bayle. I am not crazy. I only killed a dishonest man who did me harm by a false affidavit. . . . My name is Joseph Émile Philipponet, born August 19, 1886 at Lyons. . . ."

While the incredible news spread through Paris, Benoit learned the background of the crime. Ever since January 1926 Philipponet, a self-righteous psychopath, had been engaged in a suit with a landlord named Dichamp on the Rue Rochechouart. Dichamp demanded a payment of thirty thousand francs on the basis of a contract that Philipponet had made with him in connection with the transfer of an apartment, while Philipponet claimed that the contract had been forged and that he owed only thirty-five hundred francs. During the preliminaries of the controversy a private graphologist named Vigneron had filed an affidavit attesting that the contract was indeed a forgery prepared with the aid of an ink eradicator. At the next stage Bayle had been assigned to examine the document, and on the basis of chemical analysis had concluded that it was genuine, since no ink eradicator had been used.

Bayle had never met Philipponet, but that affidavit proved to be his own death sentence. The murderer summed up the story in a few words which told more about his personality than would have been discovered by a lengthy investigation: "In breach of truth and justice Monsieur Bayle came to a conclusion harmful to me. I decided to avenge myself. I waited near the stairs that lead to his office for the author of my misfortunes. He was halfway up the stairs when I called out to him. He turned around and I fired. Monsieur Bayle's despicable action was the cause of my shooting him, and I would have fired even if I had known, as you now tell me, that he was the father of five children."

Whether or not weaknesses of character marred the last years of Bayle's life, his end seemed like a blind whim of fate. The assassin's bullet destroyed a talented pathfinder in forensic chemistry and biology. Paris was left with only the foundations of the great criminalistic laboratory which was to arise under Bayle's successors, Sannié and Ceccaldi.

13

Two and a half years after Bayle's death, in December 1931, London suffered one of those crimes which make even humanitarian reformers of the penal code sometimes doubt their own arguments. Certainly no one disagreed with Superintendent G. W. Cornish of Scotland Yard when he wrote in his memoirs in 1935: "One of the most abominable . . . crimes which I have had to deal with was the murder of little Vera Page, and I shall always regret that we could not bring her unknown murderer to the gallows. If ever a man deserved hanging, he does."

The scene of the crime was that mixed district of London north of Shepherd's Bush and Holland Park. Here shabby middle-class houses bordered on slums, and along Notting Hill the police made a point of patrolling in pairs. Miles of poor streets abutted unexpectedly upon elegant squares and avenues. On Addison Road in the finer part of the district, a milkman unsuspectingly entering the tradesmen's entrance to No. 89 came upon a little girl lying motionless on the lawn. The milkman recalled the previous day's newspaper accounts of the disappearance of Vera Page, a ten-year-old child who lived at 22 Blenheim Crescent, Notting Hill. Vera Page had been missing since the evening of December 14, after visiting an aunt who lived near her parents' home. The newspapers had printed pictures of an unusually attractive girl who inevitably awoke everyone's sympathy. Although the face of the child in the garden of the house on Addison Road was blackened by coal dust, the milkman thought he recognized the features of Vera Page. He roused the cook, and both set out in search of a constable.

Superintendent Cornish happened to be at the Paddington police station that morning. Together with Detective Inspector Mallet and the police surgeon, Dr. Calvell, they drove out to Addison Road, forced their way through the crowd that had already gathered, and saw that Vera Page had indeed been found. The child could have been deposited there only in the early morning hours. During the preceding night it had rained almost continually. But the girl's dark hair and her clothes were quite dry, except her back, which had been in contact with the wet grass. Her coat and face were soiled with coal dust and also spotted with candle grease. Dr. Calvell found signs of strangulation and, when he opened the coat, injuries stemming from an unusually brutal rape.

315

When Dr. Calvell moved the body and unbent the crooked left arm, a finger bandage smelling strongly of ammonia dropped from it. Sir Bernard Spilsbury, who shortly afterward performed the autopsy, concluded that the child had been murdered after seven o'clock on December 14. The body, he believed, must have lain for a considerable time in a warm room before it was taken to the house on Addison Road.

From the very beginning of the investigation, Cornish pinned his hopes on the finger bandage. He suspected that the murderer must have worn the bandage and lost it as he laid the child down on the lawn. While Mallet began the routine inquiries, Cornish asked Roche Lynch, the Home Office Analyst, to examine the "fingerstall." Lynch reported that it consisted of a layer of bandage and another layer of lint. The bandage must have been in contact with ammonia and water for some time. On the inside of the fingerstall he found blood, bacteria, and white blood cells, indicating that the wound had bled and suppurated.

Impelled by the wave of indignation that swept through London at the bestial murder of this child, whose big dark eyes spoke appealingly to millions in newspaper pictures, Cornish sent all available men to the area between Shepherd's Bush and Holland Park. Within a day the persons who had last seen Vera Page alive had been located. After the girl had left her aunt about five o'clock in the afternoon, she had apparently not taken the most direct way home, but had succumbed to the lure of lighted shopwindows. At five-thirty or six o'clock she had been seen in front of a druggist's window near her home. Probably the pleasures of window-shopping had lured her along Montpelier Road. A friend of her father's had seen the child from across the street on Montpelier Road about seven o'clock. But when he turned to look back at her, she had vanished. Not only the parents—who cannot always be believed when they make such statements—but everyone who had known Vera Page declared firmly that she would never have gone with an unknown man. The murderer must have been someone she knew, whom she trusted. Cornish therefore sent his force out hunting for a man who might have known Vera Page, who had had an injured, suppurating finger on December 14 and 15, and who had worn a bandage.

Cornish's men, among them Detective Sergeant Charles Tracey, tramped from house to house and street to street as they had done in many similar cases. By the time the investigation approached its end in February 1932 they had conducted a thousand interrogations and worked through several thousand letters of advice from seers, fortune-tellers, diviners, and visionaries. But they tracked down only a single man who had known Vera Page and who also had a wound on the little finger of his left hand. He was Percy Orlando Rush, a workman at Whiteley's laundry, to the south of Olympia. Tracey discovered him early in the investigation, and on December 18 brought him to the Notting Hill police station for questioning.

Percy Orlando Rush was forty-one years old, a small, stocky man with unusually bushy eyebrows, a bushy mustache, and thick, dark, horn-rimmed glasses which hid his eyes. His left little finger showed an injury only partly healed. For ten years he had been living with his wife on the top floor of 128 Talbot Road, quite near the area in which Vera Page had last been seen. Even more remarkable was the fact that Rush's parents lived in the same house as the Page family, 22 Blenheim Crescent, and that Rush visited his parents several times a week, had keys to their apartment, and on December 18, when Tracey and Mallet for the first time unexpectedly asked him about Vera Page, had stated: "I knew Vera Page. She was a pretty, sweet little kid. I liked her. I always looked upon her as a nice little child." As if he felt he had said too much, he promptly added: "I have never given her sweets, money, or toys. I have seen her playing in the streets outside her own house. I last saw her about three weeks ago."

When Mallet asked Rush where he had been on the afternoon and evening of December 14, he learned that Rush, who ordinarily left Whiteley's laundry about six fifteen and took the bus to Notting Hill Gate, arriving home quite quickly, had on December 14 not reached his home until 8:15 P.M. He said that his wife had been visiting his mother that evening and he had not wanted to go home to the empty house. To while away the time until his wife would be back, he decided to walk home by way of Kensington High Street. He had dropped in at Woolworth's, then proceeded down Church Street to Notting Hill Gate and Kensington Park Road. He had no witnesses to testify that he had actually taken this route. His clothes were soiled with coal dust, like the dead girl's clothes. Tracey had found a rug in Rush's home which was stained with candle grease. Rush was the only tenant of the house who had the keys to the cellar and who used candles in order to find his way about in the darkness of the unlit cellar. Was it possible that he had met Vera Page on Montpelier Road, lured her to his home, satisfied his lust and killed her, then hidden the body in his cellar until he had an opportunity to drive or carry it to·Addison Road?

These factors weighed heavily against Rush. The results of Tracey's investigation into the wound on Rush's finger seemed even more incriminating. According to the statements of the workmen in Whiteley's laundry, Rush had injured the little finger of his left hand on December 9, and had come to work next day with a homemade bandage to protect the wound against the ammoniated water in which he had to work. Mallet and Tracey suddenly confronted Rush, at their first interrogation on December 18, with the bandage that had been found in the crook of the dead girl's arm, and asked whether he recognized it. Rush said he would have to examine it more closely. Seemingly he used the brief interval to master his rising uneasiness. Then he declared that the bandage did look very much like the ones his wife had made for him on December 9 and the next few days. But he had worn the last bandage on Saturday, December 13, and lost it in the street. After that he had not bandaged his finger.

So he had not worn a bandage on December 14, Mallet commented. Did he know Charles John Miles? Rush said he knew him; they worked together at Whiteley's. Well, Mallet continued, Charles John Miles was prepared to state that he had seen Rush with a bandage on December 14 and 15, and that Rush had said he had to wear it because the ammonia burned the sore.

Rush replied that Miles must be lying. He had tried to protect the sore against ammonia only during the first few days, when the finger was still quite bad. Aha, Mallet said, so the sore had been better on Tuesday. Would he care to see the statement from the doctor at the laundry who had looked at Rush's finger on December 15 and advised him to keep it bandaged?

Nevertheless he had not worn a bandage again. He had decided he wanted to "harden" the finger. Mallet and Tracey were convinced that he was lying. But he did not deviate from the story he had given the detectives.

On December 19 Cornish turned to Roche Lynch once more. He asked how they could prove by chemistry that the fingerstall was a bandage that Percy Orlando Rush had worn. Lynch replied that on the Continent attempts were being made to determine correspondences of textiles by comparisons of fiber and texture. This work was usually undertaken not by chemists but by biologists, since the material involved was wool, cotton, linen, or hemp, and thus organic. But if Cornish could bring him the material that Rush's wife had used to bandage the sore finger, he would try to demonstrate correspondence microscopically.

Cornish sent Tracey to Talbot Road. Tracey was received by Rush and his wife in an extremely obliging manner. They handed him a strip of gauze and a bandage from which pieces had been cut. Tracey suspected that this material might not be identical with the bandage materials that had actually been used. Something about Rush's smile disturbed him. He had the feeling that he and Mallet, in ignorance of the possibilities of further investigation, had confronted Rush too soon with the bandage they had found, thus warning him and giving him the opportunity to destroy the genuine bandage material.

On the other hand, Roche Lynch was an excellent serologist and chemist, but the field of textile studies was new to him, and he did not arrive at a definite conclusion. The fibers of the bandages corresponded, but bandage was far too common a material. The same was true for the gauze. He found no peculiarities which could have proved the identity of the fingerstall and the bandaging materials. In fact, the lesser width of the bandages seemed to suggest that there was no identity.

Cornish did not yet abandon the idea of catching Rush through the bandage. He took up Tracey's suspicion that Rush had turned over spurious bandaging materials, and from the end of December 1931 to early February 1932 he had inquiries made in many shops, trying to discover whether Rush or his wife had bought bandage. He also checked in all public first-aid stations where Rush might have gone to have his finger bandaged. But all these efforts came to nothing. He could not find a single witness, not a salesman or nurse, who could definitely recall Rush or his wife out of the hosts of customers and patients with whom they dealt every day.

When Rush appeared before the London Coroner Ingleby Oddie on February 10, for the inquest, the suspicion that rested upon him had by no means diminished. It was evident in the faces of the members of the jury and the spectators, who expressed their fury in such outcries as "That man is telling lies!" It was also evident in every one of Oddie's questions—Oddie himself was an exception among the medically and legally ill-trained coroners in England at that time. Again and again his questions returned to the problem of the bandage. He attacked the point from various angles, hoping to drive Rush into a corner, to catch him in a contradiction. The record of Rush's interrogation by Oddie revealed the Coroner's strategy:

"You know a bandage was found on Vera Page?"

"I do, sir."

"And when it was shown to you you said it was like yours?"

"I did, sir."

The coroner leaned forward and said sharply: "Was not that bandage yours?"

Rush, who was nervously drumming his fingers on the witness box, replied: "No, sir."

"Do you know it smelled of ammonia?"

A covert smile passed across Rush's face, and the coroner reproved him: "Don't smile; it is nothing to smile at. . . . You say that the bandage was not yours?"

"That is quite so."

"And you say you never got a bandage anywhere else excepting at your own home?"

"That is right, sir."

"Didn't you go to the welfare center at Whiteley's? Is there not one?"

"There is, but I had no time to go."

"Why didn't you go to the welfare center on the Monday? Did you go there at any time?"

"No, sir."

"Why not?"

"Because I did not wish to. I preferred dressing it myself."

"Did you not know that the people at the welfare center are more skilled in the application of bandages than your wife?"

"I know, sir."

"Then why didn't you have one put on there?"

Rush hesitated, then said: "That I cannot answer."

The coroner leaned forward again and said sternly: "Have you had a bandage put on anywhere else, not by your wife?"

Again Rush hesitated and then replied: "No, sir."

"You don't seem very sure about it. You could have easily gone into a chemist's shop."

"Yes."

"Did you do so?"

"No, sir."

Everyone could sense Oddie's keen suspicion, which made him revert to the same subject, the decisive question: Where was the real bandage material that Rush and his wife had used? But Rush remained steadfast. In the end Oddie could do no more than remind Rush he had sworn on the Bible to tell the truth: "Do you swear that you did not meet Vera Page on the night of Monday, December 14?"

Rush answered: "I swear that."

"Do you swear that you did not wear a finger bandage after Saturday, December 12?"

"I swear it."

After only five minutes of conference the jurymen gloomily decided that there was not sufficient evidence for them to return a verdict against Rush.

Cornish's indignation at the outcome of the Page case reverberated three years later in the account he gave of it in his memoirs. That feeling coincided with the outrage felt by hundreds of thousands of persons after Rush was released from "official suspicion." The *Times* commented that Rush would certainly have been charged if it had been possible to prove a correspondence between the material of his bandage and the remainder of the bandage in the possession of Rush and his wife. This remark focused the attention of the public on the problem of criminalistic textile studies to such an extent that the case of Vera Page may be regarded as a significant factor in the further development of such studies.

Those who looked back from the vantage point of the 1930's to the first suggestions that textiles could be compared for criminological purposes would once again encounter Hans Gross. A chapter in his "Manual for Examining Magistrates" was entitled "Examination of Cloth, etc." Thus, in 1893 he had this to say on the matter.

"Textiles can be of importance if the identity of cloth, canvas, or threads is involved. . . . If the matter is of considerable significance, the opinions of drapers etc. are insufficient. A trained microscopist should be asked to determine the number of threads per inch, their strength, the fineness of the material as determined by the manner of twisting. He will then study the individual threads to determine whether they are composed of cotton, linen, wool, silk, etc., consider subsidiary factors, and finally be able to say whether the scrap that has been found comes from a given article of clothing, whether the burlap comes from a given dozen lots of burlap. . . . The cases in which such a study is indicated are more numerous than is generally thought. It will only be necessary to be careful, when identity of materials is involved, not to be content with deciding that a given material 'undoubtedly' looks just the same as the comparison material. In every case the microscopist must first be consulted. . . . Anyone who conducts experiments of this sort will be convinced that many things thought to be different are similar, and that some look identical when they are not."

Among the first to take up Gross's ideas were Paul Jeserich, the Düsseldorf chemist Look, and later Edmond Bayle. They first made a specialty of cord, and were often called upon to compare cord used in robberies to tie the victims with cord found in the possession of suspects. Bayle was able to unmask a group of burglars who had used a rope to climb a wall. Another rope was found on their own premises, from which a piece had been cut off. Bayle showed that the two ropes were identical.

Jeserich, Look, and Bayle went to textile mills to learn the methods and techniques by which yarns, twines, threads, cords, and ropes were made. They studied the raw materials, from flax to sisal. They learned the significance of left and right twisting in the spinning of yarns, and how many kinds of yarn there are which can be distinguished solely by the type of twisting and the combination of threads with different twists. They learned, furthermore, how yarn is doubled. Bayle made large collections of different threads, yarns, and ropes, and could prove such fine points as that a button torn from a thief's jacket by his victim had threads clinging to it that corresponded with the threads still in the jacket. From threads and yarns they inevitably went on to study whole fabrics. Look assembled a veritable gallery of magnifications of textile patterns in his Düsseldorf laboratory, ranging from plain interlacing weaves to twills and satin weaves. Though all fabrics are created by running weft threads through warp threads in looms, the weft passing through the warp by means of the shuttle, the possibilities are almost endless. In plain interlacing weave, for example, the weft thread passes over the first warp thread, under the second, over the third and so on. In twill weave the weft passes over one and under two warp threads, over one and under three, and so on, thus producing a kind of stepped pattern. The combination of various basic weaves produces composite weaves ranging from the simplest to the most complicated forms.

Bayle, then, mastered the whole subject of weaves and could tell one cloth from another at almost a glance. Nevertheless, he early realized that this kind of comparison had its limits, and was only a starting point for the criminalist. Given the mass production of complicated fabrics, it meant little in the case of a theft, for example, if a scrap of fabric found on a suspect was identical in weave and color with the stolen goods. The piece of fabric need not have come from a given lot, since the same material was to be had almost everywhere. The similarities would have to be narrowed down to the most minute particulars, to the characteristics, say, peculiar to a given bolt, before anything could be proved.

Bayle had received an unforgettable lesson in this regard in 1926, when he was called to the scene of a murder on the bank of the Seine.

The victim, a fifteen-year-old girl named Christienne Paquet, nude except for silk stockings, high-heeled shoes, and a girdle, was lying on a strip of muddy ground. The only clue to be found was the imprint of a cloth pattern pressed into the soft soil. It was in the hollow of another imprint made by a knee. Probably the murderer had knelt beside the girl. After some investigation it was discovered that Paul Paquet, the dead girl's fourteen-year-old brother, had trousers of the same pattern. It seemed particularly suspicious that the boy had freshly washed and ironed them after the time of the murder. All in all, the case was full of bizarre angles. Christienne was the daughter of a prosperous factory owner, Jacques Paquet. When her brother was questioned, he told a story that seemed to incriminate him all the more. When Christienne was a mere twelve, it seemed, she had obtained possession of a "Manual of Love" and had tried out every imaginable form of the sex act with her younger brother. This had gone on for three years and practically next door to their parents' bedroom. As a result Paul was completely enslaved and felt that he could no longer live without her. About four months earlier his sister had suddenly turned away from him, declaring that she no longer needed an apprentice, since she now had a master. He described how he found out that she met a Moroccan waiter every night, and how he had been filled with desperation and hatred. But he stalwartly denied any part in the murder. The Moroccan, Joseph Chaman, was arrested. He admitted that he had met Christienne in a hotel but denied having killed her, and his alibi proved that he could not have been the murderer.

When Bayle once again studied the plaster cast of the imprints, examining every inch under the microscope, he discovered another, smaller imprint of the same pattern, which must have come from contact of the shin with the ground. In this imprint, however, there was an anomaly which Bayle could explain only on the assumption that the trousers must have been darned at this spot. Bayle once again checked Paul Paquet's trousers, but could find no sign of repair anywhere. He therefore informed the examining magistrate that Paul Paquet could not be the murderer. The boy was released, the story given to the newspapers, and two weeks later Bayle received a package containing a pair of trousers of the identical pattern, but with a darned spot below the right knee whose stitches corresponded precisely with the imprint. The package also contained a card with a note: "Congratulations. The murderer." The sender was never found. The nymphomaniac girl must have had a third lover whose identity was never discovered.

From this case Bayle drew a conclusion that remains valid to this day. The correspondence in material and weave between two textiles makes it only probable that they come from the same article of clothing. Proof of identity can be supplied only by unmistakable individual characteristics. These characteristics may be of several kinds. There may be a patched place, or a change in the fabric due to heat, aging, or wear; there may also be flaws in the weave caused, say, by a tearing of the warp. Again it was Bayle who provided a sterling example of the possibilities available to criminalistics when the investigator succeeded in tracking down one such peculiarity.

The case concerned a Paris bank messenger named Deprez who failed to return from one of his errands. Suspicion fell on a mason named Nourric, since Deprez had made all his rounds up to the call on Nourric, and had made no others afterward. Proofs against Nourric were not forthcoming until Deprez's dead body was pulled out of the Marne a week after his disappearance. His hands were tied behind his back with a handkerchief, a cheap cotton handkerchief with red stripes. At first it seemed hopeless to find any features which would mark the handkerchief as Nourric's property; such handkerchiefs were manufactured by the millions. But then Bayle caught an irregularity. There were six more cotton threads in one of the red stripes than in any of the others. This was a weaving fault due to a temporary disturbance in the raising of the warp beam. Examination of Nourric's stock of handkerchiefs led nowhere. But Bayle went to the mill and thence to the factory which had bought the flawed batch of cloth and made eight dozen handkerchiefs out of it. He pursued his investigation to the retail shops. A shop was found which had sold six of the handkerchiefs to Nourric's mother. She still had five; one she had given to Nourric. This little fact closed the circle of evidence.

The Paquet and Deprez cases did not make much of an impact outside France, and with Bayle's sudden death, textile studies were more or less dropped. Only a few chemists and biologists continued to work in this field. So textile criminalistics was still in its beginnings when the Vera Page case in 1932 so emphatically indicated the need for better and more refined analyses. Even so, eight years passed before a similar event in England drew upon this branch of criminalistics. This time it more than vindicated itself.

14

November 3, 1940, was a stormy night in the northwest of England. The rain was beating down wildly when, past midnight, the telephone rang in the Preston home of James Brierley Firth, director of the Home Office's North-Western Forensic Science Laboratory. Firth lifted the receiver and learned that a dead girl had been found in a blockhouse in the little town of Seaforth on the coast of the Irish Sea. The Lancashire Constabulary in Seaforth needed his help, and a police car was already on its way for him.

Firth, a lean man in his fifties, with a thin, furrowed face, was a chemist. For some twenty-five years he had been attached to University College in Nottingham, while also advising the authorities on ways to combat pollution in the rivers Trent, Ouse, and Cam. In this capacity he frequently appeared in court as an expert, and by the twenties had established close contacts with the police in Nottingham. In 1938 the Home Office, by now fully convinced of the importance of forensic science laboratories, added to the Metropolitan Police Laboratory of Scotland Yard six more laboratories in Birmingham, Wakefield (later moved to Harrogate), Bristol, Nottingham, Cardiff, and Preston. Firth was appointed director in Preston. The term "Forensic Science Laboratory" was something of an exaggeration for the two small rooms in an old house on Jordan Street, where Firth worked with a single police constable for assistant. But in the two years of its existence, the laboratory had accomplished as much as was expected of it, and more. Firth was known in all the police headquarters of the northwest and was called in on all capital crimes, all major burglaries and fires.

That November night was not only blustery and wet; it was also extraordinarily dark. Because of the German air raids on England, the blackout was total. The constable who came for Firth knew the roads. Nevertheless, it was 1:30 A.M. before the car reached Brook Vale bridge which connected Waterloo and Seaforth. The wind puffed out the coats of the policemen standing about and lashed Firth's face as he approached the blockhouse entrance and paused just inside the doorway, beaming his flashlight over the bare, dirty interior. The floor of the blockhouse was covered with refuse. In the midst of the filth lay the motionless figure of a girl, bloodstained bruises and dirt around her eyes, nose, and lips. Strangulation marks were plainly visible on both sides of her neck. Detective Inspector Floyd gave Firth a brief summary of what was known so far.

The dead girl was Mary Hagan, a fifteen-year-old schoolgirl from Waterloo. At 6:45 P.M. she had left her home and crossed the bridge to Seaforth to buy the evening newspaper and cigarette papers for her father. About seven o'clock she was seen in two shops on Lawson Road, where she spent 2d. on cigarette paper and 1½d. on the newspaper. Then she must have started back across the dark bridge. When she did not come home, her father and several neighbors set out to look for her, and toward eleven o'clock the child was found in the blockhouse. Dr. Bradley, the police surgeon of Seaforth, had examined her body about an hour before. It seemed likely that she had been dragged into the blockhouse and strangled shortly after seven o'clock, on her way home. The change that remained from her purchases, 1s. 8½d., was gone. Possibly the murderer had observed Mary shopping and attacked her on the way back in order to rob her; then, finding that he had killed her and that his booty was next to nothing, had used the opportunity for a perverse pleasure. Dr. Claude Horace Bradley had discovered unequivocal evidence of violation. As yet there were no suspects.

Flashlight in hand, Firth examined the dead girl once more, then gave permission to have her transferred to the Seaforth morgue. Otherwise the body was not to be touched until he himself had the opportunity to remove the clothing. He then searched the floor of the blockhouse for almost an hour, concentrating especially on the spot where Mary Hagan had lain. A few years earlier the sight of a proper gentleman down on his hands and knees on the filthy concrete floor would have aroused amazement and derision among the police. But now men like Detective Inspector Floyd were accustomed to such proceedings, and Floyd personally helped to pack up the various finds and samples of soil and refuse. Among the items of interest were a newspaper, the Liverpool *Echo* of November 2, which was found spread out directly under Mary Hagan's body, a cotton handkerchief, a woman's glove, and samples of soil from the interior of the blockhouse and from outside the entrance. Finally Firth discovered a piece of dirty fabric, apparently a finger bandage, with blood and some kind of salve clinging to the inside.

By three o'clock that morning Firth had finished his work. Chilled through, he drove over to the morgue. The rain had changed to hail. The morgue was drafty and cold, like most such places in England. But in spite of the difficult circumstances, Firth carefully removed Mary

Hagan's clothing piece by piece, and wrapped up each piece separately. In the course of this work he once again examined the strangulation marks, and observed a kind of thumbprint in blood on the right side of the neck. The print was useless for fingerprint determination. But since none of the girl's injuries had bled, he thought of the finger bandage and wondered whether the bandage could not have come from a killer with an open wound on his thumb who had lost the bandage during the struggle and pressed his bleeding thumb against Mary Hagan's throat. This was only a fleeting surmise that sprang into Firth's mind shortly before he got into the car, shivering, and started back to Preston.

During the week from November 3 to 10, Firth systematically examined his bits of evidence, from Mary Hagan's rain-soaked shoes to the curious bandage. He prepared notes on each separate study. Concerning the bandage he wrote: "This fabric was associated with a layer of mud. On removing the mud, the general appearance indicated that it was a bandage from a finger or thumb. . . . The bandage was found to be made up of three pieces." The outer bandage was of a brown, water-repellent material. The inner bandages were soaked with a disinfectant and smeared with salve. Chemical tests proved the disinfectant to be acriflavine, which was used almost exclusively in military bandage materials. The salve was zinc ointment. The blood was heaviest at the tip of the bandage; the wound therefore must be toward the tip of the finger. Firth's general conclusion was that the bandage came from a military first-aid kit which had been used on a severely bleeding thumb wound. The culprit might well be some member of a military unit. The Seaforth barracks were, indeed, not far away.

Firth prepared similar notes on every other item. But only the finger bandage seemed to provide significant clues—that is, if it really came from the killer and had not been lost by some couple holding tryst in the blockhouse, or otherwise tossed in with the other rubbish.

On November 10 Firth reported his first findings to the Constabulary. They reached Inspector Floyd just after he had at last had some leads concerning a possible murderer. Among the information on suspicious persons who had been observed in the vicinity of Brook Vale bridge on the evening of November 2 was a repeated reference to a man of about twenty-five or thirty. Witnesses had seen him both on October 30 and on November 1. A man named Hindley had noticed him about five thirty-five on the afternoon of November 2, and believed that he had recognized him as Samuel Morgan, whose parents lived on Berkeley Drive in Seaforth. His description of the fellow strikingly accorded with that of a man who on October 4 had attacked a woman named Anne McVittie, robbing her of her purse. Hindley believed that Morgan had been in the Irish Guards since 1936 and should by all rights have been in barracks. It puzzled him that the man should have been loitering by the bridge.

This puzzle was clarified by an inquiry at the barracks. Samuel Morgan had been transferred back to Seaforth the previous December after a spell of field duty. On September 22 he had left the barracks without leave, and had been missing since. He was characterized as a poorly educated and undisciplined type. Inquiries at Morgan's parents' home revealed that he had turned up there in September and said he would be staying a week. Actually he had stayed until the end of October, by which time his father became irate and ordered him out of the house. His parents maintained that they did not know where he had been staying since.

This was the state of affairs when Firth's report arrived. His suggestion that the criminal might be some person in the services fitted so neatly into Floyd's results that he asked Chief Constable Hordern to institute a search for Morgan. On November 13 he learned from Scotland Yard that Morgan had been picked up in London. Floyd rode to London on November 14. Samuel Morgan, a tall, weedy-looking young man, was brought to him at the Streatham police station. On the thumb of the man's right hand Floyd saw what he took to be a badly healed wound. Since the inspector as yet had no proofs of Morgan's part in the murder of Mary Hagan, he accused him only of the attack on Anne McVittie on October 4, took him back to Seaforth in spite of his denials, and confronted him with Anne McVittie. She recognized him at once, and he was arraigned before the magistrate in Islington. In jail Morgan was examined by Dr. Bradley, who noted a badly healed wound on the thumb, perhaps caused by barbed wire, between one and two weeks old.

Morgan himself refused to make any statement. Floyd and Sergeant Gregson therefore went to see Morgan's parents for the second time. Once again Morgan's mother insisted that she knew nothing about her son's activities after October 30. But she was an old, worn-out woman who lacked all talent for play-acting. Floyd sensed that she was one of those mothers who become particularly attached to their sons who have gone astray, and that she was capable of any kind of lie. The father said nothing; he was obviously afraid of his wife. However, he advised Floyd, as he was conducting the detectives to the door, to call on one of his older boys, Thomas Edward Morgan, who lived on Molyneux

Road, Seaforth. Thomas Edward, as it turned out, was not at home, but his wife Mildred was there. As yet she knew nothing about her brother-in-law's arrest or that he was suspected of the sensational crime. She admitted without hesitation that Samuel had come to her house on October 30. He had said he had quarreled with his father, and she let him stay on condition that he report at the barracks as soon as possible. After some resistance, he promised that he would report next day. On the morning of October 31 he had left the house, supposedly to go to the barracks. But two hours later he had returned with a heavily bleeding thumb. He said he had cut himself on barbed wire, took a field dressing from his pocket, and had her bandage the cut. She took possession of the rest of the bandage materials. On November 1 he set out for the barracks once more and again returned, nervous and ill-humored. She used more of the first-aid kit to make a new bandage for him, and put some zinc ointment on it. He then remained until about four o'clock in the afternoon on November 2. At this time he spoke of wanting to try to borrow money from their brother-in-law, James Shaw. Since then she had not seen Samuel, and was rather glad of it.

Floyd asked for Shaw's address and found that he too lived on Berkeley Drive and could be reached in the afternoon.

Shaw proved to be much less friendly. He had read of the arrest in the newspapers and weighed his every word. All the same, he admitted that Samuel Morgan had made an appointment with him on November 2. Shaw had arranged to meet him in the Royal Hotel in Seaforth between seven and eight o'clock. A younger Morgan boy, Francis, was also to be present. Francis was eighteen and served at the Seaforth barracks. Shaw had arrived at the Royal Hotel about seven-thirty, and Francis shortly afterward. Samuel Morgan came five minutes later. He asked them for money because he wanted to leave Seaforth. Shaw tried to persuade him to report back to the barracks. But he wanted at all costs to get away from Seaforth. Finally they gave him what money they had on them, and they parted.

During this dragging, hostile interview, Floyd calculated the time needed to reach the Royal Hotel from Brook Vale bridge. If Samuel Morgan had attacked Mary Hagan shortly after seven o'clock, he had enough time to walk or run to the Royal Hotel.

Had Shaw noticed anything unusual about Samuel Morgan? Floyd asked.

No.

Had Morgan been excited or injured?

He couldn't say, Shaw replied evasively. He had not noticed.

Had he really noticed nothing at all? Whether, for example, there was a bandage on Morgan's right thumb? Or a bleeding cut?

Again Shaw dodged the question: he really could not remember.

Floyd and Gregson left and drove straight to the barracks to question Francis Morgan before Shaw had a chance to get in touch with him. At the barracks, however, they learned to their surprise that in the meanwhile Francis Morgan, too, had overstayed his leave of the preceding day. Like his brother he was inclined to be undisciplined, the detectives were told, and in fact was too much attached to his elder brother for his own good.

Floyd wasted no time; he ordered a new search, this time for Francis Morgan. That took only a few hours. By five o'clock Gregson had the boy at the police station. He was pale with fear because he assumed that he had been arrested for overstaying his leave. Questioned about his meeting with his brother on the evening of November 2, the boy was so preoccupied with his own trouble that he reported things he surely would have concealed otherwise. On November 2 he had arrived at the Royal Hotel at seven thirty-seven. His brother Samuel came in five minutes later. Samuel was breathing hard as if he had been running. His finger was bleeding. He had cut himself a few days earlier and lost the bandage. Francis went outside with him to bandage up the thumb again with a field dressing. While he was doing this, he noticed a bloodstain on Samuel's cap, but asked no questions. Later Samuel accompanied him as far as their parents' house on Berkeley Drive and then vanished, allegedly setting out for Warrington or London. Since then Francis had not heard from him.

Floyd was worried lest Francis Morgan deny everything he had said as soon as his own fear abated. That had happened all too often in his career as detective. He tried to avert such a possibility by giving Morgan all the time he needed to read every word of the interrogation record and sign every page.

Floyd then rang up Preston, to let Firth know the results of the day's work, in particular the part played by the bandage, and hear what further steps they could take. Firth instantly asked after the bandaging material that Mildred Morgan mentioned having kept. Had Floyd taken possession of it before it occurred to any of the Morgans to destroy it? Had he also obtained the zinc ointment?

For a moment Floyd feared he had committed a serious error. Mildred

Morgan might already have realized how dangerous her revelations were. He hurried Gregson off to Molyneux Road and did not breathe easier until the sergeant returned with the rest of the bandage and the salve. Relieved, Floyd informed Firth, who asked to have the materials sent to Preston as soon as possible. He also wanted the clothing Samuel Morgan had worn on November 2.

In examining the clothing, Firth found traces of soil here and there, and in the left breast pocket another opened package of field dressings. Firth sent to Seaforth for standard field dressings issued in the barracks. He then began his studies to detect correspondences between the finger bandage he had found in the blockhouse and the bandage that Mildred Morgan had used for Samuel Morgan's finger, the remainder of which he now had on his laboratory table. If identity could be proved, it would amount to gravely incriminating evidence against Samuel Morgan.

Firth very well recalled the unfortunate Vera Page affair, and he also knew a good deal about the dubiousness of textile comparisons. On the other hand, he had more experience than Roche Lynch had had. Microscopic examination of the bandaging materials soon convinced him of complete correspondence in the outer wrappings and the inner gauze. The impregnation with acriflavine was the same on the blockhouse finger bandage and the field dressing from Mildred Morgan's home. The remains of salve on the bandage and Mildred Morgan's zinc ointment were the same. But in view of the immense quantities of bandaging of the same type that had been made since the beginning of the war, and the widespread use of zinc ointment, these correspondences meant virtually nothing.

In his search for special peculiarities Firth noticed one item that seemed to him significant. In the gauze layers of the bandage were portions of selvage. The selvage was unusually narrow and differed in the number of warp and weft threads from the bandaging materials that Firth had obtained from the Seaforth barracks. On the other hand, the selvage matched that of the bandage material from Molyneux Road. Firth consulted a firm that manufactured surgical dressings, Vernon & Company. Its textile engineer informed him that there were no specifications for selvages, and that the selvages of each firm differed. This was natural enough, since a number of mills provided the gauze for the bandages. The correspondence of the selvages thus served as a significant indication, but not conclusive evidence because the same narrow selvages might be found in other bandages made from gauze obtained from the same mill. These were not qualities which could be considered peculiar to the Morgan bandaging material and the blockhouse bandage alone.

Meanwhile Firth was being kept abreast of further developments in the case. Samuel Morgan was behaving in a curious manner. On November 16, before he had been openly accused of the murder, he unexpectedly called Inspector Floyd to his cell and delivered himself of a strange confession. Apparently he was undergoing a crisis; he must have suspected that his arrest because of Anne McVittie was only a pretext, and that a net was closing around him. His confession, written out by himself on an official statement form Floyd had given him, read as follows:

"I have been very worried since being arrested and want to tell what happened. On Saturday evening, November 2, 1941, I got hold of a girl on Brook Vale bridge and she fell down. I carried her into the blockhouse and laid her on the floor.

"She had 1/6 or 1/7 in her hand and I took it. I then went to the Royal Hotel at Seaforth, where I met my brother Frank and brother-in-law Jim Shaw. I did not intend to harm the girl at all."

Floyd felt that the confession, as happened so frequently, had sprung only from a momentary fear of discovery and was a crude attempt to give an innocent appearance to the events. Once again he must expect the confession to be recanted at the earliest opportunity, with a lawyer eventually attempting to represent the confession as extorted by police pressure. He could not rely on such confessions, and therefore asked Firth to do his best to supply proofs that would stand up in court.

Firth had made it his custom to lay aside materials to be investigated for a while and turn to them anew after an interval. In so doing he frequently noticed details he had previously overlooked. He followed this practice now, and meanwhile compared the traces of soil on Morgan's clothing with the soil samples from the blockhouse which he had taken on the night of November 3. Microscopic examination for mineral components revealed a distinct correspondence in the sand, the quartz, and the coal particles. Since Popp's first soil investigations, chemists had more and more turned to examining soil by special analysis in cases where the techniques of microscopy, mineralogy, botany, and bacteriology were not useful. This was especially so with soil samples taken from cities and industrial areas, in which the botanical or microbiological components were scarcely distinctive. In samples of this sort, the typical factors were generally industrial deposits of trace metals or other chemicals. Spectral analysis could reveal the presence of almost infinitesimal quantities of such elements. And in fact the tests showed Firth that the same trace elements, chiefly copper, lead, and manganese, were present in the soil samples from the blockhouse and from Morgan's clothes. With this confirmation of Morgan's presence in the blockhouse, Firth once again turned to the examination of the bandage materials.

During his first set of studies he had noticed the stitch holes along the seams in both the finger bandage and the bandaging material obtained from Mildred Morgan. The gauze layers were folded and sewed along the sides, as well as being stitched to the brown outer covering. When the threads were cut and the gauze layers unfolded, they displayed only one row of stitch holes in all the dressings from the Seaforth barracks. But in the gauze on the blockhouse finger bandage and in Mildred Morgan's bandaging material, two irregular, parallel lines of stitches were discernible. Firth promptly asked for more packages of bandages from Seaforth. In all of them he found only a single row of stitches. Had he discovered an unmistakable characteristic of this particular bandaging material? Once again he consulted the textile engineer, Ronald Crabtree, and Crabtree quickly found the explanation. The gauze pads were sewed by machine, but folded by hand. The result was slight deviations in the seaming. In the present case there had been an unusually gross deviation. The seamstress had been careless about folding the gauze, and a narrow extra fold had been included and stitched. The result was that when the folded bandage was opened out, a double row of stitching appeared.

Crabtree and Firth forthwith examined several hundred different bandages. In no case did they discover another with a double row of stitching. To obviate all doubts, Firth asked the Manchester Chamber of Commerce Testing House to check all the results of his examination. Only after this laboratory had confirmed his findings did he send the items of evidence to the prosecution, along with his opinion that the bandage from the blockhouse in which Mary Hagan had been found and the samples of bandage obtained from Mildred Morgan "were both torn from the same field dressing pad."

A month and a half later, on February 10, 1941, Samuel Morgan was tried before Mr. Justice Stable and a jury at the Liverpool Assizes. As Floyd had foreseen, Morgan now averred that he had never seen Mary Hagan. He had written his partial confession of November 16, he said, under coercion by Floyd. Francis Morgan repudiated his statements of November 15 on the same grounds. He said that Floyd and Gregson had exploited his fear of being charged with desertion and had dictated the words he had written. Now he claimed that he had been at the Royal Hotel not at seven thirty-seven but ten minutes earlier. His intention obviously was to abbreviate the time that could have been at the disposal of Samuel Morgan for committing the murder, so as to exclude the possibility that he had done it. His brother, he testified, was calm and quite as usual, and had had an undamaged finger bandage on. So patent was it that the boy was lying that the judge granted an application by the prosecution to treat him as a hostile witness. But in any case all the lies and retractions were destroyed by two circumstances. Mildred Morgan abided by her statements about the bandage she had put on the defendant's thumb, and identified the rest of the bandaging material. And Firth's proof of the correspondences between the block-house and this bandaging material could not be shaken, despite the greatest efforts by Edward Wooll and E. E. Edwards, the defense attorneys.

On February 17, 1941, the jury accepted the version of the crime sketched by G. Justin Lynskey for the prosecution. Lynskey described an unruly deserter who committed robberies because he was short of money and, too broke to go to prostitutes, had assaulted, robbed, and killed a schoolgirl. On April 4, 1941, all appeals denied, Morgan was hanged.

The Second World War, already under way when the murder of Mary Hagan took place, paralyzed the development of forensic chemistry and biology. Nevertheless, the case of Mary Hagan remained one of the great exemplary cases, a lesson in what really counted in criminalistic textile work: meticulous searching for individual details, for which the general knowledge of the processes of weaving and textile manufacture could provide only the background.

15

The enormous technological advances of the postwar years created the premises for a type of crime that brought to the fore another area of forensic chemistry—one that had a long, slow evolution behind it, but which only in the changed postwar world acquired growing importance and circulation.

Patrick Simard, an eel fisherman from Sault-au-Cochon, Quebec, on the north bank of the St. Lawrence, was on his way home toward noon on September 9, 1949. It was a cool day with an almost cloudless sky. The roar of a plane's motors sounded down along the riverbank, and Simard, welcoming any event in this solitude, watched the twin-engined plane soaring above the wooded slopes of Cap Tourmente toward the northeast. It was a Douglas DC-3 of Quebec Airways which made three flights a week from Montreal via Quebec and Baie Comeau to Seven Islands. Three times a week it appeared at eleven forty-five, passed overhead, and vanished into the distance. Simard looked at his watch and noticed that this time the plane was five minutes late. Almost at the same moment he heard the crack of an explosion. Simard thought he saw something come hurtling out of the fuselage. Then the plane dipped sharply to the left and plummeted toward the peak of Cap Tourmente.

After a moment of consternation, Simard began to run. He had to contend with the dense underbrush of the mountain slopes, and it was almost an hour before he came upon the first vestige of the plane. Several woodcutters had joined him by this time. Between fragments of suitcases and sundry scattered material lay motionless human bodies. Undeterred by the dangerous reek of leaking fuel, the men pressed toward the plane. It must have struck the ground almost vertically, for there was no swath of destruction; not a tree had been knocked down. The entire front of the airliner was a twisted mass of wreckage. The wings had been ripped off. The rear of the fuselage jutted from the ground. In vain Simard and the woodcutters looked for signs of life. Twenty-three persons, including the three crew members, the stewardess, and four children, were dead.

Simard went back to fetch help. When he reached the tracks of the railway running between Cap Tourmente and the St. Lawrence, he found a number of railroad workers. One of the section hands sped off in a handcar to the village of St. Joachim, where the stationmaster transmitted the news of the crash to Quebec. From there it reached the Ancienne Lorette airport and the parent company of Quebec Airways, Canadian Pacific Airlines.

This was the company's first serious accident since 1942, and George W. G. McConachie, its President, was deeply affected. The Douglas DC-3 was an unusually reliable aircraft, and Captain Pierre Laurin a pilot of great experience.

McConachie convoked an investigating commission. Heading it was Frank M. Francis, a technical expert of the first rank. The Investigation

Department of Canadian Pacific Airlines, which dealt with criminal cases, ordered Inspectors Jean Belanger, Jules Perreault, and Gaston Delorme to the scene. Coroner Paul V. Marceau was called in. The Department of Transport, charged with investigating the causes of all major transportation accidents, informed the Royal Canadian Mounted Police, which sent officers to Cap Tourmente to guard the scene of the crash. By five o'clock the Quebec teams were assembled and took the train to St. Joachim. There they had to change to a handcar, and it was seven o'clock before they arrived at the foot of Cap Tourmente. The group climbed the mountain in darkness by the aid of flashlights. The ascent took more than an hour. As they approached the scene of the crash, their first sight was the head of a child bashed against the ground, and Dr. Marceau later declared that nothing in his whole life had been so shaking as this ghostly nocturnal encounter with death.

No fire had broken out, so there was no great difficulty in identifying the twenty-three victims, but the cause of the sudden crash seemed all the more mysterious. In the graying dawn the technical experts questioned the few witnesses from Sault-au-Cochon. Each one reported hearing the sound of an explosion. And indeed the left front luggage compartment showed marks that suggested it had been the center of an explosion which had destroyed the control system, so that the aircraft plunged vertically into the ground in a power dive. The motors themselves had continued running until impact. The tips of the propellors had dug into the ground. Francis and his men first set about determining whether the explosion could have been caused by materials that were normally aboard a DC-3. There were five possibilities.

1. Behind the copilot's seat was a fire extinguisher. The steel cylinder contained carbon dioxide under a pressure of 1000 psi. It was conceivable that such a cylinder might explode. But the cylinder in the plane was undamaged.

2. Under the floor of the aisle in every plane were two storage batteries. At least theoretically hydrogen might have been produced by these batteries and formed a highly explosive mixture with air. But both batteries in the wreckage of the plane were in their normal place, whereas they would have been shattered if they had given rise to the explosion.

3. The pressure container for the hydraulic mechanism of the retractable landing gear contained a glycerinlike fluid. The pressure was too small to account for the force of the explosion.

4. An explosion might have taken place owing to a gasoline-air mix-

ture. But such an explosion was ruled out in the present case, since gasoline explosions are always accompanied by fire.

5. An explosive mixture of air and carbon monoxide which had somehow leaked from the motors into the fuselage was conceivable. But no carbon monoxide was found in the blood of the victims.

By September 10, therefore, Francis had already concluded that the cause of the crash was a violent explosion in the left baggage compartment. It must have been caused by a substance which in normal circumstances would not be on board a plane.

This conclusion, which was kept secret for the time being, stunned the authorities in Quebec. The fact that the explosion had taken place in a baggage compartment seemed to imply that the unknown explosive had come on board in someone's baggage or as air freight. While the passengers' relatives and friends at the Canadian Pacific Airlines terminal and the Chateau Frontenac in Quebec received the grim confirmation that there had been no survivors, the investigating commission labored under the distressing sense of confronting an enemy new in the brief history of civilian air transport. Granted, attempts to eliminate political or economic competitors or rivals in love, or to dispose of a husband or wife by a deliberately planned accident without regard for the innocent persons who might also be killed, were as old as crime itself. Schemes to collect insurance by causing ships to sink were likewise not new. Instances of bombs placed in public vehicles by psychopaths or sexual deviants could be considered part of the regular repertory of criminology. Only a few months before, there had been the incident of a Philippine plane being destroyed by an explosive in the baggage compartment. It had plunged into the sea with thirteen persons on board. Chance alone had exposed a plot by five persons who had doomed the plane and everyone in it in order to eliminate one man who was in the way of his wife and her lover. Could it be that this novel method of murder was now being repeated on Canadian soil? Or was the plane crash the result of assassination with a political, economic, or security background? For by the evening of September 12 it was obvious, both in Quebec and Ottawa, that the problem was one of crime, not accident. Consequently, the Mounted Police took over the investigation of the case of "DC-3-D 280/CP-CUA."

By 1949 the Royal Canadian Mounted Police had long been one of the most efficient police forces in the world. Its twelve divisions covered the entire country. The red coat was used only on parade, and the "Mounted" was largely symbolic. Since 1937 the Mounties had been geared to take advantage of the newest scientific developments. Its first Crime Detection Laboratory was set up in Regina, Saskatchewan; at first it occupied only a single room, but within a year it was enlarged and staffed with a chemist, a ballistics and documents specialist, and a pathologist. During the Second World War a second laboratory was founded in Ottawa, and two more were planned: one to be in Sackville, New Brunswick, the other in Vancouver, B.C. In 1949 the Prosecutor-General of the Province of Ontario was preparing to establish a major laboratory. The province of Quebec already possessed a criminological laboratory with a long and rich tradition, l'Institut de Médecine légale et de Police scientifique, located on the Rue Saint Vincent in Montreal. It had been strongly influenced by French and European traditions, and was under the direction of Franchère Pépin.

Such was the state of criminal science in Canada on the afternoon of September 10, 1949, when the crash of the Quebec Airways plane became an affair for Canadian criminalistics. Since the destruction of an aircraft was a federal crime, the investigation was clearly a matter for the Royal Canadian Mounted Police. But the ever-present tensions between Quebec and the rest of Canada made it advisable that the provincial police and the Quebec municipal police also participate. A special commission was therefore established. It consisted of Inspector René Bélec and Corporal Gérard Houde of the Royal Canadian Mounted Police, Inspector Aimé Guillemette, chief of the detective division of the Quebec city police, and Captain J. Alphonse Matte of the provincial police.

16

On September 10 two clear points were already established: 1. The explosion had taken place in the left front baggage compartment, as has been mentioned. In order to speed operations during the stop in Quebec, this compartment was loaded in Montreal only with baggage destined for Quebec. Thus the compartment was completely emptied on arrival in Quebec, then loaded with baggage and freight destined for Baie Comeau. Hence the bomb, if such it was, could have been placed on board the plane only at the Ancienne Lorette airport. 2. The second point of departure was the site of the crash itself. The investigators

would have to attempt to collect wreckage strewn in a circle of more than a mile in radius.

While Inspector Bélec and the other officials began checking records in Ancienne Lorette, Franchère Pépin and Bernard Péclet in Montreal were assigned to the chemical and technical analyses.

As he reviewed the passenger lists, Bélec started when he came across the names of three important persons from New York. They were E. T. Stannard, President of the Kennecott Copper Company, and two other high officials of the same company, Arthur D. Storke and R. J. Parker. It occurred to Bélec that these industrialists might have been involved in the manufacture of atomic bomb material. The Igor Gouzenko affair, in which a network of Soviet atom spies had been uncovered in Canada, had not yet been forgotten. Might not Soviet agents have leaped at this chance of liquidating, with a single blow, three top figures in atomic development? It turned out, however, that the three executives were not connected with atomic matters. Deposits of titanium had been found near Havre St. Pierre in the Province of Quebec, and the three were going there solely to look into ways of shipping the ore.

A check of the insurance policies that passengers had taken out for the flight revealed nothing special. They were on the usual level. Examination of the lists for wives or husbands who had boarded the plane in Quebec, leaving their spouses behind, also provided no leads. Lucille Levesque, who worked at the ticket office of Canadian Pacific Airlines in the Chateau Frontenac, had made no unusual observations when she performed the depressing office of informing the survivors of the deaths of their wives, husbands, or children. Everyone had behaved as people do in such situations. None had attracted attention by coldness, indifference, or a display of bogus sorrow. Bélec of course well knew that the human capacity for dissembling could achieve astonishing heights. He therefore agreed with Inspector Guillemette that all relatives of the passengers who had boarded the plane at Ancienne Lorette should be placed under observation and their private lives investigated to determine whether they were in economic or other difficulties, whether they had extramarital involvements, and so on.

Meanwhile Bélec himself turned his attention to the luggage. The freight clerk Willie Lamonde, who had been on duty at the airport on the morning of September 9, could recall nothing unusual. Aside from the passengers' luggage various freight parcels had been shipped. But in these parts it was fairly common for important goods to be shipped by air freight. Bélec saw no other recourse than to check the senders and receivers of all parcels. He seemed to be making no headway with this tedious business until, on September 13, a detective reported from St. Simeon, ninety miles from Quebec. He had gone to St. Simeon to check on a twenty-eight-pound parcel sent by a Delphis Bouchard in St. Simeon. There was no Delphis Bouchard, the detective reported.

For the first time Bélec felt he was on the track of something. Since the package in question was addressed to Alfred Plouffe, 180 Laval Street, Baie Comeau, he sent Corporal Houde to Baie Comeau on a special plane. A few hours later Houde reported by telephone: there was no Alfred Plouffe in all of Baie Comeau. Bélec promptly drove out to Ancienne Lorette airport and pleaded with Lamonde to summon up every memory he had of the fatal day and if possible provide a description of the person who had dispatched the parcel with the false addresses. After some cogitation, Lamonde recalled that the package in question had been brought to his window by a woman, a fat, black-haired, absolutely ordinary woman who had given no impression whatsoever of being in any way unusual or nervous. A cab driver had carried the package to the scales for her. The woman had paid $2.72, taken the receipt, and gone.

Bélec was convinced that the mystery of the plane crash was at last beginning to unfold. But the description of the unknown woman was so scanty that he saw scarcely any chance of finding her, unless questioning all the cab drivers in the city of Quebec provided information. Before he left the airport he asked Inspector Guillemette to alert the drivers, and almost at once he had results. The questioning of the taxi drivers had scarcely begun when a cabby named Granowski reported that one of his fellow drivers, a Yellow Cab man, had talked to him on the afternoon of September 9, shortly after the first news of the crash, about a woman with a parcel whom he had driven to the airport that morning. The name of the Yellow Cab driver was Paul Pelletier. Guillemette at once sent a detective to Pelletier's home. The young driver recalled his female passenger quite well. Distinctly fat, middle-aged, and with dark eyes and black hair, he said. He had picked her up at the Palais railroad station. She had had the package with her, and had not spoken a word during the ride. Since she wanted him to drive her back to the city, he carried the package to the freight window for her. On the return drive she asked to be dropped off at the Chateau Frontenac. Just before they reached it, she changed her mind and asked to be driven to the rear of the hotel. There she got out and set off toward

Lower Town, the old part of Quebec. From her accent, Pelletier guessed that she came from the poorer quarters of Quebec.

It seemed an almost hopeless undertaking to find a fat, black-haired, plebeian-looking woman in Quebec, even if the search were confined to Lower Town. Nevertheless, the attempt had to be made, and in addition the relatives of the passengers must be checked, if only to see whether there was anyone among them who could be matched with Pelletier's description.

Time was pressing. Coroner Marceau had set September 14 for the date of the inquest. Almost at the last moment, Guillemette telephoned Bélec to report that in checking over the relatives of the crash victims he had stumbled on an item that might be important. It concerned a man named Albert Guay, the husband of Rita Guay, who had been killed in the disaster. Guay, who was thirty-two years old, ran a small jewelry shop in Quebec. The previous June he had been fined twenty-five dollars for illegal possession of a weapon, in connection with which misdemeanor he had also spent a night in jail at the time. The background of his arrest had its piquant aspects. On the evening of June 23 he had molested a pretty eighteen-year-old waitress who was on her way to work at the Monte Carlo Café. He had threatened her with a revolver, and the waitress had called a policeman, who escorted her to the café. But shortly afterward Guay himself burst impetuously into the café, where the policeman arrested him. The waitress' name was Marie-Ange Robitaille. Guillemette wondered whether she might not be the "woman in the case." The incident certainly suggested that Guay was interested in women other than his wife. Marie-Ange Robitaille lived with her parents at 205 du Roi Street. At the moment she would be working in the Monte Carlo.

Bélec at once set out to meet Guillemette, and the two proceeded together to the café. Marie-Ange was undoubtedly a striking girl, with heavily rouged lips and a provocative shape which was more emphasized than hidden by her waitress' uniform. When the inspectors identified themselves, she betrayed agitation. Obviously she knew whom they were interested in. Asked whether she knew Guay, she answered yes without hesitation. She had met him in the spring of 1947, she said. When had she last seen him? Not for a long time, she replied, and she would not be seeing him again. The detectives thereupon asked her what her relations with Guay had been, and what had impelled Guay to behave as he had done on June 23. Did she have to answer that question? the girl asked. She no longer understood her own conduct during that period. She had long ago returned home to her parents and wanted her peace.

This reply struck Bélec as highly significant. But his instinct warned him against pressing the girl. He therefore said that he had no intention of prying into her private life. All he wanted was certain information, and then he would no longer trouble her. He would like to know whether Guay had any dealings with a black-haired, rather fat woman. From the speed with which Marie-Ange answered, it was clear that she wanted above all to put an end to this conversation. The woman must be Marguerite Pitre, 49 Monseigneur Gauvreau Street, she said. Could she go back to her work now?

Bélec and Guillemette left the Monte Carlo and conferred. If they could manage discreetly to confront the cabby Pelletier with Marguerite Pitre, and if Pelletier recognized her, they would know they were on the trail of something important. Immediately after the inquest they sent for Pelletier and found him glad to help. Their plan was for Pelletier to call at 49 Monseigneur Gauvreau Street, ring Marguerite Pitre's doorbell, and ask whether she had ordered a cab. Perhaps she herself would open the door, or be called to it, so that he would have a chance to look at her before he apologized, saying he must have the wrong house. But when Pelletier rang, a neighbor opened the door. She said Mrs. Pitre was still in bed, which scotched all hope of Pelletier's seeing her. All that remained was to place Pelletier in a police observation car and wait to see whether his erstwhile passenger left the house. At the same time two detectives were assigned to gathering information on Marguerite Pitre.

On September 15 what Bélec had expected and feared occurred. The newspapers were filled with lurid accounts of the Cap Tourmente disaster. The accident was attributed to everything from a plot by Communist agents to the act of a madman. One article stood out, however. Le Canada in Montreal published a story by Edmond Chasse, an experienced reporter who had apparently done a bit of private sleuthing around the Ancienne Lorette airport. He reported on the mysterious parcel and the mysterious woman who had dispatched it. The police were on the trail of the unknown woman, he concluded. Bélec was of two minds on the value of Chasse's detective work. It might warn the suspect in time, and on the other hand it might lure her out of her hiding place.

September 15 and 16 passed, and Marguerite Pitre did not leave her house. The investigation of her produced nothing striking. She worked sometimes as a waitress and was married—her second marriage—to Arthur Pitre, a harmless petit bourgeois. She was a native of Quebec and had two brothers: Jean Marie Ruest and Généreux Ruest, the latter a cripple who could get about only on crutches and was for the most part confined to a wheel chair. He was employed as watchmaker in a shabby workshop on St. François Street. There was really nothing in the gray, commonplace life of such a family that suggested a propensity for criminal acts. Certainly they did not seem to possess the intelligence to devise a plan for blowing up an airplane in flight.

Similarly, the information accumulated on Albert Guay seemed hardly to add up to the portrait of a deep-dyed villain.

Guay had been born in 1917, the son of a railroad worker. As a child he was reputed to have displayed a neurotic pride and entertained exaggerated dreams about the future. During the war he worked in the Quebec arsenal and dealt in watches and jewelry on the side; this became his principal occupation after the war. During his days in the arsenal he had met Rita Morel, and after a brief acquaintance married her. For a time he had tried his luck as a traveling salesman, then had established a jewelry shop in Seven Islands, which he gave up after a while. Finally in 1948 he opened his present shop on St. Sauveur Street. There was local gossip of his having some kind of love affair with a girl of sixteen or seventeen, but no one knew Marie-Ange Robitaille. The name the neighbors mentioned was a Nicole Cote. But apparently Madame Guay had known of the liaison and trusted it would come to an end of its own accord sooner or later.

On the morning of September 9 Guay had accompanied his wife to the Chateau Frontenac. Lucille Levesque at the ticket window recalled that he had kissed her good-by. Later, when he heard the fatal news— he had his daughter Lise in his arms—he had collapsed weeping into a chair. Neighbors reported that he had kept vigil beside the coffin for three days, and after the funeral service in St. Roch Church had walked with tear-stained face through a crowd of the curious.

Detectives tend to feel distrust for too much show of emotion. Bélec, Matte, and Guillemette certainly reacted in this way. Nevertheless, none of the information really incriminated Guay. Uncomfortably, the inspectors read the more and more voluminous accounts in the newspapers, which puffed the disaster up into the "greatest event since the Quebec Conference." Reporters from all of Canada were by now pouring into

Quebec. The detectives wondered whether they had become obsessed with a false trail. Were they perhaps overlooking clues to some other possible culprit?

17

In the existing uncertainty, all eyes turned to the laboratories in Montreal where Franchère Pépin and Bernard Péclet had been engaged for six days examining the wreckage of the DC-3 for remains of the bomb. Pépin was a chemist with a great deal of experience in the investigation of explosions. The application of chemistry to crimes and accidents involving explosions was some fifty years old in September 1949—far, far newer than this class of crime. The appearance of gunpowder in Europe around 1300 had very soon led to murders with explosives. At the time of the Renaissance the gunpowder chest had become a dangerous weapon. Disguised as a gift, as for instance a pretty jewel box, it had proved the nemesis of many a happy recipient who had guilelessly opened it, thus producing by a spring or lever a spark which exploded the charge of powder.

Whatever the reasons for such murders—whether enrichment, acts of revenge, or thwarted love—since those early days explosives had played a part in crimes of violence. Every new development in kinds of explosives had soon fallen into the hands of political or private murderers. Aside from a few scattered cases, probably the last occasion on which gunpowder was employed to fearful effect as a private weapon was in 1875. On December 11 of that year a tremendous explosion took place in the port of Bremerhaven. A wagon was bringing a large amount of freight, belonging to a merchant named William King Thomas, to the docks, to be loaded aboard the steamer *Mosel*. The driver suddenly had to check the horse-drawn wagon, whereupon the entire load blew up, killing more than a hundred persons assembled for embarkation. Thomas, who was already on board, committed suicide, but not before he had confessed his murderous scheme. The goods, among which a barrel of powder was concealed, were consigned to New York aboard the *Mosel*. The clockwork of a fusing mechanism was set so that the explosion would not take place until the ship reached the open Atlantic, after Thomas himself had left the vessel at Southampton. His idea was

344

to set the ship afire and collect a large sum of insurance for his supposedly valuable freight.

By then, however, there were many more modern explosives than gunpowder. Since 1799 mercuric fulminate had been known; it can be detonated by a blow or friction. After 1818 it began to be used for detonating material in percussion caps. Some thirty years later Ascanio Sobrero of Turin created nitroglycerin, an oily, odorless liquid which develops tremendous explosive power when jarred however slightly. The explosive power of nitroglycerin is one hundred times that of gunpowder.

In its liquid condition nitroglycerin was too sensitive to be used. In 1866 the Swedish inventor and manufacturer Alfred Nobel succeeded in converting it to a transportable explosive by mixing it with kieselguhr (a siliceous earth). In 1875 gelatin dynamite was developed, a firm, cuttable, extraordinarily explosive material consisting of 93 per cent nitroglycerin and 7 per cent collodion cotton, gun cotton, a nitrated cellulose. To the present day, mining and construction would be inconceivable without Nobel's invention. But Nobel was also providing political killers with a new weapon, which in conjunction with mercuric fulminate played a part in many an assassination. The spectacular nature of political assassinations diverted attention from thousands of other cases in which dynamite was used for lethal ends. At the same time new explosives now appeared in rapid succession. After 1885 the extraordinary explosive power of picric acid became widely known; it had been discovered by the chemist Hausmann decades before. Called melinite or lyddite, it was employed in billions of shells during the First World War. Around 1890 the chemist Häussermann discovered that a pale yellow crystalline substance called trinitrotoluene, already known for a quarter of a century, likewise could develop extraordinary explosive power. Known as tri or tulol in Germany, tolite in France, TNT in the United States, it became the most common material for shells and aerial bombs. Almost immediately there followed the use of nitrocellulose, also known as guncotton, an innocent-looking white substance made by a process of nitration from cotton cellulose. Nitrocellulose was so explosive that it had to be "gelatinized" by admixture with alcohol and ether in order to diminish its violence, enabling it to be used in smokeless powder or cartridges. In 1916 the Swiss chemist Stettbacher experimented with pentaerythritol tetranitrate, a sugarlike crystalline powder which could be manufactured from formaldehyde and acetaldehyde. It was given the name nitropenta (PETN) and proved to be the most formidable of all explosives at that time—143 times as powerful as gunpowder.

But no sooner was the First World War over than an even more violent explosive was discovered in 1920: hexogon (cyclotrimethylene trinitramine, RDX). It had been produced synthetically as early as 1899, but its explosive power, 145 times that of gunpowder, remained unknown for twenty years. It was the ultimate in destructiveness during the years between the wars. The Second World War, however, ushered in numerous new explosives and combinations of explosives (aside from the atom bomb). There were explosives of the chlorate type; there was a combination of RDX which increased the explosiveness of TNT by 50 per cent; and there were the new "plastics." The latter were essentially PETN, RDX, or TNT rendered kneadable by admixtures of vaseline or paraffin.

The number of detonators had also increased steadily in the years preceding 1949. The classical fuse invented by the English scientist Bickford in 1831—a jute cord coated with tar—had been refined into cords soaked in nitropenta and hexogen. The number of explosive caps that followed Nobel's first in 1867 was legion. Mercuric fulminate or lead azide enclosed in small copper or aluminum shells was placed in contact with the actual explosive. Both were so sensitive to the slightest shock, heat, or electric spark that they instantly exploded, detonating the main charge. Some fuses were elaborate chemical devices. Mechanical effects could shatter a glass vial containing sulfuric acid. The acid reacted with a mixture of potassium chlorate and sugar, generating a dart of flame which set off the explosive charge. Electrical fuses generated a spark for the same purpose. By 1949 criminals who wished to operate with explosives had more resources at their disposal than ever before. During the recently ended war, moreover, a great many persons had learned how to handle explosives. Nor was it beyond the capability of criminals to manufacture the high explosives that had appeared since the development of picric acid. There had been countless instances of murderers, burglars, safecrackers, and even adventurous adolescents having produced such destructive materials as RDX and TNT. For the manufacture of RDX, for example, they employed concentrated nitric and sulfuric acids, and hexamethylene tetramine, the latter fairly easy to obtain because it was used medically in the treatment of kidney and bladder diseases. In fact the modern high explosives lent themselves more readily to home manufacture than did gunpowder, whose components, saltpeter, sulfur, and charcoal, called for a degree of pulverization almost impossible to achieve by hand.

With the increased uses of explosives in crime, by 1949 there were a good many chemists in police laboratories who had specialized in the investigation of explosives. Pépin, too, had turned his attention to this field, and when Bernard Péclet of Montreal University joined him in 1946 he acquired an assistant who was thoroughly versed in the highly important field of spectral analysis.

Pépin had no illusions, however. For all the experience that had been gathered in the composition of explosives and in determining their components from trace remains, the subject was still a matter of patchwork. Nowhere did a comprehensive summary of it exist, and the explosives industry was racing far ahead of forensic chemistry. Year after year new situations cropped up, requiring fresh experiments, novel analyses.

On September 10 Pépin and Péclet had looked over the crash site in person and hunted for metal parts belonging to the shattered baggage compartment. They had also hunted for remains of luggage and freight, most of which had been blasted to bits by the explosion and strewn far from the plane itself. It was lucky that the aircraft had not plunged into the St. Lawrence River, where all clues would have been lost. Inspection of the Duralumin parts of the luggage compartment showed what technicians call a "shattering effect." The smooth sheet metal was rippled and showed a bluish-yellow discoloration.

Every explosion results from the generation of gases which expand more or less quickly. Powder explosions develop a relatively slow production of gas. The pressure wave results in bulges and tears in the materials that block its expansion. At the same time, flame marks are left behind. The various nitro explosives developed in the wake of nitroglycerin detonate at high velocity, producing a wave of tremendous pressure that literally "shatters" everything in its path. Such explosions are accompanied by extraordinary heat. In the present case, the appearance of the metal indicated that some nitro explosive had been used. The question was, which one?

Given the many possibilities, Pépin and Péclet had to examine the metallic parts and remnants of baggage for particles of explosive or the deposits of gaseous detonation products. If they could determine the chemical composition of such deposits, they could draw conclusions about the type of explosive. As soon as the first bits of wreckage arrived in Montreal, they began the toilsome procedure of inspecting everything under magnifying glass, microscope, and spectrometer, and of testing for chemical reactions. First Pépin examined tiny particles of material that had been embedded in metal, wood, or leather parts. These particles proved to be bits of copper. Since copper vaporizes at a temperature of

4230 degrees Fahrenheit, it was evident that there had been some spattering of copper in liquid form. There were also blackish and brownish deposits on metal parts and pieces of wood; these obviously came from the gases of the explosion. Transparent crystals were found among the darker spots. The discovery of copper suggested the copper sheath of a blasting cap. Since copper blasting caps, which are used chiefly in mining, are filled with lead azide as the detonator, the logical next step, therefore, was to look for traces of lead. But Pépin focused his attention instead on the colorless crystals, which dissolved easily in distilled water, yielding a bitter taste. Qualitative analysis showed them to be crystals of sodium nitrate, which is found in nitrate explosives of the dynamite type, such as gelatin dynamite D-1. Could it be a case of dynamite? Pépin wondered, and pushed on with his studies. Chemical and spectrographic tests of the black and brown deposits showed traces of lead, thus supporting the hypothesis that a copper blasting cap containing lead azide had been used. The other trace elements and compounds found, calcium, nitrites, and nitrates, sulfates, sulfites, and sulfides, seemed so untypical that no progress was made. Pépin then decided to proceed in reverse order. He would explode various types of dynamite in a closed chamber and analyze the deposits. Among other things, he wanted to find out whether the admixtures of "meal" in various kinds of dynamite are completely destroyed by the explosion and heat, or whether it was possible to discover remains of meal which might provide a clue to the firm that manufactured the explosive. Meal is a regular additive to dynamite, to ensure better combustion. Since such experiments could be carried out only in adequately shielded rooms, Pépin appealed to Ottawa for assistance. In Ottawa a mock-up of the baggage compartment of the DC-3 was created. Various types of dynamite and detonators were then exploded inside it. It turned out that gelatin dynamite D-1 produced exactly the same effects on metallic parts and pieces of luggage as those discovered in the wreckage of the unfortunate plane. Chemical deposits of sodium nitrate crystals, nitrates, nitrites, sulfates, sulfites, and sulfides, calcium, lead, and copper were found. On the other hand, not the slightest trace of meal remained.

Back in Montreal, meanwhile, Pépin and Péclet made no less than five hundred chemical and spectrographic analyses of the deposits on the wreckage, without ever being able to locate any meal. But they did consistently find all the trace elements that resulted from the Ottawa experiments. They concluded therefore that gelatin dynamite D-1, quite commonly used in Canadian industry and agriculture, had caused the explosion on the airplane. At least ten pounds of the explosive must have been employed to produce the results observed. Since home manufacture of dynamite was virtually out of the question, it must have been obtained illegally or stolen. The same was true for the copper blasting cap.

There remained the question of the time fuse. Since electric time fuses require batteries, metallic parts, and clocks, a systematic search was carried out for any vestige of such objects. In sorting through the Duralumin pieces of the baggage compartment, Pépin and Péclet noticed one spot on which there was an unusually heavy white, yellow, and black deposit. It seemed as if some hard object had been hurled against this spot with great force. Péclet analyzed solutions of the deposit and found traces of zinc, carbon, manganese, lead, tin, ammonium, sodium, copper, calcium—almost all elements that are components of dry batteries. Péclet therefore inferred that a battery had been blown against the compartment wall.

He made no further progress until there arrived from Cap Tourmente a piece of metal painted blue on both sides; it had been found lodged in a parka dangling from a branch. Pépin made comparative studies of all dry batteries on sale in Canada. It turned out that the only battery with the metal painted blue inside and out was an Eveready No. 10. Péclet's spectrographic analysis indicated that the components of the paint on the piece of metal corresponded with the components of the paint on Eveready batteries. Returning to the deposit on the piece of compartment wall, Pépin ascertained that all its elements were those contained in the battery except for one: tin. Pépin assumed that the tin must have belonged to the clock which formed part of the time fuse. No parts of the clock itself were found.

18

On September 17 the elaborate scientific study was in full swing. In Quebec, meanwhile, the day passed without Marguerite Pitre's having shown herself outside her house. Either she had read Le Canada and, guilty, scented trouble, or else there was some perfectly innocent explanation for her staying within doors. Cautious inquiries led to the information that she generally avoided activity, sometimes spending whole days in bed being tended by her good-natured husband. The uncertainty and the doubts remained.

At last, on the evening of the 17th and the morning of the 18th, Matte's and Guillemette's detectives obtained additional data which reinforced their feeling that they were on the right track. They learned that during the war Marguerite Pitre had worked in the Quebec arsenal and had met Albert Guay there. Apparently she was under obligations to him, for he had lent her sizable sums of money several times. Her crippled brother Généreux Ruest worked as a watchmaker for Guay, attending to the repair jobs that came to Guay's jewelry shop. At this point in the investigation it may have been premature to wonder whether Ruest might have helped make a time fuse, but still the detectives asked themselves that question.

In the course of the day, the tenuous connecting threads acquired more substance. Nicole Cote, who had been spoken of as Guay's mistress, was evidently one and the same as Marie-Ange Robitaille and had apparently lived for some time in a back room of the Pitre apartment. At any rate, descriptions of a lodger in Marguerite Pitre's house, a girl who had called herself Nicole Cote, corresponded completely in appearance with Marie-Ange. Had Marguerite Pitre accommodatingly set up a love nest where Guay could visit his mistress without attracting attention? Finally, on the night of September 18 Guillemette received a letter from a workman named Lucien Carreau who wrote that the jeweler Albert Guay back in April had offered him five hundred dollars if he would bring his wife Rita Guay a bottle of poisoned liquor. As the police well knew, such letters might or might not deserve credence. Sometimes they were the product of sheer fantasy or a desire to be important.

But on the following day Guillemette received an excited telephone call from a tavernkeeper. One of his waitresses was a girl named Thérèse Noël who, he said, was engaged to the brother of a Marguerite Pitre of Monseigneur Gauvreau Street. Altogether distraught, Thérèse Noël had just told him the following story: that morning an old friend of Marguerite Pitre's, a man named Albert Guay, had turned up at the Pitre apartment and shown Marguerite an article from *Le Canada*. The gist of the article was that the bomb which caused the air crash had been taken to Ancienne Lorette airport by a woman. Guay had told Marguerite she knew what she was up against now, and had given her sleeping pills. He had recommended that she commit suicide. Marguerite had actually taken some of the pills. A doctor had been called and was now trying to get her into a hospital. But there would not be a bed available at the Infant Jesus Hospital until next day, September 20.

This story, with all its particulars, could not be the product of an overstimulated imagination. The outlines of the real culprits were beginning to appear, but until Marguerite Pitre was definitely identified as the woman who delivered the package to the airport, Bélec and Guillemette could take no measures against her. However, the watchers on Monseigneur Gauvreau Street were alerted and instructed to pay the closest attention next morning.

Toward nine o'clock on September 20 the sentinels saw a cab drive up to 49 Monseigneur Gauvreau Street. Immediately afterward a slightly stooped, heavily swathed figure of a woman appeared, supported on both sides. The walk to the cab was long enough for Pelletier to have a good look at her. He had no doubt that the woman who was helped into the cab was his airport passenger of September 9.

As soon as Bélec and Guillemette were informed of the identification, they temporized no longer. They ordered a guard placed around the hospital, and gave orders for Marguerite Pitre to be arrested as soon as she left the hospital. They had sufficient grounds temporarily, since attempted suicide is a punishable offense in Canada. At the same time more detectives were assigned to shadow Guay every minute. It turned out that Guay had left the apartment he had behind his shop and moved with his daughter to his mother's place in the suburb of Limoilu. Otherwise he went about his ordinary affairs as if nothing had happened.

After two more uneasy days Guillemette learned that Marguerite Pitre, after one halfhearted attempt to take more sleeping pills on the sly, was sufficiently recovered for her to be discharged from the hospital on September 23. When she stepped through the hospital gate that morning, two detectives took charge of her and drove her to her apartment. There Bélec, Guillemette, and—in the background—Pelletier were waiting for her.

The character of Marguerite Pitre, soon to be given the sinister name "the Raven" by the Quebec press, remained for a long time murky and dubious. In one light she seemed a stupid, slovenly woman, careless about money matters, who had repeatedly borrowed from Guay since their days at the arsenal and was by now so deep in debt that she had to carry out his wishes, whether these involved providing quarters for him and his mistress or a murder. In another light she seemed a totally unscrupulous woman, familiar from her youth with the shady sides of life, who had deliberately collaborated on a murder plot in order to settle her debts with Guay, and was now trying to save her own skin. Probably there were elements of both these extremes in her character.

At any rate, the moment she confronted Guillemette—squat, fat, pale, with nervously darting eyes half hidden under heavy lids—she tried to deny her expedition to Ancienne Lorette airport. When the inspector called in Pelletier, her attitude changed at once. She dropped into a chair, breathing heavily, and admitted that on the morning of September 9 she had taken a parcel to the airport. But this admission was only a small step, for she claimed that a stranger had stopped her at the Palais railroad station and asked her to deliver the package to the air freight office for him, since he had to travel on by railroad. He had given her the sum of thirty dollars for doing this favor.

She changed her story for the second time when she realized that Guillemette was aware of her relations with Guay, of Marie-Ange Robitaille's stay in her apartment, and of Guay's visit on September 19. Her grayish face bedewed with perspiration, she now declared that Albert Guay had made an appointment for her to meet him at 8:30 A.M. at the Palais station. There he had handed her a parcel and instructed her to take it to the Baie Comeau plane. Unasked, the woman went on to make a series of hectic, far-ranging statements. She told of having met Guay at the arsenal in 1942 and having found him customers for his jewelry among the employees there. Later, as a waitress, she had done the same service, and because her commissions were small had asked him for a loan. She owed him six hundred dollars. He had been taking advantage of these debts for years to blackmail her. In 1947 he had made her take Marie-Ange, then only sixteen, into her Richelieu Street apartment. Marie-Ange Robitaille had run away from her parents and was hiding out under the false name of Nicole Cote. Guay had not cared about the risk to her, for she could be prosecuted for contributing to the immorality of a minor. With the same ruthlessness he had sent her to Ancienne Lorette on September 9, telling her that the parcel had to reach a customer in Baie Comeau by the weekend. There was an old statue in it, he had said. She had not known that Rita Guay was taking that very plane. She learned that only after the crash, and had begun to have her suspicions when Guay called on her on September 16 and ordered her to send for Marie-Ange without telling the girl that he would be appearing. She had lured Marie-Ange to her place by saying she had something important to tell her. In that way Guay and Marie-Ange had met, and she had overheard part of the conversation. Guay had said that he could not see Marie-Ange for the next six months, but he was free now and as soon as she was twenty-one he would marry her. Guay had turned up again on September 19, tossed *Le Canada* onto the table, and bellowed that he wanted to know whom she had given the package to so that a bomb could be slipped into it. The police would find her if she didn't choose to kill herself. He gave her a box and commanded her to swallow the pills in it. She had actually taken them, but then her brother had turned up and fetched the doctor.

Marguerite Pitre's fat body was literally bathed in sweat by the time she reached this point in her confession. The sweat poured down her neck, ran into the line between her doughy breasts, soaked her dress at the armpits, glistened on her forearms and hands. She solemnly declared that this was all she had to say and she was glad to be able to relieve the weight on her heart. But her eyes still darted about so furtively that Bélec did not believe her. Coldly, he said that there was only one way she could convince the law that her involvement in the murder of twenty-three persons was innocent—if she concealed nothing, nothing at all. For a while she writhed in her seat, ran her sweaty hands over her sticky brow, breathed in rattling gasps, fluttered her hands over her pudgy thighs. At last she produced an additional statement which at first sounded so wild it was difficult to believe. On August 13, she said, Guay had called on her. He offered to tear up all her I.O.U.s if she would do him a favor. He had a friend named Mrs. Cote, he said, who ran a farm in Rivière-aux-Pins. Mrs. Cote had to dispose of some tree stumps and needed dynamite for the job. He had promised to bring the dynamite next time he visited. But it wasn't so easy for him to buy explosives. Marguerite had once told him that one of her neighbors was friendly with a salesman in an agricultural implement store. Through a connection like that it should be easy for her to obtain dynamite.

The neighbor, Mrs. Parent, proved willing to help out when she learned that the "favor" Marguerite wanted was so important to her. The women went together to Mrs. Parent's acquaintance, Leopold Giroux, who worked for the firm of Samson & Filion. Mrs. Parent introduced Marguerite Pitre as Mrs. Cote and convinced Giroux that the dynamite was needed for agricultural purposes, and that Mrs. Cote had a certificate for its purchase which she had forgotten at home. They bought ten pounds' worth of dynamite sticks and nineteen blasting caps.

Marguerite Pitre signed the receipt in the name of Cote. That evening Guay came to the restaurant to collect the package. But he had forgotten to bring his I.O.U.s with him.

This story sounded so fantastic that Guillemette sent for Mrs. Parent. She admitted, in great perturbation, that since Marguerite Pitre's suicide attempt she had suspected certain connections, but had been afraid to tell the police of her foolish part in the affair. The salesman, Giroux, had experienced similar emotions. Now, however, he provided precise data on the type of explosive and blasting caps: gelatin dynamite D-1 and copper caps. Bélec communicated with Pépin in Montreal and learned that these facts coincided with the conclusions the scientists had arrived at on their own.

Whatever Bélec and Guillemette may have thought on September 23 about the truth underlying Marguerite Pitre's statements, they at any rate now had sufficient grounds to obtain a warrant for Albert Guay's arrest. At eleven o'clock in the evening of September 23 he was arrested in his mother's home in Limoilu. Although so late an hour had been deliberately chosen, the usual crowd assembled immediately—a threatening and sensation-hungry crowd, eager to set eyes on the man suspected of having sent his wife, and twenty-two other persons along with her, to sudden death. They stared at the spindly man of thirty-two whose looks were certainly nothing to boast of. Pale, but with studied poise, he strode through the group of spectators as though nothing could ever shake his confidence.

The first interrogation produced no results whatsoever. Guay denied having had any part in the crash of the DC-3 on Cap Tourmente. He denied having given Marguerite Pitre a package, let alone having urged her to commit suicide. The whole story was a fairy tale, he asserted. He was clever enough not to deny having known Marguerite Pitre, having used her as an intermediary to obtain customers, and having employed her crippled brother. He also admitted calmly that Marie-Ange Robitaille had been his mistress. But he insisted that this affair with "the little girl" had been over before his wife's death. His wife had known about the whole thing, as various people could vouch, and there had not been the slightest reason for him to want to kill her. He only wished his wife were still alive, for his little daughter missed and needed her terribly. The detectives would be well advised to spare him the accusations of such common creatures as the Pitre woman.

That day the public excitement reached the first of many climaxes. A special police squad had to protect the house on Monseigneur Gauvreau

Street from mobs of the curious. The fact that Marguerite Pitre had no scruples about accepting $150 from photographers for letting them get a picture of her, and that she "posed" for them, struck the detectives as indicative that she was no blackmailed victim but a willing, avaricious accomplice. Possibly she had assisted Guay for a promised share in the insurance money.

At the same time reporters from the entire continent besieged the Monte Carlo Café to interview and photograph Marie-Ange Robitaille. Guillemette's men had some difficulty protecting the girl from them, which they had to do if they were to find out just what kind of relations had actually prevailed between her and Guay.

Marie-Ange Robitaille had by now realized that she was compromising herself in keeping silent. After some hesitation, therefore, she told the whole story. In 1947, when Guay met her at a dance, she was sixteen, filled with rebellious teen-age longings for a change in the monotony of her life in Lower Town and in her petit-bourgeois parental home. Guay, who told her about his career as a jeweler, his big deals and travels, seemed to her the man to free her from her narrow life. But he must also have been the first to have awakened her sexuality, and he succeeded in implanting in her a blind susceptibility to illusion. Although she soon learned that he was married, and that his jewelry shop was only a hole-in-corner affair, she introduced him to her parents under the pseudonym of Roger Anger, lived with him in a cheap rooming house (instead of the mansion she had dreamed of), and when Rita Guay informed her parents of what was going on, left home entirely for a dark little room in Marguerite Pitre's apartment. For months Marie-Ange had lived in the Pitre place, without money, in hiding for fear of the juvenile court, with no employment but to wait for Guay to come and transport the two of them, for a few hours, into erotic frenzy. Finally the dreariness of her life impelled her to break with Guay. She borrowed fifty dollars, returned to Quebec, intending to telephone her parents and ask whether she might return home. But Guay drove madly from Montreal to Quebec, met her at the railroad station, and brought her back to Montreal. More months passed in a shabby rented room on St. Angèle Street, until May 1949. Once she was on the point of going voluntarily to the juvenile court. Guay again prevented her, took her to Havre St. Pierre, and promised that he would soon divorce his wife. She lived in a hotel as Mrs. Guay until ennui once more overpowered her. She sold her typewriter and used the money to flee back to Quebec. Guay met her at the dock. Once more she yielded to his promises and went to Seven Islands with him. They lived as a married couple when he visited. But his limited means did not permit frequent visits. By June her disappointment outweighed passion; the knowledge that she was pursuing a phantom proved stronger than sexual appetite. She returned to her parents and took the job in the Monte Carlo Café. But Guay followed her. On the street he threatened suicide, and he kept after her until on June 23 she had him arrested. But on the day of his release he sought her out again. For the last time she succumbed to his lures and went to Montreal with him. But a few days later she returned home. She received passionate letters in which Guay implored her to wait only a little longer. Since then he had seen her only once, in Marguerite Pitre's apartment, after the crash. Marguerite Pitre had reported the conversation correctly. Guay had told her that he was free now, but she replied that it was all over. Guay had refused to believe her. But it was the truth. She had known nothing, she finished, about anything he *might* have planned and might have done, nothing about any intentions to murder.

The way she used the word "might" betrayed the fact that not all her feeling for Guay was yet dead; she was still enough under his spell to find his guilt inconceivable. Nevertheless, her story left no doubt that Guay had a motive for murdering his wife.

While Guillemette was conducting the interrogation of Marie-Ange, Bélec turned his attention to Généreux Ruest. He could not shake off the idea that Ruest might have had a share in putting together a time fuse. He found the watchmaker sitting in his wheel chair in his wretched workshop on St. François Street. Adjoining was his equally shabby apartment. He received the inspector with the manner of a long-suffering invalid, showing not a trace of agitation or nervousness. Of course he knew Guay, he said. He saw him every week when Guay brought watches for repair. He had read about the charges against Guay. He had also heard about his sister's story. But his sister had never informed him of her private affairs. He was a lonely, abandoned cripple.

After much pondering he finally recalled an incident in August. Around August 20, he said, Guay had come to him and asked whether he knew anyone who was familiar with handling dynamite. He said he had bought a piece of land in Seven Islands and had to blast out the tree roots. Ruest had recalled a customer, Ovide Cote of Charlesbourg, who had worked with dynamite on road construction for the past twelve years. He mentioned Cote's name to Guay, and just at that moment the door opened and Cote himself came in with a watch for repair.

What a strange coincidence! Guay had talked with Cote about dynamite. The inspector asked whether Ruest had ever done any work installing clocks in electric time fuses? Ruest smiled incredulously and asked whatever could have put such an idea into the detective's head.

A few minutes later, however, he recalled another incident which he had likewise forgotten, he claimed. At the end of August or the beginning of September Guay had come to see him once more. That time he had given him an alarm clock and asked him to drill a hole underneath the 12. He was still working on his dynamite problem, he had explained, and was now building an electric fusing mechanism. After the hole was drilled, Guay vanished, and a week later came the air crash.

These two recollections sounded odd to the inspector. He suspected that Ruest made these voluntary admissions to cover himself against more serious charges. Detectives who went out to Charlesbourg reported that Ovide Cote confirmed Ruest's statements; Cote, moreover, had warned Guay against handling dynamite since he was not experienced with it. But Bélec's suspicions remained, and he decided to search Ruest's workshop to see whether he could find any traces of work on a time fuse. He asked Franchère Pépin and Bernard Péclet to come to Quebec.

Ruest was away when the inspector and the scientists descended on his quarters; a sister-in-law opened the door for them. Thus they had the opportunity to make their search undisturbed. For an hour they found nothing—until Pépin and Péclet came upon an innocent-looking piece of corrugated cardboard that meant nothing to the detectives. It was damaged in many places and had so many blackish deposits—odd in a watchmaker's shop—that the scientists immediately carried it off to Montreal. There they made experiments with blasting caps of different types. They discharged the caps with electric sparks, the circuit being completed when the hand of a clock touched a contact on the clock face. Around the exploding caps they constructed a kind of shield of corrugated cardboard. When the tiny caps exploded, the cardboard received the mild shock wave. The deposits on the cardboard were then examined, and it turned out that detonation of copper caps with lead azide filling produced exactly the same kind of deposits as those on the corrugated paper from Ruest's apartment and on the walls of the front baggage compartment of the doomed plane. There could be little doubt that Ruest had experimented with blasting caps and used the corrugated cardboard to shield the detonations.

As soon as this report reached Bélec, he confronted Ruest with it. He hammered away at the "invalid" until Ruest confessed that he had built a time fuse and tried it out in his kitchen together with Guay. Tearfully, repeatedly referring to his helplessness and crippled condition, he declared that he had been afraid to admit making the time fuse because he feared he would be suspected of having known about Guay's terrible intentions. He swore that Guay had brought him the plan for the fuse, and every item including an Eveready battery, and had kept him believing that the apparatus was for the intended blasting on the property in Seven Islands. He had learned the truth only after the disaster, when Guay came to his workshop and threatened him: "Be sure you say nothing to the police about the work you've done, or you'll have to deal with me."

During the next several months, Ruest and his sister did not change a word of their story. And it was impossible to prove that they were telling lies because Guay himself continued to deny any guilt whatsoever.

On February 23, 1950, Chief Justice Sevigny and twelve jurors heard the testimony of witnesses and the scientific evidence in the case of Albert Guay. They heard Marguerite Pitre and Généreux Ruest. It was hard to fathom what prompted Guay to continue to deny the charges and thus protect the two chief witnesses against him. Silently, he listened to the significant words of Crown Prosecutor Noel Dorion in his address to the jury: "In a case like this one there might be accomplices, and the validity of the testimony of an accomplice must be verified by your knowledge of human nature. . . . You need not worry; if there are others than Guay who should be sought out by the law, they will be sought out by the law."

For the time being justice seemed to be summary. After being out only seventeen minutes, the jury pronounced Guay guilty, which in Canadian law meant the death sentence. Only after he was in the Bordeaux prison in Montreal, without prospect of escaping death, did Guay write a complete account of the crime and of the participation of Marguerite Pitre and Généreux Ruest, who had worked for a promised share in the spoils and with full awareness of what was planned. When he died on January 12, 1951, he did not know that the two would follow him to the gallows. With Guay out of the way, they abandoned caution, and were in turn betrayed by relatives who had held their tongues for a time. They too were tried and condemned to death in Bordeaux; in 1952 Généreux Ruest was executed, and in 1953 Marguerite Pitre, popularly called "Madame le Corbeau."

Two years later, in August 1955, the Chicago *Journal of Criminal Law, Criminology and Police Science* published an article by Franchère Pépin and Bernard Péclet entitled "The Scientific Aspect of the Guay Case." They described their efforts to analyze the traces of the wreckage, to find the explosive used, and to force a confession out of Généreux Ruest. Even in a world overshadowed by the Cold War and menaced by an ever-increasing flood of crimes, the deliberate blowing up of an aircraft was enough of a novelty to turn the attention of criminologists to the investigation of explosives as a significant aspect of criminalistic science and forensic chemistry.

A few months later, on November 1, 1955, this novelty was a novelty no longer. In the vicinity of Longmont, Colorado, a four-engine United Air Lines Douglas DC-6B, N 37559, with five crew members and thirty-nine passengers on board exploded in flight. The FBI laboratory in Washington found the same signs in the wreckage that Pépin and Péclet had traced: dynamite. On November 14 twenty-seven-year-old John Gilbert Graham was arrested; his mother had been one of the dead passengers. He was convicted of having packed a bomb into his mother's suitcase in order to kill her and destroy the entire plane so that he could collect insurance of $37,800.

These cases, and the successful laboratory work that underlay the unmasking of the mass murderers, proved how remarkably this branch of detection had spread, in some fifty years, from its origins in Europe. The methods of trace investigation had become the common property of all nations. Only five years later this general international advance was confirmed many thousands of miles from the continent of North America, in a once remote part of the globe. But at the heart of this important criminal case were not explosives or fuses, but plant clues, which more than half a century before had entered criminology by way of Conan Doyle's imagination and Hans Gross's textbook.

19

Bondi, a suburb of Sydney, was sometimes called the "Playground of the Pacific." The name was an unfortunate choice insofar as it suggested the kind of luxurious resort that Florida boasts. Bondi's yellow sand and ocean surf could stand comparison with any place in the world. But its culture of milkbars and fish-and-chips stands represented a completely different social world from the hotels and restaurants of Florida.

In the summer of 1960 Bondi was a town of more than twenty thousand persons, native Australians and immigrants, clerks, salesmen, bus drivers, cabmen, workmen. Among this heterogeneous population were Bazil and Freda Thorne, an ordinary middle-class couple who at the beginning of the year had moved into a two-story house on Edward Street. Thorne worked as a commercial traveler. One of his two children, eight-year-old Graeme, attended Scots College, one of Sydney's finest public schools—which like English public schools are private and rich in tradition. Bazil Thorne himself was a former pupil of Scots College, which is situated in Bellevue Hill, a rather more prestigious district, although quite close to Bondi. Every morning at eight thirty Graeme set out from home in his gray school uniform. He walked to the corner of Edward and Wellington Streets, then turned downhill on Wellington and walked along the grass-lined sidewalk as far as O'Brien Street. Here he was met by Phyllis Smith, a friend of his parents, whose two children also attended Scots College. Mrs. Smith drove Graeme and her own children to Bellevue Hill in her car.

This ritual would probably not have changed for years if Bazil Thorne's moderate fortunes had not altered abruptly from one day to the next. A regular participant in Sydney's lotteries, he had bought a three-pound ticket. On June 1, 1960, while he was on a business trip in a country town, he received word that he was the winner of the grand prize in the Opera House Lottery: 100,000 Australian pounds. Most lottery winners plunge into an orgy of spending which often leads them to destruction, but Bazil Thorne was of a different temperament. To the reporters waiting for him at Sydney airport he declared that he would not squander the money, but use it to build a better future for his family. For the immediate present the Thornes continued to live as they had been living.

Toward nine o'clock in the morning of July 7 Phyllis Smith's station wagon stopped in front of the Thornes' house. As usual she had waited at the corner of Wellington and O'Brien Streets, but had seen no sign of Graeme. His mother assured her that the boy had left at eight thirty. Although she almost instantly felt a vague fear, she asked her friend to drive to Scots College and see whether Graeme might for some reason have accepted a drive with someone else. But Mrs. Smith returned with the news that Graeme had not got to school. At this point Mrs. Thorne recalled an article she had read about the kidnaping of Eric Peugeot, the grandson of the famous French automobile manufacturer. She telephoned the police station in Bondi at once.

Police Sergeant O'Shea arrived at the house within a few minutes to take down the details. His questioning was interrupted by the ringing of the telephone. Freda Thorne answered. A voice with a foreign accent spoke: "Is that you, Mrs. Thorne?"

"Yes."

"Is your husband there?"

"What do you want him for?"

"I have your son."

Freda Thorne began so to tremble that the telephone almost slipped from her hand. Thinking quickly, she handed the phone to the sergeant and in a whisper told him to pretend he was her husband. The voice repeated: "I have got your boy. I want twenty-five thousand pounds before five o'clock this afternoon."

O'Shea, who did not yet know of Thorne's new wealth, replied: "How am I going to get money like that?"

The voice irritably retorted: "You have plenty of time before five o'clock. I'm not fooling. If I don't get the money I'll feed him to the sharks."

"How am I going to contact you?" O'Shea stammered.

The reply was: "I'll contact you later."

The caller hung up. O'Shea immediately informed Sub-District No. 3 of the Criminal Investigation Branch of the New South Wales police department. There Detective Sergeant Freeman took over the case, never suspecting that the affair would keep the entire police force of New South Wales occupied for months.

In contrast to Canada, the Commonwealth of Australia had never developed a federal police force like the Royal Canadian Mounted Police. A Commonwealth Police Force did exist in 1957, but its sphere of operations was the vast expanses of the Northern Territory, an area of 523,620 square miles, inhabited by only 30,000 persons, 13,000 of them aboriginals. Many of the police stations here were linked only by radio or airplane with headquarters and one another; even in 1960 patrols in the desert regions were still carried out on camels. The Commonwealth Force also had charge of Nauru, the Norfolk Islands, and New Guinea. In addition there was a Police Force of the Australian Capital Territory, restricted to the capital city of Canberra, which since 1913 has been an enclave within the State of New South Wales. For the rest, the Australian police forces were under the jurisdiction of the states, and the police of each state had their own special and colorful history.

The Criminal Investigation Branch of New South Wales, originally called the Detective Branch, had very early adapted modern methods; by 1902 it had established its first fingerprint register, which in 1941 became the central fingerprint file for all of Australia. The superintendents of the Branch, located in Central Street, Sydney, had vigilantly followed developments in Europe and adopted whatever innovations seemed useful for Australian conditions.

But capable and forward-looking though the Criminal Investigation Branch was, on that morning of July 7, 1960, when Detective Sergeant Ernest Freeman first set foot inside the Thornes' house, the entire police force had had no experience whatsoever in cases of kidnaping. Australia's single case had taken place twenty-eight years before. In February 1932 a cattle breeder named Perrott had been kidnaped and held prisoner in an apartment on Roscoe Street in Sydney. There his abductors had forced him to sign a check for ten thousand pounds. But they were arrested while cashing the check, and Perrott was liberated. Although the police in the United States had had considerable experience (mostly grim and bitter) since the kidnaping of the Lindbergh baby, the Criminal Investigation Branch in Sydney was facing a wholly new problem. Dozens of police cars converged on the district around the Thornes' house. Police combed streets and gardens. They thereby violated one of the fundamental empirical rules of the American police, that intervention by detectives should be as discreet as possible. Kidnapers invariably threaten that informing the police will mean the child's death. They return the child for the ransom money only when they feel secure. If they know the police are after them, they prefer to disembarrass themselves of their prisoner, whose presence makes their escape that much more difficult. Even without police work, the victim is often killed, so that the parents pay the ransom to find only a corpse. Nevertheless, the fundamental rule is to be as compliant as possible, but to keep sharp watch while the ransom money is delivered, and to begin the police hunt only after the kidnaped child is in safety.

The news was kept from the press for a while. When reporters, made curious by the police concentration, asked what was going on, they were told that it was just a training exercise. But by ten o'clock they knew that Graeme Thorne had disappeared and that someone had demanded ransom of the parents. Shortly after noon the story was making headlines—about the same time that Bazil Thorne, flying home from a business trip, landed at Sydney's Kingsford Smith airport and was informed by Detective Sergeant Workman of what had happened. The reporters were on the spot, with the result that Graeme Thorne's abductor was able to read, by that evening at the latest, that the father had not returned home until afternoon and therefore could not have been present to receive the call in the morning, so that he had not spoken with Bazil Thorne but possibly with a detective. But what was done could not be undone. The kidnaping was already the talk of the city, and a wave of outrage swept through Sydney. Public opinion made it impossible for the police to withdraw at this point and continue working secretly. Commissioner Delaney saw no course but to push on and make the rather desperate attempt to catch the kidnaper before harm came to the child.

At Freeman's instructions, the Thornes' telephone number, 30-7113, was placed under a twenty-four-hour watch, so that as soon as the kidnaper called again an attempt could be made to trace the phone from which he was speaking. Detective Sergeant Paul stood by at the Thornes' to listen in on every call. A check of boardinghouses and motels, bridges, buses, railroads, piers, and airports extended from Sydney to all of New South Wales. In the course of the afternoon and evening radio and television stations broadcast appeals from Police Commissioner Delaney to the populace, asking that every suspicious circumstance be reported. Even the Premier of New South Wales, R. J. Heffron, remonstrated with the unknown criminal: "We have never thought that kidnaping a child and holding him to ransom could occur in this country," he declared. Detective Sergeant Gray thought it might be of some effect to bring Bazil and Freda Thorne before the television cameras. But the hapless couple, who repeatedly offered to give up the entire lottery winnings if they could have their child back safely, were by now little more than helpless spectators. Graeme's mother refused to leave the telephone. Gray therefore drove Thorne alone to the Bondi police station, where television facilities had been set up. Thorne addressed himself directly to the kidnaper: "If the person who has my son is a father, and has children of his own, all I can say is, for God's sake, send him back to me in one piece." When at the end of this lame little speech he burst into tears, he stirred hundreds of thousands of watchers, but certainly not the monster to whom he wanted to appeal.

During Thorne's absence the telephone in his home rang. It was 9:40 P.M. Detective Sergeant Paul answered: "Hello."

"Is that you, Mr. Thorne?"

"Yes."

"Have you got the money?"

"Yes."

"Put it into two paper bags."

"Wait a minute," Paul said, stalling for time to give the operators a chance to identify the caller's number. "I want to take your instructions down; I don't want to make a mistake."

The answer to that was a few muttered words, and the line went dead. Apparently the speaker had been put on his guard. The attempt to trace the telephone failed. Freda Thorne collapsed, and for the first time accused the police of endangering her son. Bazil Thorne was more self-controlled, but he too demanded that he be allowed to negotiate with the kidnaper alone, if another call came. Thus, late in the evening of July 7 there began the conflict between parents and police which continued throughout much of the story of the crime. The kidnaper's efforts to contact the parents ceased. Day after day the parents waited in agony. In their despair, they fell victim to frauds who pretended to have possession of their child. The police, on the other hand, could not at this late date withdraw from the case. It was not the pressure of publicity alone that kept them involved. As soon as the vultures, who try to profit by such occasions, began to swoop down, the police were compelled to intervene, to protect the parents. It has been the same in all kidnapings, and in the case of Graeme Thorne the extortionists began to be heard from by July 8.

On the morning of July 8 Freeman withdrew his men from the Thornes' house and left the parents to wait alone for a hoped-for telephone call. But within a short time he was back again to drive them to Wakehurst Parkway in the northeastern part of Sydney. An old man searching through a garbage dump for bottles had found an empty school case. Delaney sent two hundred policemen to comb the entire area. Police dogs were flown in from South Australia, helicopters were used to scan the countryside. For two days the huge force labored in vain. Then, on July 11, Graeme's cap, raincoat, arithmetic book, and lunch bag were found a mile away from the dump. But all further search led to nothing.

Meanwhile the Sydney police emergency number, 2222, was receiving a torrent of calls from the public. Within a few days the Criminal Investigation Branch was forced to set up a special Thorne case center in Bondi under Detective Sergeant Larry Foley. He was responsible for receiving and co-ordinating all information and sending out detectives to check it. Foley, a man with a keen analytical mind, soon had forty detectives on the case. Even so, he was swamped by thousands of items of "information," 98 per cent of which proved to be either mistaken or the product of hysteria, self-importance, imagination, a mania for denunciation, avarice, or insanity. Foley was being introduced to that spectacle which has made many a detective before him into a cynic or a misanthrope. The news that the kidnaper had had a foreign accent led to innumerable accusations of immigrant Australians. And immigrants, in their turn, made false confessions and volunteered the wildest statements in order to protect their fellow countrymen, Italians, Greeks, Hungarians, Czechs, Lithuanians, and what not, from further charges. Foley's men covered thousands of miles to check the information. They searched an old house in which the cries of a child had allegedly been heard, only to find a litter of kittens. Or they detained ships, such as the *Castle Felice* in Melbourne, because someone had seen a suspicious-looking woman boarding it with a boy.

Nevertheless, out of the flood of tips one piece of information seemed to Foley worth consideration. A young man named Denmeade reported that on the morning of July 7 at eight thirty he had passed by the corner of Wellington and Francis Streets, accompanied by his fiancée. He had noticed a car parked so inconsiderately up on the sidewalk that it was necessary to walk around it. Denmeade remembered the circumstance after he heard about the kidnaping. He described the car as an iridescent blue 1955 Ford Customline.

Detective Sergeants Doyle and Bateman put Denmeade through a tough test. They drove about with the young man through the streets of Sydney, and had him identify cars until they were certain that he undoubtedly knew the make and model year of virtually every automobile on the market. When he had unerringly identified a good many 1955 Ford Customlines at sight, they sent for the files on all licensed cars in New South Wales. Of a total of 270,000 Ford cars there were 5000 1955 Customline models. The cars were scattered over all of New South Wales. Special police officials visited every owner of a 1955 Ford Customline to learn where the car had been on the morning of July 7. It was clear from the very start that the job might take months.

Ten days after Graeme Thorne's disappearance, the case was as obscure as at the beginning. Bazil and Freda Thorne continued to wait in vain for the stranger's voice on their telephone. People experienced with kidnaping cases concluded from the silence that the criminal had abandoned hope of collecting the ransom safely, and that the boy had been killed long ago. Meanwhile the parents, along with the Rev. Mr. Clive Goodwin, who had publicly offered to serve as intermediary, were beset by tricksters. Over the telephone unknowns assumed children's voices, pretending that Graeme was speaking; with detailed instructions on what to do and how much money to take, Goodwin and the Thornes were lured as far as Brisbane and Queensland. As late as the afternoon of August 16 an Italian from Queensland telephoned the Thornes that he had just seen Graeme in a station wagon riding toward Townsville. "I hope this news will make you happy," he said.

On that same August 16, only a few hours later, two eight-year-old boys, Philip Wall and Eric Coughlin, in Grandview Grove, Seaforth, about ten miles from Bondi, told their parents they had found a bundle "in the bush" with "something like a head in it." By "the bush" they meant an empty lot adjoining the Coughlins' land. The boys' fathers went out with flashlights. In a shallow cave among some rocks they found the bundle the children had described. It consisted of a bright rug tied with string. When they undid the knot, they saw a child's arms, the hands bound. They telephoned the police station in Manly, and an hour later Sydney was startled by the news that Graeme Thorne had been found—dead. The boy was still wearing the clothes he had on the morning of July 7. His school blazer was carefully buttoned. In his trouser pocket he had the neatly folded, unused handkerchief he had been given before he left home. These circumstances suggested that the child had been killed shortly after the kidnaping. His feet, too, were bound. Around his neck was a knotted scarf that had been tied over the child's mouth to prevent his screaming. The lungs and upper air passages showed numerous signs of hemorrhage—indications that he had been suffocated. There was an injury on the back of the head also, which had resulted in a fracture of the skull. There was no doubt that Graeme Thorne had been killed by violence a considerable time before.

20

The reaction of Australia to the discovery of the murdered boy was, as a French correspondent reported from Sydney, "an outcry for vengeance." The police had not been able to prevent the murder. Everyone now demanded that they make up for this failure, and track down the murderer at any cost.

The detectives who swarmed into Seaforth, situated on a headland across the harbor from Sydney, canvassed every house in the hope of obtaining information. They soon had to admit that they were working in absolute darkness. The child's body had been found ten miles from his home, while the school case and other possessions had been picked up in an entirely different direction, the northeast. The murder must have taken place on July 8 or 9. Beyond that, five weeks after the kidnaping the police still had no significant starting point for investigation. A few thousand owners of 1955 Ford Customlines had been questioned. None of them, as far as could be determined, had been near the scene of the abduction on the morning of July 7. At this moment of gloom and pessimism the detectives turned their hopes to the clues that the criminal might have left on the body of his victim.

As we have mentioned, scientific criminalistics had reached Australia. In 1936 a forensic science laboratory had been established in Brisbane. Two years later another had been set up in Sydney. These laboratories, however, had dealt almost exclusively with the examination of footprints, handwriting, documents, and tool marks. Only after the Second World War had they extended their range—though they had then made great strides. As always, the impelling force had been certain capital crimes. One of these had been the murder of Bridget Guy in Tingalpa near Brisbane in 1945. Bridget Guy disappeared completely from the farm of her husband, Thomas Guy. Search parties discovered the suspicious remains of a fire in a patch of woods some miles away that belonged to Thomas Guy. It proved possible to convict Guy himself of the murder because the small laboratory in Brisbane, collaborating with doctors and biologists, demonstrated the remains of a woman's body in the ashes. There was, moreover, the track of a horse-drawn wagon between the site of the fire and Guy's farm; Guy had used the wagon to transport his wife's body to the spot. The hoof and wheel imprints corresponded with the hoofs of Guy's horse and the wheels of his wagon. Moreover, along the trail and in the vicinity of the fire bits of wool batting were discovered; these were traceable to a torn cushion on the driver's seat of the wagon.

Thanks to such successes, the art of scientific investigation had steadily increased in prestige. The Scientific Investigation Bureau in Sydney, founded in 1938, had been greatly enlarged beginning in 1948. In August 1960 it had at its disposal more than eighteen assistants under the direction of Detective Sergeant Alan Clarke. Even now, however, the Bureau did not employ scientists of its own, as had become the rule in Europe. Rather, the procedure that had been followed in England until 1938 was still in effect. The function of Alan Clarke's bureau was largely to collect clues. Clarke's assistants were all police officials trained to examine the scenes of crimes for pertinent data. All material requiring scientific investigation was passed on to various scientific institutes, which were concentrated in Sydney. That this system had fundamental defects, which stemmed from the scientists' lack of familiarity with basic criminalistic procedures, had not yet become so apparent in Sydney as in Europe. This may have been due to the fact that Clarke and his assistants were unusually familiar with scientific problems, and because they maintained relations with a number of scientists who had a distinctly criminalistic bent.

Alan Clarke and his associates Ross, White, Nixon, Stuckey, Snowden, and Lindsey, arrived at Seaforth on the morning of August 17. Some of them examined the site where the boy had been found, square foot by square foot; the others trained their attention exclusively on clues on the body, the clothes, and the rug. Later the rug and all the clothing were taken to the Scientific Investigation Bureau on Central Street in Sydney. There, to Clarke's gratification, trace clues of many sorts were found, and their number increased daily. On both sides of the rug were found animal and human hairs. There were also hairs clinging to the back of Graeme's trousers and jacket. The scarf that had served as a gag also had human hairs on it. Careful inspection and reinspection of the shoes, the seat of the trousers, the back of the jacket, and the knotted part of the scarf provided a sizable number of microscopic encrustations of soil. All of these had the same curious pink color. Like the hairs, they were placed in separate small containers. The scarf, trousers, and jacket had tiny particles of plants and leaves of indeterminate origin clinging to them. Other vegetable matter was stuck to the inner side of the blanket, partly where it had covered Graeme's back, but chiefly in the front where it had lain on the boy's chest. Finally, Clarke and his assistants noticed mold growing on the shoes, and a curious fatty substance coating Graeme's woolen socks.

Considerable time was taken up in accumulating all these trace clues. But by August 18 Clarke turned to Professor Neville Hewlett White, who taught plant pathology at the University of Sydney. He asked Professor White to determine the nature, origins, and time of development of the molds and fatty substances on the shoes and stockings. The next day Clarke got in touch with Dr. Cameron Oliver Cramp, who worked in the Office of the Government Medical Officer and specialized in hair comparisons. Clarke asked him to analyze the various hairs that had been found. The pink bits of soil were turned over to Horace Francis Whitworth, Curator of the Geological and Mining Museum in Sydney, with which he had been connected for twenty-four years. On the plant clues Clarke consulted a botanist, Mr. Johnson, and later Dr. Joyce Winifred Vickery, of the Royal Botanic Gardens and the National Herbarium in Sydney. Finally he brought into the case Malcolm Chaikin, Professor of Textile Technology at the University of New South Wales, to determine the peculiarities of the blanket and find out where it might have been manufactured.

In the seven decades since Sherlock Holmes had made profound deductions from particles of plants found at the scenes of crimes, botany had advanced step by step into the realm of criminalistics. Among the European pioneers to introduce botany extensively into their work was, once more, Georg Popp. The number of cases that Popp helped to solve between 1910 and 1930 by botanical analyses ran into the dozens. Some of these included the *causes célèbres* of the period. Others remained more or less obscure, but they nevertheless helped to sow a seed—to use a botanical image—that sprouted after the Second World War. Among the latter were the cases of Koopmann and Mieger.

In the Koopmann case, a robber broke into a farm on the Lüneburg Heath and escaped unseen. Among other suspects the culprit, Koopmann, was finally identified when Popp found on his socks particles of beets, wheat bran, and heath moss which had been used for bedding in the farm pigsty. The culprit had made his way in through the pigsty, taking off his shoes to be more silent. In the case of Mieger, Popp faced a different set of problems. Here he worked for the first time with traces of hay and grass, and demonstrated that the analysis of types of grass offered extraordinary possibilities to the criminalist because botanists had distinguished more than one hundred grasses which differed not only in the shape of the leaves but in the course of their veins, the position of the stomata, and the size and arrangement of the cells. In the Mieger case Popp was called to the village of Köppern in the Taunus Mountains in the late fall of 1917. A forester named Birkenauer had been shot by poachers. He was found in the hay of a feed rack intended for deer. The hay had not been renewed for a considerable time, and had become moldy and brittle. Some of it had been brought to the rack two or three years before, and was identifiable as early-cut hay; another, darker layer was from the second-growth crop; and both parts could clearly be distinguished. Every time the feed rack was touched, particles of hay flew up in all directions, and the killer who had hidden the forester's body there must have been covered with a powder of hay dust. Investigation led to a man named Mieger who worked in a nearby garrison and was suspected of using his furloughs for poaching. He denied ever having encountered the forester. Popp inspected Mieger's loden coat and found many places coated with hay dust. Comparison of the hay from the feed rack led to a useful supplementing of botanical findings by the techniques of microbiology. Because of the mixture of two types of hay the correspondence of the dust from the rack and the dust on Mieger's coat could be established microscopically. This result was confirmed by culturing the molds on Mieger's coat. The resultant microorganisms corresponded completely with cultures obtained from the hay of the rack.

Among the *causes célèbres* was Popp's solution of the Heidelberg Mayors murder, as it was called. At the end of June 1921 Wilhelm Busse, Lord Mayor of the city of Herford in northwestern Germany, and his friend, Mayor Leopold Werner, started out from Heidelberg to walk to the famous Königsstuhl. They did not return, and all investigations came to nothing. At last the daughter of a landlady from the nearby town of Ziegelhausen called on the Heidelberg police. She said she had noticed a briefcase in the room of their lodger, Leonard Siefert, which contained a letter to Mayor Busse. A search of the house yielded more objects that had belonged to the missing mayors. Siefert maintained that they had been placed in his knapsack by unknown persons while he was on a train. His story could not be refuted until, on July 11, Heidelberg students found the bodies of the missing men on the northeast slope of the Königsstuhl. Busse had been killed by a shot through the heart, Werner by blows from a rifle butt. The shot had been fired from a determinable direction, and above the footpath an ambush was discovered. In the cavelike recess where the murderer had waited for his victims, Popp found seven different varieties of mosses, two varieties of pine needles, husks of hazelnuts, and crumbled leaves from white and red beeches; he also found scales of buds, wisps of grasses, snail slime, and resin. Traces of the same vegetation clung to the clothes Siefert had worn on the day of the crime. Popp's work provided a decisive link in the chain of circumstantial evidence that led to Siefert's conviction.

It would take too long to pursue all the developments in the art of tracing botanical clues during the next decades. It is interesting, however, that as early as 1923 one of the first American scientists to carry European scientific criminalistic methods to America, Edward Oscar Heinrich of Berkeley, applied botany to a classic American crime. On October 11, 1923, a Southern Pacific express train was stopped by bandits in a tunnel of the Siskiyou Mountains in Oregon. The train crew were killed and the mail car was blown up with dynamite. The car caught fire, and thus the bandits destroyed the riches they had hoped to seize. All that they left behind at the scene of the crime was a worn and greasy pair of blue denim overalls. For lack of other evidence, detectives and officers of the U. S. Postal Inspection Service hit on the idea of sending the overalls to Berkeley. Heinrich's field, as was to be expected in those days of nonspecialization, ranged from the decipherment of codes to toxicology and dust analysis. But although his reports tended to sound somewhat histrionic, with strong overtones of Sherlock Holmes, there was sound work behind them. Within a few weeks he reported that the overalls had been worn by a lefthanded woodchopper who normally worked in fir forests. The man must be white, between twenty-one and twenty-five years old, no taller than five feet ten inches. He would have medium-brown hair, a light complexion, light-brown eyebrows, small hands and feet. "Apparently he works and lives in the Pacific Northwest. Look for such a man." This Holmesian diagnosis was based on the fact that tiny particles of fir needles and microscopically recognizable chips of fir wood were found in the right pocket of the overalls. Since they were only in the right pocket, Heinrich concluded (correctly as events turned out) that the unknown was lefthanded. Since he chopped with his left hand close to the blade of the ax and the right overall pocket turned toward the tree, the chips of wood naturally flew into the right pocket. In addition, five hundredfold magnification of the needle particles showed characteristics of the Douglas fir native to the Northwest. Forty years later no scientific criminalist would have ventured such an arbitrary diagnosis. But when the criminals, three brothers d'Autremont, were arrested in the course of the investigation, Heinrich's hypotheses were confirmed in every detail. The story became a legend and contributed greatly to the development of botanical trace analysis in the United States.

One of its more striking triumphs was in connection with the Almodovar case which began in New York on November 2, 1942. On the morning of that day a New Yorker walking his police dog in Central Park, near 110th Street, found a dead woman in the tall grass. A sleeve of her jacket seemed to have been torn from her shoulder in the course of a struggle. Detectives Hackett and Crosby of the Bureau of Missing Persons identified her as Louise Almodovar, a twenty-three-year-old waitress who five months earlier had married a twenty-seven-year-old Puerto Rican sailor named Anibal Almodovar. She had left him after a few weeks because he refused to give up other woman friends. Thomas A. Gonzales, Chief Medical Examiner, found that Louise Almodovar had been strangled, and suspicion fell upon her husband, who had made violent scenes of jealousy after the separation. He was arrested, and Alexander O. Gettler, head of the Chemical and Toxicological Laboratory in the medical examiner's office, found seeds of various types of grass in his trouser cuffs. He passed the seeds on to Joseph J. Copeland, Professor of Botany and Biology at City College, who determined that the seeds came from grasses growing around the spot where the body had been found. Moreover, the grasses in question—*Plantago cance-olata, Panicum dichotomiflorum, Eleusine indica*—could be found in Central Park alone, of the entire New York City area. To forestall possible alibis that the grass seeds had come from elsewhere, Copeland's affidavit stated explicitly that these types of grasses grew only at two spots on Long Island and three places in Westchester County. Almodovar at first confessed that he had arranged to meet his wife in Central Park, that they had quarreled again, and he had killed her in a fit of rage. But he soon thought better of it and maintained that the confession had been extorted from him under pressure. Thus the grass seeds served as prime evidence when he was brought to trial and found guilty.

21

Among the first reports to come in from the scientific institutes of Sydney were the findings of Dr. Cameron Oliver Cramp in regard to the hairs. Among the hairs were three different kinds of human hair and a considerable number of animal hairs. The last, identified as canine, were distinctively soft and reddish in color. Cramp maintained that they must be the hairs of a Pekinese dog. They were identical with samples he took from the coats of no less than ninety dogs of this breed. This suggested the possibility that the killer owned a Pekinese.

The studies of Neville Hewlitt White, the plant pathologist, also proved informative. He established that the mold cultures on Graeme Thorne's shoes came from four different types of fungi. The most remarkable of these was a culture of a yellowish green color which consisted of tiny globules. This proved to be *Aspergillus repens,* which developed only in a humid environment and when completely undisturbed for a given period. The problem, then, was to use these facts to establish the date when the boy had been wrapped in the rug, and hence how soon after the abduction he had been killed.

When the reproductive organs of the fungus reach maturity, they begin to open and discharge their spores. The sporophores on Graeme Thorne's shoes had just opened. Since the maturation period for this species was exactly three weeks, it was clear that they must have had a minimum of three weeks, time to develop on the boy's shoes. Moreover, for the fungus to have ripened to the point of having sporophores another two to three weeks was needed. Since this fungus could not form on the shoes while they were being walked in, the child's body must have lain on the ground at Grandview Grove for at least five weeks.

To check the precise time for these biologic processes, which were to a degree dependent on the nature of the nutritive base, the average temperature, and the degree of moisture, White cultured *Aspergillus repens* artificially on sterile pieces of shoe leather. He kept the culture under conditions corresponding to the environment of the bundle in which Graeme Thorne's body was found. Eventually White was able to inform Superintendent Clarke that the period of development came to exactly three weeks. Thus the layer of fungus on Graeme's shoes had been six weeks old, indicating that the boy had been killed immediately after the abduction.

Important though White's work was for establishing the time of death, it gave no leads to any definite milieu in which the murderer could be sought. The first such guidance came from Horace Whitworth of the Geological and Mining Museum after he had analyzed the pink encrustations of soil. Under the microscope they proved to contain various components: clay, yellow and brownish particles of pigment, and some plant fibers. The mass of the material, however, consisted of grains of sand mixed with a pinkish substance. This substance dissolved as soon as a few drops of hydrochloric acid were added, effervescing in a manner that indicated the presence of lime. Whitworth identified it as the pink mortar frequently used in Australian building, especially in one-family houses on rather high foundations. Graeme Thorne might therefore have lain in a cellar from whose walls particles of pink mortar had fallen. This seemed scarcely a helpful item, since there were countless such houses. But the fact acquired a surprising significance after the botanical studies in September had led to a preliminary conclusion.

The microscopically small plant particles that Clarke and his assistants had found on various items of Graeme's clothing and on the rug were divided into five sets. Set 1 consisted of bits of leaves and stems from the rug; set 2 of vegetable matter clinging to the scarf; set 3 of plant particles from the back of his jacket; set 4 of particles from the seat of his pants; set 5 of unusually fine particles that were shaken out of Graeme's jacket and appeared to be of vegetable origin.

The key questions were as follows: a) Could the particles be identified as coming from specific plants? b) Did these plants grow at the spot where the bundle containing the boy's body had been found? In that case, further work was pointless, since it might mean that the particles had found their way onto clothing and rug right there. They would then not indicate the still unknown spot where Graeme might have been killed or his body kept for a while or wrapped up. The botanist Johnson, whom Clarke first consulted, attempted a preliminary identification of the plant traces, and subsequently drove out to Grandview Grove with Clarke, where they made a survey of the vegetation around the site where the body had lain. After considerable work Johnson concluded that some of the plant debris adhering to Graeme's clothes had not come from that area. He was chary of making more definite statements and instead suggested that Dr. Joyce Vickery be called in; she could best deal with the matter, having been occupied with the classification of plants at the National Herbarium for more than a decade. On September 6 Dr. Vickery took charge of Clarke's five sets of traces and began examining the fragments of leaves, stems, twigs, fruits, and seeds in respect to their external structure—in other words, she tried to classify them morphologically. There were distinct limits to this, however, and she had to attack the problem in another way, preparing microscopic cross sections, longitudinal sections, and radial sections, and arrive at her classifications by the internal structure of the plant cells.

The task proved so formidable that Dr. Vickery asked Curator Anderson of the National Herbarium to call a conference of the scientific staff. Thanks to their collective work, by the middle of September the samples had been identified. The list included: *Pittosporum undulatum, Eucalyptus gummifera, Chamaecyparis pisifera,* variety *squarrosa, Casuarina,* probably of the variety *distyla, Cupressus glabra, Kunzea ambigua, Agrostis* of the "bent grass" species. Some of the plants, such as *Agrostis,* were represented only by a single seed, or at any rate were not found on all the items of clothing. The striking fact was that two plants appeared in large quantities on every piece of Graeme's clothing as well as on the rug. These were the *Chamaecyparis pisifera,* variety *squarrosa,* and the *Cupressus glabra*—both of them cypresses. The first is fairly common as a garden ornamental, the second rare.

Armed with these results, Clarke returned to Grandview Grove with Dr. Vickery. On their knees the two covered every square foot of the area. Dr. Vickery found *Pittosporum undulatum, Eucalyptus gummifera, Casuarina, Kunzea ambigua, Lantana camara,* but not bent grass and above all not a single specimen of either cypress. Since only a single seed of the bent grass had been found on the boy's body, its presence might have been a matter of chance. But the significant combination of two varieties of cypress could only have been carried to Grandview Grove with the body and therefore might be assumed to come from the spot where Graeme Thorne had been killed. To eliminate one possibility, Clarke and the botanist inspected the gardens of all the houses in the vicinity of Grandview Grove. At 16 Grandview Grove (the Coughlins' house) they came upon a *Chamaecyparis pisifera,* but it grew on the far side of the house from the place where the body had lain. Moreover, there was no sign of *Cupressus glabra* in the vicinity. Clarke therefore returned to Central Street firmly convinced that both trees or shrubs must be at the place where the boy had been killed or his body had been deposited. Since the combination, as the botanist informed him, was extremely rare, Clarke thought it wise to search the entire area around Seaforth, including Clontarf and Manly, for a house with a garden in which both plants were growing. And at this point the pink mortar acquired importance. The sought-for house would very likely be one of brick with pink mortar in the joints and seams of such mortar about the foundations. The whole combination—pink mortar and two types of cypress—at last gave the police something definite to look for.

Detective Sergeants Roy Coleman and George Shiell were assigned to the search. The Herbarium provided them with twigs of both types of cypress, so that they knew what they were looking for. The two detectives found themselves involved in one of the most wearisome tasks they had ever undertaken. Inhabitants and above all mailmen, whom they cautiously questioned, sent them chasing down a multitude of false trails. Constantly they came upon one or the other type of cypress, but not both together. Nevertheless they carried on, spurred by the awareness that none of the other investigations had as yet yielded any results.

Detective Sergeant Clarke continued his work on other clues in the meanwhile; among other things he learned that the rug had been made at the Onkaparinga Works in South Australia between May 1955 and January 1956. But the manufacturer's series comprised three thousand items, and it seemed virtually hopeless to trace the whereabouts of each rug. Clarke therefore waited with increasing restlessness for some report from Coleman and Shiell.

Toward the end of September the two detectives extended their search to Clontarf, a district of one- and two-story houses and bungalows. At last a mailman suggested that they try 28 Moore Street, Clontarf, about a mile and a half from where Graeme Thorne's body had been found. Skeptical after their many disappointments, they set out for Moore Street, and to their surprise found themselves at a house that actually met the prescribed conditions. It was a one-family brick house with pink mortar in the joints. It rose on high foundations, with a garage in the basement, and to either side of the garage door grew the cypresses, *Chamaecyparis pisifera* and *Cupressus glabra*. Sergeant Clarke informed Dr. Vickery, and himself set out at once for Clontarf. Joyce Vickery arrived shortly afterward. The ground in front of the garage and around the house was impregnated with particles of pink mortar; and Dr. Vickery definitely identified the shrubs as the two kinds of cypress. Twigs of *Chamaecyparis,* which grew on the west side of the garage door, had fallen on the garage floor and on the thresholds of the two doors that led into the cellar. Twigs of the other cypress on the east side of the garage door were also scattered around the premises.

Everyone at the Criminal Investigation Branch felt that the solution was near when Coleman presented his report on the tenants of 28 Moore Street. The present occupants of the house had no bearing on the case, for they had moved in after the kidnaping. But their predecessors were another matter. The next-door neighbors, Mr. and Mrs. Telford, reported that No. 28 had been inhabited for six months by an immigrant named Stephen Leslie Bradley, his wife Magda, three children, and a Pekinese dog. As far as they knew, Bradley was a Hungarian, had come to Australia in 1950, and worked as an electroplater. In spite of his limited income he had lately been driving two cars, a German Gogomobil and an iridescent blue Ford which he had bought early in July. On the morning of July 7, the day Graeme Thorne was kidnaped, movers had cleared out the house. That same morning Magda Bradley had taken a cab to the airport, supposedly to go to Queensland on vacation. Bradley had not been at home when his wife departed. He returned later when the movers were already at work and asked the Telfords to keep some paintings for him; he was afraid they would be damaged by the movers. On July 17 he had called for the paintings in his Ford. He had not told the Telfords his present address. But the sudden move on July 7 had struck them as so odd that they had written down the number of his car, AYO-382, and on July 19 had informed the police of their suspicions.

That the Telfords should have notified the police seemed hard to credit. But a check through Foley's files in Bondi proved that such a report was in fact filed away. Moreover, it had coincided with another circumstance. On July 21 Detective Sergeants Kelly and Ettalong had stopped Bradley's iridescent blue Ford on a street, in connection with the major check of all such Fords, and had taken down Bradley's present address, 49 Osborne Road, Manly. On July 24 Bradley had been visited at his place of work by detectives and questioned about his activities on July 7. He had given the impression of being so obliging and innocent, and had explained so plausibly that he had been moving house on July 7 and so would have had no time to drive eleven miles to Bondi, that he was stricken from the list of suspects.

Foley's file contained still another reference to Bradley. On September 26, just a week previously, Neville Atkin Browne, a neighbor of the Bradleys on Osborne Road, telephoned the Manly police station. He had been watching the Bradleys with some mistrust for quite a while, and had observed that they were selling furniture, that their blue Ford had vanished, and that they themselves departed on September 26. But the police had been receiving so many useless suggestions and false leads since July 7 that this information did not strike anyone as especially urgent. After all, Bradley had already been questioned in July and written off.

Now, however, there was no time to reflect on mistakes or omissions. Next morning, October 4, the Criminal Investigation Branch, which had been groping in the dark for months, at last had a definite goal to concentrate on. Public appeals were made for information on the missing Ford with license number AYO-382, and within a short time the owner of Ken Lindsay Motors in Granville called the police to say that on September 20 a man named Bradley had sold the car to him for £32 more than the unpaid balance of the installment payments; £593 had been owing on the car. Detectives Clarke, Coleman, Shiell, and Bateman raced out to Granville, sixteen miles from Sydney, and inspected the car. In the trunk Clarke came upon a brush full of hairs. On the floor of the trunk and under the mat he found numerous bits of plant material. They were taken to the National Herbarium at once, where Joyce Vickery identified them as the two betraying cypresses. Either the boy had been placed in the trunk after being killed in the Clontarf garage and wrapped up in the rug, or he had died in the trunk of the Ford itself. Since Clarke also found grit on the floor of the car trunk, which was quickly identified by Mr. Whitworth as the same pink mortar that had clung to the dead boy's clothes, it seemed fairly clear that twigs and leaves from the cypress, as well as mortar from the garage, must have been inside the trunk even before the murder.

By the evening of October 4 the police no longer had any doubts: they knew who was the kidnaper and murderer of Graeme Thorne. Bateman found the house at 49 Osborne Road completely empty. He learned from the real-estate agent, Harry Peachey, that he had just received a letter from Bradley, mailed in Melbourne, explaining that he had found it necessary to leave and would not be returning to the house, where he had rented the ground floor. It was clear that Bradley was trying to escape.

Within four days information coming in from travel bureaus, furniture dealers, automobile dealers, and school principals revealed how systematically Stephen Leslie Bradley had been planning his escape since August 25. On that day Magda Bradley had called at the office of the Union Steamship Company in Sydney and booked passage to England for herself and her thirteen-year-old son Peter on the *Himalaya*. Four days later Bradley booked passage for himself and his children Ellen and Robert on the same vessel. A few days later he went to a furniture dealer on Liverpool Street and arranged to sell all his household gear for £260. His story was that he was going to London for medical treatment. On September 20 the Ford and a week later the Gogomobil had passed into the hands of dealers. On September 23 he had taken his son Robert, who was deaf, out of the school for Deaf Boys in Castle Hill, leaving word that he was moving to Brisbane where better medical treatment would be available for Robert. Then he had gone to see George Wittmann, his wife's first husband, to say good-by before leaving for Melbourne. Obviously he had been trying to muddy his trail by alleging different destinations to everyone he spoke with. On September 24 he sent his Pekinese dog to Stewart's Veterinary Hospital with instructions that it be shipped to London. On September 26 he and his family had quietly boarded the *Himalaya,* which had made brief stops in Melbourne and Fremantle and now, on October 8, was on the way to

Colombo, Ceylon. While Bateman, Coleman, Doyle, and other detectives hurried from informant to informant, Clarke's men brought the Pekinese dog to Dr. Cramp. Within a short time Cramp determined that the dog hairs taken from the dead boy's clothes and the rug were indistinguishable from the hairs of this Pekinese. Meanwhile Clarke and his assistants searched the deserted house in Manly. In some refuse they discovered the negatives of photographs showing Bradley at a picnic with his family. One of the pictures revealed a rug exactly like the one in which Graeme Thorne's body had been wrapped. A last link in the chain of scientific evidence was closed when Clarke discovered a torn tassel behind Bradley's former home in Clontarf. There was one tassel missing on the rug, and the tassel fitted neatly into the row.

On October 8 the Central Court in Sydney issued a warrant for Bradley's arrest. The Australian High Commissioner in Ceylon asked the Colombo police to hold Bradley, and notified them that two detective sergeants would come to Colombo by air to transmit the arrest warrant. Bateman and Doyle landed in Colombo on October 14, where Bradley had meanwhile been taken off the *Himalaya* while his family continued on to England. There followed endless negotiations over the extradition procedures, and it was November 19 before the two detectives finally returned to Sydney with their prisoner. Until the day he was handed over to them, they had not seen Bradley, for he had refused all confrontations with the two detectives. Consequently, they made his acquaintance only during the flight. They found him a short, plump man with an olive complexion, sparse, oily black hair—altogether insignificant in appearance and without a trace of malignancy or cruelty. He had the slippery talkativeness of a salesman, and during the flight he babbled, unasked, in heavily accented and ungrammatical English, about his life. The plane was already flying over Australian soil when he suddenly declared: "I have done this thing to the Thorne boy. What will happen to me?" Doyle, who had sensed that Bradley was on the point of confession, replied: "In view of that, I have to warn you that anything you say may be taken down in evidence and used against you." Bradley replied: "Yes, I know. I have wanted to talk to tell you."

Bateman suggested that he wait until after the landing in Sydney. If he still wanted to make a confession then, he could do it in the prescribed fashion. And in fact, immediately on arrival, Bradley recounted the whole story. He stated that he had read in the newspaper about Bazil Thorne's winnings in the lottery and decided to kidnap his son for ransom. For several days he had watched the way Graeme was taken to school. Early in the morning of July 7 he had parked his car on Wellington Street. Shortly before Phyllis Smith arrived to pick up Graeme, he went up to the boy, told him that Mrs. Smith could not come that morning and that he was to drive him to school. Graeme had followed him without demur. For a while he simply cruised around, stopped at a public telephone booth and called the Thornes to demand a ransom of £25,000. Then he drove across the harbor bridge to his home. His wife and children had meanwhile departed for Queensland, and the movers would be coming at any moment. He therefore drove the car into the garage and told Graeme to get out for a while. He then seized the boy and gagged him and hid him in the trunk of the car so that the movers would not see him. After dark he opened the trunk to take Graeme out and saw that the boy had suffocated. He thereupon wrapped the child in a rug and drove out to the place where the body was found on August 16.

Bradley signed this confession. A series of questions was typed in at the bottom: "Have you written out this statement and read it over?" "Has this statement been made of your own free will?" "Were you cautioned before making this statement that you were not obliged to make any statement unless you wished, as any statement you did make may be used in evidence?" Under each of these questions Bradley wrote, "Yes." He wrote "No" under the question: "Has any threat, promise or inducement been held out to you to make this statement?"

Bateman and Doyle felt that they were well advised to take such precautions. Bradley's loquacity had inspired them with a deep distrust. They suspected that he was making the confession only in the hope of escaping a murder charge by claiming that Graeme had suffocated by accident, to the undoing of his plans to restore the child to his home. The boy's severe head injury alone branded Bradley as a liar, and it was also likely that he would recant his confession as soon as he recognized that his effort to establish mitigating circumstances had failed.

Sure enough, during his trial from March 20 to 28, 1961, at the Central Criminal Court of Sydney, Bradley asserted that he had made the confession in a state of confusion and panic. He attempted to curry sympathy by telling a life story that could scarcely be verified. It was the story of a half-Jewish Hungarian boy, István Baranyay, who at thirteen had been on the point of being shot by the Germans, but had escaped death by leaping into the Theiss River. Miraculously, he managed to reach Italy. But his experience in the Germans' prisons had so marked him that even as late as 1960 any encounter with the police filled him with horror, he said, and so he was ready to sign even the wildest confession.

If any of his listeners believed him, he quickly destroyed their sympathy by the calculating way in which he subsequently maneuvered with lies, denials, and failures of memory, refuting his own story about the trauma he had suffered and revealing himself as one of those base creatures who exploit the tragedy of the Jews for their own purposes. The part of his life that was traceable, from the moment he had set foot on Australian soil, revealed him as a person whose craving for status was in inverse proportion to his capabilities. In his quest for money and prestige he had plunged from one economic débâcle to the next, until the newspaper accounts of the kidnaping of Eric Peugeot inspired him to a similar attempt. His first wife Eva, whom he had married after his emigration in 1953, had died in a motor accident and Bradley had inherited her estate, which included a house. The circumstances of her death were just as obscure as the fire in a well-insured boardinghouse in Katoomba which he had run between 1956 and 1959, and which had brought him to the verge of bankruptcy.

On March 29, 1961, the jury pronounced him guilty, and Mr. Justice Clancy sentenced him to life imprisonment.

So ended what was probably the most sensational trial in the history of Australian crime. Its very sensationalism, however, profoundly affected the development of scientific criminalistics in Australia. It was no accident that five years later an Australian, Detective Sergeant F. B. Cocks, of the South Australian police in Adelaide, would publish in the *Australian Police Journal* an article entitled "Taxonomy and Plant Ecology in the Field of Forensic Science," one of the most important contributions to international criminology on the potentialities of botanical evidence. His examples included thefts, burglary, and safecracking and clearly demonstrated the value of botanical trace evidence to the everyday work of the police. Cocks also called for internationalization of forensic botanical research.

The Thorne case, and Cocks's studies, like the Guay case in Canada, demonstrated that scientific criminology was keeping pace with the historical changes of the twentieth century. In this, as in other matters, the "younger" countries of the world were beginning to come to the fore. Interestingly enough, the same trend was becoming apparent in the smaller European lands, countries with long historical traditions and high scientific development, which had, however, done little in the field of police science during the first half of the century—at least in comparison with France, England, Germany, or Italy. Perhaps the reason for their backwardness was, paradoxically, their greater good fortune. By avoiding military engagements, and tempering economic shocks, they had preserved a settled social system. But the more they succumbed, after the Second World War, to the technological, economic, and social forces of the age of mass culture, the more they were threatened by a rising tide of criminality. Confronted with these new problems, their police forces turned for help to the scientists.

22

The swift rise of Dr. Max Frei-Sulzer in the field of criminalistics was one of those truly personal triumphs increasingly rare in our age. He himself once commented that he was "pushed into a vacuum"—the vacuum being the state of scientific criminology in Switzerland. But the deeper reason for his achievement undoubtedly lay in his talent for microscopy, his wealth of ideas, and his gift for empathy.

Frei-Sulzer, born in Zurich in 1913, studied the sciences in his native city, and from the start was especially fascinated by microscopy. He had a fling at every aspect of science in which the microscope was utilized: chemistry, mineralogy, zoology, pathology, and histology. He also studied photography at the Technical Academy. Subsequently, he taught biology in Zurich. But this work did not offer him sufficient scope so he also taught microscopy at a school for medical technicians, and urged the girls to bring in slides of rare pathological phenomena. In the course of time he acquired a thorough knowledge of serology and bacteriology. Finally he gave evening courses in microscopy in the Zurich University extension system. And there, in 1949, he came into contact with the criminal division of the Zurich city police force.

Among Frei-Sulzer's evening students were two detective sergeants of the Identification Service, at that time the only branch of the police that dealt with trace investigations. After several lessons they inquired whether microscopy could not be employed for extremely small clues, and shortly afterward Frei-Sulzer received an invitation to call on Commandant Früh of the city police, who was aware of the necessity to combat growing criminality by modern methods. He proposed that Frei-

Sulzer set up a special course for detectives. Frei-Sulzer accepted the proposal and was soon giving bi-weekly instruction to members of the Identification Service. Before long they appeared in class with evidence from a criminal case in which a burglar had broken into a house through a skylight. No clues had been detectable by the naked eye on the frame of the broken skylight. But the detectives reasoned that the burglar might have left particles of fiber from his clothes in squeezing through the narrow opening. They therefore also brought their teacher a suit belonging to their suspect. Frei-Sulzer showed that a great many microscopic fragments of fiber from the burglar's clothes were indeed clinging to the frame of the skylight. There were red, green, and blue-green bits of fiber, some only .002 inches long, which proved to be identical with the fibers of the suspect's trousers.

Subsequently, the teaching sessions were divided into two parts. During the first hour Frei-Sulzer taught microscopy; during the second hour the detectives submitted evidence from cases that had occurred during the preceding week: thefts, burglaries, automobile accidents. The lessons soon developed into an advisory service for the police. Twice a week Frei-Sulzer went to police headquarters on Bahnhofsquai to look over their latest specimens. He retained his teaching posts but used vacations to visit European police laboratories wherever they had begun functioning again since the end of the war. Thus, as representative of the younger generation, he made contact with the old pioneers of criminalistic science. He visited August Brüning in Münster, Westphalia, now seventy-three but still lecturing on scientific criminology. In the confusion of the early postwar years Brüning had moved from Berlin to West Germany, and he lacked virtually all facilities for experimental laboratory work. Consequently, his lectures were based largely on the experiences of his earlier, "great" years. Locard, who still had his laboratory, was better off. Nevertheless, Frei-Sulzer also returned from visiting the French criminalist convinced that the postwar world, with its technological advances, demanded more refined methods than men such as Locard or Brüning had developed. There were obviously thousands of clues which slipped through the "mesh" of the methods hitherto applied. Techniques for studying such clues must be developed. The task so greatly attracted Frei-Sulzer that in 1950 he accepted Commandant Früh's offer to enter the police service full time. The attic rooms of police headquarters had always been the favorite sites for fledgling police laboratories, from the days of Bertillon on. Frei-

Sulzer, too, began in the attic of the building on Bahnhofsquai. Fifteen years later he was to head one of the most important special laboratories for criminalistic trace evidence to be found anywhere in the world.

This amazing rise began in 1951 when Frei-Sulzer put forth a new method, as simple as it was brilliant, for securing invisible microscopic traces at the scenes of crimes. Since the twenties the tradition had been, wherever micro-traces were being sought, to search directly with the magnifying glass for bits of evidence at the scenes of crimes, or on the clothing or possessions of suspects, or to collect dust with special vacuum cleaners. In the course of time this procedure had revealed a host of inadequacies. In searching with the magnifying glass, experienced scientists found many micro-traces, but they also missed a goodly number. Moreover, they themselves did not always inspect the scene. Hence there were many gaps in the securing of trace evidence. In 1950 many detectives lacked the training requisite for the task, for a man unfamiliar with microscopy was rarely able to think his way into the world of the microcosmos. But even if the detectives had training and were able to envisage the course of a crime or an accident and therefore imagine where invisible evidence might be found, the actual securing of tiny particles involved grave difficulties. Real certainty could be had only for movable objects which could be brought to a laboratory. The vacuum cleaner, moreover, had its own disadvantages. It not only picked up superficial traces that might be clinging to the clothing of a person who had come into contact with some object at the scene of a crime, but it frequently extracted from the depths of fabrics the dust that had accumulated there in the weeks and months before a crime, thus obliterating possibly significant evidence. To use the vacuum cleaner properly required a great deal of experience.

Frei-Sulzer hit on the idea of using an adhesive tape, such as Scotch tape. If the sticky side is placed on spots where invisible micro-traces are suspected, all the micro-particles on the surface of the object in question will stick to it. In this way fibers, splinters of wood, bits of lacquer or paint, shreds of grass, grains of pollen, or whatever will be picked up. The tape also made it easy to transport material for investigation to the laboratory without alteration. The strips of tape were doubled over so that they would stick to themselves, with the microscopic particles between the two layers. Each tape was then carefully labeled as to the spot from which it had been taken. The micro-traces on the tape retained exactly the position in which they had been found. In the laboratory the tapes could be opened and inspected under stereo magnifying glass and microscope. The particles could also be removed by solvents and transferred to slides, where they could be compared with corresponding particles, such as those taken from a suspect's clothing.

At the beginning this novel method led many detectives to exaggerated follies; they stuck tape all over the scenes of crimes instead of confining themselves to spots which might reasonably have been touched by the culprit. It took a while before the mean was found, so that the "adhesive tape test" occupied its proper place and filled the gaps between direct securing of trace evidence and vacuum cleaning of the scene or of clothing. For a while, moreover, questions were raised; it was suggested that the tape might affect the traces, especially the dyes of textile fibers. But years of experiments showed that this slight risk could be avoided completely by using tapes with chemically inert adhesives.

Proceeding from his fundamental discovery of the adhesive tape method, Frei-Sulzer built up a whole system of securing and comparing micro-traces which soon made him one of the leaders in the whole field of criminalistics. His practical investigations embraced everything that fell into the realm of micro-trace evidence. One of his prime achievements dealt with fiber traces. By countless experiments he demonstrated that the most fleeting contact between the clothing of a culprit and his victim, in fact even entering a room, sufficed to transfer fibers to victim or room. By the same token fibers adhered to hands, to the face, to other exposed parts of the body. They stuck to automobiles, motorcycles, streetcars, or bicycles that had been involved in an accident. Invisible particles from the clothing of murdered or injured persons clung to objects in quantities that far exceeded anything that had previously been guessed.

Among Frei-Sulzer's most dramatic experiences with the spread and the adhesiveness of such micro-fibers was a case of murder accompanied by robbery, which he succeeded in solving. It had taken place in an apartment with a billiard table. Green fibers of billiard-table felt were found clinging to the clothing of one suspect. Yet the murder had been committed in a room distant from the billiard table. Upon careful examination of the entire apartment, Frei-Sulzer discovered green fibers clinging to curtains, blankets, and furniture in every single room. In the course of time they had been sown over the entire apartment.

On the basis of this experience Frei-Sulzer developed his concept of the "trace level" in closed rooms. Taking fiber traces became a science. Among its most fundamental rules was to search not only in places that had been touched by the culprit, but also in "neutral" areas. Only such a search could show that the fibers from the criminal were not present everywhere in the area. Transportable evidence, such as clothing, rugs, and so on, was heat-sealed into plastic bags to prevent contamination with deceptive fibers. The evidence from suspects and from the scenes of crimes had to be gathered and transported by different detectives, preserved and examined in different rooms, in order to exclude misleading transfers of fibers. Frei-Sulzer even set up largely dust-free dressing rooms adjacent to his laboratory where suspects could disrobe, to counter any contentions that incriminating fiber traces had been transmitted to their clothing in the police laboratory itself. An essential question for the evidential value of fibers was whether the transmission had been only in one direction, from a victim to a culprit, say, or whether there had been a double transfer from one to the other. If, for example, in a morals crime red and yellow fibers from a victim's dress were found clinging to a suspect's clothes, and blue and gray fibers from the suspect's clothing were on the victim's dress, the evidential value of this double transfer was considerably greater than the one-way fiber transmission.

The full range of Frei-Sulzer's work came to light in the evaluation of traces, that is, in the comparison of fibers. Partly, to be sure, he was utilizing researches which had meanwhile been undertaken in other laboratories. Among these were the comprehensive studies of Constable A. K. Bergh of the Ottawa laboratory of the Royal Canadian Mounted Police, who in 1955 published an analytic guide to the ever-proliferating types of synthetic fibers, such as nylon, polyester, and acrylic fibers. But Frei-Sulzer and his associates in the Zurich laboratory also engaged in original research along these lines. The refinements essential in an age of mass production of textiles and chemical dyes became strikingly apparent in color comparison of fibers. Visual comparison under the microscope now employed a wide variety of techniques: light and dark fields, phase contrast, polarized light, fluorescence under ultraviolet light. Studies of this sort revealed distinctions of hue among fibers whose color appeared identical under normal light. Where microscopic procedures failed, spectrophotometry often exposed differences. Experience showed, however, that even this arsenal of techniques might prove inadequate in some circumstances. The technology of dyeing had developed to such an extent since the days of Georg Popp that the very same color could be achieved by a wide variety of chemical compounds. Two red textile fibers which could not be distinguished in hue either microscopically or spectrophotometrically nevertheless need not be of the same origin. Correspondence could be considered proved only if it were shown that the same chemical substances had been used in the dyeing process. It was therefore necessary to carry out chemical tests on bits of fiber which sometimes measured no more than a few thousandths of an inch. The method used was that of spot analysis, to which we have frequently referred; capillary pipettes thinner than hairs transferred minute portions of reagents to the particles of fiber. Finally, the method of paper chromatography, which began being applied to criminalistics between 1950 and 1960, enabled the forensic scientist to separate even mixed dyes into their components. The situation was complicated by the fact that the same dye would be absorbed to a different extent by different portions of the same fibers, so that shades of color were produced. Without chemical tests there was the ever present danger that fibers from the same source would appear to be different because of these shadings.

The number of possibilities and of tests was so large that long experience alone enabled the criminalist to select the right method for each case. Usually the simpler procedures were taught to detectives, to give them some idea of how to proceed with their investigations. The full arsenal of testing methods was reserved for cases that offered no other evidence and in which no confessions could be obtained. Such cases involved further problems, toward the solution of which Paul L. Kirk in Berkeley made significant contributions. There was, for example, the question of the absolute evidential value of fiber transfer. It became necessary to establish which types of fibers were transferred frequently by the natural contacts of people in cities, and which fiber transfers were comparatively rarer. In a series of studies Kirk showed that undyed wool was found most frequently in "innocent" transfers, followed by black wool. Expressed statistically, other fibers and hues accounted for 5 per cent, compared to the 95 per cent of such wool fibers scattered by natural dissemination. But such studies were only beginning in the sixties.

Another Swiss made formidable contributions to the study of fiber traces. He was Ernst P. Martin of Basel. Born in Niederschöntal near Basel in 1915, Martin was an outsider like Frei-Sulzer who had gradually made his way into criminalistics. He had started out as a photographer, later worked at the Pathological Institute in Basel and at the University Psychiatric Clinic of that city. In 1936, at the age of twenty-one, he had tried to obtain a job as a photographer with the Basel police. In

1941 he finally made the grade, but stayed in the photography division for many years. It was not until 1953 that he became head of the infant criminalistic investigating branch in Basel and set about establishing a proper police laboratory.

Martin, athletically lean and even in his forties almost white-haired, did not let his ambitions run away with him. He went about expanding the range of the laboratory at a deliberate pace. Gradually, the technical possibilities of spectroscopy, microcrystallization, and chromatography were explored. Right at the outset Martin had occasion to try out the adhesive tape test in a Basel murder case. A woman had been found hanged in an apartment house. Her husband's nightshirt was found with sleeves torn off, but the police inclined to think that it was a case of suicide. Only adhesive tape samplings from the dead woman's hands aroused suspicion of murder. On the tapes Martin found virtually no fibers of the rope that had been used in the hanging, but a large quantity of fiber from the husband's torn nightshirt. In many preceding cases it had been shown that fibers from the rope always clung to the hands of persons who placed a noose around their own necks. Such fibers were missing in cases of murder, in which the murderer had hanged his victim to conceal his act. This was the case here.

Although Martin was conducting important researches in the identification of papers and writing materials, which won international fame for the Basel laboratory, he devoted much of his time to further development of fiber comparison. Over the years he tested a wide variety of adhesive tapes to determine whether or not they altered traces, and finally collaborated with two manufacturers to develop tapes ideally suited for the purposes of police work.

One of the most remarkable of the cases in which the Swiss methods of micro-traces of fibers proved their value was that of Maria Flosky, which took place in the autumn of 1963.

23

On September 11, 1963, Maria Flosky was found in an area of sparse fir forest, near a lake known as the Kahler See in northern Bavaria. The lake and the industrial town of Kahl are not remarkable for their beauty, but the area is not far from the big city of Frankfurt am Main, many of whose inhabitants who wanted a taste of country would come out to take advantage of its large camping ground and public tennis courts.

On that September afternoon, a woman named Helene Rüth was scouring the forest about a quarter of a mile from the camping ground for fallen branches. She had a job in Kahl, and after four o'clock, when her shift ended, she was in the habit of going into the forest to gather faggots to supplement her winter fuel supply. As she was breaking up some sticks, she noticed a brown bundle on the ground some yards away. She went a few steps closer and realized that it was an elderly woman who was uttering peculiar moaning sounds. Thinking at first that the woman was asleep, she called out: "Hello there, get up. Do wake up!" But the woman did not respond, so Frau Rüth quickly sought out a passer-by and asked him to carry word to the camping ground. When the camping ground attendant arrived, the old woman was still. Dr. Becker, of Kahl, who came a few minutes later, said that she had just died. He started as he noticed a scarf tied around her neck and knotted at one side. Suspecting that she might have been strangled, he sent word to the Bavarian state police in Alzenau.

A message was also sent by patrol car to the state police criminal section in Aschaffenburg, and by 6 P.M. Inspectors Rohden and Lang were at the clearing. Surrounded by a throng of curiosity-seekers, they made the first examination of the scene. Their notes read: "Woman of delicate constitution, sixty-five or seventy years old, dressed carefully and tastefully, dress pushed up to waist. Otherwise completely clothed. A gold wrist watch on left arm. An empty basket near the body. Scattered alongside it boletus mushrooms, a pair of sunglasses, a hair net, ordinary glasses, and an opened brooch."

Rohden and Lang also observed the knotted scarf, but in spite of the doctor's remarks attributed no importance to it because it did not seem tight enough to warrant any idea of strangulation. When they turned the woman, who lay on her right side, onto her back, they saw in the moss twelve pearls from a broken necklace; the necklace itself was hidden by the scarf. At the same time the attendant of the camping ground, seeing the woman's face, exclaimed that he knew her. She was, he said, the mother-in-law of a Frankfurt businessman who had rented a permanent site for his tent for the summer. Her name was Maria Flosky. Her son-in-law had brought her to his tent in his car just that morning, because he had business in the vicinity, and was intending to drive her home that evening. She was a quiet person, afflicted by heart trouble, who had left the tent just an hour ago to pick mushrooms. Rohden asked the attendant to look up the address of her relatives and let them know what had happened, so that they could come to identify the body. Moreover, from the moment he heard about the woman's heart disease he concluded that this was a case of natural death and therefore had the body taken to the Kahl mortuary. There she was identified by her son-in-law when he arrived in Kahl, aghast at the news.

Rohden's report was at the District Attorney's office in Aschaffenburg by eleven o'clock. In it, Rohden recommended that the medical examiner check the cause of death, but stated that it was probably not a death by violence. "It may rather be assumed that Frau Flosky suffered another heart attack while gathering mushrooms, had difficulty breathing, and in reflex movements fumbled at the scarf in an effort to obtain air."

The next morning Medical Examiner Castorph came to Kahl and had the body moved to Aschaffenburg, there being no facilities for autopsy in Kahl. First, however, he cut the scarf away, and gave it into Rohden's possession. The scarf consisted of a red central square, surrounded by yellow patterned strips and a red border. The detective was still convinced it was a natural death when he drove back to Aschaffenburg. But shortly afterward Medical Examiner Castorph and Dr. Heinrichs of the Institute of Forensic Medicine of Würzburg University informed him that he was mistaken. The two doctors had found hemorrhages in the area of the larynx and a fracture of the hyoid bone—sure indications of death by strangulation. Maria Flosky had been the victim of an unknown murderer.

As soon as District Attorney Rath in Aschaffenburg heard the results of the autopsy he got in touch with the Bavarian State Criminal Office in Munich. Vexed with the poor judgment of the local police, he asked the homicide commission of the State Criminal Office to take charge of the case.

On the morning of September 14 Chief Detective Inspector Mohr, Detective Inspector Degen, and Detective Sergeant Waterloo arrived in Kahl. Mohr, a calm, balanced tactician, and Degen, an active, young, and exceedingly intelligent man, took care not to irritate the local authorities needlessly, but promptly proposed the creation of a joint homicide commission with Inspectors Rohden and Lang. Their approach succeeded, and the local detectives swallowed their pride and buckled down to the task before them.

When Mohr and Degen set to work, they found they had nothing to go by but Rohden's first report and a few photographs of the scene of the crime. In Aschaffenburg Maria Flosky's scarf and clothing had been kept, along with samples of hair from her head. In Würzburg snippets of her fingernails had been preserved, but the commission heard of this fact only much later. The body had already been moved to Frankfurt, where the burial had been set for September 16. The soft ground at the scene of the crime had been trampled by many feet, almost totally destroying whatever clues might have been there. At first glance all that showed up were four imprints from the feet of the coffin which the undertaker's men had set down at the spot on September 11, when they moved the corpse.

Mohr and Degen were accustomed, from constant contact with the laboratory at the State Criminal Office, to pursue every smallest scientific clue. They had been indoctrinated in the methods of seeking micro-traces and in applying adhesive tape. First of all, Mohr removed from the scarf the hairs and several mosslike particles of vegetation that were clinging to it. Then he sealed the cloth in a plastic sheath to protect it (even if tardily) against subsequent contact with misleading trace elements. From the scene of the crime he took samples of soil and vegetation and sent them, together with the plant particles from the scarf, to Munich for examination, in order to find out whether the two corresponded and hence whether the site where the body had been found was also the place where Maria Flosky had died. On September 15 Mohr got in touch with the dead woman's relatives in Frankfurt and learned that she was already in the mortuary chapel there. He asked permission to examine her hands before the burial. When their consent was given, he asked the Frankfurt criminal police to assist. Thus, shortly before the funeral on September 16 he obtained adhesive tape samplings from the hands. Since the body had already been washed, it seemed doubtful that this measure would yield any results. But in any case the strips of tape were sent to Munich so that they could be examined for textile fibers. Thus the results would be available for any later comparisons with the clothing of suspects.

That same day Mohr and Degen undertook the first of a whole series of belated examinations of the scene of the death. They ripped up several square yards of the moss surface and came upon nine pearls about two feet from the spot where Maria Flosky's head had lain; the pearls had been trampled through the moss into the earth beneath. Their hopes of being able to interpret something about the course of the crime from this fact diminished sharply, however, when Degen asked the under-taker to reconstruct the manner in which he had placed the body in the coffin. It turned out that Maria Flosky's head had probably been carried over the spot where the pearls lay. The pearls could thus have fallen from the broken necklace at this time. Examination of the glasses for fingerprints also proved fruitless. But a telephone call from Munich conveyed news of high significance. Dr. Röhm, the biologist of the laboratory at the State Criminal Office, had determined that a large number of fibers had been picked up by the adhesive tapes from the dead woman's hands. There were fibers of wool, cotton, and synthetics which definitely did not come from her clothing. Thus the washings had not removed all microscopic traces; a basis for later textile comparisons with a suspect's belongings had been obtained at the last moment.

From this point on, the homicide commission undertook a systematic search for possible culprits, so that the trace investigations for a while receded into the background. First the time of the crime was established · as accurately as possible. According to the punch card at the factory, Helene Rüth had left her job at 4:01 P.M. If the times given by all other witnesses, and the information that Maria Flosky had been still alive at the moment she was found, were all balanced against one another, the probable time of the murder was 4:15 P.M.

The next important point in the investigation concerned the question of motive. The fact that all of the victim's jewelry had been left with her did not exclude robbery. Possibly the murderer had been driven away by Helene Rüth. On the other hand, two circumstances pointed to the possibility of a sex crime: the raised dress and the death by strangulation. The orderly condition of the rest of the victim's clothing argued against that motive, however. And the record of the autopsy showed not the slightest indication of a sex crime. Mohr and Degen knew only too well, to be sure, that such findings meant little, since sex murderers frequently find the climax of lust not in sexual intercourse but in the act of killing itself. Moreover, the murderer could have been disturbed before he was able to carry out his designs.

A third question was whether the objects found at the scene of the crime all belonged to Maria Flosky, or whether some might have been left behind by the murderer. Degen drove to Frankfurt to show the members of the family each object, especially the scarf. All of them declared that they had never seen the red and yellow scarf in Maria Flosky's possession. In Kahl, too, Degen found a witness, Magdalena Diebold, who had stopped at the camping ground on September 11, and who as a milliner had a sharp eye for people's clothing. She had seen Maria Flosky leaving the camping area and declared definitely that she had not been wearing a scarf. The commission therefore had to assume that the scarf belonged to the murderer.

The plan that Mohr and Degen followed after the conclusion of these basic investigations had several aims. As a matter of routine they informed all the police headquarters in Bavaria and Hesse, with the usual request for any pertinent data. But they also knew that small detective forces were so overburdened that as a rule such requests were only posted, and for the most part never even read. They therefore took a further step. On September 10 a housewife named Maria Budin had been garroted with a silk kerchief in the Hofgarten at Bayreuth. This use of a kerchief possibly indicated a connection between the events in Kahl and Bayreuth. Could the same criminal have been responsible for both deaths? The Chief of the State Criminal Office proposed to the Mayor of Bayreuth that the investigation of both murders be conducted jointly. The Mayor of Bayreuth agreed, with the result that Mohr went to Bayreuth while Degen continued to head the commission at Kahl.

Degen decided that "pointed questions" aimed at the populace would probably yield more results than a general appeal for "pertinent data." He therefore placed the scarf in a display case and sent a sound truck around the town asking for information about it: Did anyone recognize the scarf or know to whom it belonged? The sound truck also broadcast the request that anyone who had been in the woods to the east of the lake between four and five o'clock on September 11 report to the police. Inside the town hall Degen set up a large map of the area, and began marking the network of forest paths on it. Since there must have been much coming and going on these paths just after the factories shut down for the day, he hoped someone might have seen any suspicious person. Alternatively, he hoped to find a path which was not used at all, or very seldom. For if the murderer had escaped unrecognized, he must have gone by some such path. He also launched the usual survey of all files at various police headquarters and public health offices in the vicinity on men who had been reported, suspected, or convicted for sex offenses. Finally he undertook to make a check of everybody who had signed in at the camping ground on September 11.

By the last week in September Degen had found twenty persons who had traversed the wooded area in various directions on the afternoon of September 11. None of them had encountered anyone who had attracted attention. When the movements of these witnesses were recorded on the map, it became apparent that a culprit who had escaped unseen could only have taken one of two paths that ran parallel in a northward direction toward a paved road. Only one witness, a pensioner named Otto Hock of Kahl, had something to report. About three thirty in the afternoon on September 11 he had been sitting on a bench along one of these paths, about half a mile north of the spot where Maria Flosky had died. An unknown young bicyclist who looked like a woodsman had pedaled by, said "Good day," and continued on in the northerly direction. The time, three thirty, made the episode meaningless, since it was long before the time of the murder. Nevertheless, Degen asked the forest administration whether any woodsmen had been working in the area in question on September 11. When he received a negative reply, he had the sound truck go about asking the bicyclist to report as a witness. But no one came in. Given the taciturn nature of the local population, not much significance could be attributed to this silence.

But on September 24 Detective Sergeant Beck of the district police, who had been assigned to cover cafés and restaurants asking whether proprietor or patrons had noticed anything unusual, called at The Trout, a refreshment place in the forest about half a mile north of the scene of the crime. The manager of The Trout recalled that on the afternoon of September 11 a bicyclist had stopped at his place—a man he knew only by the name of Tony. He was a close-mouthed fellow fond of a drop who presumably lived in Kahl. According to the description given by the manager, Tony had many gaps in his teeth and wore a "Mackie" haircut. The curious correspondence between the statements of the pensioner and the café manager stirred Degen. He forthwith began inquiries in Kahl for anyone known by the name of Tony. On September 25 he learned that the man might be Anton Flittner, a thirty-two-year-old machinist married for the second time and employed by the firm of Allstahl in Dörnigheim. Since the beginning of September he had been taking sick leave and riding around on his bicycle. That same day the manager of the café retracted his statement. He now thought that he had only seen Tony after September 11. But meanwhile the police files, as well as some witnesses, were providing information about Flittner that inevitably made him a principal suspect.

As recently as March 20, 1963, Flittner had been convicted of "indecent actions" against his small stepdaughter and sentenced to two months in jail. His second wife had frequently appealed to the local police for protection against his uninhibited sexuality and brutality. His first wife, it was learned, had obtained a divorce on grounds that he brought women home and had relations with them while his wife was asleep in the adjoining room. There were statements that he "hung around the camping area, watched women undress, masturbated, and required intercourse four and five times a day." Since 1960 he had several times been reported to the police for drunkenness and disorderly conduct, and the district police had urgently recommended that he be "committed for preventive custody." But this recommendation had gone unimplemented owing to the circumspection of the federal authorities. The heritage of the Nazi era, with its abuse of the laws governing preventive custody of dangerous defectives and criminals and its summary killings of the mentally ill, now hampered clear-cut, necessary decisions, even when the question at issue was the preventive custody of notorious sex criminals.

Flittner had been born out of wedlock and turned over by his mother to the local children's home. He had subsequently been raised by a foster family along with their own daughter. He had been attached to his foster mother, had shown no signs of mental disturbance, and had gone through a normal apprenticeship as a machinist—until his lack of self-control emerged shortly after his first marriage.

On September 26 Degen's men questioned Flittner's wife. Her replies were dull, resigned, and factual. On September 11 she had been at her job as seamstress in the Dietrich Company from 7:30 A.M. to 3:00 P.M. Since Flittner had been taking "sick leave" and not eating at his factory cafeteria, he had made a habit of riding over to his foster parents' house for lunch, and was usually back home when she returned and made coffee for them. But on September 11 he had not come home until five thirty because his foster family had been out at their garden plot in Frischoss, where they had a little cottage. On September 12 Frau Flittner heard at work about the murder of Maria Flosky, and at home had remarked to Flittner that he must have passed through the Steinkaute woods on his way from Frischoss to the camping ground. Shouldn't he answer the police appeal for witnesses? she asked him. He had not replied. That was all she had to say. She didn't talk much with her husband and did not know much about the things he did away from home.

Scanning the transcript of this inquiry, Degen decided to get some idea of Flittner for himself. Toward evening that same day, September 26, he found him at home alone. Flittner was an unprepossessing, smallish, pallid chap, with a large tuft of hair falling across a broad forehead, a prominent nose, drooping lower lip, and receding chin. Hesitantly, but without any sign of nervousness, he answered Degen's questions about his activities on September 11. Toward noon he had bicycled to his foster parents' home, had found them out, and about one o'clock had therefore set out for Frischoss where they had a cottage. He had stayed there until three o'clock, then ridden home. Asked how long the ride from Frischoss to Kahl took him, he replied: "Fifteen or twenty minutes."

Evidently he had not talked with his wife and did not know that she had given five thirty as the time of his return. When Degen pointed this out, he showed no great surprise, apologized for having forgotten. Oh yes, his foster sister had driven him over to the camping ground. How long had he stayed there? Degen asked. Flittner replied: "Awhile," and with a sly attempt at male solidarity alluded to the girls who could be seen there. Then he recalled that afterward he had spent a considerable time at "Krämer's stand" before bicycling home.

Next day Detective Sergeant Waterloo called on Flittner's foster parents and foster sister. They confirmed the fact that Flittner had visited them in Frischoss shortly after noon. The foster sister recalled the day precisely because she had painted the cottage that day and Flittner had got green paint on his trousers. She had cleaned the trousers with turpentine. Flittner had left for home around three o'clock.

Waterloo had received training in micro-trace detection and was versed in the principle of investigating any clothing worn by suspects on the day of a crime. He therefore asked what Flittner had worn on September 11. The foster sister could not remember precisely. But then she mentioned a brown and tan tweedy sports jacket, a light blue or green sports shirt, and either gray-green or brown gabardine trousers. Waterloo then proceeded to Krämer's stand near the camping ground. There he learned that Flittner had turned up at about three thirty and talked about a "fat blonde in a bathing suit" whom he had noticed in the camping area. He had drunk a glass of beer and left after twenty minutes at most. This meant that Flittner was lying when he claimed that he had cycled straight home. If he had done so, he would have been home shortly after four o'clock, not five thirty.

His suspicions more keenly aroused by this information, Degen called on Flittner once again and questioned him on the interval between four o'clock and five thirty. Flittner insisted that he had cycled directly home. But, he said, he could no longer remember just when he had done what. Possibly he had left the stand later. After all, he argued, the people at the stand didn't look at the clock every time a patron came and went.

He made no objection when Degen sent him by police car to Alzenau to obtain a medical opinion of the scratches on Flittner's forehead, which he had noticed the day before. The doctor, however, ruled that the scratches were at most three days old and could not possibly have come from the fingernails of a woman fighting for her life on September 11. Since there were no witnesses to testify that Flittner had passed through the woods after four o'clock on the day of the crime, Degen felt that he had no legal right to pursue the questioning. Before he left, however, he asked whether Flittner would let him have the suit he had worn on September 11 for examination. There was no better way, Degen said, to prove his innocence. Flittner hesitated for a moment. But then he handed over his brown gabardine trousers, assuring the detective that he had worn them on September 11. He also gave Degen his brown sports jacket and a pair of brown shoes. Noticing some gray-green gabardine trousers in the wardrobe, Degen pressed him to include those. At this Flittner seemed about to demur, but then handed them over.

When that evening Degen reviewed the incriminating factors against the only suspect who had been located so far, he had to admit that they consisted merely of an abnormal instinctual drive and a "time gap"—factors insufficient to connect the admittedly unsavory young man with the murder of Maria Flosky. Degen could only hope that further investigation would supply other evidence. As for his latest material, Flittner's clothes and shoes, there was the outside chance that some traces from Flittner's clothing had been left on the hands and clothes of the victim, or on the scarf which had throttled her. The scarf continued to haunt Degen's imagination, so much so that next day he set afoot an inquiry to find out whether Flittner had ever been seen wearing any such scarf. In vain. Neither his wife nor his foster parents, neither the waiters nor the bartenders at his customary cafés, nor the workers in his plant had ever observed Flittner wearing a scarf.

On September 29 a courier took Flittner's jacket, trousers, and shoes to Munich; also the scarf belonging to the unknown murderer. Degen asked for a determination of whether microscopic fiber transfers had taken place between Flittner's clothing and the hands and clothes of the dead woman or the scarf. As for the two pairs of Flittner's trousers, he pointed out that the ones actually worn on the day of the crime should be identifiable by traces of green paint, or by evidence that paint had been cleaned with turpentine.

On October 1 the items arrived in the old brick building, 4 Türkenstrasse, Munich, where the laboratory of the Bavarian State Criminal Office—the Criminal Technical Division, as it was called—was located.

24

The Criminal Technical Division was about fifteen years old at this time. Robert Heindl, its creator, was one of the important pioneers of criminalistics in Germany. Born in 1883, Heindl was still a student of law in Munich University in 1902 when he became aware of the importance of fingerprints—the first German to take an interest in the matter. He had visited Bertillon and Reiss, and aroused police chiefs in several German cities to the potentialities of dactyloscopy. In pursuit of further information he traveled to various European penal colonies which then existed in the Far East, and studied for a while in Scotland Yard. In 1911 he became head of the Criminal Police of Dresden, capital of Saxony. When he first sat down at his desk, he found its only equipment a revolver and a pair of brass knuckles. He thrust aside these relics of a cruder era of criminology and began applying the experience he had gained during his travels. He had developed a strong belief in the necessity for central direction of the criminal investigation branches of the police; detectives, he held, must be able to operate beyond the borders of cities and states. He set up such a centrally organized criminal police force in Saxony and was preparing to establish a police laboratory when the First World War interrupted all such plans.

After the war Heindl moved to Berlin, where he was the prime advocate of a federal law creating a central criminal police force for all of Germany, with a great scientific laboratory in Berlin. He hoped that various hindrances to this which had been present in the German Empire would disappear in the new German Republic. As Vice President of the International Criminal Police Commission, founded in 1921 in Vienna, he did help to initiate international police co-operation. But his hopes for Germany came to nothing. A Bavarian by birth, he must have found it especially painful that the traditional resistance of Bavaria to German centralization blocked the passage of the federal criminal police law he had so ardently urged. To be sure, the Nazi regime after 1933 carried out his program, unifying the criminal police on a federal basis and setting up a police laboratory in Berlin. But Heindl was opposed to the political premises that led to the realization of his dream; in 1933 he retired from public life and withdrew to his country home. There he spent the years until 1946, engaged in editorial work on Hans Gross's *Archiv für Kriminologie*. Every issue he published was a plea, in one form or another, for collaboration between scientific pursuit of trace evidence and ordinary criminological investigation.

With the end of the Nazi era, the newly formed Bavarian government called him to Munich in 1946 to set up a fingerprint and criminal report file. Thus at the age of sixty-three he found himself back where he had started in Saxony. The German police force had relapsed into a multitude of local organizations, and the idea of a federal police had again become remote. During his work in Munich between 1946 and 1949 Heindl had to content himself with preparing the ground for a later State Criminal Office. His section bore the grotesque name of Central Office for Criminal Identification, Police Statistics, and Police Intelligence. But from his first day in the job, this white-haired giant of a man did all in his power to set up a scientific laboratory in his office. He was ridiculed for the "glass bottle collection" which constituted all his laboratory equipment during those postwar years, when everything was lacking in Germany. In some rooms of his battered, partly bombed-out office building a few interested detectives and chemists gathered to learn; but when Heindl finally retired in 1949, the laboratory already could boast two spectrometers. The structure that was built on these foundations between 1949 and 1963 owed its existence to the efforts of a few men, in particular District Attorney Franz Meinert, who assumed the presidency of the Central Office in 1951, and the following year became head of the State Criminal Office. In his youth Meinert had read one of Heindl's books, *Criminal Technology*, which had made him a lasting convert to scientific criminology. He was a man of ideas who had both the energy and the diplomatic talents to find his way among the toils of federal and Bavarian police politics. In 1959 he left to his successor, Hans Schneider, the basic equipment for an excellent modern laboratory, the realization of which, however, still lay in the future.

In the autumn of 1963, when the materials from Kahl arrived in Munich, the Criminal Technical Division was still operating in the neglected, prisonlike building where it had started, 4 Türkenstrasse. Plans for a new building lay on Schneider's desk, but no one had any idea when construction would begin. Meanwhile, the laboratory was housed in cramped and scandalously shabby quarters, reminiscent of the laboratory in which Edmond Locard had begun in Lyons fifty years earlier.

Boxes and valuable apparatus for which there was no space in the rooms blocked the entrance hall. An antediluvian elevator groaned its way to the upper floors, where the same dirt and crowding prevailed. It was enough to discourage any but scientists who had a true passion for criminalistic work.

The medical-biological section, to which the specimens from Kahl were referred, consisted of two dreary lab rooms and a poky office. Here two scientists, Dr. Thoma and Dr. Röhm, along with a few laboratory technicians, struggled to keep up with an ever-growing burden of assignments. These were the conditions under which Dr. Röhm, having first determined the nature of the fiber traces on the adhesive tape samplings from Maria Flosky's hands, on October 2, 1963, began examining the materials from Kahl. The Frei method of micro-trace examination had been in use in Munich for several years. Steffen Berg had gone in person to Zurich to study Frei-Sulzer's system, and the Munich laboratory had made its own contributions to its further development. Röhm, despite his youth, had acquired considerable experience and technical skill in the use of the method, which called for extreme care. But with his heavy work load, interrupted by court appearances, it was the middle of October before he could report on his results.

Röhm had first examined both pairs of trousers for traces of paint, and quickly ascertained that it was the gray-green trousers Flittner must have worn on the day of the murder. Otherwise, the findings were disappointing. No matter how carefully he studied the scarf, he found no fibers clinging to it that corresponded with any fiber materials from Flittner's clothing. Conversely, no fiber traces from Flittner's suit could be found on a single item of the victim's clothing, nor did any fibers from Maria Flosky's clothes appear on any of the articles Flittner had worn. Informed of this, Degen began to feel gnawing doubts. Could it be that he was on the wrong track after all? Had his pursuit of Flittner been so much wasted effort?

In this moment of despair he learned for the first time of the existence of nail clippings from Maria Flosky, which had been kept at the Institute of Forensic Medicine in Würzburg. He immediately telephoned Würzburg and talked to Dr. Heinrichs there, with the result that Heinrichs examined the clippings for possible fibers. He was able to report tiny fiber traces in the right thumb nail and left ring finger nail. Degen pressed him to send the nails to Munich. He was hoping some of the fibers would prove to be from Flittner's clothing.

Eagerly, he awaited news from Röhm. But when it came, on October

18, it was only another disappointment. Röhm reported that the fibers under Maria Flosky's fingernails were not from Flittner's clothes. All of them, except for a blue-violet fiber, came from her own clothes. However, the blue-violet fiber was identical with fragments of fiber on the tape samplings from her hands. So far, Röhm said, he had only received Flittner's outer clothing. But the fibers looked very much as if they came from a shirt—possibly a colored cotton shirt. Would Flittner have necessarily worn his jacket while he committed the crime—presuming it was he? Or had it perhaps flown open? Maria Flosky's hands might have gripped her attacker's shirt. It would be profitable to have a look at the shirt Flittner had worn on the day of the crime, or else at all the shirts Flittner owned.

Next day Degen sent Detective Sergeant Rudingsdorfer to Flittner's home. Flittner had meanwhile decided that he was in good health again, and was back at work. But his wife gave Rudingsdorfer twenty-three different shirts; the shirt Flittner was wearing at the moment, she declared, had only been bought on September 11.

These shirts were on their way to Munich when Röhm for the first time uncovered a correspondence between the fibers from the dead woman's hands and Flittner's clothes. At 6:30 P.M. on October 25 Degen received a teletype message from Munich. It read: "In the tape sampling from the left palm is a textile fiber similar to the fibers in Anton Flittner's gray-green trousers." There was, however, a reservation: "Little evidential value can be ascribed to this correspondence, since fibers of this type are relatively common."

Nevertheless, this news was felt to be the first upswing in the case, the more so because it coincided with a surprising event in Kahl itself.

25

During the first three weeks of October the investigation in Kahl had proceeded methodically. Detectives Rohden and Beck had continued interviewing additional witnesses who had passed through the woods on September 11. As their routes were traced on the map, it became absolutely clear that there were only two paths by which the killer could have escaped unseen. These were, as has been stated, the two parallel paths running north to the Emmerichshofen-Alzenau paved road. In reviewing their data, the detectives again came upon the pensioner Otto Hock's account of an unknown bicyclist. That statement had been shelved because the time Hock gave, 3:30 P.M., was at least three quarters of an hour before the murder. Now, in reviewing the record, the detectives came upon the statement of another pensioner, a native of Kahl named Josef Herzog. Herzog had also taken a walk on September 11. At five o'clock he had been sitting on a bench in the southern part of the woods when Hock, on his way home, coming from the northerly direction, had joined him.

Rohden and Beck, who by this time knew the woods backwards and forwards, began to suspect that Hock might have erred by an hour in stating the time. Even granting that a man of sixty-eight would walk slowly, he could at most have taken half an hour from the spot where he saw the bicyclist to the bench where he met Herzog. Hence the cyclist would have passed him at four thirty, fifteen minutes after the murder. Rohden at once communicated this point to Degen, who instructed him to call on Hock without delay and check the question of the time. When Rohden went to see Hock on October 24, the old man promptly corrected his statements of September. He had since talked the matter over with Herzog, whose memory was better than his. But with his phlegmatic disposition it had not occurred to Hock to inform the police of his mistake.

At this point, Degen ceased to doubt that Flittner had used the time between four o'clock and five thirty to ride back into the woods from Krämer's stand. He was sure that Flittner had committed the murder and then fled north, returning to Kahl by way of the paved road. Yet when he recalled how stubbornly Flittner had denied having anything to do with the murder, he doubted whether there was any point in interrogating the man once more, unless he had more evidence than an old man's correction of a previous misstatement. Thus Röhm's cautious teletype message arrived just at the psychological moment; it overcame Degen's qualms and prompted him to take action.

October 26 was a Saturday, and for Flittner a day off. Degen asked the pensioner, Otto Hock, to sit beside the path where he had been resting on the day of the murder, to observe every passing cyclist, and to report later whether he recognized the cyclist of September 11. After noon Detective Sergeant Rudingsdorfer called on Flittner, waked him from what seemed a placid midday nap, and requested him to take his bicycle and accompany him. He himself mounted a bicycle and rode along with Flittner to the cottage of Flittner's foster parents. From there he pedaled along the path that Flittner claimed to have taken from Frischoss to the camping ground on September 11. They stopped awhile at the camping ground and then went on to the Krämer stand. Throughout the trip Flittner pedaled very slowly. Rudingsdorfer then took Flittner to Alzenau.

Degen was waiting there. About three thirty he, Rudingsdorfer, and Flittner cycled to the scene of the crime, and from there northward to the spot where Hock was waiting. Rudingsdorfer rode on ahead, with Flittner behind him and Degen following at some distance. After Rudingsdorfer and Flittner had passed Hock, Degen stopped to talk with the old fellow and asked whether he had recognized the cyclist he had seen on the day of the murder. Hock replied that the young man behind the first cyclist (Rudingsdorfer) certainly looked awfully like the man he had seen. He'd also been struck by the fact that the man said "Good afternoon" to him, although they were not acquainted. The cyclist of September 11 had likewise said "Good day."

On the paved road to Alzenau Degen caught up with Rudingsdorfer and Flittner, and began flinging questions at the suspect. Had he noticed the old man sitting beside the path? Why had he greeted him? Had he ever seen him before on the same spot? Perhaps on September 11, when he took the path after the murder? At any rate the old man remembered him and recalled clearly that Flittner had passed him at four thirty, fifteen minutes after the murder. That meant that he had not ridden straight home from the stand, but into the woods, that he had killed Maria Flosky and fled northward and returned home by way of the paved road.

Flittner submitted to the barrage of questions with lowered head, without replying. But his tongue kept licking out over his fleshy lower lip and his hands twisted the grips on the handle bars of his bicycle—until abruptly, without raising his eyes from the ground, he declared: "I must correct my statement. I did not ride directly home from the stand, but cycled once more along the camping ground and to the north."

Such was the dry official record of what he said, although undoubtedly he put this admission in different words. He added that it had been such a fine day that he was enjoying the ride and had decided not to bother going home for coffee. He had also passed an old man and greeted him, and had later ridden back by the paved road. But he had not passed by the scene of the crime. He had never seen Maria Flosky. He'd kept quiet about this ride because he was afraid of being suspected. He knew what it was like to be "in stir" and he didn't want to be back there. As he spoke, his dull eyes suddenly seemed so harried and frightened that his explanation sounded almost credible, and Degen had to fight off an impulse of momentary sympathy. As they reached Flittner's house, pedaling so slowly that they could barely keep the bicycles stable, Degen pointed out that their total time for the whole trip had been fifty-five minutes. There was still a time gap of at least half an hour.

On the strength of this, Degen had Flittner taken to headquarters in Alzenau, and immediately began an interrogation that went on until nearly eight o'clock at night. All his questions centered around that missing half hour. Could Flittner offer any other explanation than that he had spent the time at the spot where Maria Flosky had been killed? Flittner refused to change his story. He had cycled northward, but had seen nothing of the scene of the crime. Perhaps he'd stopped for a call of nature, perhaps he'd lingered here or there to look at the trees or the flowers. He hadn't had anything to do with the murder.

Throughout the interrogation Flittner had maintained his dulled expression, but it was obvious that he was inwardly alert. His tension relaxed only after he noticed that Degen was no longer having a record kept of the questioning. Degen took advantage of this moment to drop the whole matter of the murder and begin a personal conversation: on Flittner's circumstances, his past, his foster parents. After half an hour of this Degen had a surprise. Flittner's head drooped, he began to weep in a strange fashion and to whimper that he wouldn't go to the pen on account of an old woman. Besides, he couldn't confess to anything and bring shame on his foster mother. Then he declared he was exhausted. They must give him time. Maybe he would talk tomorrow.

Degen, familiar as he was with the surprising sentimental outbursts in emotionally deficient personalities, imagined that Flittner was approaching a collapse and would confess if avenues of hope seemed to be closed off. He therefore pronounced him under arrest, telling him that he would be brought before the examining magistrate the following day. But by the time Flittner appeared before District Judge Rauh on the morning of October 27, he had completely recovered his composure. In fact, he was defiant, insisting: "I had nothing to do with it. My conscience is clear!" and demanding a lawyer.

The court appointed Dr. Benno Imhoff of Aschaffenburg as counsel. After talking with his client, he demanded Flittner's release. Skillfully, he argued: What did half an hour's difference in time matter, given the uncertainties known to every court whenever witnesses were required to

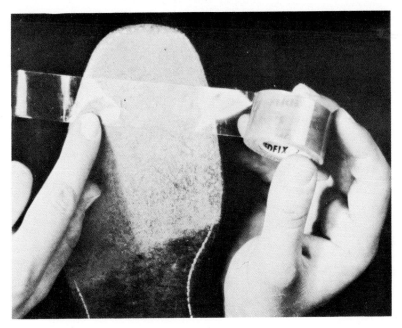

The adhesive tape method, one of the most important innovations in the technique of obtaining micro-trace evidence

ABOVE: Application of the tape to the shoe sole of a man suspected of theft in a jewelry workshop

Greatly magnified particles of a precious metal which clung to the thief's shoes when he entered the workshop

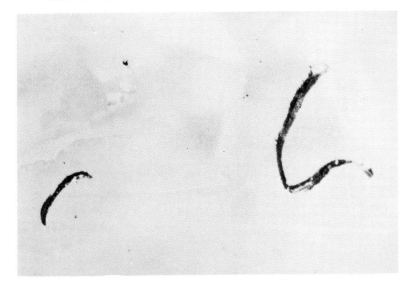

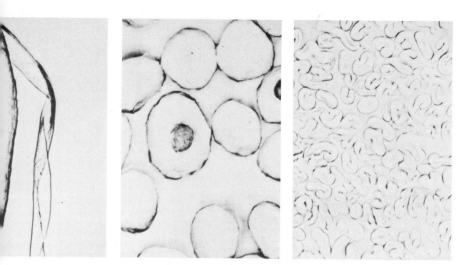

Criminalistic comparison of textile fibers encountered increasing difficulties with the development of synthetic fibers and the mass production of identical articles of clothing. Natural fibers such as wool and cotton (LEFT); cross-sections of wool and cotton (CENTER and RIGHT), greatly magnified

Synthetic fibers present a smooth surface and uniform round cross-section (LEFT and CENTER). RIGHT: rayon, a later development, with irregular cross-section

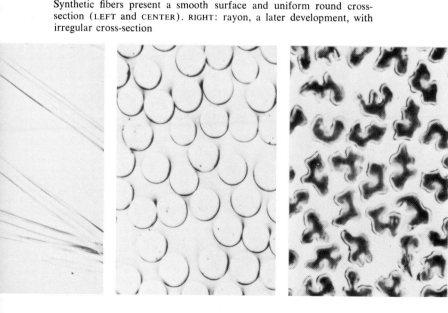

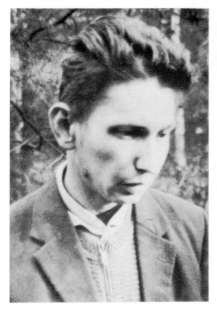

Anton Flittner

The basket at the scene of the crime

The victim's scarf

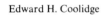

Pamela Mason

Edward H. Coolidge

The chemists Michael Hoffman and Maynard Pro of the U.S. Alcohol and Tobacco Tax Division laboratory in Washington (BOTTOM RIGHT) applied neutron activation analysis to hair clues in the Coolidge case

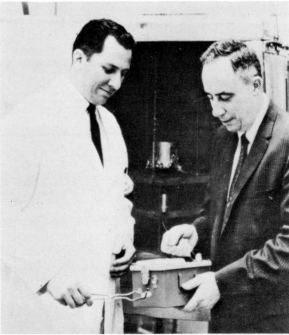

testify about times? Moreover, there was the matter of the scarf, which investigation had shown not to belong either to the murdered woman or to Flittner. Consequently, Flittner could not be the murderer. It was much more likely that the murderer had been some unknown camper who had used the scarf for gathering mushrooms.

Imhoff put the case for Flittner so persuasively that the magistrate expressed his doubts, but agreed to Degen's plea to hold the man for a few more days. Anxiously, Degen telephoned Munich, only to learn that the studies had provided no further incriminating evidence. Deeply disturbed, Degen hung up. Despite Imhoff's arguments, he could not rid himself of his sense of Flittner's guilt. In confronting Otto Hock with Flittner he had used up his only chance of corroborating his theory by a witness. He was also certain that Flittner had been close to the point of confession at the end of the previous night's interrogation, but that he would never confess once he was set at liberty.

Conscious that micro-trace evidence offered his last chance, Degen went to the scene of the crime on October 28 and again on October 30. There he tried to imagine all conceivable movements by the assaulter and the victim. Standing in the woods reconstructing the crime, he kept noticing a solitary fir tree which stood a short distance from the spot where Maria Flosky's body had lain. Was it conceivable that the victim had retreated to this tree before or during the struggle? Or could the murderer have touched the tree and left traces of his clothing on it? It was worth a try. Degen pasted adhesive tape on the tree up to the height of a man, removed the strips of tape, and sent them to Röhm. He was also thinking over the question of the scarf, from which Imhoff had drawn such good arguments for Flittner's release. Once more he pored over all the testimony, in particular the statement of the milliner who had noticed Maria Flosky leaving for the woods and had emphasized that she was not wearing a scarf. Suddenly Degen hit on a solution which, he realized to his horror, should have occurred to him before. Might not Maria Flosky have used the scarf to line her basket for the mushrooms she was going to pick? Would that be why no one had seen it? The murderer might have taken the scarf out of the victim's basket. After a series of telephone calls to some of the other detectives and to Röhm, the basket was dispatched to Munich for study. Perhaps the scarf had left some typical fiber fragments inside it.

Aware that he was now pressed for time, and that Flittner would soon be released unless he produced some tangible evidence, Degen himself went to Munich to stand by while the tests were going on. Early in November he at last received word that Röhm had discovered correspondences between fibers from Maria Flosky's hand and one of Flittner's shirts. But as yet, he warned, he could not present any definite conclusions. Finally, on November 4, came a message Degen had scarcely dared hope for. On the trunk of the fir tree, from which he had taken the surface samplings at his last visit to the woods, were fibers from that same shirt of Flittner's. Final results were promised for November 6.

After two days of almost unbearable suspense Degen at last received Röhm's definitive finding:

"1. On the adhesive tape samplings taken from Maria Flosky's palms are fragments of blue and blue-violet cotton fibers. These correspond to blue and blue-violet fibers in a blue and green checked shirt belonging to the suspect Flittner, and are indistinguishable from these fibers. 2. The tapes taken from the fir tree in the immediate vicinity of the scene of the crime contain fragments of light blue cotton fibers, and a fragment of a blue-violet cotton fiber. These fibers are indistinguishable from corresponding fiber traces on the victim's palms and from the fibers of the blue and green checked shirt belonging to the suspect. 3. On the inside of the basket are several white synthetic fibers. These fibers correspond in hue and quality to the fibers of the scarf. Furthermore, on the inner rim of the basket are a blue cotton fiber and a light ocher woolen fiber. Both fibers occur in the fabric of Flittner's sports jacket."

In speaking to Degen, who could barely contain his excitement, Röhm added that there were also black and colorless woolen fibers clinging to the trunk of the fir tree which were indistinguishable from corresponding fibers of Flittner's jacket, but that such fibers occurred so commonly in fabrics as to have only limited evidential value.

For all the caution with which these findings were expressed, they constituted an unequivocal confirmation of Degen's work and of his hunch—a confirmation by clues that no human eye could see unaided. On November 9 Mohr, Degen, and Rudingsdorfer went to Aschaffenburg, prepared to begin the decisive interrogations of Flittner. It seemed at first that Flittner would not yield an inch. He continued to insist that he had never set foot on the scene of the crime, had never seen Maria Flosky; if he had previously lied or been inaccurate about times, it was only because of his fear of the police. For hours the questions rained down upon him—until Degen abruptly cast the whole time question aside. How, he demanded, flinging his surprise information at the man, was Flittner going to explain that woolen and cotton fibers from his jacket, his shirt, and his trousers were found clinging to the murdered woman's hands? How could he explain that fibers of his jacket were in the basket? What had he been looking for in it? What had he taken out of it?

The transformation that these words wrought in Flittner took even these hardened detectives by surprise. Had he been unnerved by the unsuspected nemesis in a few fibers of cloth? Flittner abruptly declared his willingness to talk. His first admission was only a nod in response to a question: Had he met Maria Flosky on that afternoon of September 11? But that nod was the prelude to a complete disclosure. To be sure, it was days before his resistance entirely collapsed. On November 9 he was still offering an innocent version of what had happened on the fatal afternoon. His story was that he had ridden from the stand back to the woods, just to get a little air before supper. He had seen Maria Flosky looking for mushrooms. She had told him to "go about your business." At that, he said, he had come nearer, asserting that he could stay where he pleased. An argument took place. He shook her by the shoulders. Suddenly she fell to the ground. Fearing that she would complain about him to the police, he snatched the scarf that lay on the bottom of the basket and wound it around her neck. He did not want to kill her, only keep her from yelling. When he rode off on his bicycle, she was still alive. She must have rolled on the ground and tightened the scarf around her own neck, so that it choked her.

Some of the story agreed with Röhm's findings, but it was full of psychological discrepancies. The detectives kept after Flittner until the whole truth came out. He was taken to the scene of the crime to demonstrate exactly what had taken place. A female detective played the part of Maria Flosky. Every word was recorded on tape, every significant movement photographed. Though Flittner tried to play-act the incident, his memory was stronger than his histrionic abilities. Before the afternoon was over, the police had the truth—a truth that accorded in every detail with the results of the trace-evidence studies. Toward four o'clock Flittner had ridden into the woods in a state of sexual excitement. His eye caught Maria Flosky, who was bending over to pick a mushroom. As he parked his bicycle, she turned around and recognized by his look what his intentions were. She snapped at him to go away, and when he seized her she feebly tried to fend him off. He gripped her throat to silence her, and the string of pearls broke. But she continued to struggle, and retreated toward the fir tree. He brushed the trunk with his shirt sleeve, which had slid out of the sleeve of the jacket. In the course of the struggle they moved away from the tree again, until his victim fell to the ground beneath him, exclaiming in a faint voice: "What a pity for such a young man. You will think of me all your life." At that he squeezed her throat so hard that he heard a "cracking." Meanwhile he heard footsteps and started in fright. He saw the scarf in the basket and wound it around the dying woman's neck to conceal the marks of strangulation. For a moment there was silence. He unclasped the brooch to open the woman's dress. Then he heard footsteps approaching again. He jumped on his bicycle and rode off north to the paved road and then home.

Such was Flittner's confession on the afternoon of November 11, 1963. In May 1964 an Aschaffenburg jury convicted him and he was sentenced to life imprisonment. When Flittner disappeared into Straubing penitentiary, he left behind many questions concerning the uncertain boundaries of psychiatry and criminology. His case raised the problem, so far confused and utterly unsolved in the Federal Republic of Germany—and elsewhere in the world—of punishment after the crime or preventive custody of instinctual deviants. But such matters lie outside the realm of criminalistics, which in this case had shown what could be done with micro-trace evidence by a detective who could fit together a score of tiny details to apprehend a dangerous character.

26

As the solution of the Flosky case was approaching its end in 1963, reports came from across the Atlantic that seemed to open up new ways overnight for forensic chemistry and biology. The achievements recorded went far beyond anything that micro-trace work had hitherto accomplished or even hoped for. To many Europeans, less familiar than Americans and Canadians with the phenomenon of atomic energy, these reports at first sounded utterly fantastic. But they were not. Behind them stood the attempts to make the most menacing but most significant discovery of the twentieth century, atomic energy, applicable to criminalistics.

The event which was to call forth these attempts lay barely five years in the past. Its scene was Edmundston, a small town in the Canadian province of New Brunswick, on the St. John River, which separates New Brunswick from Maine.

May 13, 1958, was a day like any other for the small town of twelve thousand inhabitants. The mills of the Frazer Company pumped their wood pulp in thick pipes across the St. John River to Madawaska, the American border town, where the material was converted into paper. Whatever were the differences between the French-speaking Canadian community and the English-speaking American community, Edmundston and Madawaska were as closely linked as towns in such relationships always are. At five o'clock the sirens of the twin Frazer companies howled to announce the end of the working day. No one in Edmundston imagined that this prosaic, peaceful world was becoming the scene of a murder.

At four thirty Gaetane Bouchard, daughter of the well driller Wilfrid Bouchard, left her parents' home in Edmundston East. The sixteen-year-old laid her schoolbooks on the kitchen table, tucked the ten-dollar bill her mother had given her for shopping into the pocket of her light print dress, and set off gaily for the town's main thoroughfare, Victoria Street. A pony-tail of brown hair, a bit of white, already womanly neck, a dancing skirt, bare legs, and feet in blue suède slippers—that was the last her mother saw of Gaetane.

When Wilfrid Bouchard and his fifteen-year-old son Jean Guy returned from work at six o'clock, they waited in vain for Gaetane, who was always punctual about coming home at mealtimes. At seven thirty Bouchard began telephoning his daughter's girl friends. But no one had seen her after four thirty. Like most fathers, Bouchard was convinced that he had a well-behaved and innocent daughter. Her classmates knew her as vivacious and fond of a good time. But it seemed to Bouchard unthinkable that she had already been initiated to sex, for she never missed mass or a day at Cormier High School, helped her mother with housework, and in many respects had preserved a childlike disposition.

Nevertheless, her father must have had some misgivings, for between eight and nine o'clock he began phoning to Gaetane's girl friends to ask whether she had been seen with any men. After a while he heard about a twenty-year-old American from Madawaska who had played the saxophone at the Lido Dance Hall during the past year and had often taken Gaetane on dates in his car. His name was John Vollman. He crossed the river frequently these days, had been in Edmundston during the afternoon, and had picked up Blanche Arsenault and Marcelle Gaudreau at four o'clock and driven them home. At ten o'clock Bouchard took his car, drove over to Maine, and in spite of the lateness of the hour called on fishing tackle manufacturer John Jacob Vollman in his home. From the surprised father he learned that young Vollman had in fact played the saxophone in Edmundston last year but was now working for the *St. John Valley Times* in Madawaska. He was on night duty in the printing plant this evening. Besides, he was marrying Geneva Girard, a bookkeeper; the wedding date was only a few days away. Bouchard nevertheless drove on to the building of the *St. John Valley Times*. He found John Vollman an engaging young man with curly dark hair and a tanned face, who readily admitted that he had known Gaetane. But he had not seen her for months, he said. It was correct that he had been in Edmundston during the afternoon. He had called on the Chief of Police in connection with a counterfeiting affair and had then driven home a couple of the girls he knew from dances in Lido Hall. He had not met Gaetane and had returned to Madawaska by six o'clock.

Bouchard drove back home. Gaetane had not returned. About eleven thirty Bouchard called the Edmundston detachment of the Royal Canadian Mounted Police, whose Constable Latour at once put through a message to the patrol cars. Unable to rest, Bouchard and his son Jean Guy, along with a friendly neighbor, Stanley Gauthier, drove all over town. When this cruising proved fruitless Charles Emile, Gauthier's son, told his father about some of the places where Edmundston couples parked their cars to pursue their more or less advanced petting. Toward one o'clock in the morning Charles Emile led the small column to an abandoned gravel pit on Boucher Office Road, which was a favorite haunt of lovers.

When they got there, the pit lay in total darkness. There was nothing to be seen, not even the muted interior light of a car. But Bouchard was in so desperate a mood by now that he insisted on searching this apparently deserted area. By the light of two flashlights they stumbled among the stunted pines. After a while Jean Guy Bouchard felt something underfoot. When the cone of light fell upon it, he recognized his sister's blue suède slipper. Only a step away lay a second slipper, and seconds later the light caught an unevenness in the ground. Face down on the gravel lay the figure of a girl in a bright print dress. Bouchard did not need to see her face to know who lay there. He placed his right hand on the back of her leg and felt the chill of death.

Constable J. A. B. Latour heard the news as he was cruising along a street in Edmundston East, and roared to Boucher Office Road. A short time later other police cars arrived. Sergeant J. R. LaPointe, head of the Royal Canadian Mounted Police detachment, informed the RCMP

Crime Detection Division in Fredericton, 128 miles away, and routed out an Edmundston physician, Dr. J. B. Gaudreau. RCMP officials arrived in rapid succession: Constable Ralph Esau, Corporal J. R. Quintal, Constables Robicheau and Frank Fedor from the Identification Service in Campbellton. By the light of automobile headlights, Gaudreau knelt beside the girl. He was only a general practitioner and contented himself with the observations he could make on the spot: bruises and contusions of the left eye, lower lip, and skin of the bare legs. He had the impression that Gaetane had been dragged over the rough ground. She had died from a sizable number of stab wounds in the chest and back. Twenty-five feet away Constable Esau discovered a large dark spot where blood had trickled into the gravel, and the tire prints of a car. Apparently Gaetane had been killed beside the car and afterward dragged off to one side before the murderer left the gravel pit. Although the automobile tires had made scarcely any imprint in the hard ground, Esau tried to take a cast of the track. As he was doing this, he noticed two tiny, green particles: splinters of paint from a car. One was barely larger than the head of a pin, the other somewhat bigger and heart-shaped. Apparently both particles had been knocked off when the wheels of the car kicked up stones.

While one car took the dead girl to Edmundston, Sergeant LaPointe asked Wilfrid Bouchard about his daughter's habits, noted the addresses of her girl friends, and asked about boy friends. Bouchard denied that she had had such "boy friends." Since LaPointe had fewer illusions about the love lives of teen-agers, he discounted this point. He did not press the issue, however, for Bouchard, he could see, was at the limit of his endurance. Consequently he did not hear about Bouchard's nocturnal visit to Madawaska and John Vollman.

At dawn LaPointe and his men set out to trace Gaetane Bouchard's movements. Edmundston seemed too small for a pretty girl to vanish from sight on the way to Victoria Street in the afternoon. The constables questioned Jacqueline Dumont and Joan Fyffe, two classmates who had strolled with Gaetane after school ended at 3:30 P.M. They had promptly gone to Soucy's Restaurant on Victoria Street for a soda. A waitress with the high-flown name of Jeanne d'Arc Asselin had sold Gaetane two bars of milk chocolate. Gaetane had then walked home, said good-by to Joan Fyffe at four thirty, stayed briefly at home, and returned to the center of town. Here there was a gap. Gaetane had been seen again at five o'clock, once more in front of Soucy's. Weeda Martin,

411

who worked in a drugstore just across the street, said she had noticed Gaetane there. The girl therefore must have reached Victoria Street before disappearing.

Toward nine o'clock LaPointe received a report from Dr. J. F. Harrigan, who likewise was not a forensic physician but who conducted the autopsies in the Edmundston area. He had found nine stab wounds, one directly into the heart. Partly digested chocolate in the stomach led him to the conclusion that Gaetane had died within three hours of the time when she had eaten the chocolate. Since she had bought chocolate at four o'clock, she must have been killed between four and seven. Aside from scratches on her thighs, Harrigan had found no indications of a sexual assault. If the murderer had attempted one, he had not carried it out. Medically, Gaetane was still a "virgin."

By this time news of the murder had spread, and the first volunteer witnesses called at RCMP headquarters. Among them was Marcel Bosse, a farmer from St. Joseph. He had been sitting in his car on the Soucy's Restaurant side of Victoria Street at five o'clock. He knew Gaetane by sight and had noticed her about to cross the street in front of his car with a girl friend. A light green Pontiac came up from behind, and the girls stopped to let it pass. The driver slowed down, however, and called out something like, "Do you want a ride?" When they answered "No," he drove on. Bosse also drove on. He noticed Gaetane a second time at the corner of Victoria and George Streets. This time she was alone. Bosse recalled the time precisely because shortly afterward the Frazer Company sirens went off, as they did every day at five o'clock. The driver of the green Pontiac was a young man with dark, curly hair and tanned face, he said. His car bore a yellow license plate from Maine, across the river. Asked whether he would recognize the driver again, Bosse replied that he thought he would.

Soon afterward a girl confirmed the farmer's statements. Jo Ann Gilbert, a seventeen-year-old who knew Gaetane from high school, had been out in her father's car shortly after four o'clock. As she was about to turn into Victoria Street Extension at five o'clock, she noticed a green Pontiac, and Gaetane in the front seat beside the driver. She had not been able to recognize the driver. A few minutes later another witness, Paul Emile Levesque, had likewise driven down Victoria Street Extension and noticed a green Pontiac, probably a 1952 model, with a yellow license plate, whose driver signaled a turn. The car had turned into Boucher Office Road. There was a girl sitting beside the driver. Finally still another witness appeared: Willard Martyn. He had been driving along Boucher Office Road with his children between five and six o'clock.

The children wanted to skip pebbles over the pond at the gravel pit. But at the entrance to the gravel pit he had noticed a light green car. Since he knew that the pit was a favorite spot for "parking," he drove on. Twenty minutes later, on his way back, he saw the car still there. He did not see anyone in it.

The statements fitted into a pattern. They indicated that Gaetane Bouchard, instead of going shopping, had ridden off with an unknown man, probably an American, to a place whose significance as a trysting place she undoubtedly knew. Most remarkable of all was the correspondence between all the references to a light green American Pontiac and the splinters of light green paint that Constable Esau had found.

As soon as Sergeant W C. Hetherington of the Crime Investigation Division in Fredericton arrived in Edmundston, he got in touch with the Maine State Police. Madawaska is in Aroostook County, and the chief of the criminal investigation division of the State Police was Otis N. Labree in Houlton. Labree promised to look into the matter of who owned light green Pontiacs, with the help, possibly, of local secondhand car dealers.

Hetherington then studied the autopsy report. It did not satisfy him. Sex crimes did not necessarily lead to anatomical injuries, and without a laboratory study no definite conclusions would be possible. Even if the studies proved negative, that would not be the final word. Teen-agers had a special relationship with the world of sex, a fact which the French, long before the notion of "teen-ager" had been coined, had recognized in the word *demi-vierge*. There was that half-instinctive play with the preliminaries of sex and a whole host of one-sided and mutual practices of arousal up to a point—the point being preservation of the anatomical badge of purity, the hymen. That curb remained as a relic of middle-class morality. In the natural curiosity of youth Gaetane might well have done nothing more than "play" with the murderer—never suspecting that in an uninhibited escort she might awaken forces or abnormalities which could not be restrained. Hetherington therefore ordered the body to be sent to Fredericton, where Dr. D. F. Brunsdon could examine it more carefully.

The dead girl was taken by car to Fredericton about noon, while Hetherington and LaPointe together continued to explore the matter further on the local level. LaPointe had another talk with Gaetane's girl friends Blanche Arsenault and Marcelle Gaudreau. He asked whether they could imagine Gaetane's getting into a car with a complete stranger, or whether they knew of any American she had been acquainted with. Only now did LaPointe hear that there was such an American, and that his name was John Vollman. In fact LaPointe himself knew Vollman as a reporter of the *St. John Valley Times* and also as Deputy Director of Civil Defense in Madawaska—in which capacity he had gone around giving talks at schools and meetings. It was hard for LaPointe to imagine Vollman as a potential murderer. Nevertheless he questioned Blanche and Marcelle more closely about the young man. He learned that Vollman had driven by as the two of them left Soucy's Restaurant at four o'clock. He had stopped and offered to drive them home. Once there, however, he had tried to coax them to take a ride out into the country with him. Both had refused because they had heard from other girls who had gone for rides with "Johnny" that he was "hard to put the brakes on" when it came to the above-mentioned "point." The two girls also described the car—an oldish light green Pontiac.

Though LaPointe still felt many reservations, after these statements he and Hetherington could not help regarding Vollman as a prime suspect. Nevertheless, the reservations remained, especially after LaPointe telephoned the *St. John Valley Times* and learned that Vollman was making preparations for his wedding. Of course the impending wedding need not necessarily have stopped the young man from seeking a last bachelor's fling. Also, however, proceeding against an American citizen involved complications which only powerful incriminating evidence could justify.

A little later Otis N. Labree telephoned to say that a car dealer in Van Buren had sold a green 1952 Pontiac on April 23 to a twenty-year-old boy from Madawaska, John Vollman. At that Hetherington and LaPointe proposed a meeting with Labree in Madawaska.

Toward three thirty the Canadians drove up to the building of the *St. John Valley Times.* Vollman's Pontiac was parked on the street. While they waited for Labree, Constable Esau inspected the car. Before long they discovered a newly chipped place on the rocker panel under the right front door. The heart-shaped particle of paint fitted precisely into this chip. This was so impressive that Hetherington and LaPointe discarded a considerable portion of their reservations. Labree, who arrived shortly afterward, was equally impressed. The combined authorities called on Vollman and told him bluntly that they had business with him. Vollman's immature, boyish face paled slightly when Labree ex-

414

plained that the Canadians wanted to ask him a few questions about the violent death of a girl named Gaetane Bouchard. He would be well advised to answer the questions, Labree said.

Vollman replied that he was afraid he couldn't tell them much. He'd been feverish and sick for days, had taken a sedative, and his mind wasn't very clear. He had met Gaetane Bouchard at the Lido and gone dancing with her in Edmundston, but had not seen her for weeks. As a matter of fact, he'd told all this to Gaetane's father last night.

Very well, Labree said, but there were witnesses in Edmundston who said they had seen him yesterday afternoon when he stopped on Victoria Street in his green Pontiac and invited Gaetane to ride with him. And there were other witnesses who had seen Gaetane in a light green Pontiac with yellow and black license plates. The Canadian officers would like to know more about his activities in Edmundston yesterday.

Vollman replied that he had used the morning for collecting advertising copy that was to go in the paper. Right after lunch he had driven to Edmundston for information on a counterfeiting story, then returned to Madawaska because he had to deliver a talk on civil defense, and subsequently had driven back to Edmundston. He gathered more information and was on his way home when two girls he knew from the Lido, Blanche Arsenault and another, waved to him and asked him to drive them home. He had done so, although he could feel his fever rising. Immediately afterward, at four thirty, he had returned to Madawaska, gone to bed for a while, and later reported for night duty, which lasted until six thirty in the morning. He had had practically no sleep and could scarcely stay on his feet. He had not seen Gaetane, and if anyone had seen him with her, that person must have mistaken someone else for him. As for the Pontiac, everybody knew how many light green Pontiacs there were around. Even the Chief of Police in Edmundston drove one that resembled his own to a T.

That was true, Labree said, but the chief's car had Canadian plates. Besides, the Canadian detectives had found splinters of green automobile paint, and one splinter fitted exactly into a damaged spot on John's Pontiac, which raised certain suspicions. The best way to dispel those suspicions was to let the Canadians examine his car. It would be well for him to do so voluntarily, before measures were taken to force him to turn the car over to them.

Vollman hesitated until Labree once more explained that if he had nothing to do with Gaetane's murder he had nothing to fear; it would be best for him to co-operate. Still hesitant, Vollman finally handed

Labree the car keys. Labree passed them on to Corporal Esau, who drove the Pontiac to the Edmundston firehouse for a closer examination.

Hetherington meanwhile went on to say that they had not come to make hasty accusations. He was certain that the murderer must have got blood on his clothes. The simplest way for Vollman to dispel all possible charges was to show him the clothes he had worn yesterday in Edmundston.

Vollman answered, surprisingly, that he was so dazed now he could no longer remember which suit he had worn.

Labree asked if he were serious. When Vollman said he was, Labree suggested, with unmistakable signs of distrust, that they drive to Vollman's home and that he show the Canadians all his clothes. Vollman replied that he couldn't just walk off his job, and yielded only when Labree once again warned that it would be better for him not to wait for legal measures to be taken.

Labree, Hetherington, LaPointe, and Vollman proceeded to Vollman's home and searched the young man's clothes closet. Vollman repeated that he no longer knew which clothes he had worn. He was still seeing everything in a haze. Since there were no signs of bloodstains on any of the suits, Labree and the Canadians left the house and were making for Labree's car when Hetherington suddenly stopped and went over to the household trash burner. When he lifted the lid, he saw the charred remains of freshly and by no means completely burned clothes. Were these the clothes that Vollman had worn on the preceding day and burned after the murder?

Undoubtedly this was a crucial moment. Vollman denied having had anything to do with the burned clothes. But the tone of Labree's questions indicated that he no longer believed in his fellow American's innocence. He gathered up the burned remains, and when Vollman proved unable to recall any witness who could confirm his claim that he had returned home by 4:30 P.M. the day before, Labree ordered him to come to the Madawaska police station with the Canadian detectives. There they found a report from Fedor and Esau to the effect that the light green particles of paint correspond microscopically with the chipped part of Vollman's car, and that the glove compartment held a bar of chocolate, Caramilk, bitten into and smeared with lipstick. Hetherington, more and more convinced that Vollman was the culprit, proposed that they get hold of the farmer, Bosse, who had said he would recognize the driver of the green Pontiac. Labree agreed. It took until late afternoon before Bosse was located, but when he was confronted with

Vollman he declared without hesitation that this was the fellow who had called out to Gaetane on Victoria Street in Edmundston.

That recognition practically decided Vollman's fate for the present. After negotiations and a flurry of telephone calls, he was taken that evening to the Canadian jail of Madawaska County. At the same time Hetherington received word from Fredericton that Dr. Brunsdon had performed the requested second autopsy of Gaetane Bouchard. He too had found no indications of sexual intercourse—but Corporal Gongas, the identification service official of the Royal Canadian Mounted Police who as a matter of routine attended all autopsies, had made a discovery. While taking the fingerprints he had found clenched in Gaetane Bouchard's right hand a single hair two and a half inches long that possibly came from the murderer rather than the dead girl herself.

Gongas proposed that samples of hair be obtained from Vollman's head and sent to the RCMP laboratory in Sackville. Hetherington and LaPointe received this information with the elation of detectives who see before them prospects of further and perhaps decisive evidence. Early in the morning of May 15 Vollman was asked whether he would provide a sample strand of hair. Either he was really suffering from loss of memory, or malingering. With pronounced indifference he let samples be cut from his head, which were taken that afternoon by Corporal Quintal to Sackville. There he met Gongas, who already had samples of the victim's hair and the single hair found in her fingers. They entrusted this material to Rolande Andrée Rouen, the laboratory chemist— neither of the detectives then suspecting that they were contributing to a development of extraordinary importance.

27

Fifty years had passed since the murder of Germaine Bichon, in which interval continuous efforts had been made to refine criminalistic hair analysis. Between the two world wars, criminal investigators on both sides of the Atlantic had increasingly relied upon results of hair studies. The applications extended from murder to theft, from sex crimes to traffic accidents. In the latter, for example, the hairs of a killed or injured victim frequently clung to the vehicles of hit-and-run drivers. All in all, a good deal of progress had been made in the field since 1909.

In 1931 John Glaister, an English forensic scientist who worked in Cairo, had published his *Study of Hairs and Wools Belonging to the Mammalian Group of Animals, Including a Special Study of Human Hair, Considered from the Medico-legal Aspect.* The seventeen hundred photomicrographs printed in this book revealed the structure of hair in man and other mammals to an extent hitherto impossible. Another monumental work was published in 1938, Theodor Lochte's *Atlas der menschlichen und tierischen Haare* ("Atlas of Human and Animal Hair"). Lochte, who had worked as a forensic scientist in Göttingen until 1934, developed the first method for "de-aerating" hair, that is, for removing the air content in the medulla which interfered with precise examination. He used a low-pressure chamber in which the vacuum released the disturbing air. The Lochte method was complicated, but it prepared the way for simpler procedures developed after the Second World War. The simplest of all was devised by Otto Martin in Wiesbaden. He found that wetting agents used in the textile industry for treating textile fibers had the ability to penetrate swiftly into hair and displace the trapped air.

About the same time new techniques were developed for making the cuticle more visible. In 1930 the German scientist Schröder devised a method for using photographic plates in whose gelatin the hair was embedded, to make highly accurate casts which could be used for microscopic examination. In 1937 Alan R. Moritz, a young American forensic scientist, arrived at an even simpler procedure. He brushed a thin layer of fingernail polish, mixed with amyl acetate, on a slide and placed a tautly stretched hair into it. Within ten minutes the layer of polish dried and the hair could be removed. The remaining impression provided photographs of a precision hitherto unattainable by direct microscopic observation of the hair cuticle.

Procedures were likewise being developed for preparing and photomicrographing fine cross sections of hairs. In 1935 the American scientist Kneberg embedded hairs in fish gelatin and by using a microtome produced sections of incredible thinness. In 1957 Boller employed sheets of celluloid for embedding the hairs. During these same years electron microscopes were used to determine hitherto unknown aspects of the fine structure of hair.

Thus there had been great strides in the technical basis for such studies since the days of Victor Balthazard. The problem of distinguishing animal from human hair had become a routine matter by the middle of the twentieth century. But distinguishing among human hairs was another matter. Improved techniques of cuticle observation demonstrated that the patterns of the cuticle, which had originally appeared so uniform, were variable, but these variations remained minor and were hard to define. As for color, it was now possible to distinguish between a diffuse, evenly distributed pigment that conferred a general look of blondness and darker pigments which produced shades up to black. The latter pigments were present in the form of granules and arranged in a very definite way. Otto Martin pointed out a third type of pigment which he called "freckles." These spots of pigment were larger than the granules and had special shades of their own.

Finally, studies of cross sections of hair had provided much new information. Contrary to the older theory that smooth, stiff hairs were generally round and curly hairs oval, it was now known that smooth hairs, too, could have oval cross sections, whereas naturally wavy hair was never round. Distinct differences also existed among the human races in the cross-sectional characteristics of their hair. But—unfortunately from the point of view of forensic scientists—the hair of the same individual was subject to far greater diversity than had been assumed in 1909. Aside from the differences in head hair, the other body hairs of individuals were by no means uniform. Only 60 per cent of pubic hair agreed in color with the head hair of its possessor. About 45 per cent of armpit hair showed a reddish coloration, irrespective of the color of the head hair. Such variations left most specialists in hair analysis with the uneasy feeling that in spite of technical advances they were not really much better off than their predecessors in 1909. It was not yet possible to say with certainty that a hair found at the scene of a crime came from a specific individual. Even if a sizable quantity of hair was available, the scientists could in most cases speak only of a "probability," rarely of a "certainty."

Nevertheless the hope that new methods would be devised had not faded. When Paul Kirk published the first edition of his *Crime Investigation* in 1953, he wrote:

"That hair is actually characteristic of the individual is very probable since, if it were not, it would be the exception to the general rule of biological individuality. It therefore merits the most careful and extensive investigation aimed at fulfilling the tremendous possibilities that it presents in this direction. . . . Simple and rapid methods capable of producing decisive results in this field may be possible, but not without much more extensive and thorough research investigation. . . . It seems safe to predict that such efforts might well be rewarded ultimately with one of the most valuable sets of techniques for establishing personal identification, . . . as fingerprints are at present."

The chief constituents of hair are carbon, nitrogen, hydrogen, oxygen, phosphorus, and sulfur. But Kirk foresaw the possibility of using the trace elements, of which only the tiniest quantities are present in hair, for identification.

"The *minor constituents* of hair [he wrote] have received only limited attention and it is possible that these may lead to considerable advance from the standpoint of criminal investigation. . . . The intake of arsenic, lead, silica, and other minor constituents which are regularly detected in hair is certainly variable and to some extent a function of the occupation, diet, and medication of the individual. Thus these constituents might be expected to vary accordingly and to be useful in determining the source of a hair, provided that sensitive enough methods for the analysis can be developed and applied without destruction of a prohibitively large amount of available evidence."

Rolande Andrée Rouen, the chemist at the RCMP laboratory in Sackville, who on May 15 took over examination of the hair samples in the Bouchard case, as yet had no thought of such possibilities. She was not too well acquainted with the field of hair analysis. She therefore turned to the RCMP laboratory in Ottawa, where Constable Francis M. Kerr (a scientifically trained young officer) was engaged in hair and fiber studies. A few days later the samples of hair were dispatched to Ottawa.

28

In 1952, six years before the Bouchard affair, a young man of twenty-five joined the group of Canadian scientists working at the atomic laboratories of Chalk River, northwest of Ottawa. The Chalk River complex was established in the same year that the American atom bomb fell upon Hiroshima. But from the start the plant at Chalk River was destined for scientific and industrial, not military, purposes. Atomic Energy of Canada, a federal atomic authority, set up two reactors using natural uranium and assembled several hundred scientists and technicians for research into chemical, physical, metallurgical, biological, and medical problems.

The young man who came to Chalk River in 1952 was Robert E. Jervis. Born in Toronto in 1927, he had studied chemistry and physics at the university of his native city. In the course of his work he came upon publications dealing with the application of atomic radiation to the detection of extremely small quantities of trace elements in chemical, biological, or metallic substances. As early as 1936 G. Hevesy and A. Levi in Denmark had undertaken the first experiments to show the presence of trace elements, which could not be detected spectrographically, by making them artificially radioactive. After the Second World War this type of detection developed at an accelerated pace under the shadow of the atom bomb. It was called neutron activation analysis, and its underlying principle appeared to be fundamentally simple. Many of the familiar chemical elements, from beryllium and sodium to iron and zinc, that are not radioactive in the natural state can be transformed into radioactive elements if they are bombarded with neutrons. Each of these nonradioactive elements can, when made radioactive by bombardment, be distinguished by the type and quality of the radiation it emits.

Radioactivity can occur in three different forms. There is alpha and beta radiation, emission of particles in the most literal sense, consisting of disintegration products of atomic nuclei. Beta particles possess varying degrees of energy, which is expressed by their speed; they can reach speeds up to two thirds the speed of light. Particles of alpha radiation, on the other hand, are relatively slow, averaging only a hundredth of such speeds. Finally there is the third type of radiation, called gamma radiation. It is a "hard" electromagnetic radiation a thousand times more penetrating than ordinary X-rays. In contrast to the particle radiation, which is measured by the number of emitted particles and their velocity, gamma rays are measured by intensity and frequency.

In the attempts to determine the nature of trace elements by observation and measurement of their beta radiation, an important unit of measure was the familiar "half-life." This is the time in which half the radioactive atoms of an element disintegrate. It differs for all elements—for some amounting to seconds, for others minutes, hours, days, months, or years. Arsenic has a half-life of 26½ hours; calcium, of 164 days. The characteristic half-lives provide a means for identifying unknown trace elements. Since beta radiation can be measured with the aid of Geiger counters and other instruments, a feasible approach seemed to be to place materials to be investigated for trace elements in a nuclear reactor in which neutrons are produced by the disintegration of uranium. After the materials have been subjected for varying periods of time to the neutron flux, as it is called, and made radioactive, the nature of their trace elements can be determined by measurements. The beta radiations of the materials are repeatedly measured at intervals in order to determine, from their diminution or disappearance, the rate of disintegration of the activated elements. Their identity can be established from their half-lives.

There are difficulties in this procedure, for strongly radiating elements, such as sodium, tend to cover up weaker radiations. In such cases it is necessary to treat the material for investigation with chemicals which expunge the strongly radiating elements, thus removing their disturbing effect. Such treatment, however, necessarily destroys to some degree the material for examination.

When Jervis read these early reports, neutron activation analysis was only in its beginnings. In 1951 Taylor, Havens, and Anderson had just started employing gamma radiation for the analysis of trace elements. The peaks which appeared in the curves when the intensity and frequency of the radiation were measured reached different heights in different positions for specific elements. In this way the presence of the trace elements could be determined. Measurement of the gamma rays at intervals also permitted determination of the half-lives, since the decay of the radioactive isotopes was also expressed in the strength of their gamma radiation. By comparison with the radiation of known quantities of trace elements the quantity could thus be arrived at.

The whole "state of the art" was in active evolution. Henri Griffon, head of the toxicological laboratories of the Prefecture of Police, in Paris, was the first to utilize the novel method of analysis for criminalistic studies of poisons. This was in 1951. It had long been a toxicological axiom that in cases of arsenic poisoning arsenic tends to concentrate in the victim's hair. Frequently, the beginning and duration of poison intake can be determined from the length of hair segments containing arsenic. Since it was assumed that normal hair also contains small quantities of arsenic, it was important for toxicologists to measure the normal quantity in order to know what amounts of arsenic would indicate poisoning. Because the "normal" amounts are so minute, Griffon tried neutron activation analysis to determine them. He placed samples of hair in plastic containers and bombarded them for varying lengths of time in a nuclear reactor. Along with the samples he placed precisely weighed quantities of arsenic in the neutron flux of the same reaction. After eliminating the disturbing sodium radiation by chemically removing the sodium from the hair samples, he succeeded in detecting the trace arsenic and measuring its quantity. At first he employed only the beta radiation, identifying the arsenic by its half-life. If within 26½ hours, the half-life of arsenic, the radiation diminished by half, arsenic was present. Comparing the measured radiation with the radiation of the arsenic sample of known quantity, he could arrive at the quantity of arsenic in the sample hairs. If, for example, the counter showed 1000 "clicks" for the known quantity of arsenic, but 1500 for the sample hairs, the quantity of arsenic in the hair must be one and a half times as large as the known quantity.

When Dr. Robert E. Jervis joined the team in Chalk River, he found the development of neutron activation analysis in full swing. A multitude of possibilities were still open. There were innumerable substances used in chemistry and technology whose trace elements it was important to determine. Biologists and medical researchers were interested in the part played by trace elements in the metabolism of healthy and sick human beings. Under the direction of Dr. W. M. Campbell, Chalk River carried on a highly variegated neutron activation research program, in which Jervis participated. But he was already much interested in the work of Griffon and of H. W. Smith and J. M. A. Lenihan in Glasgow on criminalistic applications of this new method. In 1955 an inquiry from the director of the Royal Canadian Mounted Police laboratory in Ottawa provided the first impulse toward practical applications to criminalistics. Superintendent James Churchman of the RCMP had heard of the Glasgow experiments of Dr. Smith and Dr. Lenihan and asked Chalk River to check five cases in which attempted murder by arsenic were suspected. By experiments on many samples of hair Jervis and his assistant Alma Crowder established that the normal arsenic content of hair ranged from 0 to 2.5 ppm (parts per million). Less than 2 per cent of normal hair showed more than 3 ppm. On the basis of these findings, Jervis found that in three of the cases presented to him by the RCMP the hair contained five to ten times the normal content of arsenic and thus unequivocally indicated poisoning. But these studies only led him into the field of research to which he subsequently devoted so much time—in the beginning, only his leisure hours. For in the course of the arsenic tests he found that there were many other trace elements in hair, whose presence had hitherto gone unsuspected. Having learned from the police officers of the difficulties involved in microscopic comparison of hair, he hit on the idea that NAA (neutron activation analysis) might be crucially important for such comparisons. Like Kirk, he proceeded from the assumption that the kind, number, and quantity of trace elements in human hair would differ from person to person, because nourishment, environment, constitution, and hereditary factors were likewise different. Might not the trace-element pattern in each human hair be typical of the hair from a given individual, and different from the hair of every other individual?

In October 1956 Jervis for the first time presented his ideas and experiments to a conference of the Forensic Society of Canada. His lecture aroused the interest of other Royal Canadian Mounted Police officials. They pressed Campbell and Jervis to continue the experiments, and at Campbell's suggestion an agreement was reached for the laboratory in Ottawa to send one of its scientific associates to Chalk River, to study the NAA technique under Jervis' direction, and to aid Jervis in carrying out extensive hair experiments. The choice fell upon Francis M. Kerr, who like Jervis had studied in Toronto. In 1957 Kerr came to Chalk River for several months, and a regular program for the detection of trace elements in hair was initiated. In addition to Jervis, Kerr, and Alma Crowder, an older nuclear chemist who had studied in Glasgow, William Mackintosh, participated. By gamma ray measurements such additional trace elements as zinc and bromine, in addition to arsenic, sodium, and copper, were found in hair. They seemed to appear in different combinations and different proportions in individuals.

The work in Chalk River had progressed to this point when Francis M. Kerr, who meanwhile had returned to Ottawa, received the hair of the Bouchard case from Sackville in May 1958. At first he analyzed the hairs by the usual microscopic procedures. Later he was to write: "In this particular case sufficiently large samples of the known hairs were available to the examiner, but only one hair was available from the scene of the crime. The two known samples (from different individuals) were sufficiently alike (and indeed were similar in all but a very few microscopic characteristics), that the examiner's task was extremely difficult."

In fact, the comparison of the single hair weighing about one milligram that had been found in Gaetane Bouchard's hand provided all possible difficulties which could arise in microscopic hair studies. Kerr took his samples to Regina to have them examined in the RCMP laboratory there. In the course of June the laboratory finally concluded that the single hair could not belong to Gaetane Bouchard, but *might* have come from John Vollman. The few characteristics which supported this were so difficult to establish that Kerr asked Inspector Mason-Rooke to check the microscopic findings by neutron activation analysis of the trace elements. Since there were no precedents for criminalistic hair investigation of this sort, Inspector Mason-Rooke first took up the matter with the prosecutor in the Vollman case, Albany M. Robichaud, to have the procedure approved.

Developments in the Vollman affair meanwhile made the prosecutor's affirmative reply a foregone conclusion. Since May 14 the investigation had made virtually no progress. On the afternoon that Corporal Gongas found the single hair clutched in the victim's hand, Dr. Brunsdon had determined that the nine stab wounds in Gaetane Bouchard's chest and back were caused by a sharp instrument, perhaps a hunting knife, which had not been driven in up to the hilt. Hetherington and LaPointe had made every imaginable effort to find the murder weapon. They even located a witness, Lawrence Boutol, a casual friend of Vollman's who had ridden in the suspect's Pontiac two weeks before the murder, and had noticed a large hunting knife in the glove compartment. But this was the sole reference to any such weapon. It had disappeared and could not be found. The work of Rolande Rouen in Sackville showed that the splinters of paint from the scene of the crime were identical in chemical and physical constituents with the paint of Vollman's Pontiac. But there always remained the possibility that the splinters had come from another car of the same color. Unfortunately, no damaged spot on Vollman's Pontiac could be found into which the second splinter of green paint fitted. According to the chemist's analysis, the red color on the bar of chocolate came from lipstick, but there was no proof that the lipstick was Gaetane Bouchard's. There were too many lipsticks of the same type. Since, oddly enough, no search had been made for micro-fiber clues, this important area was excluded from the case. The prints of the tire tracks from the gravel pit were worthless, since they did not show enough characteristic peculiarities to permit identification with the worn tires of Vollman's car. Finally, every attempt to discover what clothing Vollman had worn on May 13 failed. To Hetherington and LaPointe, it was plain that Vollman had burned his clothes, but they had no proof. Blanche Arsenault and Marcelle Gaudreau, the girls whom Vollman had driven home, could not recall definitely what he was wearing, and the farmer, Bosse, had noticed Vollman's face, not his clothes.

As the days passed, Vollman retreated more and more behind that curious failure of memory he had first shown on May 14. He contended that the police action against him had sent him into a state of psychic shock, and drew attention to the fact that he was highly unstable and had been under psychiatric observation during his service in the U. S. Air Force. In fact he had given up high school in 1955 and served in an administrative post at Westover airfield, among other places. From Westover he was sent for psychiatric treatment to Parks Air Force Hospital in California. In July 1957 he had been discharged and after a period of rapid change of jobs had, with his mother's help, settled into the work at the *St. John Valley Times.*

To get to the bottom of this curious loss of memory, Crown Prosecutor Robichaud placed Vollman under a month's observation at the Provincial Hospital in Lancaster. Dr. Gregory, the psychiatrist there, obtained Vollman's record from Parks Hospital in California. The record showed that Vollman had been treated for "disturbances" that had little to do with failures of memory, but certainly could be connected with the murder of Gaetane Bouchard. The trouble was "difficulties in association with women"; as Vollman himself had expressed it: "I had no control over myself with women." Gregory, after his month's examination, concluded that Vollman was a sexual psychopath but not suffering from any type of mental illness which would involve loss of memory. Vollman was then transferred to the St. John County Jail to await trial. But he maintained his silence, and it seemed unlikely that he would confess. Robichaud therefore welcomed any attempt, even of the most unusual sort, to obtain more convincing material evidence. At the end of July Kerr took the samples of hair to Chalk River.

The idea that neutron activation analysis was to be utilized in a practical criminal case excited everyone in Jervis' laboratory. Under Jervis' direction, William Mackintosh, Alma Crowder, and Kerr bombarded the sample hairs and the single hair for periods ranging from 48 minutes to 18 hours. Kerr, in his microscopic studies, had found it remarkably difficult to distinguish between the samples of hair from Gaetane Bouchard and John Vollman. But measurements of the gamma radiation showed that the hair of each contained four or five differing trace elements, so that there could be no question about differentiating the hair of these two individuals. When the single hair was measured, however, the gamma radiation proved too weak for conclusions to be drawn about trace elements. This was a disappointment, and Jervis saw that much preliminary work remained to be done before single hairs could be compared by gamma-ray spectrometry. There remained, however, the possibility of measuring the beta radiation.

Since the single hair was the sole piece of evidence, and therefore could not be subjected to chemical treatment to eliminate the sodium content, beta-ray comparisons would necessarily be limited. The chances were almost nil that the precise quantities of each trace element could be determined. All the scientists could do was measure the strength of the beta radiation of all the elements taken together.

On August 12 and 13 the single hair and the sample hairs were subjected to an eight-hour activation and subsequently the "crude" total beta radiation was measured. These measurements were repeated several times in the course of the month. It proved possible to distinguish two elements by observation of the half-lives; these were not, however, the true trace elements of hair, but the ordinary major constituents, phosphorus and sulfur. The phosphorus radiation, 1.71 Mev, was distinctly strong; that of the sulfur, .167 Mev, quite weak. By introducing an aluminum screen into the counting apparatus, the sulfur radiation could be shielded so that pure values were obtained for the phosphorus and the proportion of sulfur to phosphorus radiation could be determined. For Gaetane Bouchard's hair sample it came to 2.02, for John Vollman's hair to 1.07, and for the single hair to 1.02. The difference in values between the Bouchard and Vollman hair seemed as striking as the close correspondence between Vollman's hair and the single hair found in the dead girl's hand. But to check the evidential value of this crude beta-ray measurement, Jervis asked Kerr to obtain thirty samples of hair from Royal Canadian Mounted Police recruits—and, moreover, hair that differed "microscopically." The same beta-ray measurements were undertaken with this hair as in the Bouchard case, and it was learned that more or less large differences existed from hair to hair in the phosphorus and sulfur radiation. Only then did Dr. Jervis agree to the test results being cited in court. He himself, however, was not able to appear as an expert because he had accepted an invitation to teach at the University of Toronto. Kerr, Mackintosh, and Alma Crowder therefore became the first to represent neutron activation analysis in court.

29

On November 4, 1958, the Vollman trial opened in Edmundston. No one except for a few insiders knew of the prospective appearance of "the atom as detective" (as the newspapers later put it). The trial aroused the greatest interest, for it was the first time that an American citizen was going on trial in a capital case in Canadian Madawaska County. Nevertheless, it at first remained a local affair. Vollman sat with his dark curls tumbling over his forehead, his eyes half shut, frequently chewing his lower lip, between a guard and his father. After he had pleaded "Not guilty," there began the struggle between Albany M. Robichaud and Vollman's attorney, J. A. Pichette, before Judge Arthur L. Anglin and the twelve-man jury. Pichette knew how few witnesses Robichaud could call on, and he did his best to undermine their testimony and to sow doubts about the prosecution's evidence. He would decide later whether he could dare to aim for an acquittal or content himself with saving Vollman from a mandatory death sentence by seeking a verdict of manslaughter committed in a momentary state of unconsciousness.

During the early stages, Pichette was notably unsuccessful. He could not, for example, shake the witness Marcel Bosse. Asked whether he recognized the driver of the American car he had seen in Edmundston on May 13, the farmer replied: "Sure, that fellow sitting over there in the box." On November 14 Robichaud presented a surprise witness whom he had obtained by a stroke of luck. That very day Constable Martin had come to him and reported an incident that he had suppressed for months, perhaps from fear of having violated some rule. In May he had transferred Vollman to the St. John jail and had taken along a Montreal relative of his, James F. Tobin. In Fredericton he got out of the car for twenty minutes and left Tobin to guard the prisoner. During this time Tobin asked Vollman: "How come such a smart-looking young guy as you would be in such a jam? Did you kill that girl?" To his surprise Vollman replied: "Yes, I guess there is no doubt about it. I blacked out, and when I came to, it was too late. The girl was dead. They were too easy on me when I was young. I have quite a temper. I sometimes have a hard time controlling myself. . . . I don't think they have enough on me to hang me. Enough evidence."

When Tobin appeared as a witness, Pichette lashed into him vigorously. But he had no more luck than with Bosse.

There then began days of scientific testimony, with Fedor, Mrs. Rouen, and Constable Esau taking the stand. At this stage of the trial, the defense came out better in that all three had to admit that no bloodstains and no murder weapon had been found in Vollman's car. The splinters of paint might have come from it, but only the heart-shaped splinter fitted a defect on the Pontiac. The stain on the chocolate might or might not have come from Gaetane Bouchard's lipstick. But Pichette had no chance to make much of these admissions, for after them came a stunning defeat when Francis M. Kerr took the witness stand and for the first time revealed that hair had been found in the murdered girl's fingers. Spectators and jurors listened with heightened attention. A hair torn from the head of a murderer by his victim, destined to convict him of his crime, exerted as much fascination in 1958 as it had done half a century earlier. In a hushed silence Kerr reported how the hair had been sent to Ottawa. He concluded his statement with the carefully temperate sentence: "I came to the conclusion that the single hair found in the dead girl's hand could have come from the head of the accused." Pichette sensed the dramatic effect of even so cautiously formulated a phrase. Hastily he countered: "Or from the head of another person with hair of the same characteristics." "That is correct," Kerr replied.

Robichaud quickly intervened and guided Kerr toward the climax of his testimony. It was quite true in general, he said, that the methods of hair comparison used in the past seldom attained real certainty. But in recent years a new, revolutionary method of comparison had been developed, which he would now present in court for the first time. Then he directed leading questions to Kerr: Was it correct that the laboratories in Chalk River had been working for some time on a wholly new method of identifying hair? Was Kerr prepared to inform the jury of the elements of this new method?

Pichette immediately rose to object. He guessed that Kerr's information might destroy the case for Vollman. Vehemently, he argued against the admission of an unknown, novel method in a capital case. Indignantly he protested that the jurors were being suddenly confronted with a scientific test that no one outside of Chalk River could possibly understand.

The judge overruled the objection, and Kerr provided as impressive and comprehensible a description of the new method as could possibly be given. When he was finished, Pichette resumed his objections and became involved in a violent battle of words with Prosecutor Robichaud. The judge listened with the expression of a man who had already made up his mind. He rejected the defense arguments, declared the new method admissible, accepted the hair samples as Exhibits 42, 43, and 44, and decided that Crowder and Mackintosh should be permitted to testify on their work at the next session of the court.

On November 17 Alma Crowder and William Mackintosh took the stand with their documentation. Their testimony, which took more than three hours, proved momentous enough to attract numerous representatives of the press. They described once more the basic theory of the work, explained the nature of beta radiation, and showed the differences in the beta-radiation results for the single hair and Gaetane Bouchard's own hair, the similarity of the results for the single hair and Vollman's hair. When Alma Crowder referred to these results as an *indication* of the origin of the hair, Pichette made a last attempt to sway the jurors by extracting an admission that the hair could have come from someone else with the same hair characteristics. However, he achieved the opposite of what he had intended, for he provoked Mrs. Crowder into saying more than Jervis would probably have said at this point in his researches. "It is highly improbable that you'd get the same results from two different persons' hairs, though," she declared, "there's an outside chance that in a case of, say, identical twins, hairs from the two heads would be similar."

Justice Anglin asked whether any probability calculations had been undertaken in Chalk River to determine, as in the case of fingerprints, what the odds were for finding complete correspondence of the trace elements in the hair of different persons. By then, however, Mrs. Crowder's enthusiasm had subsided somewhat and she replied with scientific caution that there had not been enough hair samples or sufficient time to make such calculations. But this reservation did not greatly detract from the effect of her preceding statements. The jury appeared convinced that the hair in the dead girl's hand had been Vollman's.

The case looked so bad for Vollman that on the last day of the trial Pichette decided to call him to the stand as the sole witness in his own defense. The lawyer had abandoned hope of an acquittal and now aimed only for a verdict of manslaughter rather than murder. To everyone's astonishment, he guided Vollman, by his questions, to an admission that he had invited Gaetane Bouchard into his car on May 13 and had driven to the gravel pit with her. According to his account, she had been "very affectionate, very responsive—but at a certain point she refused my advances. There was a struggle in the car. . . . The door flew open and we fell out onto the ground. I was not trying to rape her. The only thing I can really remember is coming back to Madawaska." Pichette asked: "Did you intend to kill Gaetane on May 13?" Vollman looked up at the ceiling and asserted: "No, no."

The whole spectacle was a too obvious attempt to escape a murder conviction on grounds of a temporary mental lapse. Robichaud, however, was not content to leave the matter at this halfway confession. In the course of an intense cross-examination he extracted admissions from Vollman that he had been "in the heat of passion" and that he thought he might have "been choking her as we lay on the ground." Vollman admitted that he had had a hunting knife in the glove compartment of his car, but said he had lost it. Then he retreated completely behind his alleged loss of memory. But his histrionic ability was so poor that the jurors were not persuaded. A picture of the girl playing with fire, and of the unstable Vollman at the height of sexual excitement being thrown into the unpredictable frenzy by Gaetane's sudden resistance, might have seemed credible, were it not for the pretended amnesia. As it was, the jurors preferred to take the prosecution view of Vollman as a murderer who after a vain attempt at rape killed his victim to prevent her from betraying him. Shortly after midnight the jury declared Vollman guilty of murder, and Justice Anglin sentenced him to death by hanging, a sentence that was commuted on February 14, 1959, to life imprisonment.

30

An article on the Bouchard case by James E. Roper and Donald Robinson, two American journalists, was given the impressive title "The Atom Becomes a Detective," and contained the following key sentence: "Dr. Robert E. Jervis says: 'A hair is as positive identification of a person as his or her fingerprints.'" Now, it is more than questionable that Jervis ever made such a statement. Perhaps the linkage between fingerprinting and nuclear analysis arose from Justice Anglin's query about the odds. For some time afterward, at any rate, the same erroneous notion appeared in almost everything written on the subject of neutron activation analysis. The reports from Edmundston had apparently given rise to the popular idea that atomic science had performed a criminalistic miracle.

Yet though Jervis himself might have been wary of any such sweeping claims for hair analysis, it is clear that he too was at times imbued with high expectations and youthful optimism. His move to Toronto to assume a teaching position in applied chemistry at the university more or less broke his connection with the RCMP laboratory in Ottawa. But he entered upon a new relationship with the Attorney General's Laboratory of the Province of Ontario, which since September 1966 has been known as the Centre of Forensic Sciences.

This laboratory, responsible for all scientific crime investigation in the province, had been in operation since the early fifties, and under its director, Dr. H. Ward Smith, had passed through a period of rapid development. (The number of cases handled rose from some five hundred in 1955 to approximately five thousand by 1962.) Its organization included a section for organic chemistry, physical chemistry, pharmaceutical chemistry, toxicology, biology, pathology, ballistics, and documents. Among the associates in the biological section was a young man named

Auseklis K. Perkons, born in Riga, Latvia, in 1932. At the age of twelve he fled to Germany from the advancing Soviet armies, and in 1951 emigrated to Canada. In 1958 he received his first degree in chemical engineering and went on to obtain his Ph. D. Perkons became a pupil of Jervis, and acted as a sort of liaison between him and the crime laboratory. The Attorney General's Laboratory decided to continue and extend the work in hair analysis that Jervis had begun at Chalk River. Jervis became adviser to the laboratory on questions of neutron activation analysis, and undertook to train Perkons and a team of young research workers in atomic techniques. Their intention was to study a large number of hair samples and prove that neutron activation analysis could indeed serve as a modern standardized method for hair comparisons.

The work began in 1959. As early as 1961 Jervis and Perkons reported their study of 90 samples of hair, each of which constituted a strand, not single hairs. The scientists concentrated on the measurement of gamma radiation. When the hair samples were left in the reactor for a sufficiently long time, the trace elements were stimulated to such strong radiation that it could be captured by a sodium iodide crystal and transmitted through a photomultiplier tube to a scintillation counter. This counter had 200 channels, each of which received rays only of a particular frequency, and indicated the pulses from the rays by small blips of light. Each channel was capable of storing 65,000 pulses. The data were recorded graphically as a gamma-ray spectrum, which looked not unlike a fever chart.

Perkons and Jervis discovered that it was necessary to activate the hair samples much longer than 18 hours. In the McMaster University reactor in Hamilton, Ontario, they exposed the hairs, packed in polyethylene envelopes, for from 48 to 72 hours to a neutron flux of billions of neutrons per second. The strong radiation of the samples thus produced made it possible for measurements to be taken on the first day after irradiation, then new measurements after seven days, twenty days, and thirty days. The disappearance of the radiation from the elements with short half-lives permitted identification of the longer-lived elements after the first week. Perkons and Jervis reported that along with the trace elements in hair previously found by others (arsenic, copper, zinc, iron, silicon, sodium, and vanadium) they had detected no less than eleven additional elements. Perkons was unable to confirm the presence of silicon and vanadium, but he had found four additional elements. His list ranged from gold, cobalt, molybdenum, and iodine to silver, mercury, and selenium.

Since it seldom happens that hair samples are taken from a suspect on the very day of a crime—in fact, the samples are usually taken a considerable time afterward—Perkons experimented with hair that had been uncut for an entire year. There seemed to be no difference in segments of the hair dating from different times, as far as the proportions of their trace elements were concerned. On the other hand, the hair of different persons sharply differed in the kind and quantity of the trace elements. Optimistically, Perkons generalized: "It is obvious from this comparison that no two hair samples are at all similar with respect to their trace element content 'patterns.'"

On December 18, 1961, Jervis and Perkons came to the United States to speak at the First International Conference on Modern Trends in Activation Analysis, held at Texas Agricultural and Mechanical College. By now they had studied 110 samples of hair from 50 persons, and after 60-hour activation of each sample had discovered even more elements. They had also refined their determinations of quantities; manganese, arsenic, copper, gold, and mercury could be detected in amounts of one ten-millionth of a gram. Further experiments confirmed the hypothesis that the element pattern of the hair seemed consistent in individuals and remained unchanged for considerable periods of time. The hopefulness of the researchers had, if anything, increased. Perkons declared: "The practical significance of these conclusions for forensic applications cannot be overestimated. Positive identification of any individual by his hair is feasible without having to worry about the exact location from which the hair was taken, or how close to the root it was cut or torn." He added a cautionary word: "A survey of thousands of hair samples is necessary to estimate the statistical probability of finding two individuals with the same micro-composition of hair, within limits of error." Nevertheless, he concluded: "The present preliminary results indicate that since there are at least 10 different components, and thus over 10 points of difference, each covering a comparatively wide range, the probability is exceedingly small indeed."

Inspired by the results of this study, Perkons undertook to analyze "other materials of forensic importance," which had hitherto resisted such techniques as spectral analysis. Once again he had noteworthy successes. In samples of raw opium from more than twenty different sources Perkons found different concentrations of trace elements, by which they could be told apart. He felt justified in expressing the hope that "With recent further improvements in the development of portable neutron generators, the time for a complete neutron activation analysis can be reduced to a day or even a few hours, and the technique can find wide applications as a routine method in every criminal laboratory."

When Jervis and Perkons returned to Toronto, they must have felt they had presented forensic science with a method whose potentialities were truly unlimited. Moreover, they had the satisfaction of knowing that American colleagues at the great atomic laboratories of Oak Ridge, Tennessee, as well as in southern California, had taken up their suggestions and were testing the criminalistic aspects of their work. Above all Vincent P. Guinn, a young nuclear chemist at the General Atomics Division Laboratories of General Dynamics Corporation in San Diego, had plunged into the new field with great energy. He had leagued himself with Raymond H. Pinker, chief chemist of the excellent crime laboratory of Los Angeles, and with the California Association of Criminalists. As a noncriminalist, he had turned to these sources to learn which types of trace analyses caused California police the greatest difficulties. The police cited the enormous numbers of automobile accidents, ordinary as well as hit-and run, where paint traces were transferred from one car to another, or from a car to the body of an accident victim. In many such cases spectral analysis failed because the traces were too small. Possibly neutron activation analysis might succeed in detecting the components of such tiny particles of paint, and thus prove correspondences. Another problem involved firearms. The paraffin test had been developed in the late thirties, and there was a tendency to believe that it afforded the necessary verification in firearm cases. Its underlying theory was as follows: with each shot, the recoil sent powder gases against the hand of the gunman, so that a layer of invisible chemical components of these gases formed on the hand. If warm paraffin were placed on the hand of the suspect, then removed and examined by chemical techniques, it would pick up these chemical components. Chemists had had considerable luck in demonstrating the presence of nitrites, a component of modern gunpowder. But it became evident that the presence of nitrites was not an adequate proof; it could be deposited on people's hands from too many other sources. Attempts were then made to show the presence of more significant components of the recoil gases, in particular lead, barium, and antimony. But if these elements were present at all, it was in such small quantities that spectral analysis could not detect them. Perhaps neutron activation analysis could close this gap.

Guinn ran a whole series of experiments on paint comparison and firearm traces, using neutron activation analysis. Valuable results were soon forthcoming. It proved possible to detect five to seven trace elements in the most minute of paint splinters, and to find barium and antimony traces from firearms. The NAA analysis was so sensitive that it showed barium and antimony even on the faces of persons who had fired guns. In view of this breakthrough, Guinn entertained the thought of proposing that ammunition manufacturers mix extremely rare trace elements, such as europium or dysprosium, in their products, thus "labeling" every type of ammunition for future criminalistic investigation.

Confidently, Jervis and Perkons resumed their work in Toronto. As of February 1964, the number of hair samples they had examined rose to 600, taken from 200 different persons. Gamma-spectrometry was by now so highly developed that they could detect as many as eighteen elements, including caesium, lanthanum, strontium, antimony, and silver. They had improved their methods of determining not only the element but its quantity. Thus Perkons could measure caesium in quantities of 2 parts per billion. The accumulated data were so vast by now that a complete statistical evaluation would of course take considerable time. Jervis and Perkons anticipated that with their progressively developing technique ten to eleven trace elements could be determined in every given sample of hair. (For not every hair contains the full complement of hair trace elements.) The possible variations in regard to the elements themselves were therefore very large. But the number of potential variations rose to infinity as soon as the scientists considered the possible differences in the quantity of each element. Jervis and Perkons computed the odds for the duplication of one and the same element pattern in both quantity and quality. The results were as follows:

If only 3 elements were measured, the probability of duplication came to 1:4800. With 5 elements measured, it was 1:126,800. With 7 elements, it rose to 1:4,250,000; and for 11 elements, 1:1,140,000,000. From these figures it followed that if in comparison of two samples of hair 11 elements of the same kind and quantity were found, identity was as good as established.

Despite these promising aspects, between 1961 and 1964 Jervis and Perkons underwent a significant psychological change. The more material they amassed, the more they encountered interesting scientific problems, so that the idea of practical criminalistics gradually faded into the background. They saw primarily the tremendous scientific task before them. Although the majority of these findings had not yet been evaluated, Perkons was already speaking of the need to study ten thousand hair samples, in order to penetrate the problem to its depths. They were now preparing to apply measuring instruments that analyzed 400 channels, and to have the values of the gamma-ray spectrograms calculated by computer and compared with the values of previously recorded spectrograms. Perkons believed that he had already assembled a sufficiently large and precise collection of comparison spectra of known elements and known quantities of elements so that an experienced scientist would not even need to undertake quantitative analyses of the elements in each individual sample. Simple comparison of the curves and peak energies of unknown hair samples with those of known hair samples appeared to be a swift and uncomplicated method of matching hair.

In February 1964 the two scientists appeared in Chicago and once again addressed the American Academy of Forensic Science. Perkons reported on past achievements and on his projected further studies of at least 1100 samples of hair. In this paper there was no mention of the near application of the analyses to criminalistic practice, although Perkons pointed out how far they had come with their system of comparing gamma spectra. "For the purpose of identification and matching of samples of hair or other materials it is not absolutely necessary to do a complete quantitative analysis based on a large volume of compiled statistical data. The analog recordings of the gamma-ray spectra show sufficient differences between dissimilar samples on the one hand, and sufficient similarity between duplicate samples from one individual, on the other hand, that purely visual identification may in some instances be feasible."

These were the words of a young man who over the past several years had evolved from a militant enthusiast and optimist in criminological matters to a research scientist who for all his optimistic leanings was increasingly engrossed by research—perhaps without even becoming aware that this was happening to him. He now viewed practical applications only as a matter for the future. Jervis, by this time thirty-six, considered the application of activation analysis in the Bouchard case only as a premature act springing from a simplehearted faith in novelty. He too was possessed by the idea of acquiring complete knowledge, complete certainty about the identification of hair, with criminalistic applications being set aside for the time being. It occurred neither to him nor to Perkons that the apparent simplicity of hair matching, which Perkons had alluded to, might lead people who were not research scientists but practical forensic chemists to attempt criminalistic activation analysis of hair without sufficient background. Such men might act out of ambition or ignorance—but act they did. While Perkons was talking in Chicago,

the authorities in Manchester, New Hampshire, were feverishly at work
on a crime that bore certain parallels to the Bouchard case, and that would
violently pull Perkons as well as Jervis out of the ivory tower of pure research to which they had retired.

31

At two o'clock in the morning on January 14, 1964, a blizzard was hurling
snow down on the small city of Manchester, New Hampshire, when Joan
Mason left the restaurant where she worked as waitress and drove home.
It took her almost an hour to reach 51 Donald Street, where she lived with
her husband and two children. Dead tired, she looked into the room where
eleven-year-old David slept. She heard him breathing quietly, and went
on to check on her daughter Pamela. But the fourteen-year-old's bed was
untouched. That afternoon someone had telephoned to ask Pamela to
baby-sit; a couple was supposed to call for Pamela between five and six
o'clock. By that time Joan Mason had left the house for her restaurant
job. But she had impressed Pamela with the rule never to let a man call
for her for a baby-sitting assignment unless he was accompanied by his
wife. She assumed that Pamela must have stayed over at a girl friend's
house because of the storm, and so she went to bed.

When she awoke a few hours later, Pamela was not yet home, and her
first talk with David left her with a feeling of uneasiness. According to
David, he and Pamela had had their supper at five thirty. At six o'clock
the bell had rung. He had gone to the door with Pamela. She was wearing
her navy-blue car coat, green stretch pants, and boots, and was carrying
a green pocketbook. Because of the heavy snow he had not seen the kind
of car that fetched her. But he was convinced that Pamela would never
get into a suspicious car. Mrs. Mason tried to reassure herself with the
same argument, but she nevertheless telephoned the high school to find
out whether Pamela had gone directly there. Hearing that she had not,
she looked for the telephone number and address of the couple, which had
been jotted on the telephone pad. Then she slipped into her outdoor
clothing and drove off into the snow. An hour later, frantic, terrified,
she sat at the desk of Police Sergeant Roger Weymans of the Manchester
city police. The address the man had given her over the telephone was
false. The couple who lived at that address had no child.

McGranaghan, the chief of Manchester's 120-man police force, promptly organized a search for Pamela, calling on the State Police and the National Guard for help. Manchester, with its 88,000 inhabitants, was one of the ten American cities with the lowest crime index, and it hoped to stay that way. Moreover, McGranaghan was deeply troubled by his recollection of the disappearance and brutal murder of another girl, which had taken place in Manchester four years before, on February 1, 1960. The killing of Sandra Valade, eighteen, and the long search, hampered by heavy snows and cold, could not be forgotten. In all those four years the police had not succeeded in tracking down the murderer. He was still at large, perhaps in the city itself.

McGranaghan made no protest when Joan Mason clung to the hope of a kidnaping. He did not interfere when she appealed on television to a mysterious unknown: "Whoever you are, for God's sake don't harm my baby. . . . I have no money. But if you want money, I'll get it somewhere. . . . " The Police Chief hoped that the events of 1960 were not about to be repeated. But hopes and reality were two different things. The information he received from Barbara Jackson, a friend of Pamela's, made him suspect that on the afternoon of January 13, a new trick had been tried to satisfy a pervert's lust. Pamela and Barbara both used the bulletin board of an automatic laundry on South Main Street to offer their services as baby sitters. On the afternoon of January 13 Barbara had received a telephone call from a man asking whether she could baby-sit for him that evening. When she asked his address, he replied evasively. He then asked her whether she could give him the address of a girl friend who baby-sat. When she said she could not, he hung up quickly. The caller who had obtained Pamela Mason's service that same afternoon had, to be sure, volunteered a name and address; but probably he had learned from the previous call and was prepared to give false information.

The trick used by the murderer of Sandra Valade on the evening of February 1, 1960, had surely been different, although nothing definite was known about it. Again it had been an icy evening and possibly he had offered to drive Sandra home from town. But otherwise the circumstances seemed similar. McGranaghan recalled the hopes of Sandra's parents that the girl might have stayed overnight at a girl friend's house, and later their desperate belief in a kidnaping. They had clung to this theory even when, a few hours after her disappearance, a watchman at the waterworks had found one of Sandra's boots caught in the filter grating of a channel, and two boys discovered Sandra's library and insurance card on Taylor Street, two miles to the south. The search had lasted many days; State

Police, National Guardsmen, and helicopters had taken part, until at last a sixteen-year-old boy noticed "something red" while driving along hilly Derry Road, something that stood out against a melting mound of snow. When he climbed the hill, he found the missing girl lying on her face, red blouse torn, naked breasts pressed into the snow, long ski pants slit open with a knife. At the autopsy in Moore General Hospital the doctors had found four bullet wounds from a .22-caliber weapon in head and back, and plain signs of rape. The years of hunting for the murderer, believed to be the owner of an old Chevrolet who had become stuck in the snow around nine o'clock on Smith Road and had rejected offered help, had been wholly in vain. By 1963 the police, after checking seven hundred suspects, had given up hope of finding the killer.

The discovery of Pamela Mason's body did not take so long. On the evening of January 20 George Charland, driving his bakery truck along Interstate Route 93 south of Manchester, noticed "something black" in a melting snowbank, but did not stop. During the night, however, he re-called the search for Pamela Mason, and when he passed the place again on January 21 he pulled over and stopped. At first he saw schoolbooks and a green pocketbook, then a lifeless body in green stretch pants, blue car coat, and fur boots. He made for the nearest telephone. Lieutenant Thomas King and Inspector Maurice Leclerc of the Manchester police, and Sergeant William McBain of the State police, arrived shortly after-ward. Pamela Mason had been found.

King and Leclerc observed the bullet wounds in Pamela's head. They saw that the girl had been stripped beneath her coat. Her underwear had vanished, and stab wounds had disfigured her rather ample body. The parallel with the murder of Sandra Valade was striking. King had the body taken to the same Moore General Hospital where the earlier autopsy had been performed.

Norman W. Leavitt, assistant chief of the Manchester police, obtained an Air Force snow-melting machine from Grenier Field, to remove the snow at the scene without destroying any clues. He found not the slightest trace of the missing underclothing. But there were a man's leather glove and a knitted white woman's glove on the ground. A pink wallet, contain-ing photographs and an identification card, were missing from the girl's pocketbook, as if the killer had made an attempt to hamper identification of his victim. Meanwhile Dr. Manuel A. Villaverde, a young physician, had performed the autopsy. He removed two .22-caliber bullets from the girl's head, one of which was totally deformed by impact with the bone and the second considerably deformed. There were four deep stab wounds in chest and nape of neck. In the stomach were the remains of a meal of fried eggs, which Pamela had prepared for herself and her brother before she hurried off to baby-sit. Villaverde concluded that she must have been killed between two and four hours after her last meal. He did not find signs of rape. But he noticed that there were scarcely any tears in the girl's clothes. The stab wounds could not have been inflicted through the clothing at all. Had the murderer undressed the girl, then later replaced the outer clothes on the dead body? Had he driven around in the blizzard until at last he hid the body on Interstate 93? There could be no answers to such questions. Assistant Chief Leavitt took charge of the clothing. Since hairs could plainly be seen clinging to the stretch pants, Leavitt also took hair samples from the body, to determine whether the hair on the pants came from the girl herself or from someone else.

Inspectors Maurice Leclerc and Donald F. Glennon, aided by Sergeants William McBain and Paul Doyon of the State Police, took over the main work of investigation. The parallels with the murder of Sandra Valade were so obvious that the detectives redirected their attention toward the suspects who had been checked between 1960 and 1963: the men with records, the deviants, anyone who owned an old Chevrolet and a .22-caliber firearm. Once more the endless search began. Only a chance find, or a witness who had observed a car on the night of January 13 near the spot where the body had been found, could narrow the vast circle of possibilities. And in fact two musicians, Joseph A. Bushey and Gerard Gravel, who had been driving home from Derry to Manchester the night of January 13, provided a first clue. At about nine thirty they were passing the spot where Pamela Mason had been found and had seen, barely a stone's throw from the place, an old Pontiac stuck in a snowdrift. Dimly, they could see the outlines of a man at the wheel. They called out to him asking whether he needed help, but he said no. Bushey and Gravel were able to give a close description of the Pontiac, but not of the driver. If the killer was the same man who had been involved in the Valade case, he had changed cars, and the search must now focus on Pontiacs.

On January 23 a more direct clue was forthcoming. The police of Haverhill, directly across the border in Massachusetts, received a telephone call from a local tavernkeeper, William J. Lemire of Comeau's Tavern. Lemire employed a bartender named Benny Speros, who also worked as a bakery products driver for the Cote bakery. Another bakery truck driver from Manchester, an Edward H. Coolidge, had called on Speros about an hour ago and asked him for a favor. He had been out with another woman, he said, and his wife had learned about it. Would

Speros say that he had been with him at Comeau's all the while? "As long as it's only your wife I'll go along with you," Speros replied. "It's not only my wife—it may be the police," Coolidge said.

The Haverhill police informed the State Police in Concord. Edward H. Coolidge's address was quickly traced. The twenty-seven-year-old bakery truck driver lived with his wife Joan and a young daughter at 302 Seames Drive. It turned out that he had been one of the suspects in the Sandra Valade case because he owned a Chevrolet of the type then sought. As the detective noticed, he now drove a Pontiac such as Bushey and Gravel had described. Doyon and Leclerc began questioning Coolidge's neighbors. On January 28 Doyon called on a friend of Mrs. Coolidge's named Dorothy Maheu. She had been playing Scrabble with Joan at the Coolidge home from early in the afternoon until quite late at night on January 13. At two o'clock Coolidge had come home from his bread route, but left again shortly afterward. He appeared briefly at the house around five o'clock, but stayed so short a time that he left the motor of his Pontiac running. Then he had vanished until eleven fifteen at night, returning home with his trousers soaking wet.

At seven thirty that same January day Doyon and Leclerc called at the Coolidge house and found Coolidge extremely obliging. He readily showed them his Pontiac, and the two detectives noticed nothing unusual about it. Asked about firearms, he just as obligingly showed them a loaded Mossberg 410 shotgun, a Martin carbine, and a Remington rifle which he used for hunting. Just as pleasantly he described his actions on January 13: he had gone home from his bread route about two o'clock, returned to the bakery, made preparations for next day's route up to five o'clock, driven home, stayed home from five ten to seven thirty, at seven thirty gone shopping in the Pontiac to the business center of Manchester. Finding the stores already closed, he had dropped in at the Syrian American Citizens Club for a drink. Then he decided in spite of the snowstorm to drive to Haverhill because he thought the shops there would still be open. But Haverhill was also shutting down. He chatted here and there with storekeepers who were just shutting up, among others with Ronald Sweet of Lafayette Fruit. Then he stopped in at Comeau's Tavern and afterward drove back to Manchester on Interstate 93. About ten o'clock he got stuck in the snow at the Derry exit, refused an offer of help from some drivers who passed by, and got himself out. He had been home by about eleven. Doyon and Leclerc accepted his story for the present. As they left, Coolidge said that he would be glad to go to the police station at any time if they had any further questions.

The contradiction between Dorothy Maheu's statement and Coolidge's contention that he had been home between five and seven could not be overlooked. Why was he lying about the hours during which Pamela Mason had been abducted? What had really impelled him to leave the house for approximately seven hours during such awful weather? Why did he mention getting stuck in the snow, a fact that coincided with the statements of the two musicians, except that Coolidge indicated a location distinctly farther south than the place where Pamela Mason's body had been found? Did he want to avoid a possible confrontation with these witnesses, who had addressed him and might recognize him? Next day the detectives drove to Haverhill and made inquiries around town. No one had seen Coolidge there on the afternoon and evening of January 13; nor did anyone recall seeing him at the Syrian American Citizens Club of Manchester.

On February 2, Coolidge was asked to call at the police station, where Leavitt, Leclerc, Glennon, Doyon, and McBain were waiting for him. He was forced to admit that he had been telling lies about his itinerary on the afternoon and evening of January 13. Abruptly he reversed himself and declared that he had had a rendezvous with a married woman in Haverhill and hadn't wanted to talk about it in his wife's presence. He had preferred a lie, even though his wife knew he had not been home. He refused "as a man of honor" to reveal the woman's name. As the questioning advanced he dropped the story of the married woman and spoke of an unknown girl who had been in his car with him. Finally he offered a third version: that he had left home about five o'clock and driven to the Syrian American Citizens Club to play gin rummy with a friend, George Vlangis. Between six and seven Ferris Ebol, who ran the restaurant at the Club, had served him dinner. Then he had driven to Haverhill in the hope of picking up some woman. He had had no luck and finally landed at Comeau's. He could not understand that no one remembered seeing him there and in the stores he had visited. As for the return drive to Manchester, he insisted that he had been stuck in the snow at the Derry, not the Londonderry, exit.

Prompt inquiries at the Syrian American Citizens Club yielded the information that Ferris Ebol had not served dinner to Coolidge on January 13. It was true that Coolidge had been there, but he had left shortly after five o'clock. Vlangis had not gone to the club at all on January 13. From Haverhill came word that Coolidge had not been seen in a single store. But on January 22 or 23 he had approached Richard E. Loosian, manager of Sykes Variety Store in Haverhill, and tried to persuade him to provide a false alibi. According to Loosian, Coolidge had said: "I need an alibi and I'd appreciate it if you would help me out. . . . When there was a murder, the Sandra Valade case, my car was impounded for three weeks. And I'm afraid with this new murder that has showed up, I'm going to be questioned again."

When the detectives confronted Coolidge with these statements, he admitted that he had not been seeking an alibi on account of his wife, but from fear that he would be suspected again as he had been in the Sandra Valade case. Very well, Leavitt said to him, why did he need false witnesses if he had nothing to hide? Coolidge then pleaded failure of memory. He no longer knew exactly where he had been during the day in question. Finally he came up with the name of one member of the Club who would certainly remember seeing him there. He had just recalled that he had played gin rummy at the Syrian American Citizens Club with Habid Nassoura.

By now it was evening and Nassoura could not be found. The discrepancies in Coolidge's story were so huge that Leavitt, remembering the hairs on Pamela Mason's ski pants, demanded that Coolidge give him samples of his hair. Coolidge complied. At the same time McBain went to Seames Drive to search the house. Joan Coolidge let him in, and looked on, pale, unhappy, and laconic, while he made a thorough search. When McBain asked her to show him her husband's guns she produced, to his surprise, a fourth gun in addition to the three Coolidge had shown him. The fourth was a .22-caliber Mossberg rifle. McBain then inspected the Pontiac and discovered a box of .22 ammunition and a pair of gray slacks with spots that seemed to him suspicious. These were the trousers Coolidge had worn on January 13, Joan Coolidge told him, and resignedly she handed over the red and black hunting jacket he had also been wearing on the fateful day. Coolidge was allowed to go home "for the present."

The Mossberg rifle and several test bullets that Leavitt fired from it were sent next day to Lieutenant Roger Beaudoin of the State Police laboratory in Concord. Glennon and Leclerc meanwhile set out to check again on Coolidge's various alibis. Toward noon they found Habid Nassoura in the SAC Club. He remembered January 13 very well. Coolidge had been there before five o'clock, and Nassoura had suggested their customary game of gin rummy. But contrary to Coolidge's habit, he had refused to play. He had left by the back door of the Club by five thirty at the latest.

During the next few days the two detectives tracked down other witnesses whom Coolidge had asked to falsify an alibi for him. He had spoken to Lawrence Pendoleris, son of the owner of Hope's Diner in Plaistow, as well as Anthony Norcia, a Massachusetts bakery driver whom he knew only casually. He had told both that the police were likely to suspect him in the case of Pamela Mason. He had told another bakery driver, John Arohvites, on January 21—*before* the discovery of Pamela Mason's body: "Now I really need that alibi." He was sure to be suspected in the Mason case, he had told Arohvites.

By February 10 William Maynard, the Attorney General of New Hampshire, decided that the time had come to arrest Coolidge. But knowing the many possibilities of error inherent in the statements of witnesses, he decided to wait until the results of the laboratory tests on the Mossberg rifle were available.

The groundwork of the science of forensic ballistics had been laid in the twenties by, among others, Calvin Goddard, who with the aid of the comparison microscope had demonstrated that tiny variations in the manufacturing process left special marks on the barrel or firing pin of every gun. These marks were transferred to the bullets fired from the gun, making it possible to identify the weapon by a bullet taken from the body of a murdered person. Murder bullets compared with test bullets fired from the fatal weapon would show the same marks under the comparison microscope.

Lieutenant Beaudoin in Concord was a ballistics expert. He reported that the two bullets which had killed Pamela Mason must have been fired from Coolidge's Mossberg rifle. The examination had been extraordinarily difficult, however, owing to the severe deformation of the bullets. Beaudoin, whose small laboratory in Concord had only limited equipment, therefore consulted a larger laboratory. The same procedure was undertaken in the examination of Coolidge's and Pamela Mason's clothing and of the Pontiac. The Attorney General enlisted the aid of the Pastore Crime Laboratory at the University of Rhode Island, in Kingston. The Laboratory had been set up in 1953 on the basis of an agreement between the Attorney General of Rhode Island and the University, in order to provide scientific assistance to law enforcement agencies in major criminal cases. The underlying idea was that the Laboratory could call upon the specialists in various departments of the University, according to need. Nominally, the Laboratory was headed by Professor W. George Parks of the Department of Chemistry. The practical work was largely handled by Dr. Harold C. Harrison, a fifty-seven-year-old chemist. Since the requirements of Rhode Island scarcely sufficed to keep a laboratory fully occupied and did not afford sufficient experience, Harrison had from the first sought assignments in neighboring states. He had for some time maintained connections with the Attorney General of New Hampshire. Thus Maynard naturally turned to him for assistance in the Coolidge case. In addition he appointed a predecessor of Beaudoin, Carroll A. Durfee, as a kind of "special expert" for trace examinations.

Durfee, a white-haired man of seventy-three, had retired in 1963, but still retained his youthful vigor. During his term of office he had won a measure of local fame, and had had a fruitful collaboration with Harrison. Since the bullets constituted prime evidence, Durfee first had a look at the Mossberg rifle and the bullets, but he was unable to hand down a clear verdict. Harrison, a chemist, could scarcely claim to be a ballistics expert of the first rank. Durfee therefore passed the rifle and bullets on to the gunnery expert of the Rhode Island Fish and Game Department, Leo Grandchamp. Grandchamp came to the conclusion that the bullets which had killed both Pamela Mason and Sandra Valade had come from the Mossberg rifle. But even before the final results of the tests were in, Deputy Chief Leavitt had called at Seames Drive on the night of February 19 and arrested Coolidge. As the handcuffs were placed on him, Coolidge asserted: "My rifle never left my house that night."

Since in subsequent interrogations Coolidge became involved in repeated contradictions but continued to deny any part in the murder of Pamela Mason, the weight of the investigation shifted steadily toward Durfee, Harrison, and the attempts to prove by means of trace evidence that Coolidge and Pamela Mason must have been in physical contact, or that the girl had been in Coolidge's Pontiac. As the trial was to show, these efforts were ill-fated. Harrison, whose experience in the field of micro-traces was later to be vehemently called into question, examined the clothing of Pamela Mason and Coolidge for significant traces. He observed a certain number of hairs and other particles, and placed them— without for the present classifying them—in covered glass dishes to have them available for later comparisons. Subsequently he vacuumed the clothes and placed all the particles he obtained in glass dishes. The Pontiac was examined mainly by Chief Leavitt, who contented himself with vacuuming portions of the interior and sending the dust and other particles thus gathered to Kingston. Specialists like Frei-Sulzer, Martin, or Kirk would certainly have frowned at such summary vacuum-cleaning procedures. The examinations of the car and the clothing were indeed casual and routine; no attempt was made to find rare and hence significant micro-traces. Samuel J. Golub, a textile expert hired by Coolidge's defense, examined the sealed Pontiac many months later. He found a whole series of characteristic traces which had obviously been overlooked and were never considered in the comparative studies. Among these were the large and conspicuous scattering of white cattle hairs which very probably would have stuck to Pamela Mason's clothing had she been inside the car. Golub also was the first to look for rare types of fiber on the girl's clothing—fibers which, if they had been sought and found in the Pontiac or on Coolidge's clothing, would have provided reliable evidence of mutual contact. Among other things he discovered some Dynel fibers which had never been mentioned in Harrison's studies. He also found vegetable matter clinging to Pamela Mason's clothes, including dandelion seeds. These were a strange find in the middle of winter, but apparently no one had thought of pursuing this oddity. On the whole, instead of a painstaking, detailed search for significant elements, the scientific investigators had contented themselves with routine examinations that later exposed Harrison in particular to fierce attacks by the defense in court, and to impatient questions from the judge.

If Harrison had known of or employed the adhesive tape technique, even his routine methods might have secured important micro-traces from the Pontiac. Instead, the routine vacuum-cleaning fetched up that dangerously irrelevant mixture of dirt in which micro-elements that had been caught in the fabric for many months and had no relation to the murder confused the whole picture.

On April 8 Durfee went to Kingston to help Harrison sort out the assembled traces. The clothes were vacuumed once more. Aside from hairs, which were sorted according to origin (Mason or Coolidge clothing, Pontiac) and placed on microscope slides, no effort was made to determine precisely what the micro-particles were or how frequently or rarely they occurred. Harrison contented himself with identifications such as "a blue particle, apparently of plastic," or "red dye on white paper." He made not a single exact determination of the material of any one particle. The sorting was done by color, red with red, blue with blue, yellow with yellow. Subsequently, the particles were placed under the microscope and those having the same structure were grouped together. By means of various microscopic techniques of illumination, they determined whether the hues of red, blue, or yellow were the same. Micro-traces from the clothing of Pamela Mason and Coolidge, and from dust extracted from the Pontiac, were regarded as identical on the basis of these cursory tests. Apparently Harrison did not know the intricacies of this field, or the pitfalls of simple color comparisons. To be sure, he tried to confirm the identity of the particles by some further physical and chemical tests. Thus he took their refractive index and solubility. In some instances he also determined the melting point of the unknown materials. Where he thought the particles might be of paper, he used the Hirtzberg test, one of the numerous color tests of the paper industry which is employed to grade, roughly, the cleanliness of cellulose. But none of these tests, applied singly or in combination, could really prove that two particles of unknown origin consisted of the same material. Different materials might even have the same solubility and melting point. And when Harrison later argued in court that one kind of cellulose was the same as any other, he could only arouse doubts of his competence.

In this manner Harrison selected 54 micro-trace particles, of which 27 came from the clothing of Pamela Mason and 27 from the clothing of Coolidge or from the Pontiac. He set them up in pairs and considered their identity substantiated on the basis of color, structure, refractive index, melting point, or Hirtzberg test. On the basis of these tests he concluded that one or several parts of the clothing of Pamela Mason had been in physical contact with the Pontiac or with Coolidge's jacket, or both.

During these same spring and summer months of 1964 during which Harrison and Durfee were engaged in this comparison of micro-particles, they also sorted out the hairs which had been obtained from various articles of clothing and the Pontiac. These amounted to quite a conglomerate. The sorting was done according to shade and to the categories of "human" and "animal." Later Durfee refined this somewhat by measuring the medullas, the cross sections, and so on. He came to the conclusion that several hairs from the jacket and two single hairs from Pamela Mason's ski pants might have come from Coolidge's head hair and pubic hair, and that two samples of hair from the Pontiac were identical with the hair from the dead girl's head. The hair studies, too, were later sharply contested in court. Samuel J. Golub pointed out, for example, that among the hairs found on Pamela Mason's clothing, which allegedly had come from Coolidge, was a crushed hair. Such crushing was characteristic of hair that had been subjected to heavy pressure, such as that from large automobile or truck tires. It therefore seemed more likely that this hair had come from the road surface of Interstate 93 rather than from Coolidge.

But whether or not Golub was right about this single case, Harrison and Durfee themselves seem to have felt some misgivings about the evidential value of their work during the summer of 1964. At any rate they looked for some confirmation of their conclusions. In February 1964 Harrison had attended the meeting of the American Academy of Forensic Science in Chicago. He had heard Perkons' paper and exchanged some words with Dr. H. Ward Smith of Toronto. Early in August he convinced

Durfee that neutron activation analysis must be applied to the hair studies. Eager to try this novelty, and with no notion of its complexities, he got in touch with Dr. Corliss of the University of Rhode Island and proposed that he undertake experiments with the technique. The University had had no experience in neutron activation analysis, but a research reactor was to be available in September. Harrison therefore turned to Toronto for information on the method. He wrote to Dr. H. Ward Smith explaining that he was engaged in a case and asking to be instructed on procedure.

32

When Harrison's letter arrived in Toronto, Jervis and Perkons undoubtedly regarded it as just one more among many inquiries from interested persons, but hardly as betokening a serious intention to use NAA almost immediately in a real criminal case. At Chicago in February they had not spoken of imminent criminalistic application of their work because they were completely absorbed in their scientific research. Since then, moreover, things had happened in their laboratory which flatly forbade practical applications. The use of a computer in the gamma-ray spectrometry of hairs, and their further evaluation of some 1000 samples, had alarmingly upset premises which but a few months ago had seemed securely established. The computer, which excluded subjective errors, revealed that errors could indeed creep in in their previous manual recording of the gamma-ray spectra, and, more significantly, that it was not advisable simply to compare the resultant spectra visually. Such simplified methods might at some future time be feasible when the results of measurements could be automatically recorded. For the present, however, it seemed unwise to forgo quantitative determinations for the various elements. Even more alarming were the conclusions following from evaluation of the studies of the 1000 hair samples. Even while this work was in progress, disturbing information had reached Toronto concerning the researches of several Brazilians, F. W. Lima, H. Shibata, and L. T. Atalla. These upset the assumptions underlying the previous work in hair comparison, in particular the assumption that the pattern of trace elements in the hair from the head of one individual would be similar. The Brazilians had found that there could be considerable differences in trace element content even in hairs taken from the same strand. And Francis M. Kerr, of Ottawa, had even found a reason for this unnerving fact. He called it "the hair cycle." The mass of hair on a human head was constantly changing, owing to growth and loss of some hair. After a single hair grew out of the hair root, there followed a lengthy period of quiescence, at the end of which the hair was expelled and a new hair began growing. Each hair root was independent of its neighbors, so that any strand of hair contained growing hairs alongside static hairs. Since the nourishment of the hair roots changed in keeping with changes in body nutrition, a static hair would contain different element patterns from a growing hair, and even in the growing hair much depended on its age. A hair comparison by means of neutron activation analysis could therefore provide reliable results only if the hairs were carefully selected beforehand and those of the same growth compared. In Kerr's opinion this was possible, but it imposed considerable restrictions on the hoped-for systematic application of NAA. Special precautions were necessary, and in a good many cases the technique simply could not be applied.

A further surprising difficulty arose from the discovery that the quantitative content of different elements in hair was interdependent. That is, the amount of one element influenced the possible amounts of other elements. In their evaluation of the 1000 hair samples Jervis and Perkons found that the amount of rubidium in the hair depended on the amount of sodium, the amount of strontium on the amount of bromine. This reduced the number of possible variations of trace element patterns and influenced the calculation of probabilities. Study of the hair of whole families revealed a certain tendency to congruences. The hair of newborn infants resembled the mother's hair in trace element patterns. Twins showed correspondences which diminished with increasing age. Persons who lived in particular regions or sections of cities might also share certain trace elements. All this affected the certainty of hair comparison by neutron activation analysis. Most puzzling of all remained the new knowledge of the differences in element patterns in the hair of the same individual. Jervis and Perkons had become aware that in their hair studies they were dealing with "living" substances which were subject to numerous changes in response to as yet largely unknown laws. They did not take this as a cause for resignation. NAA comparisons remained a method far superior to all previous microscopic techniques. But until they had faced up to the last possible surprises and limitations that the method held in store, it was unthinkable to introduce neutron activation analysis of hair into criminalistic practice and make it a routine procedure.

On August 20 Dr. H. Ward Smith had the requested information sent to Harrison. With it, however, went a personal letter warning Harrison against applying neutron activation analysis in its present state of development. The Toronto scientists, he wrote, regarded the whole area as insufficiently investigated to serve as a base in legal proceedings.

As far as Jervis and Perkons were concerned, that should have taken care of the inquiry from Rhode Island. In April 1965 the two flew to Texas to report to the Congress on the many-faceted problems that had arisen from studies of 1100 hair samples, and their tentative conclusions therefrom. From Texas they continued on to San Diego, where Vincent P. Guinn was holding a seminar on criminalistic neutron activation analysis. The United States seemed to be on the way to assuming leadership in the development of the new method. Guinn himself obviously realized that the future of criminalistic neutron activation analysis might well lie not in the realm of comparing organic materials, which were subject to constant change, but in dealing with stable, unchanging inorganic trace elements. After a series of initial experiments with powder and paint traces, Guinn had undertaken some experiments in comparing wood and soils. But he had soon run into the thorny problem of the alteration of living materials, which made it so very dangerous to conclude from the formal correspondences of trace elements that certain woods or soils were actually identical. Advised by the experienced criminalists of Los Angeles, Guinn and his growing staff of associates had systematically continued their research into neutron activation analysis in connection with synthetic textiles, automobile tire rubbers, automobile greases, glass, and paints. They were astounded at the accuracy with which activation analysis revealed a wide variety of trace elements in plastics. Up to eleven elements could be detected and their quantities determined. With plastics of homogeneous composition, only formal comparison was necessary to determine correspondence or noncorrespondence. Difficulties appeared only in nonhomogeneous plastics. The same was true for tires, greases, paints, and glass. All these materials could supply significant trace clues not only in crimes, but in tens of thousands of traffic accidents.

On July 3, 1964, Guinn had achieved a success that attracted wide attention. For the first time an American court in San Mateo County, California, admitted neutron activation analysis as evidence and arrived at a verdict solely on the basis of a comparison of paint traces. On October 25, 1963, the police in South San Francisco were alerted by the burglar alarm of the Buri Buri Liquor Store. When they reached the rear entrance of the store, they found that someone had attempted to break in. By the door lay a tire iron that had apparently been used as a burglary tool.

Nearby stood a young man, William Ray Woodward of Daly City, who said he had just happened by and was on his way to his car, which was parked in a side street. Possibly he would have got away with this alibi if the police had not noticed a flake of light blue paint on the tire iron, resembling the light blue color of Woodward's car. There were also cracked bits of paint in the trunk of the car. Paul M. Dougherty, of the Sheriff's office in Redwood City, examined the flakes of paint and the tire iron. On the iron he discovered another trace of paint, this time of a brown hue that resembled the paint on the back door of the liquor store. Both paint traces were so tiny that comparison by traditional methods seemed hopeless. As a result of the excellent rapport between Guinn and the California criminalists, Dougherty telephoned Pinker in Los Angeles, reported his find, and was advised to fly to San Diego. He arrived in San Diego on December 5, bringing with him the flakes of paint, some paint samplings from Woodward's car, and a section of the brown door frame. Donald E. Bryan was assigned to conduct the comparisons by gamma-ray measurement. Because of the differing measurement intervals, the testing lasted from December 6 to 27. But by then a final and indisputable result was obtained. The blue particles of paint and the samples of paint from Woodward's trunk contained five of the same elements in the same proportions: titanium, aluminum, sodium, copper, and manganese. The brown paint samples contained seven of the same elements in corresponding proportions: manganese, sodium, antimony, zinc, indium, aluminum, and titanium. When Woodward came to trial on July 3, 1964, all the efforts of his lawyer failed to shake the results of the analyses. But more important than the verdict was the precedent that had been established in favor of this type of testimony.

By the spring of 1965 the Woodward case was widely known throughout the United States as a model of the criminalistic potentialities of neutron activation analysis, and Guinn was much encouraged to intensify his work in San Diego. Jervis and Perkons, for their part, had reported on an admirable series of experiments and had arrived at new insights in the field of hair analysis. But Perkons concluded his report this time on a cautious note: "It is possible that in the near future, criminalists should be able to introduce evidence of comparisons of this type in the law courts, supported by the results of a large number of hair studies such as are reported in this paper. It is, however, not yet reliable to extend the activation 'matching' or 'individualization' method to single hair evidence commonly encountered in crime investigations."

On April 29 Jervis flew back to Toronto. He was deeply absorbed in the "two aspects of neutron activation analysis," of which he had chosen the most difficult, the biological aspect. In Toronto a telephone call from New Hampshire was put through to him. A man he had never heard of, a lawyer named Matthias J. Reynolds, explained that he was representing a young man, Edward H. Coolidge of Manchester, who was accused of having murdered a girl. The trial of Coolidge was scheduled to begin on May 17. Maynard, the prosecutor, with the aid of a Lieutenant Durfee and a Dr. Harrison of Rhode Island, had accumulated a considerable amount of scientific evidence, much of which was based on neutron activation analysis which might well make a great impression on the jurors. Some fifteen hairs and some plastic particles had been examined by NAA. The conclusion had been reached that the hairs found on the dead body were identical with Coolidge's hair. . . .

Startled and alarmed, Jervis asked who had carried out the studies. It seemed that the university reactor in Rhode Island had not been ready in time, and the reactor at the Massachusetts Institute of Technology was not available. Maynard had therefore turned to the laboratory of the Alcohol and Tobacco Tax Division of the U. S. Treasury Department in Washington. The hair studies had been concluded in January; they had been carried out by two chemists, Maynard Pro and Michael Hoffman. Pro had stated that his work was based on the researches of Drs. Jervis and Perkons. Therefore, Reynolds now asked, would Dr. Jervis be willing to advise the defense and to check the reliability of the opinion from Washington? In view of the references to Jervis's own research as the basis of the analyses, the court was agreeable to having him check the work of the Washington scientists as an expert for the defense.

The name Pro meant nothing to Jervis. Consequently Jervis uneasily sensed something was afoot which in view of the problems that had arisen might result in irrevocably casting discredit on his whole enterprise. In the course of the telephone call, he recalled Harrison's inquiry and Smith's warning reply. Reynolds, who found the reference to the correspondence with Dr. Smith highly interesting, promised to report in greater detail by letter and to send copies of the Washington studies.

The Alcohol and Tobacco Tax Division of the Treasury Department had long maintained a laboratory in Washington. During Prohibition its major task had been to assist in tracking down illegal stills. Since the end of the Second World War the battle against tax evasion by clandestine manufacture or importation of alcohol and narcotics had risen to new highs. The small laboratory had been enlarged, and in 1950 Maynard J. Pro, a New York chemist, had entered the Treasury Department with the principal assignment of modernizing the technical equipment. Pro, an inconspicuous, quiet, but ambitious "idea man," had studied at Columbia University and during the war had worked on poison gases at Edgewood Arsenal.

In 1956 Pro had first turned his attention to the possible contribution of nuclear chemistry to the task of the Treasury Department. For decades the Internal Revenue Service had been concerned with a special problem: how to verify the age assigned to imported spirits. Since 1952 the test explosions of hydrogen bombs had discharged large quantities of tritium, a radioactive isotope of hydrogen, into the atmosphere. This tritium united with ozone and reached the earth as water. Water used for the manufacture of alcohol after 1952 should therefore be characterized by a higher tritium content. If this tritium could be identified, there would be some indication of the age of the alcohol under investigation.

Pro had been dealing with this problem for some years when the news from Edmundston of the first application of neutron activation analysis in the Bouchard case aroused his interest. Because large quantities of opium and other narcotics were reaching the United States particularly during the years 1959 and 1960, the idea arose of examining confiscated drugs by neutron activation analysis in order to determine their place of origin. It seemed likely that the poppy plants from which the opium came would take in quantities of trace elements from the soil in which they grew, and that these elements would be different in China, India, and other opium-growing areas. If so, NAA would supply hints as to the countries of origin. The Treasury Department got in touch with the Atomic Energy Commission, which referred it to George W. Leddicotte, a young chemist who headed the Nuclear Analysis Division in the atomic laboratories at Oak Ridge, Tennessee. George Anslinger of the United Nations obtained standard samples of narcotic drugs from all the producing areas of the world, and Leddicotte embarked on an extensive program of research. Perkons had led the way in this field also, having already analyzed some twenty-eight opium samples from different locations.

Maynard Pro was necessarily drawn into this work to a certain extent. Before long the Oak Ridge team had extended its experiments to traces of soil, paints, and drugs other than opium. Such substances could be important for Treasury agents who wanted to know, for example, where confiscated trucks with loads of smuggled liquor had come from. Soil clinging to the wheels could be compared with samples of earth from around houses in which illegal distilleries were suspected. Paint studies were also significant because the alcohol often contained traces of paint

453

from containers or distilling apparatus. Pro devoted himself more and more to the application of neutron activation analysis to clues of this type. He was not a research chemist in the deeper sense of the word. He was a practical man who was enthusiastic about a new method, who realized that it had a great future and wanted to make its potentialities available to himself and his Washington laboratory as quickly as possible. Whether he was impelled by excessive ambition to move too fast, as later critics asserted, must remain an open question. In 1961 and 1962 the Internal Revenue Service placed some $80,000 at Pro's disposal to be used for measuring instruments for gamma-ray spectrometry, thus eliminating the trips to Oak Ridge that had previously been necessary, and calls upon the time of the scientists there. From 1963 on Pro worked with several assistants, including Howard Schlesinger and later Michael Hoffman, on neutron activation analysis in his own small Washington laboratory. Activation of the materials to be investigated was largely done in an atomic reactor of the Armed Forces Radiobiology Research Institute in Bethesda, Maryland, which was conveniently near. And as early as July 1964 the Alcohol and Tobacco Tax Division sent out a little brochure entitled *Physical Evidence* to law enforcement officers of all sorts. It described the scientific investigation facilities of the Washington laboratory. Of the pamphlet's twenty-three pages, eight were devoted to neutron activation analysis. The laboratory offered neutron activation studies of the following materials: mash and alcoholic distillates, paints, soils, tobaccos, debris on clothing and vehicles, drugs, coins, gunpowder residue, automobile greases, wood, pipe and wire, glass, plastic, hair, and "other physical evidence." Since the pamphlet was addressed not only to agents of the Division, but also to police authorities all over the country, it gave advice on how physical evidence could be secured, packed, and sent to Washington for analysis.

This whole program was marked by a striking lack of the restraint and caution with which such men as Guinn in San Diego and Pinker in Los Angeles operated. Even before the Guinn team had first taken the results of a neutron activation analysis into court in the Woodward case, Pro had already made two appearances before federal justices. On March 16, 1964, some liquor dealers were found guilty of having transported a truckful of illegal brandy from a distillery in Atlanta to New York. Schlesinger and Pro had compared soil traces on the truck tires with soil from the vicinity of the distillery by means of gamma-ray spectrometry. In both cases they had determined the *qualitative* presence of nine of the same trace elements and concluded that the soil was the same. Barely nine weeks later, on May 21, a federal court in Cincinnati convicted a man who had sent his brother a radio set filled with dynamite. The set was so constructed that it would explode when plugged in. Pro's laboratory examined adhesive tape strips and putty from the radio bomb and tape strips and putty from the garage of the presumed culprit. Six corresponding trace elements were found on the tapes and seven in the putties. In both the New York and the Cincinnati cases Pro curiously enough contented himself with determining the kinds of elements and disregarding the proportions involved.

Be that as it may, knowledge of the work of the Washington laboratory and its successes in court prompted Attorney General Maynard in Concord to turn to Pro. In January 1965 Durfee went to Washington with his hair clues, which for months had lain preserved in distilled water and glycerin. The exhibits consisted mostly of single hairs. There were: 1. Head hair of Pamela Mason. 2. Pubic hair of Pamela Mason. 3, 4, and 5. Hair from Pamela Mason's jacket. 6. Hair from Pamela Mason's ski pants. 7. Hair from Coolidge's Pontiac. 8. Hair from Coolidge's jacket. 9. Hair from Pamela Mason's jacket. 10 and 11. Pubic hair from Coolidge. 12. Head hair from Coolidge. 13. Hair from Coolidge's Pontiac. 14. Hair from Coolidge's chest. 15. Hair from Coolidge's forearm.

Pro's assistant, Hoffman, placed each of the samples, without cleaning them beforehand, in a plastic capsule and drove to Bethesda, accompanied by Durfee. There the hairs were exposed to the neutron flux of the reactor for two hours. Hoffman and Pro then began their first gamma-ray measurements, and on January 28 they sent Attorney General Maynard a six-page report on their study. Attached to it were copies of the gamma spectra, with some thirty graphs. Their conclusions were that the hairs of Pamela Mason and Coolidge showed different trace-element patterns and could therefore be distinguished. The two hairs from Coolidge's car fitted into the pattern of Pamela Mason's hair. The hair from Pamela Mason's jacket and pants corresponded in its trace elements with Coolidge's pubic hair.

Hard upon this report, Michael Hoffman himself went to Rhode Island to see whether the micro-traces that Harrison had examined would also lend themselves to neutron activation analysis. He took some of the particles back to Washington and after a while reported that the trace-element patterns of a number of them corresponded. At this point Harrison, Durfee, and the prosecutor became firmly convinced that they had in hand an unbreakable chain of factual evidence against Coolidge, and that the NAA opinions represented a trump card that would surely make the deepest impression upon any juror. Defense Attorney Reynolds could see the ominous prospects for his client. His sole hope was that Dr. Jervis might find some fault with the work of the Washington experts.

When Jervis received Maynard Pro's report and copies of the gamma-ray spectra of the hair studies, he quickly found his worst fears confirmed. Pro's spectra at best were of the kind he and his colleagues had prepared years ago. Pro had consistently determined about seven trace elements instead of ten to fourteen, and had supplied no data on the quantity of hair in the various samples. Neither did he disclose how many of these results had been based on single hairs—which at least for the present were ineligible for hair comparison studies. From the photocopies of the spectrograms alone Jervis concluded that several "peaks" had been wrongly indicated. The elements potassium and antimony, which Pro claimed he had found in the head hair of Pamela Mason as well as the hair from Coolidge's Pontiac, were simply not present, or at least there was no evidence for their presence. In the spectra for the hairs from Pamela Mason's jacket and slacks, and for Coolidge's pubic hair, Jervis could not find the "peaks" which supposedly indicated the presence of chlorine and silver. The elements calcium and bromine were cited in other spectra when there were no signs of their presence. Jervis could accept the analysis of only five peaks: for sodium, manganese, copper, zinc, and mercury—the very elements that counted least for hair comparisons because they were too widely distributed. Sodium was to be found in all hair, mercury in 751 of 776 hairs, and copper in 629 of 776 hairs, as Perkons had shown in his studies.

Not only were there errors in the determination of the kind of elements: Jervis was utterly confounded by the fact that Pro had apparently not undertaken to determine the quantities of the various elements. For the differing quantities alone would provide the characteristic trace-element patterns. In the analysis of Pamela Mason's head hair, the hairs from the Pontiac, Coolidge's pubic hair, and the hairs from Pamela Mason's jacket and slacks Pro had contented himself with a visual comparison of the height of the peaks for copper, manganese, and mercury, from which he had drawn vague and highly dubious conclusions about the quantitative proportions of these elements. There were no actual quantitative determinations at all. Jervis also found it incredible that the activation of the hair samples had been limited to two hours, whereas his and Perkons' years of experiments had shown the need for irradiation periods twenty to thirty times as long if a useful number of trace elements were to be identified. In his appended comments, Pro made the point that the correspondence between the hairs from the car and the victim's head hair was especially confirmed by the presence of antimony and silver in both, since these two trace elements occurred so rarely in hair. In Perkons' series of studies he had found silver in at least 60 per cent and antimony in 65 per cent of all hairs. As for Pro's concluding remarks that "head hairs from one person, taken at different times, have the same composition," they indicated that he had simply not followed the most recent warnings in the literature.

Highly exercised, Jervis informed Defense Attorney Reynolds of his reaction, and recommended that he ask the prosecution for the original records, on the basis of which Pro had drawn the spectra by hand. He suspected that other mistakes might have arisen in the process of transfer. At any rate it was unthinkable that these inadequate spectra might in some circumstance decide the fate of a defendant.

Reynolds did not succeed in obtaining the original documents from the prosecution. He could only assure Jervis that they would certainly be available during the trial itself.

33

On Monday, May 17, 1965, Justice Robert F. Griffith opened the trial of Edward H. Coolidge in a jammed courtroom in Manchester. The case of Sandra Valade was "reserved," and Coolidge was charged with the murder of Pamela Mason. Three weeks later, on June 8, Jervis for the first time set foot in a courtroom, prepared to defend the cause of neutron activation analysis against the dangers of inadequate or premature applications.

Reynolds had hitherto accomplished little against the witnesses who exposed Coolidge's lies about the evening of the crime and his efforts to establish false alibis. Reynolds had also not challenged the opinions of ballistics experts, from Beaudoin to Grandchamp, that the bullets from Coolidge's Mossberg rifle had killed both Pamela Mason and Sandra Valade, although the inclusion of evidence from the Valade case was not really admissible. In fact Reynolds' restraint had struck observers at the trial as so unusual that they sensed some adroit chess move behind it. And in fact Reynolds was planning a coup for the later days of the trial. He was in a position to prove that the Mossberg rifle had first come into Coolidge's possession at Christmas 1961 as a prize in a competition held by the Coca-Cola Bottling Company, of which Coolidge was an employee.

If, therefore, the prosecution experts claimed that this rifle had killed not only Pamela Mason in January 1964 but also Sandra Valade in January 1960, their verdict must be faulty and worthless. But the gun question was of secondary importance and had to wait. The decisive struggle would be the scientific one, which was set for June 9 and 10.

The prosecution had set June 9 as the date for the testimony of Lieutenant Durfee and Dr. Harrison on the comparative tests of the hair and particle clues. But that was only the prelude to the court appearance of the Washington experts, Maynard Pro and Michael Hoffman. The sensational revelations that were expected were foreshadowed in the pages of the *Manchester Union Leader* and other newspapers. On June 7 the *Leader* announced: "Two federal experts will testify for the state. . . . Both are experts in the field of 'neutron activation analysis,' a science regarded as the most revolutionary development since the perfection of the fingerprint system. They are Maynard Pro and Michael Hoffman. . . . The scientific evidence to come from Pro and Hoffman is expected to climax the state's charge against Coolidge. . . . The state will seek to show through testimony by Pro and Hoffman that two strands of hair found in Coolidge's 1951 Pontiac sedan match hair snipped from Pamela's head after her body was found." The article added that Pro and Hoffman were also ready to prove by neutron activation analysis that thirty to forty particles taken from the victim's clothes corresponded with particles found on the clothes of Edward H. Coolidge and in the interior of his car.

Jervis sat listening with intense interest to the testimony of Durfee and Harrison. Once more he recalled Harrison's letter to H. Ward Smith and Smith's clear warning against premature experiments. Had Harrison actually disregarded these warnings? Had he failed to mention them to the prosecution?

At the beginning of the June 8th session three more scientists joined Jervis: Constantine J. Maletskos, senior scientist at the Cancer Research Center in the New England Deaconess Hospital, who had performed radioactivation studies from 1956 to 1960 and had investigated the role of trace elements in the human body; Samuel J. Golub, textile fiber and hair expert; and C. S. Hurlbut, Professor of Mineralogy at Harvard. Reynolds had turned to them and they had pointed out weaknesses in Harrison's methods. The journalists could sense the ferocity of the coming disputes. Jay Hanlon and Jim Stack reported in the *Manchester Union Leader*: "A clash of experts was assured yesterday with the appearance in the courtroom of four defense witnesses who come armed with impressive credentials of their own. . . . Dr. Jervis, notably, was described by a defense attorney as 'a pioneer in the field of neutron activation analysis,' the revolutionary crime detection technique on which the state is banking heavily in its case against Coolidge."

The struggle began with preliminary skirmishing between Reynolds and Carroll Durfee. The stalwart retired State Police Lieutenant, who had acted mostly as a technical assistant, withstood Reynolds' attacks. Harrison withstood them somewhat less well. His methods of particle comparison offered so many openings for question, and Harrison himself displayed so much uncertainty, that he was frequently hard pressed even before Reynolds fired his first shot on the question of neutron activation analysis: the matter of Harrison's letter to Toronto and Smith's warning reply. Was it true, he inquired, that Harrison had appealed to Toronto in August? Was it true that he had obtained information about NAA?

After a great deal of argument back and forth, Reynolds persuaded Harrison to read the letter he had addressed to Smith at the time. He then asked about the answer. Had not Smith cautioned him? At this moment Attorney General Maynard rose to his feet, as if he sensed the danger to his cause. He protested that the content of Smith's answer could not be presented to the jurors because Dr. Smith was not present as a witness and the prosecution therefore could not cross-examine him about the content of the letter. On legal grounds Justice Griffith sustained his objection and forbade the reading of the letter. But Reynolds did not give up. Repeatedly interrupted by Maynard's objections, he tried to extract from Harrison the sense of Smith's letter and why Harrison had disregarded a plain warning. He tried at least a dozen times, until the judge banned any further questions along those lines.

Thus the first attack evidently had failed—but it only seemed that way. June 10 became a dramatic day behind the scenes. Justice Griffith was informed on two matters: the contents of Smith's letter and Reynolds' vain efforts to obtain from the prosecution the original documentation of Pro's and Hoffman's measurements. As for the letter, it turned out that Harrison had never transmitted it to Maynard. But the original measurements were not available either. The prosecution had never received them. Maynard Pro reported that owing to lack of space in the Washington laboratory they had been destroyed, and that this had also been done with all other NAA reports he had hitherto filed. This information sowed such strong misgivings in Justice Griffith that he decided to hear Pro and Hoffman testify on June 11 in the absence of the jury for the time being, and to listen to the opinions of Jervis and Maletskos also. He would then decide whether to let the jury be informed of the reports by the Washington chemists.

On the morning of June 11 Maynard Pro appeared to testify about his studies. He spoke in a low, nervous voice. Within a short time it became apparent that Maynard, disturbed by the events of the preceding day, must have conferred with Pro or Hoffman to dispel his doubts. Apparently he had reassured himself once more that Pro had carried out his work on the basis of publications by Jervis and Perkons. Pro's testimony began with a listing of the fundamental lectures and publications by Jervis and Perkons between 1961 and 1965. With what seemed a clear conscience, Pro admitted that he had made no quantitative determination of the elements. He had merely drawn and compared the graphs and the peaks. He referred to Perkons' statements in Chicago in the spring of 1964 that "for the purpose of identification and matching of samples of hair or other materials it is not absolutely necessary to do a complete quantitative analysis based on a large volume of compiled statistical data. The analog recordings of the gamma-ray spectra show sufficient differences between dissimilar samples on the one hand, and sufficient similarity between duplicate samples from one individual, on the other hand, that purely visual identification may in some instances be feasible." Pro insisted that he had performed the comparisons in accord with the literature on the subject.

Jervis began to understand what had happened. Unhappily he realized that not only inadequate experience and excessive haste were to blame here, but also his own and Perkons' premature optimism of earlier years. Remarks that had been intended only for researchers had misled a man like Pro into rashly applying simplified methods which, given his limited experience, he should not have applied at all. It was true that Perkons had made the statements to which Pro now appealed—but under vastly different circumstances, against a background of far more experience in the making and analysis of spectrograms—even before the computer was employed in Toronto. When Maynard asked what information was necessary for carrying out gamma-ray measurements, Pro replied that the apparatus was extremely simple, that the whole problem was as easy as pressing a button. With a sinking heart Jervis heard Pro once more defend the correctness of his results: "It could be said with a high degree of reliability the hair came from the same source."

At eleven thirty Pro's direct testimony was finished, and the judge adjourned proceedings until one thirty. Then Reynolds began his cross-examination of Pro. By this time Jervis must have realized that as soon as he took the witness stand himself he would have no choice but to admit his and his associates' own mistakes and excessive optimism, in particular their underestimation of the effect of their own publications on persons with less experience in the field than their own. But that was certainly not the whole story. More careful study of the literature should have warned Pro against picking out only the methods that seemed simple and routinely applicable.

Opening his cross-examination after the lunch recess, Reynolds, well cued by Jervis and Maletskos, subjected Pro to a severe grilling. It lasted until after five o'clock and on the following day, a Saturday, from ten in the morning until well into the afternoon. Reynolds' innumerable questions drew from Pro admissions proving that he had ventured into a field he had not mastered. He had thought it sufficient to determine seven elements qualitatively. Determination of twelve or more elements seemed to him impossible and in any case unnecessary. He did not think there was anything wrong in having based his study on single hairs. Quantitative analysis of the elements seemed to him superfluous. He regarded the presence of seven corresponding elements, without consideration of their different quantities, as proof that the hairs had come from the same source, and maintained that the probability of a repetition of such a combination was $1:4,150,000$. He was not bothered by the fact that the hairs had been placed in the reactor without having been cleaned, and considered two hours long enough for activation. He dismissed the idea that longer activation would reveal more, at least fourteen elements, and denied that the manual transfer of the measurements to spectrograms, as had been done in Washington, could introduce errors. He saw no harm in having destroyed the original data. Still and all, he more and more frequently resorted to such phrases as "I think" or "I do not think" or "the literature says this is not necessary."

It was a depressing spectacle. Yet during those two days Jervis repeatedly reflected on the question of where the fault lay. He saw clearly what distinguished him from Pro. It was a highly significant, a fateful difference. Because of the extent of his work on human hair he had seen still unsolved problems in nature, which Pro had not noticed at all. He had recognized difficulties where Pro found everything settled and arranged in a neat formula. He had learned that nature constantly revealed new aspects which could not be grasped formalistically. Even in the technological age things were not going to be open and shut in the field of crime investigation, nor would those problems disappear that arose from the multifariousness of living phenomena. And so, when he himself took the witness stand on June 12, he defended neutron activation analysis as an excellent method when applied with care. But he pointed out that he and his colleagues would never venture to compare hairs by the methods that Pro and Hoffman had applied, or even by the methods that they themselves had applied in the past. But even though this was an admission of his own errors of the past, he could not avoid, in the course of the questions and cross-examination, condemning Pro's carelessness. The climax of his testimony was reached when he observed that the five elements whose presence he could recognize from Pro's data occurred in the hair of every other human being and without qualitative determinations had no significance as evidence whatsoever. This point alone demolished the whole scientific report.

On June 15, 1965, the *Manchester Union Leader* announced: "Defense lawyers for Edward H. Coolidge Jr. won a major victory in Superior Court today when Justice Robert F. Griffith ruled out certain key scientific testimony presented by prosecution experts. At the outset of today's session the judge told the all-male jury he was excluding from the evidence the neutron activation analysis of human hair. . . . The effect of his ruling was considered to be a damaging blow to the prosecution."

Griffith justified his action to the jurors as follows: "I have excluded it [neutron activation analysis] because I feel it would be misleading since it was presented to you with perfectly good faith by the state as evidence as reliable as fingerprints in identification. . . . The court is of the opinion that this field offers great opportunity in the future for analysis and identification. It does not believe it should accept evidence not acceptable by the scientists in general. The court feels that to accept Dr. Jervis' work as a basis and then deny the statements of Dr. Jervis, who does not feel it was properly done at this trial, would be improper." He concluded by saying that he would admit the NAA analysis of the plastic particles because these apparently belonged in another field.

Griffith's decision indicated a realization, even by a layman, that there was a dividing line within the nuclear methods between investigation of "static" inorganic substances and "living" organic substances.

It represented a triumph for Reynolds. For Jervis, it only confirmed the knowledge he already had: that he and all other researchers in the field of hair analysis still faced many years of arduous studies before they could present hair comparisons with any degree of assurance.

Reynolds did not enjoy his triumph for long. The exclusion of the hair analyses no more prevented Coolidge's conviction than his trump card in regard to the origin of the Mossberg rifle. It turned out that Mossbergs had no serial numbers, hence there was no proof that Coolidge's Mossberg was the weapon he had received as a prize at Christmas 1961. The whole of the scientific evidence in the case came to nothing. But Coolidge settled his fate when he was called as a witness in his own cause and during the cross-examination entangled himself in such a net of contradictions that on June 23 the jurors pronounced him guilty. He was sentenced to life imprisonment. To Reynolds this meant the "loss" of a case, at least for the present, to which he had devoted enormous pains, intelligence, and passion. But to Jervis the struggle in Manchester was a critical test for the whole scientific field he and his colleagues had pioneered. He knew that he, Perkons, and other researchers in the field must do everything in their power to prevent any more such premature applications of their work.

Nine months later, Perkons and Jervis published another account of their studies of trace elements in human head hair, warning against over-enthusiasm. A long way still lies ahead before activation analysis becomes a routine tool in crime detection, but that it will eventually benefit detection work seems a reasonable conclusion.

Bibliography

Adelsberger, L., and Schiff, F., "Die Blutgruppendiagnose als forensische Methode," *Ärztliche Sachverständigen Zeitung,* XI (1924), 101–03.

Adler, O. u. R., "Über das Verhalten gewisser organischer Verbindungen gegenüber Blut, mit besonderer Berücksichtigung des Nachweises von Blut," *Hoppe-Seylers Zeitschrift,* Jahrg. 41 (1904), 59.

Albert, "Unterscheidung von Blutflecken und rothen Färbeflecken in Kleidungsstücken," *Henkes Zeitschrift für Staatsarzneykunde,* 1855.

Anliong, Chen, "Ist eine Individualdiagnose beim menschlichen Haar möglich?" *Archiv für Kriminologie,* CXVIII (1956), 145–48.

Archibald, Bill, *The Bradley Case.* Sydney, 1961.

Arnau, Frank, *Warum Menschen Menschen töten.* Düsseldorf, 1964.

Ashton-Wolfe, Harry, *The Invisible Web (From Documents Supplied by Dr. Edmond Locard).* London, n.d.

Balthazard, Victor, *Précis de médecine légale,* 6th ed., rev. Paris, 1943.

Balthazard, Victor, and Lambert, Marcelle, *Le Poil de l'homme et des animaux,* 1910.

Balthazard, Victor, *et al.,* "Étude des gouttes de sang projeté," *Annales de médecine légale,* XIX (1939), 19.

Baly, E. C. C., *Spectroscopy I–IV.* London, 1927.

Barclay, Weston, "The Case of the Man Who Kneaded Candy," *New York World Telegram,* December 1, 1945.

Barni, M., "Sulla determinazione dei sottogruppi A_1 e A_2 nelle macchie di sangue," *Atti dell' Accademia Fisiocritici,* XIII (1954/55), 399.

Bate, L. C., and Pro, M. J., "Applications of Activation Analysis to Forensic Science," *The International Journal of Applied Radiation and Isotopes,* XV (1964), 111–14.

Baud, Linda, *Tagebuch einer verbotenen Liebe, Die menschlichen Hintergründe im Prozess Jaccoud.* Bern, 1960.

Bayle, Edmond, "Une Affaire Criminelle vue au laboratoire," *Bulletin de l'Association des Élèves de l'Institut de Criminologie de l'Université de Paris,* II, 1 (January-February, 1927), 3–8.

Beck, W. V., "Untersuchungen zur Feststellung der Gleichartigkeit von Bindfäden," *Archiv für Kriminologie,* CII (1938), 209.

Behrens, Wilhelm, *Hilfsbuch zur Ausführung mikroskopischer Untersuchungen in botanischen Laboratorien.* Braunschweig, 1883.

Bell, H. W., *Sherlock Holmes and Dr. Watson.* London, 1932.

Bendigo, C. W., *Textile World's Synthetic Fiber Table.* New York, 1945.

Bercher, J. H., *Étude médico-légale de l'œuvre de Conan Doyle et de la police scientifique au XXe siècle.* Thèse du laboratoire de médecine légale de Lyon. Lyon, 1906.

Berg, Karl, "Bericht über die 15. Tagung der Deutschen Gesellschaft für gerichtliche und soziale Medizin in Düsseldorf vom 18. bis 23. September 1926," *Deutsche Zeitschrift für die gesamte gerichtliche Medizin* (1926), 60–7.

Berg, Steffen, "Die Beweiskraft medizinischbiologischer Untersuchungsergebnisse," *Grundfragen der Kriminaltechnik.* Bundeskriminalamt Wiesbaden, 1958.

———, "Die Bedeutung zytochemischer Methoden für die Auswertung von Blutspuren, insbesondere deren Altersbestimmung," *Archiv für Kriminologie,* CXXXVI, 1st and 2nd Series (1965), 14–21.

Bibliography

———, "Die Blutgruppendiagnose aus Speichelspuren und anderen Körpersekreten in der kriminalistischen Praxis," *Archiv für Kriminologie*, CVI (1955), 81.

———, "Entwicklungen in der polizeilichen Kriminaltechnik," *Archiv für Kriminologie*, CXXXV, 3/4 (1965).

———, "Kriminalwissenschaftliche Tagungen und fachliche Situationen der staatlichen Sachverständigen," *Kriminalistik* (February, 1962), 75.

———, *Der Sexualverbrecher*. Hamburg, 1963.

Bergh, A. K., "Einige Aspekte der Identifizierung von synthetischen Fasern," *Internationale Kriminalpolizeiliche Revue* (October, 1955), 246.

Bertillon, Suzanne, *Vie d'Alphonse Bertillon*. Paris, 1940.

Bickerich, R., and Pettenkofer, H., "Zur direkten Bestimmung der Blutgruppe O aus Blut und Sekretflecken," *Archiv für Kriminologie*, CXX (1957), 129.

Blakeney, Thomas S., *Sherlock Holmes: Fact or Fiction?* London, 1932.

Blickenstorfer, Walter, "Peinliche Fragen zum Fall Jaccoud," *Züricher Woche* (May 13, 1960).

———, "Zum Fall Jaccoud, War die 'Rote Hand' im Spiel," *Züricher Woche* (April 22, 1960).

Block, Eugene B., *The Wizard of Berkeley*. New York, 1958.

Boller, Werner, "Vorschlag einer neuen forensischen Haaruntersuchungsmethode," *Archiv für Kriminologie*, C (1937), 8.

Bonnefoy, Marcel, "Les Expertises judiciaires nous font frémir," *Constellation*, CXLIV (April, 1960).

Bovard, Pierre-André, "À propos de l'affaire Jaccoud," *Revue de Science Criminelle et de Droit Pénal Comparé* (Nouvelle Série 1960), I.

Boyd, W. C., and Shapleigh, E., "Specific Precipitating Activity of Plant Agglutinins (Lectins)," *Science*, CXIX (1954), 419.

Brahn, B., and Fisch, F., "Das chemische Verhalten der serologischen Gruppenstoffe A und B, ihr Vorkommen und ihr Nachweis in Körperflüssigkeiten," *Klinische Wochenschrift*, VIII (1929), 1523.

Browne, Douglas G., and Tullet, E. V., *Bernard Spilsbury: His Life and Cases*. London, 1952.

Brüning, August, "Aus den Erinnerungen eines gerichtlichen Chemikers," *Chemiker-Zeitung*, LXVI (1942), 242–7.

———, "Beiträge zur Überführung von Verbrechern durch den Nachweis von Leitelementen an ihrem Körper und ihrer Kleidung," *Archiv für Kriminologie*, LXXV (1923), 266–69.

———, "Überblick über die historische Entwicklung der naturwissenschaftlichen Kriminalistik," *Archiv für Kriminologie*, CXIX, 3/4 (1957).

———, and Harder, O., *Die Kriminalität bei der Post*. Berlin, 1924.

Brussey-Malville, Jacques de, "Le Docteur Paul va fêter sa 100,000e autopsie," in *La Nouvelle République*, Bordeaux, August 28, 1947.

Budvári, R., "Über eine neue Methode der Blutgruppenuntersuchung in Blutflecken mittels Agglutininelution," *Deutsche Zeitschrift für die gesamte gerichtliche Medizin*, LIV (1963), 24.

Burns, Creighton, *The Tait Case*. Melbourne, 1962.

Burt, Leonard, *Commander Burt of Scotland Yard, By Himself*. London, 1959.

Carr, John Dickson, *The Life of Sir Arthur Conan Doyle*. New York, 1949.

Carr, William H. A., "The Murder Doctor: A Look at the City Medical Examiner Office," *New York Post*, August 19, 1964.

Casanova, Ed., "Un Crime mystérieux," *Le Figaro*, July 19, 1909.

Ceppellini, R., "Leone Lattes (In Memoriam) 1887–1954," *Boll. Ist. Sierotera-pèutico Milanese*, XXXIII (December, 1954), 649–50.

Cherrill, Fred, *Cherrill of the Yard*. London, 1954.

Civil Aeronautics Board, *Accident Investigation Report United Air Lines, Inc., Douglas DC-6 B N 37559, Near Longmont, Colorado, November 1, 1955*.

Clarke, A. F., "Scientific Aspects of the Thorne Kidnapping and Murder in July 1960," *The Australian Police Journal*, XVI, 3 (July, 1962).

Bibliography

Clavetie, Georges, "Gazette des Tribunaux—Cour d'Assises de la Seine: La pluie de sang," *Le Figaro,* February 8, 1910.

Cocks, F. B., "Taxonomy and Plant Ecology in the Field of Forensic Science," *The Australian Police Journal,* XIX, 3 (July, 1965).

Cohan, M., *et al.,* "Activation Analysis of Physical Evidence Connected with Illicit Distilleries," *Journal of the Association of Official Agricultural Chemists,* XLVIII (June, 1965).

Coombs, R. R. A., and Dodd, B., "Possible Application of the Principle of Mixed Agglutination in the Identification of Blood Stains," *Medicine, Science and the Law,* I (1960/61), 59.

Coombs, R. R. A., *et al.,* "A and B Blood Group Antigens on Human Epidermal Cells, Demonstrated by Mixed Agglutination," *Lancet,* XXI (1956), 461.

———, "Detection of Weak or Incomplete Rh-agglutinins," *Lancet,* II, 15 (1945).

Cornish, G. W., *Cornish of the "Yard."* London, 1935.

Cramer, James, *The World's Police.* London, 1954.

Curry, A. S., *Methods of Forensic Science.* New York, 1964.

Cuthbert, C. R. M., *Science and the Detection of Crime.* London, 1958.

Cuyahoga County Coroner's Statistical Report 1958. Cleveland, 1959.

Dahl, Günter, "Das Abgründige in Dr. Jaccoud," *Der Stern,* Nr. 3 (1960).

Dankworth, P. W., *Lumineszenz-Analyse im filtrierten ultravioletten Licht.* Leipzig, 1934.

Däubler, C., "Über die Untersuchung menschlichen und thierischen Blutes durch Messung von Grössenunterschieden rother Blutkörperchen," *Vierteljahresschrift für gerichtliche Medizin,* 3rd series, XVIII (October, 1899).

Davidson, W., and Smith, D., "A Morphological Sex Difference in the Polymorphonuclear Neutrophil Leucocytes," *British Medical Journal,* II, 6 (1954).

Deen, Van, "Tinctura guajaci und ein Ozonträger als Reagenz auf sehr geringe Blutmengen," *Archiv holländischer Beiträge zur Natur- und Heilkunde,* III (1861–64), 228.

Derobert, Léon, and Hausser, Guy, *La Pratique médico-légale.* Paris, 1938.

Dettling-Schönberg-Schwartz, *Lehrbuch der gerichtlichen Medizin.* Basel, 1951.

Diamond, Louis K., *et al.,* "Identification of the Kell Factor in Dried Blood Stains," *Journal of Forensic Medicine,* II (1955), 243.

Dilnot, George, *Great Detectives and Their Methods.* Boston and New York, 1928.

Dodd, B., and Hunter, D., "Saliva Stains: A Comparison Between the Inhibition and Mixed Agglutination Technique for the Detection of Ab and H," *Proceedings of the Third International Meeting in Forensic Immunology, Medicine, Pathology and Toxicology,* London, 1963.

Dodinval, P., "Sensibilité de la réaction d'inhibition de l'antiglobuline appliquée à la détermination du caractère humain des taches de sang." *Acta Clinica Belgiae,* XII (1957), 169.

Domenici, F., "Leone Lattes (1887–1954)," *Minerva Medicalegale* (Turin) (Nov.-Dec., 1954).

Doyle, A. C., *The Complete Sherlock Holmes.* New York, 1930.

———, *Memoirs and Adventures.* London, 1924.

———, *The Memoirs of Sherlock Holmes.* London, 1894.

Duclos, J., and Ruffié, J., "Recherches médico-légales des antigènes sanguins du type rhésus dans les taches de sang sec," *Acta medicinae legalis et socialis,* Liège, VII (1954), 111.

———, "Absorption des anticorps anti-fy par le sang désséché," *Comptes Rendus des Séances de la Société de Biologie,* LXIII (1957), 393.

Dungern, Von, and Hirszfeld, L., "Über gruppenspezifische Strukturen des Blutes," *Zeitschrift für Immunitätsforschung,* VII (1911), 526.

Dupin, Arthur, "Qui l'a assassinée?" *Le Journal,* July 19, 1909.

Elbel, Herbert, "Zur Technik der Untersuchung auf die Bluteigenschaften M und

Bibliography

N," *Deutsche Zeitschrift für die gesamte gerichtliche Medizin,* XXIV (1935), 242.

Emmert, C., *Lehrbuch der gerichtlichen Medizin.* Leipzig, 1900.

Evans, W. E., "The Examination of Hairs and Fibers," in Gradwohl, R. B. H., ed., *Legal Medicine.* St. Louis, 1954.

Falkenheim, H., "Zur Lehre von den Anomalien der Haarfärbung," *Vierteljahresschrift für Dermatologie und Syphilogie* (1883), 33.

Farran, Jean, "La Justice des hommes condamne la justice d'un père," *Paris Match* (June 27, 1959).

Finzi, Marcello, "Das Kriminal-Museum von Lyon," *Archiv für Kriminologie,* LXXXVII (1930), 125.

——, "Das Polizeilaboratorium in Lyon," *Kriminalistik,* III, 9/10 (1949).

Fiori, Angelo, "L'agglutinazione mista nell' Identificazione degli antigeni ABO in tracce di sangue," *Medicina Legale e Assicurazione,* IX (1961), 205.

——, "Detection and Identification of Bloodstains," *Methods of Forensic Science,* I (1962), 243–290.

Fiori, Angelo, et al., "Modified Absorption-Elution Method of Siracusa for ABO and MN Grouping of Blood-stains," *Journal of Forensic Sciences,* VIII (1963), 419–567.

Firth, J. B., *A Scientist Turns to Crime.* London, 1960.

Floriot, René, *Au Banc de la défense.* Paris, 1959.

Fontaine, G., and Muller, P., "Identifizierung von biologischen Produkten durch immunchemische Methoden," *Deutsche Zeitschrift für gerichtliche Medizin,* XLIX (1960), 420.

Forsythe, Wm. E., "Samuel S. Gerber," *The Bulletin,* Academy of Medicine, Cleveland (June, 1964).

Frécon, A., *Des Empreintes en général et de leur application dans la pratique de la médecine légale.* Lyon, 1889.

Frederic, J., "Untersuchungen über die Rassenunterschiede der menschlichen Kopfhaare," *Zeitschrift für Morphologie und Anthropologie,* IX (1906), 248–324.

Freeman, R. Austin, *Dr. Thorndyke: His Famous Cases.* London, 1929.

——, *Dr. Thorndyke's Crime File.* New York, 1941.

Frei-Sulzer, Max, "Beitrag zur Spurenkunde des Suicids durch Erhängen und Erdrosseln," *Kriminalistik* (September, 1955), 345.

——, "L'Analyse des traces au laboratoire de Police scientifique de Zurich," *Revue Internationale de Criminologie et de Police technique* (January-March, 1956), 49.

——, "Colored Fibers in Criminal Investigation with Special Reference to Natural Fibers," in A. S. Curry, ed., *Methods of Forensic Science* (New York, 1965), IV, 141.

——, "Die Beschaffung des Vergleichsmaterials für kriminalistische Gutachten," *Kriminalistik* (March, 1958), 98.

——, "Farbphotographie im Dienste der Kriminalistik," *Kriminalistik* (January, 1956), 16.

——, "Indizienbeweis durch Textilfaserspuren," *Kriminalistik* (March, 1954).

——, "Die Methoden der Faservergleiche in der Kriminalistik," *Kriminalistik* (May, 1963), 197.

——, "Die Mikrobiologie in der Kriminalistik," *Kriminalistik* (November, 1958), 452.

——, "Mikroskopische Analyse von Verbrecherspuren," *Mikroskopie,* IV, 11/12 (1949).

——, "Mikroskopische Befunde an Trinkgefässen," *Kriminalistik* (February, 1953), 43.

——, "Mikrospuren bei der Abklärung von Unfällen," *Kriminalistik* (June, 1956), 211.

——, "Die Sicherung von Mikrospuren mit Klebband," *Kriminalistik* (October, 1951).

Bibliography

_____, "Le Travail de l'expert sur le lieu de l'incendie et au laboratoire," *Bulletin Association des établissements cantonaux d'assurance contre l'incendie*, I-IV (1962).

_____, "Nachweisreaktionen auf dem Gebiete der Kriminalistik," *Chemische Rundschau*, XVI (1963).

_____, "Naturwissenschaften im Dienste der Kriminalistik," *Ringiers Blatt für Alle*, XIX/XX (1963).

_____, "Spurenuntersuchungen bei Sachbeschädigung," *Kriminalistik* (February, 1955), 54.

Freund, Valentin, and Lautenbach, Lothar, "Die Aufklärung eines Falles von Tötung und Leichenbeseitigung als Ergebnis gerichtsmedizinischer und kriminalistischer Zusammenarbeit," in Franz Meinert, ed., *Gerichtliche Medizin und Kriminalistik, Festschrift zum 60. Geburtstag von Prof. Dr. Emil Weinig.* N.d.

Friedberger, E., "August v. Wassermann †," *Zeitschrift für Immunitätsforschung*, I (1925), 1–12.

Friedenreich, V., and Hartmann, G., "Über die Verteilung der Gruppenantigene im Organismus der sogenannten Ausscheider und Nichtausscheider," *Zeitschrift für Immunitätsforschung*, XCII (1938), 141.

Friedländer, Hugo, and Sello, Dr. E., "Die Ermordung der achtjährigen Lucie Berlin," *Interessante Kriminalprozesse von kulturhistorischer Bedeutung*, IV. Berlin, 1922.

Fujiwara, K., "Einige Erfahrungen mit der Blutgruppenbestimmung an Flecken in Kriminalfällen," *Deutsche Zeitschrift für die gesamte gerichtliche Medizin*, XV, 1930, 470.

Furneaux, Dupert, *Famous Criminal Cases*, VIII, London, 1962.

Gabard, Charles E., "Kriminaltechnisches Labor Los Angeles," *Internationale Kriminalpolizeiliche Revue* (December, 1956), 313–17.

Galloro, Giovanbattista, "Ricerche sperimentali sull'utilizzabilità delle proprietà gruppe-specifiche della saliva nella pratica medicolegale," *Archivio di Antropologià Criminale*, LX (1940), 853–56.

Gamper, D., "Offener Brief an Prof. Marbe," *Archiv für Kriminologie*, XCII (1933), Heft 5/6, 204.

Garçon, Maurice, "Mort du docteur Paul," in *Le Monde*, January 28, 1960.

Gayet, Jean, *Manuel de Police Scientifique.* Paris, 1961.

Gerber, S. R., "The Coroner Will Rule . . . ," *The Bulletin*, Academy of Medicine, Cleveland (March, 1964).

_____, "New Coroners' Offices, Laboratories and Mortuary," *The Bulletin*, Academy of Medicine, Cleveland (March, 1953).

Gerteis, Walter: *Detektive: Ihre Geschichte im Leben und in der Literatur.* Munich, 1953.

Géry, Gérard, "Jaccoud: Deux Cœurs mis à nu," *Paris Match*, Nr. 564 (January 30, 1960).

_____, "Le Jury a dit 'Oui,' " *Paris Match*, Nr. 566 (February 13, 1960).

Gibb, T. R. P., *Optical Methods of Chemical Analysis.* New York, 1942.

Giesecke, Karl, "Über den Staub in den Kleidungsstücken und seine Bedeutung für die Kriminaluntersuchung," *Archiv für Kriminologie*, LXXV (1923), 14–40.

Gillies, Donald A., "Scientific Evidence in the Sheppard Case," *The Journal of Criminal Law, Criminology and Police Science*, XLVII (1956), 136–42.

Gilroy, R., and Harrison, H. C., "Firearms Discharge Residues," *Journal of Forensic Sciences*, IV, 1 (1959).

Glaister, John (1856–1932), *A Study of Hairs and Wools Belonging to the Mammalian Group of Animals, Including a Special Study of Human Hair, Considered from the Medico-legal Aspect.* Cairo, 1931.

Glaister, John (1892–), *Medical Jurisprudence and Toxicology.* Edinburgh, 1931; 11th ed., in collaboration with Edgar Rentoul, Baltimore, 1962.

Glaister, John (1892–) and Smith, Sidney, *Recent Advances in Forensic Medicine.* London, 1939.

Bibliography

Godwin, John, *Killers in Paradise*. London, 1962.

Goroncy, Kurt, "Blutgruppenbestimmungen in der gerichtsärztlichen Praxis," *Deutsche medizinische Wochenschrift* (1929), 306–8.

Goroncy, Kurt, "Zur Frage der individuellen Blutdiagnose," *Deutsche Zeitschrift für die gesamte gerichtliche Medizin*, V (1925), 178–82.

Grassberger, Roland, "Hans Gross, Fondateur de la criminalistique," *Revue Internationale de la Criminologie et de Police technique*, VII, 194.

Griffith, Arthur, *Mysteries of Police and Crime*. London, 1898.

Gross, Hans, *Handbuch für Untersuchungsrichter*. Munich, 1893.

Guglielmo, Giovanni di, "Leone Lattes," *Haematologica*, XXXVIII (1954), III-IV.

Guinn, V. P., "Recent Developments in the Application of Neutron Activation Analysis Techniques to Forensic Problems," *Journal of the Forensic Science Society*, IV, 4 (October, 1964).

Haase, Dr., "Der Totschlag bei R. . . , Untersuchung auf Blut und von Haaren," *Vierteljahresschrift für gerichtliche Medizin*, 3rd Series, XXIII (1902), 75.

Halstuch, B. E., *Textile Chemistry in the Laboratory*, New York, 1950.

Hanausek, T. F., *Lehrbuch der technischen Mikroskopie*. Stuttgart, 1901.

Hartmann, L., and Tolliez, M., "Microméthode d'étude en gelose de la réaction antigène-anticorps (variante du procédé d'Ouchterlony)," *Revue Française d'Études Clin. et Biol.*, II, 2 (1957), 1997.

Hausbrandt, F., and Judkuweit, A., "Untersuchungen zur Untergruppenbestimmung (A₁ und A₂) an Trockenblut," *Deutsche Zeitschrift für gerichtliche Medizin*, XLV (1956), 355.

Hausman, I. A., "Structural Characteristics of the Hair of Mammals," *American Naturalist*, LIV (1920), 496.

Haycraft, Howard, *Murder for Pleasure*. New York, 1941.

Hegg, Pierre, "En marge de la Criminalistique, Techniques et appareils nouveaux," *Revue Internationale de Criminologie et de Police technique*, Geneva (1958), 43–45.

———, "Bathiscope Détector," *Revue Internationale de Criminologie et de Police technique*, Geneva (1952), II, 189–96.

———, "Une méthode nouvelle en Suisse pour relever les empreintes digitales de comparaison et ses applications pratiques," *Revue Internationale de Criminologie et de Police technique*, Geneva (1949), I, 58–62.

Hegg, P., and Undritz, E., "Die morphologisch-hämatologische und cytologische Untersuchung eingetrockneter Blutflecke," *Schweizerische Medizinische Wochenschrift*, XLI (1959), 1959. Part II, *ibid.*, XLIII (1960), 1223–30.

———, "Die morphologische Untersuchung eingetrockneter Blutflecken und ihre forensische Bedeutung," *Wiener medizinische Wochenschrift*, CXII (1962), 294–96.

———, E., *Rapport d'Expertise. Affaire: Jaccoud, Pierre, Crime de Plan-les-Ouates du 1. mai 1958; Victime: Zumbach*.

Heindl, Robert, "Chemie und Photographie im Dienst der Verbrechensaufklärung," *Archiv für Kriminologie*, XX (1905), 3–5.

———, "Der Mordprozess Halsmann," *Archiv für Kriminologie*, XCII (1930), 177.

———, "Naturwissenschaftliche Kriminalistik," *Archiv für Kriminologie*, CXVIII (1956).

Heuberger, Dr. Josef, *Die Entwicklung der Haushaltsstaubsauger*. Verlag Elektrolux, Berlin, 1930.

Higuchi, S., "Über den Nachweis der vier menschlichen Blutgruppen in Blutflecken," *Zeitschrift für Immunitätsforschung*, LX (1928), 246.

Höfer, Otto, *Die Farbe des menschlichen Haares in forensischer Beziehung*. Dissertation, Göttingen, 1916.

Hofman, Eduard von, "Einiges über forensische Untersuchung von Blutspuren," *Vierteljahresschrift für gerichtliche Medizin*, XIX (1873), 113.

———, *Lehrbuch der gerichtlichen Medizin*. Vienna, 1898.

Bibliography

_____, "Über Haare in gerichtsärztlicher Beziehung," *Prager Vierteljahresschrift für gerichtliche Medizin,* CXII, 77.

Höhnel, E. von, and Ritter, Franz, *Die Mikroskopie der technisch verwendeten Faserstoffe.* Vienna and Leipzig, n.d.

Höhnke, Wilfried, "Verbrechen und Affären, Aus Düsseldorfer Kriminalakten," *Düsseldorfer Nachrichten,* Nr. 85–130 (1965).

Holländer, L., "Über die Blutgruppe Duffy und ihre Verteilung in Basel," *Acta haemat.,* VI (1951), 257.

Holländer, L., and Hässig, A., "Zur klinischen Bedeutung des Lewis-Blutgruppensystems," in *P. H. Anderson: Papers in Dedication.* Copenhagen, 1947.

Holledge, James, *Crimes Which Shocked Australia.* Sydney, 1962.

Holmes, Paul, *The Sheppard Murder Case.* New York, 1961.

Holzer, Franz Josef, "Blutgruppenstoffe im Speichel," *Zeitschrift für ärztliche Fortbildung,* XXXVII (1940), No. 3.

_____, "Ein einfaches Verfahren zur Gruppenbestimmung an vertrocknetem Blut durch Agglutininbindung," *Deutsche Zeitschrift für die gesamte gerichtliche Medizin,* XVI (1931), 445–58.

_____, *Erinnerungen an meine Arbeit bei Karl Landsteiner* (unpublished notes).

_____, "Karl Meixner," *Deutsche Zeitschrift für die gesamte gerichtliche Medizin,* XLIV (1955), 341–42.

_____, "Die Untergruppen in der Blutgruppenforschung," *Klinische Wochenschrift,* XVI (1937), 481.

_____, "Untersuchungen über die gerichtlich-medizinische Verwertbarkeit der Ausscheidung von Blutgruppensubstanzen," *Deutsche Zeitschrift für die gesamte gerichtliche Medizin,* XXVIII (1937), 234.

_____, "Verwendung der Herzbeutelflüssigkeit zur Blutgruppenbestimmung an Leichen," *Klinische Wochenschrift,* VIII (1928), 2427.

_____, "Zur Erkennung des verletzenden Werkzeugs aus Wunden," *Deutsche Zeitschrift für die gesamte gerichtliche Medizin,* XXXIX (1948), 35–45.

Hoover, J. E., "Physical Science in the Crime Laboratory," *Review of Science Instruments,* IX (1938), 335–40.

Hrabowski, H., "Die Bedeutung botanischer Hilfsindizien für die Aufklärung von Tatbeständen," *Archiv für Kriminologie,* CXXII (1958), 179–87.

Hübner and Müller-Hess, "Die sexualpathologischen, psychiatrischen und gerichtlich-medizinischen Lehren des Hussman-Prozesses," *Deutsche Zeitschrift für die gesamte gerichtliche Medizin,* Vol. XIV, I, 1929.

Im Obersteg, Jürg, "Salomon Schönberg†," *Deutsche Zeitschrift für die gesamte gerichtliche Medizin,* XLVIII (1958), 1.

_____, "Gerichtliche Medizin," in *Lehre und Forschung an der Universität Basel zur Zeit der Feier ihres 100 jährigen Bestehens.* Basel, 1960.

Inglis, K. S., *The Stuart Case.* Melbourne, 1961.

Jacob, Madeleine, "Le Docteur Paul," in *Libération,* October 8, 1952.

_____, "Les Secrets du Docteur Paul," in *Libération,* January 27, 1954.

Jagič, N., and Landsteiner, K., "Über die Verbindungen und die Entstehung von Immunkörpern," *Münchner Medizinische Wochenschrift,* L (1903), 764–68.

Jervis, R. E., and Perkons, A. K., "Application of Radioactivation-analysis in Forensic Investigations," *Journal of Forensic Sciences,* VII, 4 (October, 1932).

_____, *Hair Individualisation Studies* (manuscript, 1964).

_____, "Trace Elements in Human Head Hair," *Journal of Forensic Sciences,* XI, 1 (January, 1966).

Jervis, R. E., et al., "Activation Analysis in Forensic Investigation," *Proceedings of International Conference on Modern Trends in Activation Analysis.* Texas, Agricultural and Mechanical College Press, 1962.

_____, "Computer Analysis of Complex Gamma Ray Spectra," *11th Annual Meeting of the Society for Applied Spectroscopy,* San Diego, October, 1963.

Bibliography

Jeserich, Paul, "Auf den Spuren des Verbrechens," Parts I and II, *Berliner Illustrierte Zeitung,* XIX/XX.

——, *Die Mikrophotographie auf Bromsilbergelatine bei natürlichem und künstlichem Licht unter ganz besonderer Berücksichtigung des Kalklichtes.* Berlin, 1908.

——, "Über forensisch-chemische Untersuchungen," *Tageblatt der 55. Versammlung deutscher Naturforscher und Ärzte in Eisenach,* VII (1882), 157–61.

Jeserich, Rudolf, "Der sprechende Stein," *Deutsche Polizei,* VI (1952), 91–4.

Joffroy, Pierre, "Jaccoud: L'amour a fait de lui un accusé," *Paris Match,* No. 563 (January 23, 1960).

Jungwirth, J., "Eine Schnellmethode zur artspezifischen Differenzierung menschlichen Blutes," *Deutsche Zeitschrift für die gesamte gerichtliche Medizin,* XLV (1956), 527.

Karsten, Kettel, and Thomsen, Olaf, "Quantitative Untersuchungen über die menschlichen Isoagglutinine Anti-A und Anti-B," *Zeitschrift für Immunitätsforschung,* LXV (1930).

Kelly, Vince, *Rugged Angel: Australia's First Policewoman.* Sydney, 1961.

——, *The Shark Arm Case.* Sydney, 1963.

Kempen, P., *Untersuchungen zur Blutalters und Geschlechtsbestimmung an Blutschüppchen.* Dissertation, Bonn, 1961.

Kerr, F. M., "The Application of Neutron Activation Analysis to a Forensic Science," *Royal Canadian Mounted Police Gazette,* XXI, 9 (1959), 13.

——, *A Study of the Influence of the Hair Cycle on the Trace Element Content of Human Hairs by Means of Neutron Activation Analysis.* Thesis, University of Ottawa, 1964.

Kind, S. S., "Absorption-elution Grouping of Dried Blood Stains on Fabrics," *Nature,* CLXXXVII (1960), 789.

——, "Absorption-elution Groupings of Dried Blood Smears," *Nature,* CLXXXVIII (1960), 397.

Kirk, Paul L., *A Brief Sketch of the History of the School of Criminology.* University of California (manuscript).

——, *Crime Investigation, Physical Evidence and the Police Laboratory.* New York, 1953.

——, *Crime Investigation,* New York, 1960.

——, *The Crime Laboratory, Organization and Operation.* Springfield, 1965.

——, "Human Hair Studies," I and II, *Journal of Criminal Law and Criminology,* XXXI (1940), 486; XXXI (1941), 627.

——, "Human Hair Studies—Applications of the Microdetermination of Comparative Density," *Journal of Criminal Law and Criminology,* XL (1952/53), 263.

Kirk, Paul L., and Brown, Charlotte L., "Individuality of Blood, Electrochromatophoretic Patterns of Dry Blood," *Journal of Forensic Medicine,* VIII, 1 (1961), 34–41.

Kirk, Paul L., and Sylvia, Frederic R., "A Density Gradient Study," *Journal of Forensic Medicine,* IV (1957), 58–64.

Kirk, Paul L., *et al.,* "Casting of Hairs—Its Technique and Application to Species and Personal Identification," *Journal of Criminal Law and Criminology,* XL (1949), 236.

——, "Hair Studies—Refractive Index of Crown Hair," *Journal of Criminal Law and Criminology,* XXXI (1940/41), 746.

——, "Some Problems in Blood Testing and Grouping," *Journal of Criminal Law, Criminology and Police Science,* XLV (1954), 80–4.

Kisser, J., and Sekyra, L. W., "Die mikroskopische Diagnose heimischer Holzarten in zerkleinertem und pulverisiertem Zustand," *Archiv für Kriminologie,* CIII (1938), 19.

Kling, André, *Méthodes actuelles d'expertises employées au laboratoire municipal de Paris etc.* Paris, 1922.

Bibliography

Koch, J. H., and Yoe, J. H., *Trace Analysis.* New York, 1955.

Kögel, G., "Typen der Fluoreszenz- und Ultraviolettphotographie," *Archiv für Kriminologie,* LXXX (1927), 81–9.

Kögel, P. R., "Die Anwendung der Palimpsestphotographie auf forensischem Gebiet," *Archiv für Kriminologie,* LXXI (1919), 85–102.

Kratter, Julius, *Lehrbuch der gerichtlichen Medizin.* Stuttgart, 1912.

———, "Über den forensischen Werth der histologischen Methode zur Unterscheidung von Thier- und Menschenblut," *Archiv für Kriminologie,* X (1902).

Künkele, F., "Blutgruppenuntersuchungen bei Speichelresten aufgeklebter Briefmarken," *Verhandlungen des 1. Internationalen Kongresses der gerichtlichen und sozialen Medizin,* Bonn (1938), 132–33.

Lacassagne, A., *Précis de médecine légale.* Paris, 1910.

Landé, P., *Étude médico-légale des taches de sang.* Bordeaux, 1909.

Landsteiner, Dr. Karl, "Über Agglutinationserscheinungen normalen menschlichen Blutes," *Wiener klinische Wochenschrift,* XLVI (1901).

———, "Zur Kenntnis der antifermativen, lythischen und agglutinierenden Wirkungen des Blutserums und der Lymphe," *Centralblatt für Bakteriologie, Parasitenkunde und Infektionskrankheiten,* XXVII (1900).

Landsteiner, K., and Levine, P., "A New Agglutinable Factor Differentiating Individual Human Bloods," *Proceedings of the Society for Experimental Biology and Medicine,* XXIV (1927), 600.

———, "Further Observations of Individual Differences of Human Blood," *Proceedings of the Society for Experimental Biology and Medicine,* XXIV (1927), 941.

Landsteiner, Karl, and Richter, Max, "Über die Verwerthbarkeit individueller Blutdifferenzen für die forensische Praxis," *Zeitschrift für Medizinalbeamte,* III (1903), 85–89.

Landsteiner, K., and Wiener, A. S., "An Agglutinable Factor in Human Blood Recognized by Immune Sera for Rhesus Blood," *Proceedings of the Society for Experimental Biology and Medicine,* XLIII (1940), 43.

Langemann, Hans, *Das Attentat.* Hamburg, 1956.

Lassaigne, J. L., "De l'examen physique des poils et des cheveux," *Annales d'hygiène publique, VIII,* 2nd Series (1857), 226.

Lattes, Leone, "Le Diagnostic individuel des taches de sang," *Annales de Médecine Légale et de Criminologie,* V (1923).

———, "Due casi pràtici di diàgnosi individuale del sangue umano," *Archivio di Antropologia Criminale,* XXXVII (Vol. VII, Series IV/1916), 298–308.

———, *L'individualità del sangue.* Messina, 1923.

———, "Methoden zur Bestimmung der Individualität des Blutes," in Abderhaldens *Handbuch der biologischen Arbeitsmethoden* (1927).

———, "Praktische Erfahrungen über Blutgruppenbestimmung in Flecken," *Deutsche Zeitschrift für die gesamte gerichtliche Medizin,* IX (1927), 402–10.

———, "Sull'applicazione pràtica della prova di agglutinazione per la diágnosi specifica ed individuale del sangue umano," *Archivio di Antropologia Criminale,* XXXIV (Vol. V, Series IV/1913), 310–25.

———, "Sulla tècnica della prova di isoagglutinazione del sangue," *Archivio di Antropologia Criminale,* XXXVII (Vol. VII, Series IV/1916), 400–08.

Lauer, A., "Zur Technik der Blutfleckendiagnose nach M und N," *Deutsche Zeitschrift für die gesamte gerichtliche Medizin,* XXII (1933), 86.

LeBreton, R., *Betrachtungen zu den Befunden der gerichtsmedizinischen Sachverständigen im Prozess Jaccoud* (manuscript).

———, *Identification du sang et des cellules d'organes humains dans les taches: Limites de la méthode microscopique* (manuscript).

———, *Valeur des méthodes sur l'identification du sang humain dans les taches* (manuscript).

Ledden-Hulsebosch, J. C. van, "Die 'sieben goldenen W.' des Kriminalisten," *Archiv für Kriminologie,* CXV (1955), 8–9.

Bibliography

——, "Die Bedeutung von am Tatort hinterlassenen Fäkalmassen," *Archiv für Kriminologie*, LXXIV (1922), 273.

——, "Verwendung der ultravioletten Strahlen in der Kriminalistik," *Archiv für Kriminologie*, LXXIII (1926), 1–7.

Lender, Dr., "Gutachten über die Haare an den Beilen der Warsiner Höhle," *Vierteljahresschrift für gerichtliche und öffentliche Medizin*, XXIII (1863).

Lenz, Adolf, "Hans Grosst, Gedenkrede," *Zeitschrift für die gesamte Strafrechtswissenschaft*, XXXVII, 595.

Leppmann, F., "Der Fall Berger und die ärztliche Sachverständigentätigkeit," *Ärztliche Sachverständigenzeitung* (January 1, 1905), 5–7.

——, "Rückblick und Ausblick (Bemerkungen zum Krantz- und Hussmann-Fall)," *Ärztliche Sachverständigenzeitung*, I (1929), 17–18.

Lesser, Fritz, "A. v. Wassermann," *Dermatologische Wochenschrift*, LXXX (1925), 621–22.

Levine, Philip, "Review of Landsteiner's Contribution to the Human Blood Groups," Keynote Address, Am. Ass. Blood Banks, 13th Annual Meeting, San Francisco, August 22, 1960.

Levine, Philip, et al., "The Role of Isoimmunization in the Pathogenesis of Erythroblastosis Fetalis," *American Journal of Obstetrics and Gynecology*, LXII (1941), 925.

Lewis, W. B., "Research in the Atomic Energy Field," *The Canada Year Book*. 1963–4.

Lindenau, H., and Niceforo, A., *Die Kriminalpolizei und ihre Hilfswissenschaften*. Berlin, n.d.

Locard, Edmond, "Beiträge zur kriminalistischen Staubuntersuchung," *Archiv für Kriminologie*, XCII.

——, *Le Crime et les criminels*. Paris, n.d.

——, *Le XVIIe siècle médico-judiciaire*. Lyon, 1902.

——, *L'Enquête criminelle et les méthodes scientifiques*. Paris, 1920.

——, *L'Identification des récidivistes*. Paris, 1920.

——, *Instructions pour les recherches techniques dans les enquêtes criminelles*. Lyon, 1924.

——, *Manuel de technique policière*. Paris, 1923.

——, *Mémoires d'un criminologiste recueillis par Robert Corvol*. Paris, 1957.

——, *Les Méthodes de laboratoire dans l'expertise en écriture*. Lyon, 1921.

——, *La Poroscopie*. Lyon, 1923.

Lochte, Th., *Atlas der menschlichen und tierischen Haare*. Leipzig, 1938.

——, "Über die Kronenbildung des auffallenden Bluttropfens und ihre Beziehung zu sekundären Blutspritzern," *Deutsche Zeitschrift für die gesamte gerichtliche Medizin*, XXII (1933), 387.

Longhetti, A., and Roche, G. W., "Microscopic Identification of Man-made Fibers from the Criminalistic Point of View," *Journal of Forensic Science*, III (1958).

Loth, David, *Crime Lab*. New York, 1964.

Lynch, Roche, "The Technique of the Precipitin Test and Its Forensic Value," *Analyst*, LIII (1928), 5–23.

Makins, F. K., *The Identification of Trees and Shrubs*. London, 1948.

Makris, John N., *The Silent Investigators*. New York, 1959.

Mannheim, Herbert, *Pioneers in Criminology*. Chicago, 1960.

Maresch, Wolfgang, *Aide-Mémoire zum Prozess Jaccoud über die Fragen, welche einer erneuten Klärung bedürfen* (manuscript).

——, "Die Entwicklung der gerichtlichen Medizin an der medizinischen Fakultät in Graz," *Wiener klinische Wochenschrift*, LXXV (1963), 437–39.

——, "Zum Nachweis von Gewebsteilchen an Tatwerkzeugen," *Deutsche Zeitschrift für die gesamte gerichtliche Medizin*, LI (1961), 560–62.

Maresch, Wolfgang, and Wehrschütz, E., "Moderne Methoden der Blutfleckendiagnostik (Agargeldiffusion und Mischagglutination)," *Archiv für Kriminologie*, CXXXII (1963), 1.

Bibliography

Maresch, Wolfgang, and Werkgartner, Anton, *Gutachten in der Strafsache gegen P. Jaccoud vom 22. Jänner 1960* (manuscript).

Martin, E. P., "Comportement des fibres textiles colorées en présence de la colle des bandes transparentes adhésives," *Revue Internationale de Police Criminelle* (May, 1965).

——, "Die Photographie als Hilfsmittel zur Unterscheidung gefärbter Textilfasern," *Photographie und Wissenschaft*, V, 2/3 (1956).

——, *Einige Daten zur Entwicklungsgeschichte der Kriminaltechnik in Basel* (manuscript, 1966).

——, "Sicherung und Auswertung von mikroskopischen Tatortspuren," *Das Polizeiblatt für das Land Baden-Württemberg*, XXV (February 2, 1922).

——, "Zur Frage der Brennbarkeit moderner Textilgewebe," *Chimia* (1964), 48–56.

Martin, Otto, "Die angewandte Biologie im Dienste der Kriminalistik," *Schriftenreihe des Bundeskriminalamtes*, Wiesbaden (6769), 117–21.

——, *Aus den Erinnerungen eines forensischen Biologen* (manuscript).

——, *Entwicklung und Grundlagen des Textilvergleichs* (manuscript, 1965).

——, "Kriminaltechnische Untersuchungen an Textilien," *Kriminalistik* (December, 1955).

——, "Zum Nachweis winzigster Blutspritzer, ausgebürsteter und ausgewaschener Blutspuren," *Kriminalistik* (April, 1955), 144–47.

Marx, Hugo, "Ein Beitrag zur Identitätsfrage bei der forensischen Haaruntersuchung," *Archiv für Kriminologie*, XXIII (1906), 75.

——, *Einführung in die gerichtliche Medizin für praktische Kriminalisten*. Berlin, 1907.

Meiners, Walter P., "Sprengstoffe und Zündmittel—ihr verbrecherischer Gebrauch," *Kriminalistik* (October, 1962).

Meinert, Franz, "Exekutive und Kriminaltechnik," *Die Polizei/Polizeipraxis* (1959), 141.

Meixner, Karl, "Die Blutgruppen in der gerichtlichen Medizin," *Wiener klinische Wochenschrift*, IV/V (1928).

——, "Lehren des Halsmannprozesses," *Beiträge zur gerichtlichen Medizin*, X (1930), 47.

——, "Offener Brief an Professor Marbe als Erwiderung auf dessen Schrift, 'Der Strafprozess gegen Philipp Halsmann,' " *Archiv für Kriminologie*, XCII (1933), 192.

Mellon, M. G., *Analytical Absorption Spectroscopy*. New York, 1950.

Michon, R., "Les procédés d'analyse par radioactivation et leur intérêt en médecine légale," *Acta Medicinae legalis et socialis*, XI (Liège, 1958), 119–28.

Migerka, T., *In den gewerblichen Betrieben vorkommende Staubarten in Wort und Bild*. Vienna, 1895.

Minakow, P., "Über die Veränderung der Haare durch die Hitze," *Vierteljahresschrift für gerichtliche Medizin, Supp.* (1896), 105.

Moore, Jacqueline, "Murder in the Sky," 4 parts, *Weekend Picture Magazine* (March 14, 21, 28, and April 4, 1953).

Moretti, Carlo, "La Police à Genève," *Revue Internationale de Criminologie et de Police technique*, I (1948), 23.

Mortisch, Paul, "Kann das Blut verschiedener Individuen unterschieden werden?" *Archiv für Kriminologie*, LXXVIII (1926), 12–23.

Mostar, Gerhart Hermann, and Stemmle, Robert A., *Der Neue Pitaval*, I. Munich, 1963.

Moureau, P., and Servais, O., "Determination of Blood Groups in Bloodstains," in Lundquist, *Methods of Forensic Science*, New York, 1963, II.

Moureau, P., *et al.*, "Méthodes classiques et modernes d'identification des taches de sang," *29. Congrès International de Médecine Légale et de Médecine Sociale*, Marseilles, 1962.

Bibliography

Mueller, Bernhard, "Der Schwurgerichtsprozess in Kaiserslautern gegen den Zahnarzt Dr. Richard Müller," *Archiv für Kriminologie*, CXX (1957), 165 ff.

Mueller, Berthold, *Gerichtliche Medizin*. Berlin, 1953.

——, "Technik und Bedeutung der Blutgruppenuntersuchung für die gerichtliche Medizin," *Staatsmedizinische Abhandlungen*. Leipzig, 1939.

Muenscher, W. C. L., *Keys to Woody Plants*. Ithaca, New York, 1946.

Müller, B., "Das Agglutin-Anreicherungsverfahren, ein neues Verfahren zur Blutgruppenbestimmung an altem, eingetrocknetem Blute," *Deutsche Zeitschrift für die gesamte gerichtliche Medizin*, XI (1928), 120.

Muller, Maurice, *Aide Mémoire sur: Méthodes classiques pour la recherche du sang en médecine légale, Détermination de l'origine du sang, Conclusions* (manuscript).

——, "Une Nouvelle Méthode de lecture de la réaction précipitante en médecine légale," Deutsche *Zeitschrift für gerichtliche Medizin*, XLII (1954), 550–54.

Muller, M., *et al.*, "Application médico-légale de la réaction antigène-anticorps en milieu gélifié," *Lille Médical*, XXX, 4 (1958), 218–23.

——, "Identification médico-légale des différents liquides biologiques par les réactions immunologiques en milieu gélifié," *Lille Médical*, XXX, 12 (1958), 773–76.

Nachtrieb, N. H., *Principles and Practice of Spectrochemical Analysis*. New York, 1950.

Nakai, Ryohei, "Über die Blutgruppenuntersuchung von Speichelflecken auf Papier," *Archiv für Kriminologie*, CVII (1940), 43.

Nepote, Jean, "L'Identité judiciaire de Paris," *Revue Internationale de Criminologie et de Police technique*, III (Geneva, 1961), 118–28.

——, "Die Kriminaltechnik in Frankreich," *Internationale Kriminalpolizeiliche Revue*, CXLIX (June-July, 1961).

Newman, F. H., "The Use of the Spectrographic Criminal Investigation," *The Police Journal*, XI (1938), 343–9.

New South Wales Police Force, 1862–1962. Centenary brochure.

Nickolls, L. C., and Pereira, M., "A Study of Modern Methods of Grouping Blood Stains," *Medicine, Science and the Law*, II (1961/2), 172.

Norman, R. D. Van, "Die Polizei im Norden Kanadas," *Internationale Kriminalpolizeiliche Revue* (October, 1961).

O'Brien, G. M., *The Australian Police Force*. Melbourne, 1960.

Oesterlen, O., *Das menschliche Haar und seine gerichtsärztliche Bedeutung*. Tübingen, 1874.

O'Hara, Charles E., and Osterburg, James, *An Introduction to Criminalistics*. New York, 1963.

Ouchterlony, A., "Antigen-Antibody Reactions in Gels," *Acta Pathologica et Microbiologica Scandinavica*, XXVI (1949), 507–15.

——, "Antigen-Antibody Reactions in Gels, II: Factors Determining the Site of the Precipitate," *Arkiv for kemi, mineralogi och geologi*, I, 7 (1949), 43–48.

——, "Antigen-Antibody Reactions in Gels, III: The Time Factor," *Arkiv for kemi, mineralogi och geologi*, I, 9 (1949), 55–59.

Palaiseul, Jean, "Un crime a été commis et voici le docteur Paul," in *Noir et Blanc*, March 9, 1949.

Pate, B. D., and Smales, A. A., "Determination of Arsenic in Biological Materials," *Analyst*, LXXVII (1952), 188–96.

Péclet, Bernard, and Pépin, Franchère, "The Scientific Aspect of the Guay Case," *Journal of Criminal Law, Criminology and Police Science*, XLVI (1955/56), 272.

Pereira, M., "The Identification of MN Groups in Dried Blood Stains," *Medicine, Science and the Law*, III (1963), 268.

——, "Observations on the Grouping of Dried Stains of Body Fluids," *Proceedings of the Third International Meeting on Forensic Immunology, Medicine, Pathology and Toxicology*, London, 1963.

Bibliography

Perkons, A. K., *Hair Individualization Study by Neutron Activation.* Doctoral thesis. Toronto, 1963.

Pfaff, Emil Richard, *Das menschliche Haar in seiner physiologischen, pathologischen und forensischen Bedeutung.* Leipzig, 1869.

Pitchandi, N., "Forensic Science Laboratories in Britain," *The Indian Police Journal,* IV, 4 (April, 1958).

Pittman, Patricia, and Wilson, Colin, *Encyclopedia of Murder.* New York, 1962.

Plaa, Gabriel L., *et al.,* "Evaluation of Textile Fibers as Evidence," *The Journal of Criminal Law, Criminology and Police Science,* XLIII (Chicago, 1952/53), 382.

Ponsold, Albert, "Ein Mikroabsorptionsverfahren zum Nachweis der Blutuntergruppen A_1 und A_2," *Deutsche Zeitschrift für die gesamte gerichtliche Medizin,* XXVIII (1937), 248.

Popoff, N. W., "Isoagglutination und ihre forensische Anwendung in Russland," *Deutsche Zeitschrift für die gesamte gerichtliche Medizin,* IX (1924), 411–25.

Popp, Georg, "Die Beobachtung und Deutung von Blutspuren bei Kriminalforschungen," *Zeitschrift für öffentliche Chemie,* XIX (1904).

———, "Bomben, Erdspuren und Instrumenten-Untersuchung," *Zeitschrift für öffentliche Chemie,* XXI (1910).

———, "Botanische Spuren und Mikroorganismen im Kriminalverfahren," *Archiv für Kriminologie,* XIV (1939), 231–37.

———, "Der Indizienbeweis im Heidelberger Raubmordprozess," *Deutsche Strafrechtszeitung,* III/IV (1922), 94.

———, "Mord oder Selbstmord bei aufgehängten Leichen," *Archiv für Kriminologie,* LXXXVIII (1931), 79.

———, "Nachweis von Arsen in Leichenaschen," *Zeitschrift für angewandte Chemie,* XXXI (1928).

Popp, Hans, *Erinnerungen an meinen Vater Georg Popp.* Record of a conversation about Georg Popp with Jürgen Thorwald.

Potter, Edith L., "The Rh-Factor," *Modern Medicine* (1951).

Prokop, Otto, *Lehrbuch der gerichtlichen Medizin* (Historischer Teil). Berlin, 1960.

Prokop, Otto, and Uhlenbruck, Gerhard, *Lehrbuch der menschlichen Blut- und Serumgruppen.* Leipzig, 1963.

Putkonen, T., "Über die gruppenspezifischen Eigenschaften verschiedener Körperflüssigkeiten," *Acta Soc. med. Fin. Duodecim.,* XIV (1930), 107.

Radin, Edward D., *Headline Crimes of the Year.* Boston, 1952.

———, *Twelve Against Crime.* New York, 1961.

———, *Twelve Against the Law.* New York, 1950.

Reiss, A., *Manuel de police scientifique.* Lausanne, 1911.

Reiss, R. A., *Einiges über die signaletische Photographie.* Munich, 1902.

———, "Étude sur l'Escroquerie au Trésor," *Archives d'Anthropologie Criminelle de Médecine légale et de psychologie normale et pathologique,* Lausanne (March, 1907).

———, *Les Méthodes scientifiques dans les enquêtes judiciaires et policières.* Lyon, n.d.

———, "Die Photographie von Krankheitserscheinungen," *Internationale photographische Monatsschrift für Medizin,* VII, 6 (Munich, 1900).

Renkonen, K. O., "Studies in Hemagglutinins Present in Seeds of some Representatives of the Family of Leguminosae," *Annales Medicinae Experimentalis et Biologiae Fenniae,* XXVI (1948), 66.

Reuter, Karl, "Naturwissenschaftlich-kriminalistische Untersuchungen menschlicher Ausscheidungen," in *Abderhaldens Handbuch der biologischen Arbeitsmethoden,* Berlin/Vienna, 1934, IV, 305.

Rhodes, Henry T. F., *In the Tracks of Crime.* London, 1952.

Richter, Max, *Gerichtsärztliche Diagnostik und Technik.* Leipzig, 1905.

———, "Über Häminkrystalle," *Vierteljahresschrift für gerichtliche Medizin* (1990), Heft 3.

Bibliography

Rippel-Baldes, *Grundriss der Mikrobiologie.* Berlin, 1952.

Ritter, Bernhard, "Zur Geschichte der gerichtsärztlichen Ausmittelung der Blutflecken," *Henkes Zeitschrift für Staatsarzneykunde,* LXXX (1860).

Root, Lin, "Atomic Energy Solves a Crime," *American Weekly* (December 2, 1962).

Ruch, Rodney R., *et al.,* "Neutron Activation Analysis in Scientific Crime Detection—Some Recent Developments," *Journal of Forensic Sciences,* IX, 1 (January, 1964).

Sannié, Charles, "La Détection scientifique du crime," in *Science et Société,* IV, 3 (1952), 149–72.

———, *La Recherche scientifique du criminel,* Paris, 1954.

———, "Le Rôle du Service de l'Identité Judiciaire de la Préfecture de Police à Paris dans la lutte contre le Crime," *Revue Internationale de Criminologie et de Police technique,* IV (Geneva, 1951), 291–98.

Schaidt, G., "Eine neue Methode zur Darstellung der Haarcuticula," *Kriminalistik,* VIII (1954), 127.

Scheller, H., *Einführung in die angewandte spectrochemische Analyse.* Berlin, 1960.

Schiff, Fritz, *Die Blutgruppen und ihre Anwendungsgebiete.* Berlin, 1933.

———, "Die gerichtlich-medizinische Bedeutung der serologischen Eigenschaften M und N von Landsteiner und Levine," *Deutsche Zeitschrift für die gesamte gerichtliche Medizin,* XVIII (1932), 41.

———, *Die Technik der Blutgruppenuntersuchung für Kliniker und Gerichtsärzte.* Berlin, 1929.

Schiff, F., and Sasaki, H., "Der Ausscheidungstypus, ein auf serologischem Wege nachweisbares menschliches Merkmal," *Klinische Wochenschrift,* XI (1932), 1426.

Schleyer, Friedrich, "Investigation of Biological Stains with Regard to Species Origin," *Methods of Forensic Science,* I (1962), 291–333.

———, *Neuere Methoden zur Blutarterunterscheidung, eine kritische Übersicht* (manuscript, 1965).

———, "Vergleichende Untersuchungen über den optimalen Nachweis von ABO-Agglutinogenen in Blutflecken," *Zeitschrift für Immunitätsforschung,* CXIV (1957), 244.

Schlunegger, U. P., and Wyttenbach, A., "Neutronenaktivierungsanalyse zur Identifizierungsüberprüfung von Autolacksplittern," *Kriminalistik* (1965), 296.

Schneider, Albert, "Police Microscopy," *Journal of the American Institute of Criminal Law and Criminology,* XI (1920), 219.

Schnug, G., "Die methodischen Möglichkeiten beim Nachweis der Bluteigenschaften in Blut- und Sekretspuren," *Grundfragen der Kriminaltechnik.* Bundeskriminalamt Wiesbaden, 1958.

———, "Über den P-Nachweis an Blutflecken," *Deutsche Zeitschrift für die gesamte gerichtliche Medizin,* XLI (1952), 451–53.

Schorr, M., *Zur Geschichte der Bluttransfusion im 19. Jahrhundert.* Basel/Stuttgart, 1956.

Schütze, A., and Wassermann, A., "Über eine neue forensische Methode zur Unterscheidung von Menschen- und Thierblut," *Berliner klinische Wochenschrift,* VII (1901), 187–90.

Schwartz, Fritz, "Heinrich Zangger, 1874–1957," *Deutsche Zeitschrift für die gesamte gerichtliche Medizin,* XLVI (1957), 353.

Schwarzacher, W., "Über die Grundlagen der vergleichenden Haaruntersuchung," *Archiv für Kriminologie,* CXIII (1943), 11.

Schweder, Paul, *Die grossen Kriminalprozesse des Jahrhunderts.* Hamburg, 1961.

Seelig, Ernst, "Hans Gross," *Zeitschrift des historischen Vereines für Steiermark,* XXXVI, 1.

Seith, W., and Ruthardt, K., *Chemische Spektralanalyse.* Berlin, 1948.

Sheppard, Sam, *Endure and Conquer.* Cleveland, 1966.

Shew, E. Spencer, *A Companion to Murder.* New York, 1961.

Bibliography

Silk, Stafford, *The Bogle Mystery.* Sydney, 1963.

Smith-Hughes, Jack, *Nine Verdicts on Violence.* London, 1956.

Smith, H. Ward, *New Horizons in the Administration of Justice.* Report of the Attorney-General's Laboratory, Province of Ontario.

Smith, Sydney, *Mostly Murder.* New York, 1959.

Söderman, Harry, *Auf der Spur des Verbrechens.* Cologne, 1957.

———, "Zur Frage des kriminaltechnischen Staubsaugeverfahrens," *Archiv für Kriminologie,* XCIII (1933), 156–68.

Specht, Walter, "Die Chemilumineszenz des Hämins, ein Hilfsmittel zur Auffindung und Erkennung forensisch wichtiger Blutspuren," *Deutsche Zeitschrift für die gesamte gerichtliche Medizin,* XXVIII (1937), 225.

Speiser, Paul, *Karl Landsteiner.* Vienna, 1961.

———, "Sechzig Jahre Blutgruppen," *Medizinische Welt,* L (1961), 2666.

Sprecher, Jean, and Weitz, Ludwig, "Jaccoud—Opfer oder Mörder—Schweizer Bürger laufen Sturm gegen die Justiz," *Revue,* III (December, 1960).

Strassmann, Fritz, "Arthur Schulz†," *Deutsche Zeitschrift für die gesamte gerichtliche Medizin,* XIX (1932), 264.

Strassmann, Georg, "Über individuelle Blutdiagnose," *Deutsche Zeitschrift für die gesamte gerichtliche Medizin,* V (1925), 184–92.

Strauch, C., "Der serodiagnostische Nachweis von Menschenblut vor Gericht," *Ärztliche Sachverständigen Zeitung,* XXI (1905), 429–33.

Sutermeister, H. M., "Kriminalpsychologie und Medizin," *Praxis,* XLIX (1960), 580–88.

———, "Kritische Bemerkungen zum Fall Jaccoud," *Züricher Woche* (August 19, 1960).

Sutherland, W. W., "The Crime Detection Laboratory," *The Indian Police Journal,* I, 4 (1955), 46.

Taylor, Alfred Swaine, *The Principles and Practice of Medical Jurisprudence.* London, 1873.

Taylor, H. B., "The Government Analyst's Laboratories and the Police," *The Australian Police Journal* (October, 1954).

Tetsuichi, Dr. Ito, "Über einige Anwendungen ultravioletter Strahlen zu gerichtlich-medizinischen Zwecken," *Deutsche Zeitschrift für die gesamte gerichtliche Medizin,* IX (1924), 726.

Thiénard, A., *L'Assassinat.* Paris, 1892.

Thoinot, L., *Précis de Médecine Légale.* Paris, 1913.

Thoma, K., "Combined Saliva and Blood-Group Determination in Traces," *Archiv für Kriminologie,* CXXVIII (1961), 44.

———, "Determination of Blood-Groups A, B, AB and O in the Finger and Toe-nails," *International Criminal Police Review,* LXXVII (1955), 107.

Thomas, Frederic, "Milestones in Forensic Medicine: The Belgian Contribution," in *Medicine, Science and the Law,* III (1963).

Thorwald, Jürgen, *The Century of the Detective.* New York and London, 1965.

Titmus, F. H., *World Timbers.* London, 1958.

Tully, Andrew, *The FBI's Most Famous Cases.* New York, 1965.

Türkel, Siegfried, *Beiträge zur kriminalistischen Symptomatologie und Technik.* Graz, 1931.

———, "Bemerkungen zur Technik der Staubextraktion aus Kleidungsstücken," *Beiträge zur kriminalistischen Symptomatologie und Technik.* Graz, 1931.

Uhlenhuth, Paul, "Das biologische Verfahren zur Erkennung und Unterscheidung von Menschen- und Tierblut sowie anderer Eiweisssubstanzen und seine Anwendung in der forensischen Praxis," *Ausgewählte Sammlung von Arbeiten und Gutachten.* Jena, 1905.

———, "Eine Methode zur Unterscheidung der verschiedenen Blutarten, im besonderen zum differentialdiagnostischen Nachweis des Menschenblutes," *Deutsche medizinische Wochenschrift,* Nos. 6, 7, February, 1901.

Bibliography

———, "Über die Entwicklung des biologischen Eiwissdifferenzierungsverfahrens im Dienste der gerichtlichen Medizin unter besonderer Berücksichtigung eigener Forschungsergebnisse," *Zeitschrift für gerichtliche Medizin*, XXXIX (1948).

Ullyet, Kenneth, *Crime out of Hand*. London, 1963.

Undritz, Erik, "Bedeutung und Schönheit der Farben in der Hämatologie—der Wissenschaft vom Blut," in *Palette*, Sandoz AG, IV, 11 (1962).

———, "Blut und Knochenmark im Alter," in *Krankheiten der über Siebzigjährigen*. Bern and Stuttgart, 1964.

———, "Erythrozyten bei Mensch und Tier," *Sandoz Panorama*. December, 1962.

———, *The Sandoz Atlas of Hematology*. New York, 1952.

Undritz, Erik, and Steinemann, Aida, "Die Blutkörperchen der Ascidien, dieser merkwürdigen Meerestiere, die ihren Platz zwischen den Evertebraten und den Vertebraten einnehmen," *Schweizerische medizinische Wochenschrift*, XCIII (1963), 1477.

Unger, Hellmuth, "Karl Landsteiner, 1868–1943," in *Via Triumphalis*, ed. R. Erckmann. Munich, 1954.

Villebrun, Émile, *Des Ongles, leur importance en médecine judiciaire*. Thesis. Lyon, 1883.

Virchow, R., "Identität oder Nichtidentität von Haaren," in *Gesammelte Abhandlungen* (Berlin, 1879), II, 552.

Vogel, G., "Untersuchung von Blutspurenmaterial," *Kriminalistik* (October, 1962), 439–41.

Volta, A. Dalla, *Trattato di medicina legale*, I and II. Milan, 1935.

Vuillemin, Georges, *Des Poussières au point de vue médico-légal*. Thesis. Lyon, 1884.

Wachholz, Leo, "Über Veränderungen der Haarfarbe," *Archiv für Kriminal-Anthropologie und Kriminalistik* (1905), XIX.

Walcher, Kurt, "Beiträge zur Beurteilung von Blutspritzern," *Deutsche Zeitschrift für die gesamte gerichtliche Medizin*, XVI (1931), 272.

———, *Gerichtlich-medizinische und kriminalistische Blutuntersuchung*. Berlin, 1939.

Waldeyer, W., *Atlas der menschlichen und tierischen Haare*. Lahr, 1884.

Walker, J. T., "The Spectrograph as an Aid in Criminal Investigation," in *Proceedings of the Sixth Scientific Conference on Spectroscopy and Its Application*, New York, 1939, 1–5.

Wallach, Otto, *Tabellen zur chemischen Analyse*, Bonn, 1910.

Weigert, F., *Optische Methoden der Chemie*. Leipzig, 1927.

Whitehead, Donald F., *The FBI Story*. New York, 1956.

Wiener, Alexander S., *Blood Groups and Transfusion*. Springfield, 1943.

———, "Cases from the Files of the Serological Laboratory of the Office of the Chief Medical Examiner of New York City," *Journal of Forensic Medicine*, IX, 4 (1962).

———, "Dr. Karl Landsteiner," *The Scientific Monthly* (September, 1943), 280–83.

———, *Dr. Kari Landsteiner: Les Prix Nobel en 1930*. Stockholm, 1931.

———, "A New Test (Blocking Test) for Rh-sensitization," *Proceedings of the Society for Experimental Biology and Medicine*, LVI (1944), 173.

———, "The Rh-Factor," *British Medical Journal* (1949), 404.

———, and Gordon, Eve B., "Examination of Blood Stains in Forensic Medicine," *Journal of Forensic Science*, I (1956), 89.

———, *et al.*, "Medicolegal Applications of Blood Grouping Tests," *Journal of the American Medical Association*, CLXIV (1957), 2036.

———, *et al.*, "A New Serological Test (Inhibition Test) for Human Serum Globulin," *Proceedings of the Society for Experimental Biology and Medicine*, LXXI (1949), 96–99.

Wiesner, Julius, *Die Rohstoffe des Pflanzenreiches*. Leipzig, 1903.

Wolz, Regierungsrat, "Kriminaltechnische Neuerungen auf der Internationalen Polizeitechnischen Ausstellung Karlsruhe 1925," *Archiv für Kriminologie*, LXXVIII (1926), 94–105.

Bibliography

Yada, S., "Determination of the ABO Blood Groups of Blood Stains by Means of Elution Test," *Japanese Journal of Legal Medicine*, XVI (1963), 290.

Yamakami, K., "The Individuality of Semen, with Reference to Its Property of Inhibiting Specifically Isohemoagglutination," *Journal of Immunology*, XII (1926), 185.

Ziemke, E., "Über die Blutbesudelung des Täters bei Tötung durch Halsschnitt," *Vierteljahresschrift für gerichtliche Medizin*, LXI (1922), 172–84.

Index

Index

Gerber, Dr. Samuel R., 133-148, 155
Gettler, Alexander O., 112, 372
Gilbert, Jo Ann, 412
Girard, Geneva, 410
Girardi, Renzo, 38-42
Girardi, Mrs. Renzo (Andrea), 38-41
Giroux, Leopold, 353-354
Glaister, John, 418
Glennon, Inspector Donald F., 440, 442-443
Goddard, Calvin, 444
Golub, Samuel J., 445-446, 447, 458
Gongas, Corporal, 417, 425
Gonzales, Thomas A., 112-113, 372
Goodwin, Rev. Clive, 366
Gouffé (victim), 281
Gourbin, Émile, 284-285
Gouzenko, Igor, 339
Grabar (scientist), 214
Grabowski, Michael S., 136
Graham, John Gilbert, 359
Graham-Knoll (scientist), 181, 183, 186
Grandchamp, Leo, 445, 457
Granowski (taxi driver), 340
Gravel, Gerard, 440, 441
Gray, Detective Sergeant, 363
Gregory, Dr., 426
Gregson, Sergeant, 328, 330-331, 333
Griffat, Emilie, 270
Griffith, Judge Robert F., 457, 459, 462
Griffon, Henri, 422-423
Griguard (chemist), 284
Gross (criminal), 242
Gross, Hans, 234-235, 236, 242, 245, 246, 252, 281, 282, 287, 296, 321, 359, 399
Gryczykowski (carpenter), 9
Guay, Albert, 341-343, 350-359, 381
Guay, Mrs. Albert (Rita), 341, 343, 350, 352, 354, 355
Guay, Lise, 343, 351, 354

Guérin, Inspector, 313
Guillemette, Inspector Aimé, 338-343, 350-352, 354-356
Guinn, Vincent P., 434-435, 450-451, 454
Guth, Detective, 76
Guy, Thomas, 367
Guy, Mrs. Thomas (Bridget), 367

Haase, Dr., 264
Hablutzel (peddler), 275-276
Hackett, Detective, 372
Hagan, Mary, 326-334
Hall, Vivian, 86
Halsmann, Philipp, 64-65
Hamard, Octave, 256-260, 266-279
Hanlon, Jay, 458
Hansen (scientist), 181, 182, 203
Hansen, Detective Secretary, 119
Harrigan, Dr. J. F., 412
Harrison, Dr. Harold C., 444-448, 450, 452, 455, 458-459
Harsch (student), 56, 61
Hartmann, L., 214
Hasebrink (farmer), 121
Hässig, Dr. Alfred, 181-182
Hastrong, Examining Magistrate, 255, 272, 276-277, 280
Hausmann (chemist), 345
Häussermann (chemist), 345
Häussler, Franz, 70
Havens (scientist), 422
Hawke, Justice, 95
Hawthorne, Detective John A., 106, 108-109, 111-113
Hayes, Susan, 137-138, 143-146
Heberger, Inspector, 210-213, 218-222
Heffron, R. J., 363
Hegg, Pierre, 175, 177-179, 181-187, 190-199, 206
Heindl, Robert, 398-399
Heinrich, Edward Oscar, 149, 371
Heinrichs, Dr., 390, 400
Hendrich, Frau, 119
Hennig, Dr., 236-237
Hennion, Céleste, 294-295

Index

Index